THE POLITICS OF SCIEN

THE POLITICS OF SCIENCE

Readings in Science, Technology, and Government

EDITED BY

WILLIAM R. NELSON

United States Air Force Academy

New York

OXFORD UNIVERSITY PRESS

London   Toronto   1968

PREFACE

The allocation of funds by the United States government for the support of science and engineering now exceeds $15 billion a year, and might be found to be as much as 20 billion if all secondary and indirect aid could be attributed accurately. Not only is this more than the total cost of the World War II scientific effort, but it also exceeds the entire federal budget for the year immediately preceding the attack on Pearl Harbor. This impressive sum provides a good indication of the importance that the government is attaching to science, and there is every reason to believe that the emphasis will become even greater in the future. The heavy financial commitment of the government to the support of basic and applied research is a relatively recent phenomenon, even though a decision to encourage the development of science can be traced back as far as the adoption of the Constitutional clause providing for the protection of patent rights; and the actual assistance given over the years to certain fields of experimentation, especially in agriculture, has been considerable. The complexity and scope of this new obligation pose problems for the public official that were unknown just a few years ago.

At the outbreak of World War II, science hardly could have been considered to be a significant factor in government. Although there were a handful of scientific offices scattered throughout the various executive departments, the vast potential of the scientific revolution that was about to burst forth in a frenzy of wartime activity lay in the colleges and universities of the country, and to a lesser extent in the large manufacturing corporations. It was certainly not within the formal structure of government. Thus in building the immense military atomic project, the Manhattan Engineering District turned primarily to the Universities of Chicago and California for scientific support and to such industrial leaders as Union Carbide and Carbon and the Du Pont Corporation for technical assistance.

The $2 billion invested in the Manhattan project far outstripped the

v

total funds that government had spent on science and technology in all the previous history of the country. This was understandable in view of the magnitude of the war effort, but the feature that distinguished the undertaking from other temporary crash projects was the fact that large-scale government spending on research and engineering did not end with the defeat of Japan. A new agency, the Atomic Energy Commission, was created to administer the peacetime atomic program, and it was later joined by two other important scientific organizations—the National Science Foundation and the National Aeronautics and Space Administration. Also, under the stimulus of the Cold War, the military services undertook large programs for the development of new weapons, primarily by going outside of their own laboratories and making liberal use of the government contract and grant.

With the continuing appropriation of a substantial portion of the national budget to science and technology came new problems of allocation and administration. The process of decision-making in determining the distribution of federal funds became increasingly political, with various groups, special interests, and spokesmen competing against each other for a bigger share of the available government resources. The major universities were acutely aware of the influence that went with large grants and contracts. They also discovered that distinguished scientists and well-known researchers not only went where the government research awards were, but that the awards frequently followed an important scientist from one school to another. For example, one sure way to receive substantial government support for a research project was to designate a Nobel laureate as manager of the project. This situation resulted in a somewhat uneven competition for the services of such luminaries between the traditional prestige schools and the greatly expanded, and often larger, state universities.

A whole new complex of private corporations that are almost solely dependent upon the receipt of government contracts for research and development services also has arisen. This complex maintains elaborate contacts with both Congress and the Administration, and, since with many of the new organizations the government is the sole client and awards contracts by negotiation rather than competitive bidding, their status as private commercial concerns is more of a facade than a fact.

It would be pointless to argue the merits of the expanded emphasis upon science and technology, or even the necessity for the creation of the specific institutions that are involved in the new programs. They are now a fact of life and must be accepted as such. However, that is not to say that every request for funds to support a scientific project is to be treated as sacrosanct by the bureaucrat and the legislator. Difficult political decisions are involved at every turn. The questions of how much money should be appropriated for science, what priorities will be given to various programs, what individuals, institutions, or corporations will be entrusted with the development of the programs, and what degree of administrative control and management should be maintained, are absolutely critical.

Even though it is impossible to determine with any degree of certitude how much money the government should spend on science and technology, there will always be a limit to the funds available. Someone must decide between the relative priorities of such competing demands as aid to Yugoslavia, the level at which the price of sugar will be supported, the mobilization of a new infantry division, and the importance of putting a man on the moon. The complexity of this type of decision (a problem that might be compared to adding such incommensurables as apples and oranges) typifies the subject matter dealt with in this book.

Our primary concern involves an application of the decision-making process, but an application requiring the quantification of variables on a scale far broader than is normally associated with the formulation of government policy. In order to reduce the range of potential error in these decisions to the realm of acceptable risk, it is necessary that every possible effort be devoted to an examination of the conflicting values involved and the most effective ways of making decisions in which these values will be given due consideration. The relative merits of proposed programs must be balanced with the apparent likelihood of successfully achieving the identifiable objectives of the programs.

The reader will note that the essays in this book illustrate the emphasis of the government upon the physical sciences. This provides a reasonably accurate indication of the priorities that have existed in officially sponsored research. Without detracting from the importance of supporting the physical sciences, it can be observed that earlier and more extensive assistance to research in the biological sciences could have been highly productive. The explanation is simply that the large mission-oriented agencies and departments saw the potentialities of a direct return on their research investment to be greater with the physical sciences and engineering. Hopefully, there is an increased recognition of the need to broaden the scope of scientific programs in order to provide a more comprehensive approach to biological research.

A rather obvious deficiency in over-all government support is the comparatively narrow interpretation given to "science" and the resultant failure to support social research on a significant scale. Efforts such as those of Senator Fred R. Harris (D., Oklahoma) to establish a "National Foundation for the Social Sciences" are an encouraging sign that Congress is beginning to recognize the need to maintain a truly broadly based program that will encompass research in a multitude of promising academic disciplines. After all, the remarkable progress made in science and technology will create as many problems as it will solve if our political and social institutions are unable to adjust to the changed environment in which they must operate. This adjustment involves a joint responsibility. Social scientists must endeavor to understand the general nature and problems of the scientific enterprise, just as scientists and engineers must learn as much as they can about the political process as it affects their work. If this book is of some value in satisfying these responsibilities, it will have served its purpose.

Colorado Springs, Colorado   W.R.N.
November 1967

CONTENTS

I   The Scientific Revolution, 3

DON K. PRICE, The Republican Revolution, 5
VANNEVAR BUSH, Science: The Endless Frontier, 26
Scientific Activities in Government, 1940–1962, 55
DON K. PRICE, The Scientific Establishment, 70
CHARLES V. KIDD, The Growth of Science and the Distribution
        of Scientists among Nations, 87

II   Organizing for Science, 105

White House Superstructure for Science, 107
MEG GREENFIELD, Science Goes to Washington, 124
The National Science Foundation, 139
JAMES R. KERR, Congress and Space: Overview or Oversight?, 176

III   The Management of Research and Development, 191

Government Contracting for Research and Development, 193
BURTON H. KLEIN, Policy Issues Involved in the Conduct
        of Military Development Programs, 220
KLAUS KNORR AND OSKAR MORGENSTERN, Science and Defense, 237

IV   The Scientist as a Decision-Maker, 269

ALBERT WOHLSTETTER, Scientists, Seers and Strategy, 271
D. S. GREENBERG, Venture into Politics: Scientists and Engineers
        in the Election Campaign, 282
DONALD R. FLEMING, The Big Money and High Politics of Science, 299
WARNER R. SCHILLING, The H-Bomb Decision: How To Decide
        Without Actually Choosing, 308
ROBERT GILPIN, The Intra-Scientific Conflict over a Nuclear
        Test Ban: The Problem of Conflicting Expertise, 328

V   Science and Foreign Policy, 357

WARNER R. SCHILLING, Scientists, Foreign Policy, and Politics, 359
EUGENE B. SKOLNIKOFF, Scientific Advice in the State Department, 384
JOHN TURKEVICH, Soviet Science Appraised, 396
WILLIAM R. NELSON, Pugwash: The Scientific Conscience and
        International Politics, 406

ix

VI   Government and the Future of American Science, 421

LYNTON K. CALDWELL, Biopolitics: Science, Ethics, and Public
         Policy, 423
EDWARD T. CHASE, Politics and Technology, 435
GEORGE C. SPONSLER, Needed: Scientists on Top, 450
EMMANUEL G. MESTHENE, Can Only Scientists Make Government
         Science Policy?, 457
EUGENE RABINOWITCH, Responsibilities of Scientists in the Atomic
         Age, 465
WILLIAM R. NELSON, Science: A Means or an End?, 475

Index, 481

THE POLITICS OF SCIENCE

I
THE SCIENTIFIC REVOLUTION

In its own way as dynamic and far-reaching as the industrial and political revolutions of the eighteenth and nineteenth centuries, the scientific revolution we have witnessed since the outbreak of the Second World War may have an even greater effect upon the future of humanity—for this revolution contains the potential for either the infinite betterment or the destruction of civilization. The beginning of this scientific revolution can be identified with the creation of the Manhattan Engineering District. It is important to note that it represented not only the most ambitious joint scientific and technological project ever undertaken, but, and probably even more important for the future pattern of development, it cast the government in the role of the chief client and benefactor of science.

The scientific revolution has unfolded in three major phases, although these phases have been complementary to each other and not entirely separate, either in direction or objectives. They have, of course, been largely concurrent rather than consecutive in emphasis, producing compatible end products without much dependence by one phase upon progress in another. The three phases can be identified as atomic development, missile development, and computer development, together with the ancillary advances that each major program has incorporated.

Don K. Price, in the first reading, describes the profound influence of science on the evolution of American government and the rise of scientists and engineers to positions of high executive responsibility. This is followed by Vannevar Bush's report to the President on a program for government in the postwar support of science. It was this report, more than anything else, that shaped the peacetime relationships between science and its principal financial backer, and, although it was temporarily bogged down in a jurisdictional struggle between the President and Congress, the National Research Foundation that Bush proposed in his report set the

3

pattern for the establishment of the National Science Foundation in 1950.

The historical development of science in the United States since the war is the subject of an essay extracted from a National Science Foundation report. Of particular significance is the fact that by 1960 there were well over 100,000 scientists and engineers directly employed by the federal government, with an even larger number in industry and universities wholly or partially supported by government contracts or grants.

Science is identified as the major establishment in the American political system in a second reading by Don K. Price. In the dimensions of its financial support and in the breadth of its influence, science has become an independent force in government. The mobility of scientists, who are largely free from political restraints and the rigidity of the classified civil service system, gives them a unique opportunity to play an important role in all aspects of national policy.

Finally, Charles V. Kidd examines the problem of the migration of scientists as one of the phenomena accompanying the growth of science. He brings up the somber possibility that only those nations that are already scientifically advanced will benefit substantially from the scientific revolution.

This first chapter, emphasizing the growth of science and the new intellectual as well as the increased material affluence of the scientific community, establishes the environment for our study of the political considerations and machinations that are integral parts of the making of national science policy. Even though emphasis is placed upon the examination and analysis of events that have taken place in the United States, the lessons to be learned from these experiences may well be applicable to any nation undertaking a substantial program for scientific development.

4

DON K. PRICE
The Republican Revolution

At the end of World War II the mood of the scientific community was in sharp contrast to that of the general public. The popular magazines were full of advertisements promising that the great advances of science during the war would lead to a postwar utopia of new gadgets. But the scientists themselves were generally not so cheerful; indeed, their very success as scientists had made them fearful or pessimistic as citizens. To them—or to some of the more far-sighted among them—the invention of the atomic bomb was a threat to the freedom of the world, and particularly to the freedom of science.

These fears have by now become more widely accepted. The United States has come to see that it is in a new kind of rivalry with the Soviet Union—a rivalry that may well turn, not on territorial or diplomatic gains, or even (in the narrow sense of the word) on military advantage. The crucial advantage in the issue of power is likely to be with the nation whose scientific program can produce the next revolutionary advance in military tactics, following those already made by radar, jet propulsion, and nuclear fission.

Partially obscured by this spectacular military aspect of the role of science, but closely related to it, is its long-range economic aspect. The same fields of technology that are crucial to military tactics—electronic communications, aeronautics, and power—are also those that may have great influence in economic competition. The massing of scientific research for attack on military problems has its industrial by-products. In these fields the tremendous military research program is probably pushing our industry farther and farther ahead of its competitors, at a time when the most difficult economic problems of the free world arise because we can produce more things more cheaply than can our allies.

American science in its relation to government is in an uncomfortable pair of dilemmas. The main article of its faith is academic freedom, which would clearly be extinguished by a Communist triumph. To prevent such a triumph, American scientists are now required to work in a complicated network of secret and confidential data, and to communicate on many subjects only with those who have been officially investigated and cleared. Then, too, science has been accustomed in the past to rely for its support (and incidentally for its independence) on a great variety of local and private institutions. Yet it is now obvious to everyone that the structure of scientific research in American universities and industry has come to depend heavily on federal grants and federal contracts.

It is not surprising that many scientists have come to look on this relationship between science and government as an unhappy shotgun marriage, into which science had been frightened by the explosive force that it now measures in millions (instead of merely in thousands) of tons of TNT. They take this view even when they realize that they have helped to create a world in which the United States cannot be defended except by the maximum development of science, and in which science cannot be protected in its freedom, or supported with funds, except by government.

A very small minority of scientists in America have followed some of their European colleagues in looking to government as the savior of science from the capitalist system. Many more have tended to look on government as an authoritative and arbitrary institution controlled by politicians or bureaucrats who have little sympathy for the advancement of knowledge or the interests of private institutions.

Neither attitude seems to me to have much to do with the way that American government actually works today. Those who react automatically in favor of business as against government, or vice versa, or for civilian as against military institutions, or for private as against public institutions, are likely to find themselves in strangely contradictory positions. By classical textbook standards the American system of government is a maze of paradoxes—a confusing conglomeration in which private institutions have a major role in the planning of government policy, in which scientific advisers are held publicly responsible for some of the most critical decisions of war planning and the ivory tower of anonymity is reserved for generals and admirals, and in which Congressional committees check on administrative details while policy is developed either by trade associations or by harassed government clerks.

Yet this system, to the wonder of the foreigner—and, even more, of the informed insider—seems to work with a surprisingly dynamic quality. It is dynamic, it seems to me, because science, which has been the most explosive force in modern society, has profoundly influenced the development of the American government ever since the scientists took a hand in the great republican revolution of the eighteenth century. Unless we look at the way in which science helped first to shatter the authority of sovereigns, and then helped to rebuild authority in quite different patterns, we cannot understand the new relationship of science to government of the mid-twentieth century.

In looking at this new relationship, I shall not try to distinguish very carefully between basic and applied science, or to decide whether social science is really science at all. For I am interested in the influence on our governmental institutions, not of any particular scientific method, but of an attitude that scientists of all descriptions have shared, by contrast with politicians, clergymen, and lawyers. The scientist does not appeal to precedent or take things on faith. He wants to observe them, experiment with them, and prove them. This attitude, moreover, has spread during the past century or two among the general public. Though it began with the scientists, it then spread to the allied professions and the "mechanic arts," so that it is impossible to talk about the political consequences of science and refer only to the influence of scientists. It is the modern factual and objective way of thinking, which the scientist stimulated, that has worked on our political system indirectly, by way of the general climate of informed opinion.

We may as well start at the beginning, constitutionally speaking. The American Revolution and the American Constitution were the first great practical steps toward destroying the traditional conception of sovereignty and the traditional apparatus of hereditary rule. In Europe it was the age of the Enlightenment and the Encyclopedists—the rationalists who found themselves at odds with the existing apparatus of society. But in Europe there were no practical statesmen on the order of those who shaped the changes that revolutionized America well ahead of France. Washington, the surveyor and engineer who kept up a correspondence with Arthur Young on methods of scientific agriculture; Franklin, the inventor and experimenter; and Jefferson, who took an active personal lead in stimulating a wide range of scientific studies from paleontology to meteorology—these were the men who set the intellectual tone among the leaders in the American colonies.

The first effect of their leadership was to destroy the traditional theory of hereditary sovereignty, and to substitute the idea that the people had the right, by rational and experimental processes, to build their governmental institutions to suit themselves. The new government could not rest on a basis of either dynastic authority or military force. Its basis had to be a representative republican system. That system had to depend on elections, in constituencies that did not exist by virtue of grants from the king. The people, in short, had to be the basis of political power. Accordingly, the people had to be counted, and for the first time in modern history a nation instituted a complete census.

The census thus became the ultimate basis of sovereign power in the

United States. The Constitution itself required the federal government to make the largest collection of social-science data in the world, and the census is still the most important source of materials for social-science research. There are those who believe that the government cannot properly support research in the social sciences because of their controversial nature. Yet today the most significant redistribution of political power in America is accomplished by the clerks in the Bureau of the Census, who each ten years calculate the new representation of the states in the House of Representatives. Even though the decennial census has been one of the great occasions for the distribution of political patronage, hardly anyone has questioned the integrity of the Census Bureau's basic information.

The American Revolution was so thorough—partly, of course, because it took place in a relatively new country and partly because the leading Tories were forced to emigrate—that the fundamental issues in American society developed during the next two centuries in an almost unique form. The French liberals had to spend the nineteenth century fighting the entrenched military and ecclesiastical establishments, which still exercised profound influence within the permanent institutions of government. In Great Britain the liberals were similarly engaged in restricting the royal prerogative and destroying the remnants of feudal privilege. Meanwhile, in Great Britain as well as on the Continent, the old ruling class assimilated the new captains of industry.

It was therefore very easy for the European liberal to accept Marx's view that the government was a great permanent engine for the defense of the privileged capitalist classes, and thus the more liberal wing in politics moved fairly steadily toward various forms of socialism as a solution to its problems.

In America this trend did not make much sense to anyone. The government was not permanent enough, or efficient enough, to be thought of as an engine for anything. In early America it was, indeed, the conservatives who sought to make the government an instrument of national economic and industrial planning, and it was the triumphant democracy that destroyed their dream. The intellectual center of this dream was the idea of a national university—a center for the advancement of the sciences recommended by President Washington and by several of his successors. Alexander Hamilton made the keystone of his system for the development of American manufactures a system of government bounties and subsidies to scientists and inventors, to accompany the use of tariff and other government policies for the encouragement of industrialization.[1] John Quincy Adams followed George Washington in believing that the key to the preser-

1. "Report on Manufactures" in *The Works of Alexander Hamilton* (New York: Williams and Whiting, 1810), Vol. I, pp. 235–36.

vation of the Union was the use of all the resources of the applied sciences to create a system of transportation and communications to develop the West and to link together the North and the South.

As John Quincy Adams wrote in a personal letter in 1837:

> The great effort of my administration was to mature into a permanent and regular system the application of all the superfluous revenue of the Union to internal improvement. . . . With this system in ten years from this day the surface of the whole Union would have been checkered over with railroads and canals. It may still be done half a century later and with the limping gait of State legislature and private adventure. I would have done it in the administration of the affairs of the nation.[2]

John Quincy Adams was the last of the great statesmen of the Federalist period who united with politics a deep personal interest in science. As Secretary of State he personally prepared for the Congress a *Report upon Weights and Measures;*[3] as an elder statesman in Congress he continued to fight for a wide variety of scientific programs; and he finally killed himself by traveling at an advanced age in bad weather to Cincinnati to dedicate an astronomical observatory.

His grandson, Brooks Adams, has called attention to his fundamental belief:

> He alone among public men of that period appreciated that a nation to flourish under conditions of modern economic competition, must organize its administrative, as well as its social system upon scientific principles.

But this was a futile dream. John Quincy Adams had inherited from the Federalists and the Jeffersonians alike the ideal of a competent public service. But, to quote Brooks Adams again:

> As John Quincy Adams discovered in 1828, democracy would not permit the ablest staff of officials, to be chosen by him, to administer the public trust. Democracy, on the contrary, has insisted on degrading the public service to a common level of incapacity, thereby throwing the management of all difficult public problems,

2. To the Reverend Charles W. Upham. Quoted in Henry Adams, *The Degradation of the Democratic Dogma* (with an introduction by Brooks Adams) (New York: The Macmillan Company, 1919), pp. 24–25.
3. John Quincy Adams, Secretary of State of the United States, *Report Upon Weights and Measures, prepared in obedience to a resolution of the Senate of the Third March, 1817* (Washington: Gales and Seaton, 1821). Thomas Jefferson, as Secretary of State, had submitted to the House of Representatives on July 17, 1790, a *Report of the Secretary of State on the Subject of Establishing the Uniformity of the Weights, Measures, and Coins of the United States.*

such as the use of railroads and canals, into private hands, in order
that they might escape ruin, and thence has come the predicament
in which we, in particular, and the world at large, now stand.[4]

This was a revolution even more drastic in some of its practical effects
than that of 1776. The earlier revolution denied the old theory of sovereignty; the later one made government ineffective as a working organization. In this respect the states and cities outdid the federal government. As
they adopted new constitutions and charters they not only made their personnel systems subject to political spoils, but also made their forms of organization diffuse and emasculated their powers.

This system might have worked indefinitely if America had remained the
frontier as Andrew Jackson knew it, or had developed according to the
agrarian ideals of Jefferson. But just as the philosophical scientists of the
eighteenth century had begun the process of weakening the authority of
government, so the applied scientists of the nineteenth century—the engineers and inventors—made necessary the strengthening of its structure and
authority. They built up the modern corporation, the modern metropolitan
area, and the great concentrations of economic power and social problems
that could not be dealt with by the weak governments of the frontier. For
this development the American people were intellectually quite unpre-
pared. They had neither the legal theory nor the established administrative
machinery to cope with problems that could be solved only by the steady
policies of a strong government.

Science took part in the republican revolution that destroyed the old system of sovereign authority. It was then forced, by the very changes that it
effected in society, to take part in the rebuilding of the machinery of government. Constitutional historians have always noted how the radicalism of
the Declaration of Independence had to be counterbalanced by the conservatism of the Constitution. But they have less often observed that the
pervasive weakening of authority and administration that went with the republican revolution continued for nearly a century. And then science had a
hand in developing the legal theory and the administrative machinery that
were needed to make the federal Constitution—and the state constitutions
and municipal charters—workable in modern society.

Science did so, first of all, by helping to show that government needed to
add to its legal powers to deal with modern probems. It became clear that
life in industrial cities would be intolerable without more regulation by
government than was possible under a Jeffersonian political theory. It is
hard in the mid-twentieth century to appreciate how much the city dweller
depends for his health and safety on governmental controls that were le-

4. Introduction by Brooks Adams in Henry Adams, *The Degradation of the Democratic Dogma* (New York: The Macmillan Company, 1919), pp. 61, 120–21.

gally impossible a century ago—on public health regulations, on city planning and zoning, and on fire, electrical, and building inspection, to say nothing of the positive municipal services. At the same time the farmer has gone even farther than the city dweller in requiring the government to sustain and regulate his aspect of the national economy.

The powers for these purposes were added to government only gradually, and only because the law began to find that there were issues that could not be settled entirely by legal precedent or by reasoning from abstract principles. It began to take note of proof furnished by the sciences and of the informed opinion of organized professional groups.

It is important to note that in all this process the initiative and leadership came from local scientific and professional groups or from local groups of laymen interested in science. Their interest was usually based not on the cultivation of science for its own sake, but on the solution of practical problems. But in the end it led the government not only to undertake scientific research, but also to expand its powers, its functions, and its personnel to take advantage of the new opportunities developed by research and experimentation.

Let us have a look first at the way some of the regulatory powers of government developed. Throughout the nineteenth century judges were gradually persuaded that public health regulations were necessary for the prevention of epidemics. These regulations were extended from the simple provisions of quarantine to a wide variety of sanitary regulations, and finally to the provision of authority for zoning and city planning in the interests of the public health and safety. Gradually the massing of medical evidence regarding contagious disease, and the relation of such evidence to the sociological statistics regarding urban life in general, provided the basis for the development of municipal powers in America.

The federal government, making use of its constitutional power to control commerce, began to extend its regulatory functions as soon as the local governments themselves. Alexander Dallas Bache, the great-grandson of Benjamin Franklin, was the professor of natural philosophy and chemistry at the University of Pennsylvania. Professor Bache became chairman of a special committee at the Franklin Institute in 1832 to investigate the reasons for the explosions of steamboat boilers. The Secretary of the Treasury, with the help of a special appropriation of the Congress, contributed $1,500 toward the expenses of this investigation—probably the first grant by the federal government for experimental research.

The committee reported in 1836 with a magnificent disregard for the limitations of science. It first discussed such scientific problems as the manifestations of steam pressure and the qualities of various types of iron and copper boilers, but then went on to recommend to the Congress a draft bill providing for the first program of federal regulation of business. The bill was enacted, and the Steamboat Inspection Service became the first federal regulatory agency.[5]

Progress in the physical and biological sciences, medicine, and engineering made perhaps the first important contribution to the development of government powers and programs, but the social sciences were not far behind. The regulation of business by both the federal and state governments began to develop in the late nineteenth century. This development would hardly have been possible without the economic and statistical studies that began to expand at that time. J. D. B. De Bow, who headed the Census Bureau when it conducted the census of 1850—containing some statistical series even more elaborate than those of today—founded *De Bow's Review,* the first economics journal in America, and gave great impetus to the development of this whole field of study. Not much later the studies of John R. Commons laid the groundwork for the twentieth-century advances in labor legislation, and the research of Charles Francis Adams on problems of transportation economics led directly to the regulation of the railroads, first by the states, and then by the federal government through the Interstate Commerce Commission. As for the railroads, of course, the social and natural sciences joined hands in encouraging federal regulation; the Franklin Institute, appalled by the railway wrecks as it had been earlier by the steamboat disasters, worked out a uniform code of railway signals, which was enacted into federal legislation.[6]

The history textbooks are accustomed to trace the development of governmental policy in relation to party campaigns and changes in national administration, as they are likely to credit the revolution in technology to the inventions of an Edison, Morse, or Bell. But just as these inventors were simply carrying to conclusion the work of scientists still comparatively unknown to the public, so the development of government powers and functions during the past century has been only the inevitable adoption by politicians of ideas first developed in scientific laboratories and in scholarly or professional societies.

But this is getting ahead of our story. Let us look for a moment at the way in which the government began to support science during the nineteenth century.

First of all there is the story of the agricultural sciences. In this field gov-

5. Committee of the Franklin Institute of the State of Pennsylvania for the Promotion of the Mechanic Arts, *General Report on the Explosions of Steam-Boilers* (Philadelphia: C. Sherman & Co. Printers, 19 St. James Street, 1836).
6. Thomas Coulson, "The First Hundred Years of Research at the Franklin Institute," *Journal of the Franklin Institute,* CCLVI, No. 1 (July 1953).

ernment support was no novelty, even at the time when President Washington first proposed to the Congress the establishment of a National Board of Agriculture. Parliament under the Puritan Commonwealth had granted funds for experimentation in Georgia on the growth of indigo and other agricultural products.

The creation of a federal agricultural agency, like the rest of the grand design of the Federalists for the development of the national economy, was blocked by Jefferson's strict construction of the Constitution. Nevertheless, Jefferson as an individual gave a great impetus to the support of the agricultural sciences. In 1787, for example, he smuggled rice out of Piedmont in spite of the laws prohibiting its export on pain of death, and encouraged the founding of agricultural societies and their co-operation on a national basis.

In the development of a new continent the great opportunity of the applied sciences was in the mapping of the country, the surveying of its natural resources, and the improvement of its agriculture. On the recommendation of the American Philosophical Society President Jefferson transmitted to the Congress a proposal for the establishment of the United States Coast Survey, which was set up in the Treasury Department in 1807. The American Association for the Advancement of Science was created when the American Society of Geologists and Naturalists decided to broaden its scope and change its name. Expeditions like those of Lewis and Clark, whom President Jefferson sent out to explore the West, were only spectacular extensions of the work being carried on in a great many states. The first President of the A.A.A.S. had been a state geologist in Massachusetts, New York, and Vermont,[7] and the agricultural experiment stations in the states, which began without federal support, grew out of the work of the geological surveys.

About this time began the active co-operation of the private agricultural societies with government officials. This was a reciprocal business. Public officials encouraged and stimulated the growth of the private organizations. The Commissioner of Patents in the State Department, who had begun as early as 1836 to distribute free seeds to farmers, helped organize the Agricultural Society of the United States; and after the Civil War officials in the new Department of Agriculture helped organize the National Grange. But the pressure was far more continuous and effective in the opposite direction. The national official agencies were created by the initiative and support of the private associations. The New York State Agricultural Society from 1832, and the United States Agricultural Society from 1852, worked

7. Frederick W. True, *A History of the First Half-Century of the National Academy of Sciences, 1863–1913* (Washington: National Academy of Sciences, 1913), p. 152.

steadily for the creation of state experiment stations and for the creation of a national Department of Agriculture.[8]

The support of the agricultural sciences—into which the greater part of the federal research funds went until World War II—was based not only on the recommendations of local groups of scientists, but also on the more widespread demand from the farmers and their organizations. The seeds that Jefferson smuggled out of Europe and those that American consuls sent back for experimental purposes in later years led Congressmen to the habit of sending out free seeds to their constituents—an important item of patronage for more than a century and one that helped educate Congress to the need for technical assistance to American farmers.

It was such practical politics that shaped the system of federal aid to agricultural research. In 1862 Congress might have decided to give funds for agricultural research to the principal existing universities, where the best research could have been had for the money. It might have given funds to the Smithsonian Institution or set up laboratories directly in some federal agency.

Instead the Congress, in the same year that it created the Department of Agriculture, passed the Morrill Act and the Homestead Act. These two acts followed the precedent of the grant of federal lands for education in the Northwest Territory in 1787—grants of free land for what amounted to relief purposes and for bonuses to veterans of the Revolution. The Homestead Act followed the appeal of the Republican Party to "vote yourself a farm," and the Morrill Act set up a system of grants of public lands to the states to support the creation of colleges—the land-grant colleges—for training in the agricultural and mechanic arts. By the end of the century the land-grant system had been expanded into a system of cash grants to the states for the support of experiment stations associated with the A. and M. colleges.

This policy was doubtless not the most efficient and economical way to produce first-rate basic research. It led to the support of a great many institutions that the better established universities condescendingly called the "cow colleges." It led to a great deal of research in which the practical problems of the local farmers were considered far more important than basic scientific principles. But it did cover the country with institutions for training and research in the agricultural sciences and engineering, a system that has no parallel in any other country.

Since this system owed its beginning to political pressure, it is not surprising that the distribution of grants for agricultural research was not ac-

8. A. C. True, *A History of Agricultural Experimentation and Research in the United States, 1607–1925* (Washington: Government Printing Office, 1937), Misc. Pub. No. 251, United States Department of Agriculture.

companied, in the early days, by any very effective central supervision. The funds were divided among the experiment stations according to a statutory formula rather than by administrative discretion. And it was many years before the development of the research bureaus in the Department of Agriculture, and the threat of such pests as the boll weevil, gave the Department of Agriculture a role of effective leadership over the state experiment stations.

By beginning with scientific experimentation and later moving on into research in agricultural economics, the Department of Agriculture laid the foundations of the whole range of federal programs for the encouragement, support, and control of agriculture on a national basis—a system that has made the supposedly most individualistic class in American society the enthusiastic supporters of a thoroughgoing national system of technical aid and economic regulation. In no field is there a clearer line of connection between the development of scientific research and the subsequent development of governmental authority and programs.

In other fields of science the relationship with government developed in different patterns. During the nineteenth century, two institutions deserve particular attention: the Smithsonian Institution and the National Academy of Sciences. Whereas the system of agricultural research grew up gradually, and its shape was determined by political considerations, these two institutions were created by scientists and conformed to their ideas about the proper relationship of government and science.

The Smithsonian Institution was not incorporated until 1846, but it was the fruit of the ideas of a half century earlier. James Smithson, the illegitimate son of the Duke of Northumberland, was (like Priestly) one of the English scientists who were sympathetic to the ideas of the American and French revolutions. In 1792 he was in Paris, singing *Ça Ira* and writing home letters that were unmistakably republican in sentiment. In later years he continued to live abroad, perhaps disillusioned with politics and certainly resentful of the fact that his illegitimacy barred him from the social station of his ancestors in English society. He doubtless believed that the radical and rational young republic of Franklin and Jefferson was better able than England to use his estate, as he said in his will, for "the increase and diffusion of knowledge among men."

Smithson died in 1829, the year in which Andrew Jackson became President. By the time his bequest reached the United States, democracy was no longer a theory in the United States—it was a fact that had all the imperfections of most political facts. The scientists and their sponsors in the Congress—particularly John Quincy Adams, who led the fight for the acceptance of Smithson's bequest—were no longer in the vanguard of revolutionary politics. On the contrary, they were eager to establish the Smithsonian Institution under a form of organization that would insulate it as far as possible from partisan politics and protect its privately donated capital from political abuse.

Ironically enough, the original capital was invested in bonds of the state of Arkansas, which defaulted on them, but the federal government restored the full amount and guaranteed the Smithsonian six per cent interest perpetually. Nevertheless, and although the Institution is listed as a part of the organization of the federal government, it has always liked to consider itself a private trust rather than a government agency.[9]

As far as I know, the only function ever vested by law in the President's Cabinet is that of serving as the membership of the Smithsonian Establishment. But the Establishment, though composed of the principal heads of the executive departments, has nothing to do with running the Institution. That is the responsibility of the Board of Regents; this executive board is made up mainly of officials from the judicial and legislative branches of the government and filled out by the appointment of several private citizens. It in turn delegates its executive function to the Secretary whom it appoints.

The Smithsonian defies classification, but it may well be thought of as the first American foundation of national scope. It had many of the qualities of the later private foundations, for it pioneered in a great many fields and left the further development of its ideas to other institutions. One of the seven secretaries who have served it since 1836 helped found the National Academy of Sciences; another originated the Marine Biological Station at Woods Hole, Massachusetts; and another took the lead in establishing the Carnegie Institution of Washington and in organizing the National Advisory Committee for Aeronautics. The Institution was a tremendous influence in developing the scientific activities of a dozen or more federal agencies during the nineteenth century. Its more recent history, however, suggests that there are handicaps as well as advantages in the form of government organization that is divorced from political control and from operating programs. The newer and more exciting functions have gone to other agencies, while the Smithsonian has been loaded down with the administrative burdens of a group of museums and a zoo, which take up about nine tenths of its budget.

The National Academy of Sciences was not a new idea when it was chartered by the Congress in 1863. The Civil War simply gave the scientists a chance to establish an institution of which they had been dreaming for dec-

9. The Institution proper is supported by the income of its endowments, which have grown as a result of private gifts to many times the original sum given by Smithson. The Secretary of the Smithsonian, however, administers the United States National Museum and nine other smaller federal agencies that are wholly supported by annual appropriations made by the Congress.

ades. The same men who had advocated a national university during the Federalist period had discussed the creation of a National Academy; indeed, the two ideas were sometimes indistinguishable.

By 1851 Professor Bache, in a speech as President of the A.A.A.S., had proposed the creation of a National Academy to provide scientific advice to government agencies. "There are few applications of Science," he argued, "which do not bear on the interests of commerce and navigation, naval or military concerns, the customs, the light-houses, the public lands, post-offices and post-roads, either directly or remotely."

To give the government help on such problems was one purpose of the Academy; another was to supply a kind of honorific distinction that had been missing in American intellectual life. Joseph Henry, as President of the Academy in 1867, referred wistfully to the honors and rewards given scientists by the academies of Paris, Berlin, and St. Petersburg and hoped that the Academy would supply similar incentives to encourage "devotion to original research," as contrasted with mechanical inventions. At the same time, to justify the complete detachment of the Academy from government control, its charter sought to protect it, as its first President noted, from suspicion of any "taint of self-seeking as to power or influence," or "taint of supposed desire for remuneration," [10] by simply providing that it could never be paid for its work for the government beyond the actual expense of its investigations.

The organization of the Academy was more suited to the purpose of providing honor to its members than advice to the government. It was a self-perpetuating group, limited at first to fifty members, which had to set up an *ad hoc* committee to consider each request for help from an official agency. Yet the work of the Academy was fruitful not only in furthering science, but in its effects on the operating programs of government.

For example, the scientists were the first to recognize that America was destroying its natural resources by wasteful methods of development. The A.A.A.S. had lobbied for years in favor of federal laws to protect the remaining forests. Perhaps the most crucial step toward a new federal policy, however, was the creation in 1896 of the National Academy's Committee on the Inauguration of a National Forest Policy. The report of this committee, of which Gifford Pinchot was a member, led to the creation of the United States Forest Service, and Pinchot later credited it with originating the federal forest policy.[11]

10. Frederick W. True, *A History of the First Half-Century of the National Academy of Sciences, 1863–1913* (Washington: National Academy of Sciences, 1913), p. 203.
11. *Yearbook of the United States Department of Agriculture, 1899* (Washington: Government Printing Office, 1900), p. 297. This Yearbook, as its Preface says, pre-

Similarly, it was as a result of committee reports from the National Academy that the Congress set up the Geological Survey to unify and develop the survey work of the Department of the Interior and created the Weather Bureau as a civilian agency to carry on the work originally done by the Army Signal Corps.

We have already seen how the work of the agricultural experiment stations led to the present broad programs of the Department of Agriculture, and we have noted the geological and other survey work that led to the programs of the Forest Service and of the Department of Interior. A little later the Department of Commerce and Labor was established, primarily to carry on research on industrial and labor problems. These research programs included that of the National Bureau of Standards, for which the National Academy had lobbied for some time. But they also included a wide range of social-science research. These research programs gradually broadened to form the basis of the subsequent programs of Commerce and Labor when they were set up as separate departments, and of the emergency programs of public assistance and wartime regulation of the economy. Thus the research programs of natural and social scientists laid the foundation for the development of government services, the extension of governmental powers, and the regulation of key aspects of the national economy.

The federal government, after starting with a theory that denied the traditional doctrines of sovereignty, gradually built up its powers and functions to make use of the applied sciences for the development of the new continent, and ultimately to meet the needs of an industrialized economy. In this process the national associations and organizations of scientists and their professional colleagues—working within their specialized groups without regard to partisan allegiance or to the boundaries between government and private life—supplied the most dynamic initiative.

But the same scientists who led the government to undertake its new functions were far from willing to build up the government as an authoritative central power. The public agencies that they helped to create were often so organized as to make them as independent of the heads of government as if they were private institutions. Americans learned early that it was possible, especially in the states and municipalities, to create public agencies that were a part of the general government in name and financial support only. In this respect the scientists were often in alliance with the lawyers, who were eager to leave as little discretionary power as possible in the hands of those who administered the laws. So the habit developed of

---

sented "for the first time within the covers of a single volume a fairly comprehensive review of the progress and development of a century in almost every branch of scientific inquiry having a direct practical bearing upon agriculture."

delegating new functions to independent boards or commissions, which were supposed to operate on the basis of scientific or professional judgment and with as little mixture of politics as possible.

These boards were usually staffed by government personnel and supported by public funds. Yet many of them, with the moral and political support of their professional colleagues and clients, maintained for many years a high degree of independence of the mayor or governor or legislature. They were usually not very efficient and are now going out of fashion —except, of course, in the field of education—but they may have been necessary for the creation of professional respectability and *esprit de corps* as the government undertook new functions.

In the federal government the Constitution made it more difficult to set up such independent boards, somewhat to the distress of the National Academy, which repeatedly recommended that boards of scientists be created to head research and related programs. This was all to the good, from the administrator's point of view. But a sound constitutional structure was not, by itself, enough to provide good administration. It could not provide an adequate career service or create competent executives. John Quincy Adams, for all his administrative ability as Secretary of State, saw the Patent Office fall into chaos because its head was a scientist more interested in organizing subversive movements for the freedom of the Latin-American republics than in recording new patents.[12] A little later the Jacksonian revolution swept away what little career merit system there was, and the factional tensions of the Civil War period completed the corruption of the civil service.

In the United States, by contrast with either Great Britain or the major European countries, we have not developed career groups of permanent civil servants who are predominantly general administrators. The British, for example, started with a permanent civil service covering the major administrative positions, and then sought to improve its efficiency and to supplement it with strong scientific and technical services. By contrast, in the United States the scientific services were the first to be developed on a nonpartisan and efficient basis.

The basic reason for this contrast, of course, is quite clear. The United States was building its government from the ground up, without the benefit of a strong center of established authority—indeed, with the purpose of preventing the development of any such center. Competing factions or parties intended to use administrative appointments either to put into effect their particular policies or, more crudely, to serve as bribes for their political supporters. This spoils system was put out of business less by the civil

12. Leonard D. White, *The Jeffersonians* (New York: The Macmillan Company, 1951), pp. 207–10.

service reformers than by the development of strong professional groups and of specific scientific and technical criteria for appointment to office.

It was comparatively hard to prove that the country suffered if an unqualified person became a collector of customs, or a junior diplomat, or a postal executive. It was comparatively easy to prove that it suffered if he became a public health doctor or a geodetic engineer. Moreover, there were professional bodies whose standards and *esprit de corps* gave strong moral support to those who sought to improve the public service in such scientific fields. Hence the scientific and technical positions of the government were generally the first to be taken out of politics and put on a merit basis.[13]

In part this was accomplished by developing the scientific bureaus under the wing of the military departments. Some scientists, in commenting on the history of these bureaus, argue that they would have done better if they had been entirely under the direction of civilian scientists. But I think it is probable that the military services, especially in the mid-nineteenth century, were the only parts of the federal government that could be counted on for a measure of continuity and stability in administration. As poorly as they were frequently administered, they at least were founded on the ideal of a non-partisan career system, in which provision could be made for scientific training.

West Point, it should not be forgotten, was the first engineering school in the United States, and it was the Army engineers who applied the sciences of the day to the surveying and development of the West and to the provision of internal improvements. Similarly the Navy, with its need for skills in navigation and shipbuilding, was a natural sponsor of the sciences. The Naval Observatory was one of the earliest federal agencies to undertake the support of relatively basic science; A. A. Michelson undertook his work on measuring the velocity of light as Ensign Michelson, U.S.N.

When the civil service reform movement got under way in the latter part of the nineteenth century it was no longer possible to hope that a general civilian career service could be established. If we were to take government jobs out of politics, it could not be done by setting up a separate class of career officials. Each job had to be filled by the person who could prove that he was the best able to perform its particular duties. To withstand political criticism the examination had to be as specific and as objective as possible.

By consequence, government personnel systems in the United States had

13. Lewis Meriam, *Public Personnel Problems* (Washington: The Brookings Institution, 1938), p. 317. ". . . the tendency has been to leave in the patronage fields the . . . general administrators. . . . Our national legislator and political executives have on the other hand repeatedly recognized that for scientific, technical, and professional work, competence in the field and permanency of tenure are essential."

to make use to the fullest possible extent of fool-proof testing methods. The psychologists helped to introduce into government some of the most advanced techniques of testing, selection, and classification of personnel.

Some of this was useful. But a great deal of it was not, and the public personnel system bogged down in a mass of pseudo science. Recruitment examinations were devised so as to keep the examiner from having to use any judgment. The objective short-answer test prevented the examiner from being considered partial or partisan, but it did little to help him select candidates for government jobs who would have the intellectual ability to deal with general policy issues and the personal qualities that would enable them to accept managerial responsibility. Similarly, the detailed classification of positions was suitable enough for specialized and subordinate functions, but it was a great handicap to the creation of a career service in the higher ranks of research workers or administrators.

While this defect has led to great difficulties in the development of general administrators, it has left the field free for scientists and engineers to move into managerial positions. In American government, as in American business, the top executive positions have not been pre-empted either by a single social class or by a closed career service. Consequently, in all the fields in which scientific or technical knowledge is important, scientists and engineers have tended to rise into positions of executive responsibility. In Great Britain the scientific civil servants have always complained that they were kept out of positions of top authority by the administrative class. In the United States the complaint is more likely to be the opposite—that good scientists are ruined by being taken from laboratory positions and given administrative responsibilities for which they may be poorly suited.

While the American democracy distrusted public officials as a class, it was almost equally distrustful of organized science and the professions. It is worth remarking that in the United States, by contrast with Great Britain, admission to a profession is controlled by examinations administered by a government, rather than by professional societies. Similarly, American universities are not controlled by governing bodies made up of university scholars; instead, they are headed by boards of lay trustees. Accordingly, scientists and engineers of the more ambitious sort were not content to look on their profession as a separate segment of society. Instead, they moved naturally into administrative and executive positions in business as well as government, with the purpose of applying their scientific skills to practical affairs.

This system developed, no doubt, partly because there was no group of career civilian administrators in the government (as there was a group of career military officers) to maintain general control over the administration of public affairs. The lack of such general administration has probably made for poor management in little things, but for dynamic administration in the big issues. For it puts in positions of executive responsibility men who are committed by their training to the exploiting of new ideas and the adoption of new techniques.[14] These are not, in general, the men who judge their accomplishments by the absence of criticism and by administrative convenience. They are far more likely to fall into the opposite error, of believing that the public interest is the same as their professional specialty.

In this tendency the scientist-administrator is aided by the nature of the American federal system. Like any other specialist, he can do business with his professional counterpart at other levels of government, regardless of party or of the policy of the general administration. For example, the close relation of the public health specialists—federal, state, and local—has helped to develop their program regardless of party platforms. Personnel moves from one level of government to another, and ideas are exchanged at professional gatherings. These ties, reinforced by the system of grants-in-aid, do much to strengthen many of the programs in which scientists and technicians are involved.

The expansion of government functions over the past half century has required reforms in the organization of government as well as in its personnel. In this field, too, there has been a heavy reliance on research as a preliminary to action. States and cities throughout the country, in the early nineteenth century, adopted forms of organization that were unworkable in the society created by modern science and industry. The steps toward reform, which have made impressive changes at all levels of government, have followed painstaking research by universities and research bureaus. To the foreign visitor the most striking phenomenon in American government is likely to be the extent to which private research institutions play a continuous role in the development of government administration—a subject that in most European countries, and even in Great Britain, is considered the province of the professional civil servant alone.

The emphasis on research as a preliminary to governmental action comes, of course, from an unwillingness to permit the government not only to answer a question arbitrarily but even to define the issue, present its views, and manage the administrative machinery. This unwillingness to take the answers from established authority leads to a tremendous use of research as a basis of decisions at all levels. The Congress itself, being unwilling merely to act on the recommendations of the President, relies on its

14. *Sixth Annual Report of the Advisory Council on Scientific Policy* (*1952–1953*) (London: H. M. Stationery Office), Cmd. 8874, p. 2. ". . . scientists and engineers are urgently needed not only in the laboratories and workshops, but also in the board rooms of British industry. . . . It is no accident that the enormous growth of American production has coincided with an increasing representation in management of men with a strong scientific or technical background."

committees. Those committees in turn do not like to trust the executive agencies to prepare the information on which they act, but make use of independent research staff. And in addition to regular staff members, the Congress has begun more and more to create special research commissions to provide it with programs on which to act.

It is a common observation among political scientists that the weakness of party discipline in the Congress makes it hard to develop a long-range and consistent policy in the United States government. It is less commonly noted that the indirect effects of the lack of Congressional discipline are as important as the direct effects, and that both reflect the American tradition of distrusting authority as such, and of wanting to handle each issue on its merits. These indirect effects are the government's lack of ability to maintain the kind of organization, staffed by the kind of career personnel, that can maintain through the years a steady and coherent view of national policy. As a result it is difficult to present general policy issues to the public and the Congress. Instead of a grand battle between opposing forces we have a series of unrelated skirmishes, generally on administrative or technical issues.

A country like Great Britain, which gradually grafted democratic institutions onto a strong system of traditional authority, could afford to let each current issue be settled by a contest between two clear-cut political parties, especially if the parties could be trusted to agree on fundamentals. But in a country that had started with a popular revolution and was only gradually developing a stable and authoritative system of government, this was a dangerous approach. The experience of the Civil War taught that lesson to those who did not already know it. As a result the American political system has not been based on a contest between two ideological systems. It has instead compartmentalized authority among Congressional committees and semi-independent executive authorities. This is a system that makes it hard to develop broad and consistent policies, while encouraging appeals to research on each separate problem.

As a result, long-range policy decisions do not depend on general political theory, but are frequently made (in effect) by groups of scientists and technicians, working in professional associations or in universities or research institutions, who develop the basic ideas to which the practical politicians will turn in order to deal with the next emergency.

In the long run this system, or lack of system, gives a great deal of influence in public affairs to men whose positions enable them to maintain a comprehensive view of new scientific and intellectual developments. Someone has facetiously remarked that our university presidents are the American equivalent of the British peerage—men whose opinions on public issues must be considered, but who have no formal power.

But for all their weight as general advisers, the university presidents are probably less influential on particular policies than the scientists who are leaders in their professional societies and research councils. De Tocqueville remarked that where you found a public enterprise headed in Great Britain by a man of rank, and in France by an agency of government, in America it would be headed by an association.

This has been particularly true for the government programs in which science is concerned. The origins of policies are not to be found in party platforms or the pronouncements of political leaders. They can rather be traced in the discussions that take place among leaders in scientific and professional fields, in the research studies that such discussions stimulate, and in the consequent consensus among the professionals.

During the twentieth century the influence of such intellectual leaders has been greatly extended by the financial backing of the great foundations. The foundation officials themselves, always on the lookout for new intellectual developments that may contribute to public affairs, thus make a great contribution in the long run to public policy. In part their influence has been exercised by supporting work aimed directly at problems of government, as did the Spelman Fund when it supported the organization of professional societies of public officials. But they have exercised even greater influence on government almost absent-mindedly, by their support of scientific and technical programs. The atom bomb might never have been developed if the Rockefeller Foundation had not built cyclotrons in the middle 1930's, or in the 1920's given financial support in Europe to Enrico Fermi and Niels Bohr. To take a less known and less spectacular example, the work of the Rockefeller Foundation's predecessor, in its efforts to combat hookworm and improve agricultural education, led to experiments in local government (and in grants-in-aid to local government) that undoubtedly paved the way for the federal-state-local relationships by which most of the modern government programs are administered.

To the scientific or rationalistic mind of the eighteenth century it made no sense to let the control of public affairs depend on a hereditary monarchy, supported by traditional political theory. The classical idea of parliamentary democracy sought to solve that problem (in Great Britain) by competition between two parties, each with its own political theory, or (on the Continent) among many parties—and the more numerous the parties, the more dogmatic their theories.

This idea is accepted by a great many American political scientists as the working model by which they criticize their own institutions. But it was a pattern that never really applied to American politics. To a people brought up to question dogmatic political theory, it seemed no better to be guided by two or a dozen party dogmas than by one—and perhaps not so safe. In the American political system the pragmatic and experimental method prevailed. This was the method in which each issue was dealt with on an experimental basis, with the views of the interested technical or professional groups having more weight than party platforms or political theories. It was a method that gave far more weight to research and to scientists, and created a more dynamic economic and political system than could have prevailed under a more orderly and authoritative approach.

As we look at the relation of government and science in the United States, we must learn to think without making use of the patterns or models taken for granted by most of the textbooks. The skepticism of traditional authority and the unwillingness to create permanent and highly professionalized organs of administration were deeply rooted in the American mind in the eighteenth century by rationalist and scientific currents of thought. In America the republican revolution was a thorough one. It did not stop with the substitution of a President for a King. It went deep into the fundamental fabric of government. As the sciences had destroyed the old unified philosophical and theological system of thought, the republican revolution in America swept away the unified apparatus of authority that had been based on that system. Thus the alliance between science and the republican revolution first destroyed, and then rebuilt on a different pattern, the forms of organization and the systems of personnel that determine the practical working of authority in the modern state.

These forces were at work in the whole Western world. But they were most influential in America. The lack of a career service of general administrators, the strength and independence of the scientific and professional specialties within government, and the close ties in each scientific and professional field between the federal specialists and their colleagues in the states whose programs are supported by federal grants—all these features worked together to set free the force of organized science and to let it shape the central government of the United States into a very different institution from its European counterparts. It is a system that has been rapidly adapted to the widespread support of scientific research and the rapid application of scientific data.

In recent years we have built on these foundations a markedly new system for the support of science—a system that has produced results as terrifying as they are effective. Whether we have at the same time developed an ability to understand where this system is going, or to control it, is another question.

VANNEVAR BUSH

Science: The Endless Frontier

Introduction
SCIENTIFIC PROGRESS IS ESSENTIAL

We all know how much the new drug, penicillin, has meant to our grievously wounded men on the grim battlefronts of this war—the countless lives it has saved—the incalculable suffering which its use has prevented. Science and the great practical genius of this nation made this achievement possible.

Some of us know the vital role which radar has played in bringing the United Nations to victory over Nazi Germany and in driving the Japanese steadily back from their island bastions. Again it was painstaking scientific research over many years that made radar possible.

What we often forget are the millions of pay envelopes on a peace-time Saturday night which are filled because new products and new industries have provided jobs for countless Americans. Science made that possible, too.

In 1939 millions of people were employed in industries which did not even exist at the close of the last war—radio, air conditioning, rayon and other synthetic fibers, and plastics are examples of the products of these industries. But these things do not mark the end of progress—they are but the beginning if we make full use of our scientific resources. New manufacturing industries can be started and many older industries greatly strengthened and expanded if we continue to study nature's laws and apply new knowledge to practical purposes.

Great advances in agriculture are also based upon scientific research. Plants which are more resistant to disease and are adapted to short growing seasons, the prevention and cure of livestock diseases, the control of our insect enemies, better fertilizers, and improved agricultural practices, all stem from painstaking scientific research.

Advances in science when put to practical use mean more jobs, higher wages, shorter hours, more abundant crops, more leisure for recreation, for study, for learning how to live without the deadening drudgery which has been the burden of the common man for ages past. Advances in science will also bring higher standards of living, will lead to the prevention or cure of diseases, will promote conservation of our limited national resources, and will assure means of defense against aggression. But to achieve these objectives—to secure a high level of employment, to maintain a position of

From *Science: The Endless Frontier* by Vannevar Bush, Government Printing Office, 1945.

26

world leadership—the flow of new scientific knowledge must be both continuous and substantial.

Our population increased from 75 million to 130 million between 1900 and 1940. In some countries comparable increases have been accompanied by famine. In this country the increase has been accompanied by more abundant food supply, better living, more leisure, longer life, and better health. This is, largely, the product of three factors—the free play of initiative of a vigorous people under democracy, the heritage of great natural wealth, and the advance of science and its application.

Science, by itself, provides no panacea for individual, social, and economic ills. It can be effective in the national welfare only as a member of a team, whether the conditions be peace or war. But without scientific progress no amount of achievement in other directions can insure our health, prosperity, and security as a nation in the modern world.

SCIENCE IS A PROPER CONCERN OF GOVERNMENT

It has been basic United States policy that Government should foster the opening of new frontiers. It opened the seas to clipper ships and furnished land for pioneers. Although these frontiers have more or less disappeared, the frontier of science remains. It is in keeping with the American tradition—one which has made the United States great—that new frontiers shall be made accessible for development by all American citizens.

Moreover, since health, well-being, and security are proper concerns of Government, scientific progress is, and must be, of vital interest to Government. Without scientific progress the national health would deteriorate; without scientific progress we could not hope for improvement in our standard of living or for an increased number of jobs for our citizens; and without scientific progress we could not have maintained our liberties against tyranny.

GOVERNMENT RELATIONS TO SCIENCE—PAST AND FUTURE

From early days the Government has taken an active interest in scientific matters. During the nineteenth century the Coast and Geodetic Survey, the Naval Observatory, the Department of Agriculture, and the Geological Survey were established. Through the Land Grant College Acts the Government has supported research in state institutions for more than 80 years on a gradually increasing scale. Since 1900 a large number of scientific agencies have been established within the Federal Government, until in 1939 they numbered more than 40.

Much of the scientific research done by Government agencies is intermediate in character between the two types of work commonly referred to as basic and applied research. Almost all Government scientific work has ultimate practical objectives but, in many fields of broad national concern, it commonly involves long-term investigation of a fundamental nature. Generally speaking, the scientific agencies of Government are not so concerned with immediate practical objectives as are the laboratories of industry nor, on the other hand, are they as free to explore any natural phenomena without regard to possible economic applications as are the educational and private research institutions. Government scientific agencies have splendid records of achievement, but they are limited in function.

We have no national policy for science. The Government has only begun to utilize science in the nation's welfare. There is no body within the Government charged with formulating or executing a national science policy. There are no standing committees of the Congress devoted to this important subject. Science has been in the wings. It should be brought to the center of the stage—for in it lies much of our hope for the future.

There are areas of science in which the public interest is acute but which are likely to be cultivated inadequately if left without more support than will come from private sources. These areas—such as research on military problems, agriculture, housing, public health, certain medical research, and research involving expensive capital facilities beyond the capacity of private institutions—should be advanced by active Government support. To date, with the exception of the intensive war research conducted by the Office of Scientific Research and Development, such support has been meager and intermittent.

For reasons presented in this report we are entering a period when science needs and deserves increased support from public funds.

FREEDOM OF INQUIRY MUST BE PRESERVED

The publicly and privately supported colleges, universities, and research institutes are the centers of basic research. They are the wellsprings of knowledge and understanding. As long as they are vigorous and healthy and their scientists are free to pursue the truth wherever it may lead, there will be a flow of new scientific knowledge to those who can apply it to practical problems in Government, in industry, or elsewhere.

Many of the lessons learned in the war-time application of science under Government can be profitably applied in peace. The Government is peculiarly fitted to perform certain functions, such as the coordination and support of broad programs on problems of great national importance. But we must proceed with caution in carrying over the methods which work in wartime to the very different conditions of peace. We must remove the rigid controls which we have had to impose, and recover freedom of inquiry and that healthy competitive scientific spirit so necessary for expansion of the frontiers of scientific knowledge.

Scientific progress on a broad front results from the free play of free intellects, working on subjects of their own choice, in the manner dictated by their curiosity for exploration of the unknown. Freedom of inquiry must be preserved under any plan for Government support of science in accordance with the Five Fundamentals listed on pages 48–9.

The study of the momentous questions presented in President Roosevelt's letter has been made by able committees working diligently. This report presents conclusions and recommendations based upon the studies of these committees which appear in full as the appendices. Only in the creation of one over-all mechanism rather than several does this report depart from the specific recommendations of the committees. The members of the committees have reviewed the recommendations in regard to the single mechanism and have found this plan thoroughly acceptable.

The War Against Disease

IN WAR

The death rate for all diseases in the Army, including the overseas forces, has been reduced from 14.1 per thousand in the last war to 0.6 per thousand in this war.

Such ravaging diseases as yellow fever, dysentery, typhus, tetanus, pneumonia and meningitis have been all but conquered by penicillin and the sulfa drugs, the insecticide DDT, better vaccines, and improved hygienic measures. Malaria has been controlled. There has been dramatic progress in surgery.

The striking advances in medicine during the war have been possible only because we had a large backlog of scientific data accumulated through basic research in many scientific fields in the years before the war.

IN PEACE

In the last 40 years life expectancy in the United States has increased from 49 to 65 years largely as a consequence of the reduction in the death rates of infants and children; in the last 20 years the death rate from the diseases of childhood has been reduced 87 percent.

Diabetes has been brought under control by insulin, pernicious anemia by liver extracts; and the once widespread deficiency diseases have been much reduced, even in the lowest income groups, by accessory food factors and improvement of diet. Notable advances have been made in the early diagnosis of cancer, and in the surgical and radiation treatment of the disease.

These results have been achieved through a great amount of basic research in medicine and the preclinical sciences, and by the dissemination of this new scientific knowledge through the physicians and medical services and public health agencies of the country. In this cooperative endeavour the pharmaceutical industry has played an important role, especially during the war. All of the medical and public health groups share credit for these achievements; they form interdependent members of a team.

Progress in combating disease depends upon an expanding body of new scientific knowledge.

UNSOLVED PROBLEMS

As President Roosevelt observed, the annual deaths from one or two diseases are far in excess of the total number of American lives lost in battle during this war. A large fraction of these deaths in our civilian population cut short the useful lives of our citizens. This is our present position despite the fact that in the last three decades notable progress has been made in civilian medicine. The reduction in death rate from diseases of childhood has shifted the emphasis to the middle and old age groups, particularly to the malignant diseases and the degenerative processes prominent in later life, Cardiovascular disease, including chronic disease of the kidneys, arteriosclerosis, and cerebral hemorrhage, now account for 45 percent of the deaths in the United States. Second are the infectious diseases, and third is cancer. Added to these are many maladies (for example, the common cold, arthritis, asthma and hay fever, peptic ulcer) which, though infrequently fatal, cause incalculable disability.

Another aspect of the changing emphasis is the increase of mental diseases. Approximately 7 million persons in the United States are mentally ill; more than one-third of the hospital beds are occupied by such persons, at a cost of $175 million a year. Each year 125,000 new mental cases are hospitalized.

Notwithstanding great progress in prolonging the span of life and in relief of suffering, much illness remains for which adequate means of prevention and cure are not yet known. While additional physicians, hospitals, and health programs are needed, their full usefulness cannot be attained unless we enlarge our knowledge of the human organism and the nature of disease. Any extension of medical facilities must be accompanied by an expanded program of medical training and research.

BROAD AND BASIC STUDIES NEEDED

Discoveries pertinent to medical progress have often come from remote and unexpected sources, and it is certain that this will be true in the future. It is wholly probable that progress in the treatment of cardiovascular disease, renal disease, cancer, and similar refractory diseases will be made as the result of fundamental discoveries in subjects unrelated to those diseases, and perhaps entirely unexpected by the investigator. Further progress requires that the entire front of medicine and the underlying sciences of chemistry, physics, anatomy, biochemistry, physiology, pharmacology, bacteriology, pathology, parasitology, etc., be broadly developed.

Progress in the war against disease results from discoveries in remote and unexpected fields of medicine and the underlying sciences.

COORDINATED ATTACK ON SPECIAL PROBLEMS

Penicillin reached our troops in time to save countless lives because the Government coordinated and supported the program of research and development on the drug. The development moved from the early laboratory stage to large scale production and use in a fraction of the time it would have taken without such leadership. The search for better anti-malarials, which proceeded at a moderate tempo for many years, has been accelerated enormously by Goverment support during the war. Other examples can be cited in which medical progress has been similarly advanced. In achieving these results, the Government has provided over-all coordination and support; it has not dictated how the work should be done within any cooperating institution.

Discovery of new therapeutic agents and methods usually results from basic studies in medicine and the underlying sciences. The development of such materials and methods to the point at which they become available to medical practitioners requires teamwork involving the medical schools, the science departments of universities, Government and the pharmaceutical industry. Government initiative, support, and coordination can be very effective in this development phase.

Government initiative and support for the development of newly discovered therapeutic materials and methods can reduce the time required to bring the benefits to the public.

ACTION IS NECESSARY

The primary place for medical research is in the medical schools and universities. In some cases coordinated direct attack on special problems may be made by teams of investigators, supplementing similar attacks carried on by the Army, Navy, Public Health Service, and other organizations. Apart from teaching, however, the primary obligation of the medical schools and universities is to continue the traditional function of such institutions, namely, to provide the individual worker with an opportunity for free, untrammeled study of nature, in the directions and by the methods suggested by his interests, curiosity, and imagination. The history of medical science teaches clearly the supreme importance of affording the prepared mind complete freedom for the exercise of initiative. It is the special province of the medical schools and universities to foster medical research in this way—a duty which cannot be shifted to government agencies, industrial organizations, or to any other institutions.

Where clinical investigations of the human body are required, the medical schools are in a unique position, because of their close relationship to teaching hospitals, to integrate such investigations with the work of the departments of preclinical science, and to impart new knowledge to physicians in training. At the same time, the teaching hospitals are especially well qualified to carry on medical research because of their close connection with the medical schools, on which they depend for staff and supervision.

Between World War I and World War II the United States overtook all other nations in medical research and assumed a position of world leadership. To a considerable extent this progress reflected the liberal financial support from university endowment income, gifts from individuals, and foundation grants in the 20's. The growth of research departments in medical schools has been very uneven, however, and in consequence most of the important work has been done in a few large schools. This should be corrected by building up the weaker institutions, especially in regions which now have no strong medical research activities.

The traditional sources of support for medical research, largely endowment income, foundation grants, and private donations, are diminishing, and there is no immediate prospect of a change in this trend. Meanwhile, research costs have steadily risen. More elaborate and expensive equipment is required, supplies are more costly, and the wages of assistants are higher. Industry is only to a limited extent a source of funds for basic medical research.

It is clear that if we are to maintain the progress in medicine which has marked the last 25 years, the Government should extend financial support to basic medical research in the medical schools and in the universities, through grants both for research and for fellowships. The amount which can be effectively spent in the first year should not exceed 5 million dollars.

After a program is under way perhaps 20 million dollars a year can be spent effectively.

Science and the Public Welfare
RELATION TO NATIONAL SECURITY

In this war it has become clear beyond all doubt that scientific research is absolutely essential to national security. The bitter and dangerous battle against the U-boat was a battle of scientific techniques—and our margin of success was dangerously small. The new eyes which radar supplied to our fighting forces quickly evoked the development of scientific countermeasures which could often blind them. This again represents the ever continuing battle of techniques. The V–1 attack on London was finally defeated by three devices developed during this war and used superbly in the field. V–2 was countered only by capture of the launching sites.

The Secretaries of War and Navy recently stated in a joint letter to the National Academy of Sciences:

> This war emphasizes three facts of supreme importance to national security: (1) Powerful new tactics of defense and offense are developed around new weapons created by scientific and engineering research; (2) the competitive time element in developing those weapons and tactics may be decisive; (3) war is increasingly total war, in which the armed services must be supplemented by active participation of every element of civilian population.
>
> To insure continued preparedness along farsighted technical lines, the research scientists of the country must be called upon to continue in peacetime some substantial portion of those types of contribution to national security which they have made so effectively during the stress of the present war. . . .

There must be more—and more adequate—military research during peacetime. We cannot again rely on our allies to hold off the enemy while we struggle to catch up. Further, it is clear that only the Government can undertake military research; for it must be carried on in secret, much of it has no commercial value, and it is expensive. The obligation of Government to support research on military problems is inescapable.

Modern war requires the use of the most advanced scientific techniques. Many of the leaders in the development of radar are scientists who before the war had been exploring the nucleus of the atom. While there must be increased emphasis on science in the future training of officers for both the Army and Navy, such men cannot be expected to be specialists in scientific research. Therefore a professional partnership between the officers in the Services and civilian scientists is needed.

The Army and Navy should continue to carry on research and development on the improvement of current weapons. For many years the National Advisory Committee for Aeronautics has supplemented the work of the Army and Navy by conducting basic research on the problems of flight. There should now be permanent civilian activity to supplement the research work of the Services in other scientific fields so as to carry on in time of peace some part of the activities of the emergency war-time Office of Scientific Research and Development.

Military preparedness requires a permanent independent, civilian-controlled organization, having close liaison with the Army and Navy, but with funds directly from Congress and with the clear power to initiate military research which will supplement and strengthen that carried on directly under the control of the Army and Navy.

SCIENCE AND JOBS

One of our hopes is that after the war there will be full employment, and that the production of goods and services will serve to raise our standard of living. We do not know yet how we shall reach that goal, but it is certain that it can be achieved only by releasing the full creative and productive energies of the American people.

Surely we will not get there by standing still, merely by making the same things we made before and selling them at the same or higher prices. We will not get ahead in international trade unless we offer new and more attractive and cheaper products.

Where will these new products come from? How will we find ways to make better products at lower cost? The answer is clear. There must be a stream of new scientific knowledge to turn the wheels of private and public enterprise. There must be plenty of men and women trained in science and technology for upon them depend both the creation of new knowledge and its application to practical purposes.

More and better scientific research is essential to the achievement of our goal of full employment.

THE IMPORTANCE OF BASIC RESEARCH

Basic research is performed without thought of practical ends. It results in general knowledge and an understanding of nature and its laws. This general knowledge provides the means of answering a large number of important practical problems, though it may not give a complete specific answer to any one of them. The function of applied research is to provide such complete answers. The scientist doing basic research may not be at all interested in the practical applications of his work, yet the further progress of industrial development would eventually stagnate if basic scientific research were long neglected.

One of the peculiarities of basic science is the variety of paths which lead to productive advance. Many of the most important discoveries have come as a result of experiments undertaken with very different purposes in mind. Statistically it is certain that important and highly useful discoveries will result from some fraction of the undertakings in basic science; but the results of any one particular investigation cannot be predicted with accuracy.

Basic research leads to new knowledge. It provides scientific capital. It creates the fund from which the practical applications of knowledge must be drawn. New products and new processes do not appear full-grown. They are founded on new principles and new conceptions, which in turn are painstakingly developed by research in the purest realms of science.

Today, it is truer than ever that basic research is the pacemaker of technological progress. In the nineteenth century, Yankee mechanical ingenuity, building largely upon the basic discoveries of European scientists, could greatly advance the technical arts. Now the situation is different.

A nation which depends upon others for its new basic scientific knowledge will be slow in its industrial progress and weak in its competitive position in world trade, regardless of its mechanical skill.

CENTERS OF BASIC RESEARCH

Publicly and privately supported colleges and universities and the endowed research institutes must furnish both the new scientific knowledge and the trained research workers. These institutions are uniquely qualified by tradition and by their special characteristics to carry on basic research. They are charged with the responsibility of conserving the knowledge accumulated by the past, imparting that knowledge to students, and contributing new knowledge of all kinds. It is chiefly in these institutions that scientists may work in an atmosphere which is relatively free from the adverse pressure of convention, prejudice, or commercial necessity. At their best they provide the scientific worker with a strong sense of solidarity and security, as well as a substantial degree of personal intellectual freedom. All of these factors are of great importance in the development of new knowledge, since much of new knowledge is certain to arouse opposition because of its tendency to challenge current beliefs or practice.

Industry is generally inhibited by preconceived goals, by its own clearly defined standards, and by the constant pressure of commercial necessity. Satisfactory progress in basic science seldom occurs under conditions prevailing in the normal industrial laboratory. There are some notable exceptions, it is true, but even in such cases it is rarely possible to match the universities in respect to the freedom which is so important to scientific discovery.

To serve effectively as the centers of basic research these institutions must be strong and healthy. They must attract our best scientists as teachers and investigators. They must offer research opportunities and sufficient compensation to enable them to compete with industry and government for the cream of scientific talent.

During the past 25 years there has been a great increase in industrial research involving the application of scientific knowledge to a multitude of practical purposes—thus providing new products, new industries, new investment opportunities, and millions of jobs. During the same period research within Government—again largely applied research—has also been greatly expanded. In the decade from 1930 to 1940 expenditures for industrial research increased from $116,000,000 to $240,000,000 and those for scientific research in Government rose from $24,000,000 to $69,000,000. During the same period expenditures for scientific research in the colleges and universities increased from $20,000,000 to $31,000,000, while those in the endowed research institutes declined from $5,200,000 to $4,500,-000. These are the best estimates available. The figures have been taken from a variety of sources and arbitrary definitions have necessarily been applied, but it is believed that they may be accepted as indicating the following trends:

(a) Expenditures for scientific research by industry and Government —almost entirely applied research—have more than doubled between 1930 and 1940. Whereas in 1930 they were six times as large as the research expenditures of the colleges, universities, and research institutes, by 1940 they were nearly ten times as large.

(b) While expenditures for scientific research in the colleges and universities increased by one-half during this period, those for the endowed research institutes have slowly declined.

If the colleges, universities, and research institutes are to meet the rapidly increasing demands of industry and Government for new scientific knowledge, their basic research should be strengthened by use of public funds.

RESEARCH WITHIN THE GOVERNMENT

Although there are some notable exceptions, most research conducted within governmental laboratories is of an applied nature. This has always been true and is likely to remain so. Hence Government, like industry, is dependent upon the colleges, universities, and research institutes to expand the basic scientific frontiers and to furnish trained scientific investigators.

Research within the Government represents an important part of our total research activity and needs to be strengthened and expanded after the war. Such expansion should be directed to fields of inquiry and service which are of public importance and are not adequately carried on by private organizations.

The most important single factor in scientific and technical work is the quality of personnel employed. The procedures currently followed within the Government for recruiting, classifying and compensating such personnel place the Government under a severe handicap in competing with industry and the universities for first-class scientific talent. Steps should be taken to reduce that handicap.

In the Government the arrangement whereby the numerous scientific agencies form parts of larger departments has both advantages and disadvantages. But the present pattern is firmly established and there is much to be said for it. There is, however, a very real need for some measure of coordination of the common scientific activities of these agencies, both as to policies and budgets, and at present no such means exist.

A permanent Science Advisory Board should be created to consult with these scientific bureaus and to advise the executive and legislative branches of Government as to the policies and budgets of Government agencies engaged in scientific research.

This board should be composed of disinterested scientists who have no connection with the affairs of any Government agency.

INDUSTRIAL RESEARCH

The simplest and most effective way in which the Government can strengthen industrial research is to support basic research and to develop scientific talent.

The benefits of basic research do not reach all industries equally or at the same speed. Some small enterprises never receive any of the benefits. It has been suggested that the benefits might be better utilized if "research clinics" for such enterprises were to be established. Businessmen would thus be able to make more use of research than they now do. This proposal is certainly worthy of further study.

One of the most important factors affecting the amount of industrial research is the income-tax law. Government action in respect to this subject will affect the rate of technical progress in industry. Uncertainties as to the attitude of the Bureau of Internal Revenue regarding the deduction of research and development expenses are a deterrent to research expenditure. These uncertainties arise from lack of clarity of the tax law as to the proper treatment of such costs.

The Internal Revenue Code should be amended to remove present uncertainties in regard to the deductibility of research and development expenditures as current charges against net income.

Research is also affected by the patent laws. They stimulate new invention and they make it possible for new industries to be built around new devices or new processes. These industries generate new jobs and new products, all of which contribute to the welfare and the strength of the country.

Yet, uncertainties in the operation of the patent laws have impaired the ability of small industries to translate new ideas into processes and products of value to the nation. These uncertainties are, in part, attributable to the difficulties and expense incident to the operation of the patent system as it presently exists. These uncertainties are also attributable to the existence of certain abuses, which have appeared in the use of patents. The abuses should be corrected. They have led to extravagantly critical attacks which tend to discredit a basically sound system.

● ● ●

INTERNATIONAL EXCHANGE OF SCIENTIFIC INFORMATION

International exchange of scientific information is of growing importance. Increasing specialization of science will make it more important than ever that scientists in this country keep continually abreast of developments abroad. In addition a flow of scientific information constitutes one facet of general international accord which should be cultivated.

The Government can accomplish significant results in several ways: by aiding in the arrangement of international science congresses, in the official accrediting of American scientists to such gatherings, in the official reception of foreign scientists of standing in this country, in making possible a rapid flow of technical information, including translation service, and possibly in the provision of international fellowships. Private foundations and other groups partially fulfill some of these functions at present, but their scope is incomplete and inadequate.

The Government should take an active role in promoting the international flow of scientific information.

THE SPECIAL NEED FOR FEDERAL SUPPORT

We can no longer count on ravaged Europe as a source of fundamental knowledge. In the past we have devoted much of our best efforts to the application of such knowledge which has been discovered abroad. In the future we must pay increased attention to discovering this knowledge for ourselves particularly since the scientific applications of the future will be more than ever dependent upon such basic knowledge.

New impetus must be given to research in our country. Such new impetus can come promptly only from the Government. Expenditures for research in the colleges, universities, and research institutes will otherwise not be able to meet the additional demands of increased public need for research.

Further, we cannot expect industry adequately to fill the gap. Industry will fully rise to the challenge of applying new knowledge to new products. The commercial incentive can be relied upon for that. But basic research is essentially noncommercial in nature. It will not receive the attention it requires if left to industry.

For many years the Government has wisely supported research in the agricultural colleges and the benefits have been great. The time has come when such support should be extended to other fields.

In providing Government support, however, we must endeavor to preserve as far as possible the private support of research both in industry and in the colleges, universities, and research institutes. These private sources should continue to carry their share of the financial burden.

THE COST OF A PROGRAM

It is estimated that an adequate program for Federal support of basic research in the colleges, universities, and research institutes and for financing important applied research in the public interest, will cost about 10 million dollars at the outset and may rise to about 50 million dollars annually when fully underway at the end of perhaps 5 years.

Renewal of Our Scientific Talent

NATURE OF THE PROBLEM

The responsibility for the creation of new scientific knowledge rests on that small body of men and women who understand the fundamental laws of nature and are skilled in the techniques of scientific research. While there will always be the rare individual who will rise to the top without benefit of formal education and training, he is the exception and even he might make a more notable contribution if he had the benefit of the best education we have to offer. I cannot improve on President Conant's statement that:

> . . . in every section of the entire area where the word science may properly be applied, the limiting factor is a human one. We shall have rapid or slow advance in this direction or in that de-

pending on the number of really first-class men who are engaged in the work in question. . . . So in the last analysis, the future of science in this country will be determined by our basic educational policy.

A NOTE OF WARNING

It would be folly to set up a program under which research in the natural sciences and medicine was expanded at the cost of the social sciences, humanities, and other studies so essential to national well-being. This point has been well stated by the Moe Committee as follows:

> As citizens, as good citizens, we therefore think that we must have in mind while examining the question before us—the discovery and development of scientific talent—the needs of the whole national welfare. We could not suggest to you a program which would syphon into science and technology a disproportionately large share of the nation's highest abilities, without doing harm to the nation, nor, indeed, without crippling science. . . . Science cannot live by and unto itself alone.

• • •

> The uses to which high ability in youth can be put are various and, to a large extent, are determined by social pressures and rewards. When aided by selective devices for picking out scientifically talented youth, it is clear that large sums of money for scholarships and fellowships and monetary and other rewards in disproportionate amounts might draw into science too large a percentage of the nation's high ability, with a result highly detrimental to the nation and to science. Plans for the discovery and development of scientific talent must be related to the other needs of society for high ability . . . There is never enough ability at high levels to satisfy all the needs of the nation; we would not seek to draw into science any more of it than science's proportionate share.

THE WARTIME DEFICIT

Among the young men and women qualified to take up scientific work, since 1940 there have been few students over 18, except some in medicine and engineering in Army and Navy programs and a few 4-F's, who have followed an integrated scientific course of studies. Neither our allies nor, so far as we know, our enemies have done anything so radical as thus to suspend almost completely their educational activities in scientific pursuits during the war period.

Two great principles have guided us in this country as we have turned our full efforts to war. First, the sound democratic principle that there should be no favored classes or special privilege in a time of peril, that all should be ready to sacrifice equally; second, the tenet that every man should serve in the capacity in which his talents and experience can best be applied for the prosecution of the war effort. In general we have held these principles well in balance.

In my opinion, however, we have drawn too heavily for non-scientific purposes upon the great natural resource which resides in our trained young scientists and engineers. For the general good of the country too many such men have gone into uniform, and their talents have not always been fully utilized. With the exception of those men engaged in war research, all physically fit students at graduate level have been taken into the armed forces. Those ready for college training in the sciences have not been permitted to enter upon that training.

There is thus an accumulating deficit of trained research personnel which will continue for many years. The deficit of science and technology students who, but for the war, would have received bachelor's degrees is about 150,000. The deficit of those holding advanced degrees—that is, young scholars trained to the point where they are capable of carrying on original work—has been estimated as amounting to about 17,000 by 1955 in chemistry, engineering, geology, mathematics, physics, psychology, and the biological sciences.

With mounting demands for scientists both for teaching and for research, we will enter the post-war period with a serious deficit in our trained scientific personnel.

IMPROVE THE QUALITY

Confronted with these deficits, we are compelled to look to the use of our basic human resources and formulate a program which will assure their conservation and effective development. The committee advising me on scientific personnel has stated the following principle which should guide our planning:

> . . . To get top leadership there must be a relatively large base of high ability selected for development and then successive skimmings of the cream of ability at successive times and at higher levels. No one can select from the bottom those who will be the leaders at the top because unmeasured and unknown factors enter into scientific, or any, leadership. There are brains and character, strength and health, happiness and spiritual vitality, interest and

motivation, and no one knows what else, that must needs enter into this supra-mathematical calculus.

• • •

REMOVE THE BARRIERS

Higher education in this country is largely for those who have the means. If those who have the means coincided entirely with those persons who have the talent we should not be squandering a part of our higher education on those undeserving of it, nor neglecting great talent among those who fail to attend college for economic reasons. There are talented individuals in every segment of the population, but with few exceptions those without the means of buying higher education go without it. Here is a tremendous waste of the greatest resource of a nation—the intelligence of its citizens.

If ability, and not the circumstance of family fortune, is made to determine who shall receive higher education in science, then we shall be assured of constantly improving quality at every level of scientific activity.

THE GENERATION IN UNIFORM MUST NOT BE LOST

We have a serious deficit in scientific personnel partly because the men who would have studied science in the colleges and universities have been serving in the Armed Forces. Many had begun their studies before they went to war. Others with capacity for scientific education went to war after finishing high school. The most immediate prospect of making up some of the deficit in scientific personnel is by salvaging scientific talent from the generation in uniform. For even if we should start now to train the current crop of high school graduates, it would be 1951 before they would complete graduate studies and be prepared for effective scientific research. This fact underlines the necessity of salvaging potential scientists in uniform.

The Armed Services should comb their records for men who, prior to or during the war, have given evidence of talent for science, and make prompt arrangements, consistent with current discharge plans, for ordering those who remain in uniform as soon as militarily possible to duty at institutions here and overseas where they can continue their scientific education. Moreover, they should see that those who study overseas have the benefit of the latest scientific developments.

A PROGRAM

The country may be proud of the fact that 95 percent of boys and girls of fifth grade age are enrolled in school, but the drop in enrollment after the fifth grade is less satisfying. For every 1,000 students in the fifth grade, 600 are lost to education before the end of high school, and all but 72 have ceased formal education before completion of college. While we are concerned primarily with methods of selecting and educating high school graduates at the college and higher levels, we cannot be complacent about the loss of potential talent which is inherent in the present situation.

Students drop out of school, college, and graduate school, or do not get that far, for a variety of reasons: they cannot afford to go on; schools and colleges providing courses equal to their capacity are not available locally; business and industry recruit many of the most promising before they have finished the training of which they are capable. These reasons apply with particular force to science: the road is long and expensive; it extends at least 6 years beyond high school; the percentage of science students who can obtain first-rate training in institutions near home is small.

Improvement in the teaching of science is imperative; for students of latent scientific ability are particularly vulnerable to high school teaching which fails to awaken interest or to provide adequate instruction. To enlarge the group of specially qualified men and women it is necessary to increase the number who go to college. This involves improved high school instruction, provision for helping individual talented students to finish high school (primarily the responsibility of the local communities), and opportunities for more capable, promising high school students to go to college. Anything short of this means serious waste of higher education and neglect of human resources.

To encourage and enable a larger number of young men and women of ability to take up science as a career, and in order gradually to reduce the deficit of trained scientific personnel, it is recommended that provision be made for a reasonable number of (a) undergraduate scholarships and graduate fellowships and (b) fellowships for advanced training and fundamental research. The details should be worked out with reference to the interests of the several States and of the universities and colleges; and care should be taken not to impair the freedom of the institutions and individuals concerned.

• • •

The plan is, further, that all those who receive such scholarships or fellowships in science should be enrolled in a National Science Reserve and be liable to call into the service of the Government, in connection with scientific or technical work in time of war or other national emergency declared by Congress or proclaimed by the President. Thus, in addition to the general benefits to the nation by reason of the addition to its trained ranks of such a corps of scientific workers, there would be a definite benefit to the nation in having these scientific workers on call in national emergencies. The Government would be well advised to invest the money involved in this plan even if the benefits to the nation were thought of solely—which they are not—in terms of national preparedness.

A Problem of Scientific Reconversion
EFFECTS OF MOBILIZATION OF SCIENCE FOR WAR

We have been living on our fat. For more than 5 years many of our scientists have been fighting the war in the laboratories, in the factories and shops, and at the front. We have been directing the energies of our scientists to the development of weapons and materials and methods, on a large number of relatively narrow projects initiated and controlled by the Office of Scientific Research and Development and other Government agencies. Like troops, the scientists have been mobilized, and thrown into action to serve their country in time of emergency. But they have been diverted to a greater extent than is generally appreciated from the search for answers to the fundamental problems—from the search on which human welfare and progress depends. This is not a complaint—it is a fact. The mobilization of science behind the lines is aiding the fighting men at the front to win the war and to shorten it; and it has resulted incidentally in the accumulation of a vast amount of experience and knowledge of the application of science to particular problems, much of which can be put to use when the war is over. Fortunately, this country had the scientists—and the time—to make this contribution and thus to advance the date of victory.

SECURITY RESTRICTIONS SHOULD BE LIFTED PROMPTLY

Much of the information and experience acquired during the war is confined to the agencies that gathered it. Except to the extent that military security dictates otherwise, such knowledge should be spread upon the record for the benefit of the general public.

Thanks to the wise provision of the Secretary of War and the Secretary of the Navy, most of the results of war-time medical research have been published. Several hundred articles have appeared in the professional journals; many are in process of publication. The material still subject to security classification should be released as soon as possible.

It is my view that most of the remainder of the classified scientific material should be released as soon as there is ground for belief that the enemy will not be able to turn it against us in this war. Most of the information needed by industry and in education can be released without disclosing its embodiments in actual military material and devices. Basically there is no

reason to believe that scientists of other countries will not in time redis-
cover everything we know which is held in secrecy. A broad dissemination of scientific information upon which further advances can readily be
made furnishes a sounder foundation for our national security than a policy of restriction which would impede our own progress although imposed
in the hope that possible enemies would not catch up with us.

During the war it has been necessary for selected groups of scientists to
work on specialized problems, with relatively little information as to what
other groups were doing and had done. Working against time, the Office of
Scientific Research and Development has been obliged to enforce this practice during the war, although it was realized by all concerned that it was an
emergency measure which prevented the continuous cross-fertilization so
essential to fruitful scientific effort.

*Our ability to overcome possible future enemies depends upon scientific
advances which will proceed more rapidly with diffusion of knowledge than
under a policy of continued restriction of knowledge now in our possession.*

NEED FOR COORDINATION

In planning the release of scientific data and experience collected in connection with the war, we must not overlook the fact that research has gone
forward under many auspices—the Army, the Navy, the Office of Scientific
Research and Development, the National Advisory Committee for Aeronautics, other departments and agencies of the Government, educational
institutions, and many industrial organizations. There have been numerous
cases of independent discovery of the same truth in different places. To
permit the release of information by one agency and to continue to restrict
it elsewhere would be unfair in its effect and would tend to impair the morale and efficiency of scientists who have submerged individual interests in
the controls and restrictions of war.

A part of the information now classified which should be released is possessed jointly by our allies and ourselves. Plans for release of such information should be coordinated with our allies to minimize danger of international friction which would result from sporadic uncontrolled release.

A BOARD TO CONTROL RELEASE

The agency responsible for recommending the release of information from
military classification should be an Army, Navy, civilian body, well
grounded in science and technology. It should be competent to advise the
Secretary of War and the Secretary of the Navy. It should, moreover, have
sufficient recognition to secure prompt and practical decisions.

To satisfy these considerations I recommend the establishment of a Board, made up equally of scientists and military men, whose function would be to pass upon the declassification and to control the release for publication of scientific information which is now classified.

PUBLICATION SHOULD BE ENCOURAGED

The release of information from security regulations is but one phase of the problem. The other is to provide for preparation of the material and its publication in a form and at a price which will facilitate dissemination and use. In the case of the Office of Scientific Research and Development, arrangements have been made for the preparation of manuscripts, while the staffs under our control are still assembled and in possession of the records, as soon as the pressure for production of results for this war has begun to relax.

We should get this scientific material to scientists everywhere with great promptness, and at as low a price as is consistent with suitable format. We should also get it to the men studying overseas so that they will know what has happened in their absence.

It is recommended that measures which will encourage and facilitate the preparation and publication of reports be adopted forthwith by all agencies, governmental and private, possessing scientific information released from security control.

The Means to the End

NEW RESPONSIBILITIES FOR GOVERNMENT

One lesson is clear from the reports of the several committees attached as appendices. The Federal Government should accept new responsibilities for promoting the creation of new scientific knowledge and the development of scientific talent in our youth.

The extent and nature of these new responsibilities are set forth in detail in the reports of the committees whose recommendations in this regard are fully endorsed.

In discharging these responsibilities Federal funds should be made available. We have given much thought to the question of how plans for the use of Federal funds may be arranged so that such funds will not drive out of the picture funds from local governments, foundations, and private donors. We believe that our proposals will minimize that effect, but we do not think that it can be completely avoided. We submit, however, that the nation's need for more and better scientific research is such that the risk must be accepted.

It is also clear that the effective discharge of these responsibilities will require the full attention of some over-all agency devoted to that purpose. There should be a focal point within the Government for a concerted program of assisting scientific research conducted outside of Government. Such an agency should furnish the funds needed to support basic research in the colleges and universities, should coordinate where possible research programs on matters of utmost importance to the national welfare, should formulate a national policy for the Government toward science, should sponsor the interchange of scientific information among scientists and laboratories both in this country and abroad, and should ensure that the incentives to research in industry and the universities are maintained. All of the committees advising on these matters agree on the necessity for such an agency.

THE MECHANISM

There are within Government departments many groups whose interests are primarily those of scientific research. Notable examples are found within the Departments of Agriculture, Commerce, Interior, and the Federal Security Agency. These groups are concerned with science as collateral and peripheral to the major problems of those Departments. These groups should remain where they are, and continue to perform their present functions, including the support of agricultural research by grants to the Land Grant Colleges and Experiment Stations, since their largest contribution lies in applying fundamental knowledge to the special problems of the Departments within which they are established.

By the same token these groups cannot be made the repository of the new and large responsibilities in science which belong to the Government and which the Government should accept. The recommendations in this report which relate to research within the Government, to the release of scientific information, to clarification of the tax laws, and to the recovery and development of our scientific talent now in uniform can be implemented by action within the existing structure of the Government. But nowhere in the Governmental structure receiving its funds from Congress is there an agency adapted to supplementing the support of basic research in the universities, both in medicine and the natural sciences; adapted to supporting research on new weapons for both Services; or adapted to administering a program of science scholarships and fellowships.

A new agency should be established, therefore, by the Congress for the purpose. Such an agency, moreover, should be an independent agency devoted to the support of scientific research and advanced scientific education alone. Industry learned many years ago that basic research cannot often be fruitfully conducted as an adjunct to or a subdivision of an operating agency or department. Operating agencies have immediate operating goals and are under constant pressure to produce in a tangible way, for that is the test of their value. None of these conditions is favorable to basic research. Research is the exploration of the unknown and is necessarily speculative. It is inhibited by conventional approaches, traditions, and standards. It cannot be satisfactorily conducted in an atmosphere where it is gauged and tested by operating or production standards. Basic scientific research should not, therefore, be placed under an operating agency whose paramount concern is anything other than research. Research will always suffer when put in competition with operations. The decision that there should be a new and independent agency was reached by each of the committees advising in these matters.

I am convinced that these new functions should be centered in one agency. Science is fundamentally a unitary thing. The number of independent agencies should be kept to a minimum. Much medical progress, for example, will come from fundamental advances in chemistry. Separation of the sciences in tight compartments, as would occur if more than one agency were involved, would retard and not advance scientific knowledge as a whole.

FIVE FUNDAMENTALS

There are certain basic principles which must underlie the program of Government support for scientific research and education if such support is to be effective and if it is to avoid impairing the very things we seek to foster. These principles are as follows:

(1) Whatever the extent of support may be, there must be stability of funds over a period of years so that long-range programs may be undertaken.

(2) The agency to administer such funds should be composed of citizens selected only on the basis of their interest in and capacity to promote the work of the agency. They should be persons of broad interest in and understanding of the peculiarities of scientific research and education.

(3) The agency should promote research through contracts or grants to organizations outside the Federal Government. It should not operate any laboratories of its own.

(4) Support of basic research in the public and private colleges, universities, and research institutes must leave the internal control of policy, personnel, and the method and scope of the research to the institutions themselves. This is of the utmost importance.

(5) While assuring complete independence and freedom for the nature, scope, and methodology of research carried on in the institutions receiving public funds, and while retaining discretion in the allocation of funds among such institutions, the Foundation proposed herein must be responsible to the President and the Congress. Only through such responsibility can we maintain the proper relationship between science and other aspects of a democratic system. The usual controls of audits, reports, budgeting, and the like should, of course, apply to the administrative and fiscal operations of the Foundation, subject, however, to such adjustments in procedure as are necessary to meet the special requirements of research.

Basic research is a long-term process—it ceases to be basic if immediate results are expected on short-term support. Methods should therefore be found which will permit the agency to make commitments of funds from current appropriations for programs of five years' duration or longer. Continuity and stability of the program and its support may be expected (a) from the growing realization by the Congress of the benefits to the public from scientific research, and (b) from the conviction which will grow among those who conduct research under the auspices of the agency that good quality work will be followed by continuing support.

MILITARY RESEARCH

As stated earlier in this report, military preparedness requires a permanent, independent, civilian-controlled organization, having close liaison with the Army and Navy, but with funds direct from Congress and the clear power to initiate military research which will supplement and strengthen that carried on directly under the control of the Army and Navy. As a temporary measure the National Academy of Sciences has established the Research Board for National Security at the request of the Secretary of War and the Secretary of the Navy. This is highly desirable in order that there may be no interruption in the relations between scientists and military men after the emergency wartime Office of Scientific Research and Development goes out of existence. The Congress is now considering legislation to provide funds for this Board by direct appropriation.

I believe that, as a permanent measure, it would be appropriate to add to the agency needed to perform the other functions recommended in this report the responsibilities for civilian-initiated and civilian-controlled military research. The function of such a civilian group would be primarily to conduct long-range scientific research on military problems—leaving to the Services research on the improvement of existing weapons.

Some research on military problems should be conducted, in time of peace as well as in war, by civilians independently of the military establishment. It is the primary responsibility of the Army and Navy to train the men, make available the weapons, and employ the strategy that will bring victory in combat. The Armed Services cannot be expected to be experts in all of the complicated fields which make it possible for a great nation to fight successfully in total war. There are certain kinds of research—such as research on the improvement of existing weapons—which can best be done within the military establishment. However, the job of long-range research involving application of the newest scientific discoveries to military needs should be the responsibility of those civilian scientists in the universities and in industry who are best trained to discharge it thoroughly and success-fully. It is essential that both kinds of research go forward and that there be the closest liaison between the two groups.

Placing the civilian military research function in the proposed agency would bring it into close relationship with a broad program of basic re-search in both the natural sciences and medicine. A balance between mili-tary and other research could thus readily be maintained.

The establishment of the new agency, including a civilian military re-search group, should not be delayed by the existence of the Research Board for National Security, which is a temporary measure. Nor should the creation of the new agency be delayed by uncertainties in regard to the postwar organization of our military departments themselves. Clearly, the new agency, including a civilian military research group within it, can re-main sufficiently flexible to adapt its operations to whatever may be the final organization of the military departments.

NATIONAL RESEARCH FOUNDATION

It is my judgment that the national interest in scientific research and scien-tific education can best be promoted by the creation of a National Re-search Foundation.

I. *Purposes.*—The National Research Foundation should develop and promote a national policy for scientific research and scientific education, should support basic research in nonprofit organizations, should develop scientific talent in American youth by means of scholarships and fellow-ships, and should by contract and otherwise support long-range research on military matters.

II. *Members.*—1. Responsibility to the people, through the President and the Congress, should be placed in the hands of, say, nine Members, who should be persons not otherwise connected with the Government and not representative of any special interest, who should be known as Na-tional Research Foundation Members, selected by the President on the basis of their interest in and capacity to promote the purposes of the Foun-dation.

2. The terms of the Members should be, say, 4 years, and no Member should be eligible for immediate reappointment provided he has served a full 4-year term. It should be arranged that the Members first appointed serve terms of such length that at least two Members are appointed each succeeding year.

3. The Members should serve without compensation but should be entitled to their expenses incurred in the performance of their duties.

4. The Members should elect their own chairman annually.

5. The chief executive officer of the Foundation should be a director appointed by the Members. Subject to the direction and supervision of the Foundation Members (acting as a board), the director should discharge all the fiscal, legal, and administrative functions of the Foundation. The director should receive a salary that is fully adequate to attract an outstanding man to the post.

6. There should be an administrative office responsible to the director to handle in one place the fiscal, legal, personnel, and other similar administrative functions necessary to the accomplishment of the purposes of the Foundation.

7. With the exception of the director, the division members, and one executive officer appointed by the director to administer the affairs of each division, all employees of the Foundation should be appointed under Civil Service regulations.

III. *Organization.*—1. In order to accomplish the purposes of the Foundation the Members should establish several professional Divisions to be responsible to the Members. At the outset these Divisions should be:

a. *Division of Medical Research.*—The function of this Division should be to support medical research.

b. *Division of Natural Sciences.*—The function of this Division should be to support research in the physical and natural sciences.

c. *Division of National Defense.*—It should be the function of this Division to support long-range scientific research on military matters.

d. *Division of Scientific Personnel and Education.*—It should be the function of this Division to support and to supervise the grant of scholarships and fellowships in science.

e. *Division of Publications and Scientific Collaboration.*—This Division should be charged with encouraging the publication of scientific knowledge and promoting international exchange of scientific information.

2. Each Division of the Foundation should be made up of at least five members, appointed by the Members of the Foundation. In making such appointments the Members should request and consider recommendations from the National Academy of Sciences which should be asked to establish a new National Research Foundation nominating committee in order to bring together the recommendations of scientists in all organizations. The

chairman of each Division should be appointed by the Members of the Foundation.

3. The division Members should be appointed for such terms as the Members of the Foundation may determine, and may be reappointed at the discretion of the Members. They should receive their expenses and compensation for their services at a per diem rate of, say, $50 while engaged on business of the Foundation, but no division member should receive more than, say, $10,000 compensation per year.

4. Membership of the Division of National Defense should include, in addition to, say, five civilian members, one representative designated by the Secretary of War, and one representative of the Secretary of the Navy, who should serve without additional compensation for this duty.

IV. *Functions.*—1. *The Members of the Foundation should have the following functions, powers, and duties:*

a. To formulate over-all policies of the Foundation.

b. To establish and maintain such offices within the United States, its territories and possessions, as they may deem necessary.

c. To meet and function at any place within the United States, its territories and possessions.

d. To obtain and utilize the services of other Government agencies to the extent that such agencies are prepared to render such services.

e. To adopt, promulgate, amend, and rescind rules and regulations to carry out the provisions of the legislation and the policies and practices of the Foundation.

f. To review and balance the financial requirements of the several Divisions and to propose to the President the annual estimate for the funds required by each Division. Appropriations should be earmarked for the purposes of specific Divisions, but the Foundation should be left discretion with respect to the expenditure of each Division's funds.

g. To make contracts or grants for the conduct of research by negotiation without advertising for bids.

And with the advice of the National Research Foundation Divisions concerned—

h. To create such advisory and cooperating agencies and councils, state, regional, or national, as in their judgment will aid in effectuating the purposes of the legislation, and to pay the expenses thereof.

i. To enter into contracts with or make grants to educational and non-profit research institutions for support of scientific research.

j. To initiate and finance in appropriate agencies, institutions, or organizations, research on problems related to the national defense.

k. To initiate and finance in appropriate organizations research projects for which existing facilities are unavailable or inadequate.

l. To establish scholarships and fellowships in the natural sciences including biology and medicine.

m. To promote the dissemination of scientific and technical information and to further its international exchange.

n. To support international cooperation in science by providing financial aid for international meetings, associations of scientific societies, and scientific research programs organized on an international basis.

o. To devise and promote the use of methods of improving the transition between research and its practical application in industry.

• • •

V. *Patent Policy.*—The success of the National Research Foundation in promoting scientific research in this country will depend to a very large degree upon the cooperation of organizations outside the Government. In making contracts with or grants to such organizations the Foundation should protect the public interest adequately and at the same time leave the cooperating organization with adequate freedom and incentive to conduct scientific research. The public interest will normally be adequately protected if the Government receives a royalty-free license for governmental purposes under any patents resulting from work financed by the Foundation. There should be no obligation on the research institution to patent discoveries made as a result of support from the Foundation. There should certainly *not* be any absolute requirement that all rights in such discoveries be assigned to the Government, but it should be left to the discretion of the director and the interested Division whether in special cases the public interest requires such an assignment. Legislation on this point should leave to the Members of the Foundation discretion as to its patent policy in order that patent arrangements may be adjusted as circumstances and the public interest require.

VI. *Special Authority.*—In order to insure that men of great competence and experience may be designated as Members of the Foundation and as members of the several professional Divisions, the legislation creating the Foundation should contain specific authorization so that the Members of the Foundation and the Members of the Divisions may also engage in private and gainful employment, notwithstanding the provisions of any other laws: provided, however, that no compensation for such employment is received in any form from any profit-making institution which receives funds under contract, or otherwise, from the Division or Divisions of the Foundation with which the individual is concerned. In normal times, in view of the restrictive statutory prohibitions against dual interests on the part of Government officials, it would be virtually impossible to persuade persons having private employment of any kind to serve the

Government in an official capacity. In order, however, to secure the part-time services of the most competent men as Members of the Foundation and the Divisions, these stringent prohibitions should be relaxed to the extent indicated.

Since research is unlike the procurement of standardized items, which are susceptible to competitive bidding on fixed specifications, the legislation creating the National Research Foundation should free the Foundation from the obligation to place its contracts for research through advertising for bids. This is particularly so since the measure of a successful research contract lies not in the dollar cost but in the qualitative and quantitative contribution which is made to our knowledge. The extent of this contribution in turn depends on the creative spirit and talent which can be brought to bear within a research laboratory. The National Research Foundation must, therefore, be free to place its research contracts or grants not only with those institutions which have a demonstrated research capacity but also with other institutions whose latent talent or creative atmosphere affords promise of research success.

As in the case of the research sponsored during the war by the Office of Scientific Research and Development, the research sponsored by the National Research Foundation should be conducted, in general, on an actual cost basis without profit to the institution receiving the research contract or grant.

There is one other matter which requires special mention. Since research does not fall within the category of normal commercial or procurement operations which are easily covered by the usual contractual relations, it is essential that certain statutory and regulatory fiscal requirements be waived in the case of research contractors. For example, the National Research Foundation should be authorized by legislation to make, modify, or amend contracts of all kinds with or without legal consideration, and without performance bonds. Similarly, advance payments should be allowed in the discretion of the Director of the Foundation when required. Finally, the normal vouchering requirements of the General Accounting Office with respect to detailed itemization or substantiation of vouchers submitted under cost contracts should be relaxed for research contractors. Adherence to the usual procedures in the case of research contracts will impair the efficiency of research operations and will needlessly increase the cost of the work to the Government. Without the broad authority along these lines which was contained in the First War Powers Act and its implementing Executive Orders, together with the special relaxation of vouchering requirements granted by the General Accounting Office, the Office of Scientific Research and Development would have been gravely handicapped in carrying on research on military matters during this war. Colleges and universities in which research will be conducted principally under contract with the Foundation are, unlike commercial institutions, not equipped to handle the detailed vouchering procedures and auditing technicalities which are required of the usual Government contractors.

• • •

ACTION BY CONGRESS

The National Research Foundation herein proposed meets the urgent need of the days ahead. The form of the organization suggested is the result of considerable deliberation. The form is important. The very successful pattern of organization of the National Advisory Committee for Aeronautics, which has promoted basic research on problems of flight during the past thirty years, has been carefully considered in proposing the method of appointment of Members of the Foundation and in defining their responsibilities. Moreover, whatever program is established it is vitally important that it satisfy the Five Fundamentals.

The Foundation here proposed has been described only in outline. The excellent reports of the committees which studied these matters . . . will be of aid in furnishing detailed suggestions.

Legislation is necessary. It should be drafted with great care. Early action is imperative, however, if this nation is to meet the challenge of science and fully utilize the potentialities of science. On the wisdom with which we bring science to bear against the problems of the coming years depends in large measure our future as a nation.

NATIONAL SCIENCE FOUNDATION REPORT 62–37
Scientific Activities in Government, 1940–1962

At the beginning of World War II it was apparent that the Government's scientific activities had not been adequate to meet the crisis which was upon it. New organizations were created to carry out the expanded programs of military research and development. Principally, these were the Office of Scientific Research and Development (OSRD) with its two major constituents, the National Defense Research Committee (NDRC) and

From *Federal Organization for Scientific Activities,* Government Printing Office, 1962.

the Committee on Medical Research, and the Manhattan Engineer District of the War Department's Corps of Engineers, which continued the program begun by NDRC on the nuclear bomb. For the first time the Government relied heavily upon contracts for the conduct of research and development projects, most of which applied scientific knowledge to military use. Military research and development in aeronautics were handled largely by an expanded National Advisory Committee for Aeronautics.

Immediately after World War II certain scientific activities of OSRD and other wartime agencies were continued by transfer to or by contract with the military departments. In 1947, the year following establishment of the Atomic Energy Commission, this agency took over civilian control of nuclear research and production from the Manhattan Engineer District project. In the Commission, the pattern was continued of administering scientific programs under contract with outside organizations.

Dr. Vannevar Bush, the wartime director of OSRD, submitted in 1945, at the request of President Franklin D. Roosevelt, a report on what postwar steps should be taken by the Federal Government for the support of science in the national interest. In his report, *Science—the Endless Frontier,* Bush proposed establishment of a National Research Foundation to support research and education in the sciences and dissemination of scientific information. This proposal led ultimately to the establishment of the National Science Foundation.

The principal Federal support for basic research in the years immediately following the war came from the Navy Department, which set up the Office of Research and Inventions in 1945. In 1946, by Act of Congress, this became the Office of Naval Research, which supports research in the many scientific fields of interest to the Navy. Another major source of support for such research in the life and medical sciences was the National Institutes of Health. From the Atomic Energy Commission came also support for basic research.

In 1946, President Truman, recognizing the need for a full examination of the Nation's scientific research effort, established the President's Scientific Research Board, under the chairmanship of his advisor, Dr. John R. Steelman. The following year the Board issued a report of recommendations on Federal organization for science, administration of research, training and utilization of scientific manpower, and medical research. One of the recommendations led to the establishment of the Interdepartmental Committee for Scientific Research and Development, composed of bureau chiefs, agency heads, and departmental officials having major responsibilities in science. The Committee sought to help solve administrative and personnel problems of member agencies in carrying out their research and development program.

As noted, the National Science Foundation was established by Act of Congress (Public Law 507—81st Congress) in 1950. This culminated a movement, which began in 1945 following Dr. Bush's report, when extensive Congressional hearings indicated that a majority of the Nation's scientists, educators, and business leaders favored the creation of such an agency. The Foundation was given broad responsibilities to develop national science policies and to stimulate and support basic research and science education.

The Science Advisory Committee was set up in 1951 by Executive Order and placed administratively within the Office of Defense Mobilization. This Committee was composed of fifteen eminent scientists and engineers from within and outside the Government, appointed by the President. The Committee's purpose was to advise the President, the National Security Council, and other agencies in matters relating to scientific and technological developments of significance to national security and on the utilization of science resources to assure their availability in the event of mobilization.

In 1957, the President transferred the Science Advisory Committee of the Office of Defense Mobilization (in the Executive Office of the President) to the White House, reconstituting and enlarging it as the President's Science Advisory Committee. At the same time he established the post of Special Assistant to the President for Science and Technology, whose incumbent became also chairman of the new Committee.

The new Committee, to complement its deliberations, recommended that a council be established made up of Federal officials from agencies having large research and development programs. It further recommended that the Special Assistant to the President for Science and Technology also serve as chairman of the council. Under Executive Order 10807 in 1959 the Federal Council for Science and Technology was set up with the Special Assistant to the President for Science and Technology as chairman. The Order also provided for the new Council's Standing Committee to succeed the Interdepartmental Committee on Scientific Research and Development. The combination of the Science Advisory Committee and the Federal Council provides a means for bringing to bear the best advice of scientists and engineers, both within and outside the Government, at the Presidential level.

In 1962, the President's Reorganization Plan No. 2 established the Office of Science and Technology as a new unit within the Executive Office of the President. The Office assists the President in reviewing and establishing policies, plans, and programs of science and technology in the Federal agencies. Reorganization Plan No. 2 transferred from the National Science Foundation to the new Office the functions conferred by the

NSF Act of 1950 of evaluating scientific research programs undertaken by agencies of the Federal Government. It further transferred so much of that function of developing and encouraging the pursuit of a national policy for the promotion of basic research and education in the sciences as is necessary to enable the Director of the Office of Science and Technology to advise and assist the President in achieving coordinated Federal policies for the promotion of basic research and education in the sciences. Responsibility for promotion of national policy in these two scientific areas was retained in the Foundation.

In addition to the evolution of coordinating mechanisms, the Federal organization for science has recently been enlarged. The chief expansion has been in the field of space technology, with the creation in 1958 of the National Aeronautics and Space Administration as successor to the National Advisory Committee for Aeronautics. This new agency is providing extensive support to research and development in science and engineering.

In the following pages is given a more detailed discussion of recent developments and characteristics of the Federal organization for science.

Major Characteristics

The Federal organization for science consists of components of both the Executive and Legislative Branches of the Federal Government. In the Executive Branch, 10 departments and 27 independent agencies contain units which plan, administer, conduct or support scientific activities. Within the Legislative Branch, Congressional Committees, the Library of Congress, the Botanic Garden, and the Government Printing Office engage in scientific activities. These agencies range widely in size, functions, fields of science, types of scientific and technological activities supported, contact with non-Government institutions, and types of facilities required.

A number of agencies were established primarily to promote some aspect of science and technology, for example, the National Aeronautics and Space Administration, and the Atomic Energy Commission, the latter two emphasizing engineering development. Appropriate scientific activities in other departments and agencies are performed at the bureau level on a large scale. Under the Department of Commerce, for example, are the Patent Office, the National Bureau of Standards, the Coast and Geodetic Survey, the Weather Bureau, the Office of Business Economics, and the Bureau of the Census. Many of these organizations in turn contain subordinate divisions which make contributions in their fields to science. The National Institutes of Health is but one of several scientific and technical organizations in the Public Health Service of the Department of Health, Education, and Welfare.

Often, a subdivision, not primarily engaged in scientific activity, contains subordinate units having research objectives. In the Department of Health, Education, and Welfare, for example, the Social Security Administration is responsible for studying and making recommendations and administering programs in connection with old age and survivors insurance, old age assistance, and related subjects. Although the major functions of the Administration do not involve scientific activities, several of its divisions, such as the Division of Program Research, are so involved.

Since World War II, developments in organization for scientific activities have been largely for the purpose of improving and expanding the Federal scientific effort. Recently, this trend has been characterized by: (1) an increased attempt to review and coordinate more effectively Federal scientific and technical programs at the Presidential level, (2) appointment of scientific administrators to Secretary-level posts, (3) integration or coordination of scientific activities within the subdivisions of the agencies, (4) expansion of international science activities, (5) growth of Government-supported extramural programs, and (6) emergence of the aerospace program.

DIRECTION AT THE PRESIDENTIAL LEVEL

During the past five years the trend toward greater review and supervision of Federal scientific programs at the Presidential level has become particularly evident. The Special Assistant to the President for Science and Technology, the President's Science Advisory Committee, the Federal Council for Science and Technology, and the Office of Science and Technology are all contributing to more comprehensive and effective evaluation and coordination of Federal scientific and technological activities. The Special Assistant to the President for Science and Technology is responsible for keeping informed of the progress of scientific and technical efforts in Federal agencies and for presenting his findings, evaluations, and recommendations to the President. The President's Science Advisory Committee is responsible for providing answers to questions raised by the President and for recommending ways in which United States science and technology can be advanced. The Committee serves as an important direct scientific input from the scientific community. The Federal Council considers Federal scientific and technological problems and developments affecting more than one Federal agency.

The Office of Science and Technology, headed by a director appointed by the President, serves as a permanent staff to advise and assist the President on major matters of Federal policy affected by or pertaining to science and technology. Because of the rapid growth and far-reaching scope of Federal activities in science and technology, it is imperative that the President have adequate staff support to develop policies and to evaluate programs to assure that science and technology are used effectively in the interests of national security and the general welfare. Policies in science and technology transcending agency lines often need to be coordinated and shaped at the level of the Executive Office.

SCIENCE ADMINISTRATORS AT THE SECRETARY LEVEL

In recent years positions have been established at the level of the Secretary's office in certain agencies to direct and coordinate their scientific activities. Leading scientists or engineers have been appointed to these positions. This pattern follows the action taken by the Department of Defense in the mid-nineteen-fifties.

The significance of this development has been substantial, placing as it does a staff science administrator at a level above that of the bureaus or major subdivisions which have operating responsibilities in research and development. Such an administrator has authority and supervision over subordinate units as well as the responsibility for coordinating their scientific programs. Generally, these science administrators have authority to examine scientific requirements and views of agencywide policy and program decisions in apportioning agency funds and manpower. In addition, they have the necessary status to participate effectively in interagency decision-making and in Congressional proceedings. The authority and importance of such positions within the Secretary's office have enabled the Federal Government to obtain the services of science administrators of distinction in their disciplines and with the required training and experience in operating and administering research and development activities.

The most recent example of such an appointment is the Assistant Secretary for Science and Technology in the Department of Commerce in 1962. He supervises the scientific and technical functions of the Department of Commerce and is a principal scientific and technical adviser to the Secretary. This includes the scientific and technical activities of such establishments as the National Bureau of Standards, the Patent Office, the U.S. Weather Bureau, and the Coast and Geodetic Survey. Prior to the creation of this position, the Under Secretary, four Assistant Secretaries, several bureau heads, and the Department's Science Committee shared many of these supervising and coordinating duties.

Other recent examples are: the Science Adviser to the Secretary, Department of the Interior, appointed in 1961; and the Science Adviser to the Secretary, Department of State, 1958. The Science Adviser to the Secretary, Department of the Interior, assumed some of the duties held by the bureau heads, the Administrative Assistant Secretary, and other Assistant Secretaries of the Department. He serves the Department of the Interior as principal adviser on matters of science and coordinates scientific programs of the Department. He also represents the Department on the Federal Council for Science and Technology and other interdepartmental bodies concerned with coordinating Federal scientific activities.

The Science Adviser to the Secretary, Department of State, is responsible for providing scientific advice to the Secretary of State and his staff, including the presentation for their consideration of those scientific developments at home and abroad which may have important implications in the formulation and implementation of foreign policy.

COORDINATION OF SCIENTIFIC ACTIVITIES WITHIN SUBDIVISIONS

With the acceleration of Federal scientific activities, there has been a trend towards greater integration and coordination of the administration, planning, and conduct of scientific programs. Such integration and coordination, occurring particularly in those agencies engaged in research and development, have had the effect of centralizing the organization for science. Existing organizational units have been expanded and new ones created to coordinate entire scientific programs of major subdivisions of an agency.

The trend towards greater centralization within subdivisions is illustrated by the following reorganizations. In 1956 the research and development programs in the physical and engineering sciences in the Post Office Department were consolidated under the Office of Research and Engineering. This Office develops and administers an industrial research and engineering program for the postal establishment and assists in the construction and modification of postal facilities. Prior to 1956 these activities had been conducted in the former Office of the Chief Industrial Engineer and other research and engineering units. In addition, the research and development program of this Office was centralized under the Assistant Director for Research and Development who supervises the Research Division, Development Division, and the Postal Laboratory.

In 1960, the Maritime Administration also centralized its research and development activities under the Office of Research and Development. This Office plans, evaluates, organizes, coordinates, and directs all research and development activities of the Administration including those conducted by employees of the Administration and those performed under contract with other Government agencies or private industry. It assumed the coordinating functions from other divisions of the Maritime Administration primarily concerned with ship construction and operations.

Other examples of consolidation under one office for research and development activities, formerly scattered among several organizational units within an agency or subdivision, are the Office of Research and Development, Patent Office, 1956; Office of Research and Development, Coast and Geodetic Survey, 1960; Office of Research and Development, Department of Labor, 1957; Office of Development Research and Assistance, Agency for International Development, 1961; Office of the Assistant Commissioner (Planning and Research), Internal Revenue Service, 1958; Aviation Research and Development Service, Federal Aviation Agency, 1961; and Office of Assistant Chief for Research and Development, Bureau of Supplies and Accounts, Department of the Navy, 1960.

INTERNATIONAL SCIENCE ACTIVITIES

With the increased recognition of the international character of scientific knowledge and its growing influence on the political and economic welfare of the United States, a number of Federal agencies have established units for the conduct of foreign scientific programs. In other instances, agencies reorganized their units for such purposes to give greater emphasis to their international objectives.

These organizational units permit the Nation more effectively: (*1*) to participate in worldwide scientific efforts such as the International Geophysical Year, Antarctic research, and the aerospace program including the international regulation of telecommunications; (*2*) to participate in the work of intergovernmental organizations, such as the World Health Organization, the International Labor Organization, the North Atlantic Treaty Organization, and the Organization of American States; (*3*) to aid less developed nations in science and technology, particularly in agricultural, engineering, and medical sciences; and (*4*) to acquire scientific knowledge and manpower from other technologically advanced countries for use in domestic programs.

This trend is particularly evident in the Department of State. In the reorganization of the Foreign Aid Program in the newly established (1961) Agency for International Development, a major subdivision of the Department, greater emphasis than heretofore is placed upon scientific activity. In addition to its responsibility for providing funds and technical personnel for the construction of institutes of science and laboratories and for support of advanced training of scientific personnel in foreign areas, the Agency supports other scientific activities. It has established an Office of

Development Research and Assistance which plans to conduct programs of basic and applied research and evaluation in economic and social development.

Under the State Department also are the science attachés, located in London, Paris, Bonn, Stockholm, Rome, New Delhi, Tokyo, Buenos Aires, Bern, and Rio de Janeiro. Their responsibilities include keeping the embassies and Department informed of developments in science, advising them of the impact of United States policies on the scientific activities of the host countries, and interpreting the influence that foreign policies may have on United States scientific activities.

Another agency that has significantly expanded its support of foreign science in recent years is the Department of Agriculture. The Foreign Research and Technical Programs Division, a subdivision of the Agricultural Research Service, was organized in 1958 to administer the Foreign Agricultural Research Grant Program under Public Law 480. Its purpose is to further research in agricultural sciences in many countries of the world. Financed by foreign currencies made available to the Federal Government through sales of surplus commodities abroad, the Division makes grants to foreign institutions which can provide trained personnel, laboratory space and other facilities for conduct of the proposed work. The Division coordinates that foreign research program, serving components of the Agricultural Research Service, the Forest Service, the Agricultural Marketing Service, and other subdivisions of the Department. Agricultural attachés act as liaison between the Foreign Office of the Division and the institute receiving the grant and the ambassador of the country involved.

The National Science Foundation also has given foreign science activities additional attention in the past few years. The Foundation's Office of the International Geophysical Year discharged the agency's support of the IGY during 1958 and 1959. Currently, the Office of Antarctic Programs and the Office of International Science Activities, under the Associate Director for Education and International Activities, have broad functions to meet the increased responsibilities of the Foundation in international science. The Office of Antarctic Programs coordinates and manages the Foundation's responsibility to insure that an integrated United States scientific research program is carried out in Antarctica. The Office of International Science Activities is responsible for providing staff and policy guidance on international aspects of research support, science education, exchange of science information, and on international scientific meetings. The Office maintains small staffs in Japan, France, and Brazil.

In addition to these organizational units, other offices of the National Science Foundation have subdivisions for carrying on international science activities, such as the Foreign Studies Program of the Office of Economic and Statistical Studies and the Foreign Science Information Program of the Office of Science Information Service.

Other agencies or subdivisions that have expanded their foreign scientific activities and responsibilities in recent years include the Atomic Energy Commission's Office of Assistant General Manager for International Activities, created in 1956. Activities of this Office and its Division of International Affairs have broadened the base of international nuclear knowledge and skills through the negotiation and implementation of international agreements for cooperation with foreign countries and international organizations. The Office provides assistance to foreign nationals who wish to receive training in nuclear science and technology at Atomic Energy Commission facilities.

Within the Executive Office of the President, both the President's Science Advisory Committee and the Federal Council for Science and Technology have subcommittees to consider international science problems. The President's Science Advisory Committee has a Panel on International Science. Through this Panel the Committee assists in forming national policies relating to foreign aspects of science and engineering and in furthering international cooperation in science and technology. The Federal Council established the International Committee in 1959 to promote and coordinate Federal international scientific activities.

GROWTH OF EXTRAMURAL PROGRAMS

The trend towards extramural performance of Federal science programs, initiated on a major scale during World War II, has continued. Thus, the percentage of federally supported research and development performed extramurally, i.e., by contract or grant, which had risen to approximately 65 percent of total Federal expenditures for research and development in 1954,[1] had increased to an estimated 77 percent in 1962.[2]

The impact of this development on the Federal scientific effort has been substantial. Organizationally, it has influenced the type and size of agencies and subdivisions required to administer and manage Federal support of scientific activities. Increasing emphasis has thus been placed on the management and control of federally financed contracts or grants, such

1. National Science Foundation. *Reviews of Data on Research & Development,* No. 33, "Trends in Funds and Personnel for Research and Development, 1953–61." Washington 25, D.C.: Supt. of Documents, U.S. Government Printing Office, April 1962.
2. The 1962 data in this section are drawn from the National Science Foundation publication, *Federal Funds for Science X. Fiscal Years 1960, 1961, and 1962.* (Washington 25, D.C.: Supt. of Documents, U.S. Government Printing Office, 1962.)

as those in the Atomic Energy Commission, Department of Defense, National Aeronautics and Space Administration, and the Department of Health, Education, and Welfare. These agencies reported for 1962 extramural programs representing from 74 to 98 percent of their total funds for research and development. Only three of the major agencies having research and development programs perform most of their research in their own laboratories, the Departments of Agriculture, Commerce, and the Interior.

Of the total Federal funds for extramural research and development programs in 1962, approximately 80 percent was obligated to profit organizations, 15 percent to educational institutions and the balance to other nonprofit organizations. Indications are that funds for extramural performance of federally financed research and development may increase in the future.

The advantages of performing the research and development extramurally are the organizational flexibility and availability of technical and scientific personnel. Expansion in certain areas such as the space programs in the Department of Defense and National Aeronautics and Space Administration and the atomic energy effort in the Atomic Energy Commission do not allow time for the buildup of Government-owned scientific facilities and personnel, such as has occurred in the long-established departments.

AEROSPACE PROGRAM

Acceleration of the Federal aerospace program has been an influential factor in the total expansion of Federal scientific activities. Since 1961, the National Aeronautics and Space Administration has become the Government's second largest supporter of research and development. Only the Department of Defense, another large supporter of aerospace activities, currently spends more funds for research and development activities. Increasing at a greater rate than any other agency in recent years, NASA reported $905 million in 1961 obligations for support of research and development and R&D plant and an expected increase to $3.9 billion by fiscal year 1963.[3]

Among the organizational units, in addition to those cited, which have been created since 1957 to carry out the aerospace program are the following: Advanced Research Projects Agency, Department of Defense, 1958; National Aeronautics and Space Council, 1958; House Committee

3. National Science Foundation. *Federal Funds for Science XI. Fiscal Years 1961, 1962, and 1963.* Washington 25, D.C.: Supt. of Documents, U.S. Government Printing Office. (To be published)

on Science and Astronautics, 1958; Senate Committee on Aeronautical and Space Sciences, 1958; Space Science Board, National Academy of Sciences–National Research Council, 1958; Office of Aerospace Research, Air Force, 1961; and certain units of the Air Force Systems Command, Air Force, 1961. Agencies such as the Weather Bureau, the National Bureau of Standards, the Departments of the Army and Navy, the Atomic Energy Commission, and the National Science Foundation have also established administrative units and supported facilities to conduct or sponsor research related to aerospace. Activities and organizations for this purpose are described in the detailed presentation of these agencies given in this report.

The division of space responsibilities among a number of agencies, both military (Department of Defense, particularly Advanced Research Projects Agency) and civilian (National Aeronautics and Space Administration, Atomic Energy Commission, and Department of Commerce), further emphasizes the need for a high-level policy and coordinating authority transcending agency lines, such as the Office of Science and Technology. The large anticipated requirements of the aerospace program, in terms of dollars and manpower, necessitate decisions as to most effective employment of the Nation's limited scientific resources.

Trends in R&D Funds and Scientific Manpower

The significance and impact of Federal scientific activities can be evaluated in terms of certain statistical trends. Data on funds and personnel portray the extent and direction of the Federal Government's effort in science. The following description gives, in terms of funds and personnel, (1) the data for the Federal sector in relation to data for the national aggregate and (2) statistical trends within the Federal sector.

RELATION OF FEDERAL SECTOR TO NATIONAL AGGREGATE [4]

Statistical data on funds and personnel indicate that the national scientific effort has been rising rapidly since 1954. Expenditures for the performance of research and development, by far the largest scientific activity in terms of funds, were estimated at $15 billion in 1961–62 for all sectors of the economy, almost three times the 1953–54 national level of $5.2 billion.

The major contributor to this increased national scientific effort has been the Federal Government. In the last several years, the Federal Government, as a source of funds for research and development, has provided approximately 65 percent of the national total. The balance of the total

4. Data in this section are from the National Science Foundation bulletin, *Reviews of Data on Research & Development,* No. 33, *op. cit.*

has been provided by industry, 32 percent; colleges and universities, 2 percent; and other nonprofit institutions, 1 percent. The percentage of funds provided by the Federal Government has risen substantially since 1954. In that year the Federal Government provided 53 percent of the total national funds; industry, 44 percent; colleges and universities, almost 3 percent; and other nonprofit institutions, less than 1 percent.

From the standpoint of funds spent in performing research and development, the Federal Government accounts for considerably less in the national scientific effort. The percentage distribution of funds spent by performers of research and development in 1961 [5] was: industry, 75 percent; Federal Government, 15 percent; colleges and universities, 8 percent; and other nonprofit institutions, 2 percent. The extent of the national research and development total performed by the Federal Government in 1954 was approximately 19 percent; industry's share was 70 percent; colleges and universities, 9 percent; and other nonprofit institutions, 2 percent. Although Federal intramural funds as a percentage of the total funds for research and development was less in 1961 than in 1954, in terms of actual dollars, Federal performance in its own laboratories has increased from approximately $1 billion in 1954 to an estimated $2.1 billion in 1961.

Since 1954 the number of scientists and engineers employed in research and development in the natural sciences (including engineering) has increased in all sectors of the economy. In 1954 there were approximately 223,000 scientists and engineers, in terms of full-time equivalents (F.T.E.), employed in research and development in the country. By 1958 this number had increased to 327,000 and by 1960 the total was estimated at 387,000. The increase in these personnel over this period was almost 75 percent. Funds for research and development rose more than 140 percent during the same period.

The percentage distribution of scientists and engineers engaged in research and development, by sector, for the years 1954, 1958, and 1960 was as follows:

Total Number (full-time equivalents)	1954	1958	1960
	223,000	327,000	387,000
	Per cent distribution		
TOTAL	100	100	100
Federal Government	13	12	11
Industry	74	73	74
Colleges and Universities	11	13	13
Other Nonprofit Institutions	2	2	2

5. The latest year for which national data are available by sector. These national data are based on reports by performers.

Percentages for industry and other nonprofit institutions have remained relatively stable; the Federal Government has declined a few percentage points and the college and university sector has risen. In terms of numbers of scientists and engineers (F.T.E.) engaged in research and development however, the Federal Government increased this type of personnel from approximately 29,500 in 1954 to about 42,000 in 1960.

FEDERAL SECTOR [6]

Similar to the national totals for research and development, the long-term trend of aggregate expenditures for research and development by the Federal Government has moved upward. In fiscal year 1940, Federal expenditures for research and development amounted to an estimated $74 million. It is anticipated that such outlays will reach $12.3 billion by fiscal year 1963, with every indication that growth will increase in future years.

Spending by the Federal Government for research and development since 1940 appears to have followed three major waves. The first of these dates roughly from 1940 to the readjustment to peacetime conditions which followed World War II. The second wave, extending from 1950 to 1955, was sparked by the growth of certain peacetime research and development endeavors and later by the military demands for the Korean conflict. The third, extending from 1956 to the present, has been affected by several factors, the space program, the cold war, and the public health effort. In the first period, outlays for research and development accelerated to a peak in 1945 and then receded; in the second period, these expenditures rose to a high point in 1953 and then leveled off; the third period has been one of uninterrupted growth.

The increasing importance of Federal research and development in total Federal spending is illustrated in trend data. In fiscal year 1940, research and development funds accounted for less than 1 percent of total Federal expenditures. At the peak during World War II, in fiscal year 1945, these funds represented 2 percent of the national budget. By 1953, they accounted for 4 percent of the Federal budget. In fiscal year 1961, an estimated 11 percent of Federal funds were earmarked for research and development; the same percentage was anticipated in fiscal year 1962. The stepping up of the space program of the National Aeronautics and Space Administration and the steady advances, registered by the Departments of Defense, and Health, Education, and Welfare, the Atomic Energy Com-

6. Data on trends in Federal spending are derived from *Federal Funds for Science X* (*op. cit.*), except the 1963 figure which is the total to appear in *Federal Funds for Science XI* (*op. cit.*). The totals for Federal research and development include funds for R&D plant.

mission, and the National Science Foundation, portend an even greater share of Federal funds in the future for research and development. These five agencies accounted for over 90 percent of total Federal expenditures for research and development in fiscal years 1960, 1961, and 1962.

Data on Federal employment of scientists and engineers in all activities (research and development included) support the above trend. Like the data given earlier on scientists and engineers in research and development, the number of Federal scientists and engineers has also increased, as the Government has increased its scientific and technological activities and responsibilities. In 1931 less than 14,000 scientists and engineers were employed by the Federal Government. In 1938 employment of scientists and engineers was three and one-half times as great as in 1931; almost 48,000 persons were employed in scientific occupations by that time. Relatively large increases occurred during the depression and World War II. From 1938 to 1947, such employment increased by more than one-half, to about 75,000 persons. By 1951 the number of scientists and engineers had grown to more than 100,000. The total number of scientists and engineers in Federal employment was only slightly higher in 1954 than in 1951.

Between 1954 and 1958, however, there was an increase of 20 percent resulting in a total employment of almost 121,000 in these occupations. Of this increase 13 percent occurred between 1954 and 1957 and 7 percent from 1957 to 1958, undoubtedly a reflection of the growing tempo of the Government's scientific effort.[7] In 1960, the number of federally employed scientists and engineers had increased to 128,000, or about 8 percent of full-time white collar workers employed by the Government.[8]

7. National Science Foundation. *Scientists and Engineers in the Federal Government, October 1958*. Washington 25, D.C.: Supt. of Documents, U.S. Government Printing Office, 1961.
8. The 1960 data on Federal employment of scientists and engineers are from a survey by the U.S. Civil Service Commission.

DON K. PRICE
The Scientific Establishment

Now that the federal government is spending more money on research and development than its total budget before Pearl Harbor, American scientists find it hard to figure out their new role in society. They used to assume that democracy would never be a patron of the sciences, and even after the Second World War the Executive had to urge the support of research on a skeptical Congress. But even though the last administration started to cut back on expenditures for science, it ended by quadrupling them. And this was by no means for defense alone; over those eight years the Congress multiplied the budget of the National Institutes of Health more than ninefold, giving them each year more than the President recommended. It is almost enough to make one try to apply to politics the theory of Henry Adams that science, as it becomes more abstract, increases in geometrical progression the power that it produces.[1]

In his farewell message President Eisenhower warned the nation against the danger that "public policy could itself become the captive of a scientific-technological elite." Even though he quickly explained that he was not talking about science in general, but only those parts allied with military and industrial power, this was a shock to the scientists.[2] To one who believes that science has helped to liberate man from ancient tyrannies —who in short still takes his political faith from Franklin and Jefferson

1. Adams predicted that "the future of Thought, and therefore of History, lies in the hands of physicists . . . ," and went on to speculate that a rapid acceleration of thought in the direction of the abstract sciences might "reduce the forces of the molecule, the atom, and the electron to that costless servitude to which it has reduced the old elements of earth and air, fire and water. . . ." His prediction was uncanny, except for the term "costless" (*The degradation of the democratic dogma,* 277, 303, New York, 1958; first published in 1919).
2. Quoted in *New York Times,* 22 January, 1961, p. 4E. See also the authorized interpretation of this statement by the President's Special Assistant for Science and Technology, Dr. George B. Kistiakowsky, in *Science* 133: 355, 1961. As Chief of Staff, General Eisenhower had told the Army in 1946 that "The future security of the nation demands that all those civilian resources which by conversion or redirection constitute our main support in time of emergency be associated closely with the activities of the Army in time of peace," and advised the Army to contract extensively for scientific and industrial services (Memorandum for . . . General and Special Staff Divisions, etc., "Scientific and Technological Resources as Military Assets," 30 April, 1946).

From *Proceedings of the American Philosophical Society,* 106, No. 3 (June 1962). A revised version of this essay appeared as a chapter in *The Scientific Estate* by Don K. Price, Harvard University Press, 1965. Reprinted by permission.

70

and the Age of the Enlightenment—it is disconcerting to be told that he is a member of a new priesthood allied with military power.

Yet the plain fact is that science has become the major Establishment in the American political system: the only set of institutions for which tax funds are appropriated almost on faith, and under concordats which protect the autonomy, if not the cloistered calm, of the laboratory. The intellectual problems involved in this new status are likely to trouble scientists almost as much as the fears of the apocalyptic uses to which their discoveries may be put by the politicians.

The scientists are not the first, of course, to find it difficult to adjust their political ideals to the new world of technology. For example, the old corporation executive liked the great power technology had given to industry, but wished to limit the role of government on Jeffersonian principles. But the American scientist has a better right to his political nostalgia. For while the Founding Fathers had very little idea that industrial corporations would ever exist, let alone claim freedom of enterprise as a fundamental of the Constitution, some of them had a strong faith that free science would advance the cause of political freedom.

This faith of the Enlightenment tended to persist in the political thinking of American scientists, even in the period between the two World Wars, when it came to seem naive to their colleagues abroad. Even to this day they have shown singularly little interest in the conservative political theorists who have been telling them that science cannot deal with basic values or solve the major human problems, and the radical theorists who tell them that science can, if it will only join in a political system that will give it real power over society.[3] The conservative theorists have usually supported the conventional views of those in the European parliamentary tradition who believed that major political issues should be dealt with by party leaders and career administrators, with scientists speaking on such matters only when spoken to. And the most important radicals have been the Marxists, who proposed to let science, as they defined it, determine all human values through a disciplined system that would leave no room for the disorder of liberal democracy.

If American scientists generally ignored both the conservative and radical critics of the Enlightenment, it was probably, in the main, because

3. Maritain, Unamuno, and Ortega y Gasset represent the conservative critics of the Enlightenment; J. D. Bernal may be taken as a sample on the Socialist side. Judith N. Shklar, whose *After Utopia* begins with the observation that "nothing is quite so dead today as the spirit of optimism that the very word Enlightenment evokes," goes on (p. 3) to admit that "The less reflective public, certainly until 1914, remained cheerfully indifferent to the intellectual currents of despair. . . ." In this optimistic category, I would include most American scientists, and bring the date up to the present.

they were simply not interested in political theory, or even in politics. But it may have been also because neither theoretical position seemed very relevant to their practical experience. In disregard of the conservative and conventional theory, American scientists have come to have a much more direct role in high administration and in the making of policy than their counterparts in the parliamentary systems of Western Europe. (This is not to say that they had a more satisfactory role in the performance of scientific functions in the government.) And the more influence the scientists acquire, the more they now seem to work toward the dispersal of government organization and the decentralization of decisions, a trend impossible to explain to technocrats or the theorists of Marxism.

If we wish to understand the nature of our present scientific establishment, and its role in the making of public policy, perhaps we should look at the unusual way in which the role of scientists in public affairs has developed in the United States, and what its influence has been on the governmental system. That influence, I think, has been profound, not because of anything the scientists were seeking to do deliberately, at least until quite recently, but because of the special opportunities that were offered them by the nature of American political institutions. From the Jacksonian period, indeed, American scientists rarely had any distinctive opinion about politics or its relation to science; they were most often inclined to combine the anti-political prejudices of the business community with an envy of the social status of the European scientist. But while the American scientist lacked the honorific status of a member of a European Academy, he probably found it easier to play a direct role in government policymaking.

Sir Charles Snow has written with great insight of the Two Cultures, of the persisting failure of the humanists to understand the scientists or the changes they are working in the world, and of the scientists' personal and institutional difficulties in their relationship to government administrators and politicians. He has warned Americans most cogently against the naive belief that their constitutional system protects them against the dangers that face all countries as the result of the terrible weapons that scientists have put at the disposal of politicians who still think in pre-scientific terms.[4]

But in the United States we need to understand the idiosyncrasies of our institutions, not in order to admire them, but to know how to remedy their shortcomings, which were only a minor nuisance a generation ago, but may be a mortal threat today. Our television experts and editorial writers may be addicted to oratorical overconfidence in our peculiar institutions, but our scientists and intellectuals generally—and government re-

4. See especially his *Science and government*, 55, Cambridge, 1961.

formers in particular—are rather more addicted to applying constitutional cures that do not fit the disease.

I suspect that Sir Charles has a special degree of popularity in the United States for a reason that he would probably disapprove. We enjoy what he writes not only because we see many important ways that it applies to us, but also because of ways in which it does not. We like it much as we like Anthony Trollope; we like to read about a scholarly world in which the classicists can still snub the scientists, and social scientists hardly exist at all, just as we like to read about the squire and the vicar and the butler. And American scientists like to imagine, as they read about the problems that scientists have when serving under the career administrators of the United Kingdom, that they can blame their own problems on lack of status in the bureaucracy.

Yet a look at the main outlines of the two systems gives a different picture. In Great Britain, in spite of decades of debate about the basis of recruitment of the Administrative Class, it is still dominated by men trained in the classical and historical studies; not one man in twenty among these guardians of public policy has had a scientific or technical education. In spite of recurrent criticism of its role, it still maintains a professional monopoly (though in a studiously amateur and nonscientific way) over the organization of the government departments, and a major share of influence in the formation of national policy. It thus has no great interest in maintaining easy institutional channels by which scientists could move into its membership, or the universities could work closely with it on its major policy problems.[5]

Now that we are both constitutional democracies, it makes much less difference that Great Britain has a king and the United States a president, but a great deal of difference how we set up the professional group of men who actually run the government. Our Jacksonian revolution indeed destroyed the hopes of John Quincy Adams for a continuation of the Jeffersonian alliance between science and republicanism. At the same time, by wiping out the beginnings of a career system, it prevented the development of an elite administrative corps and thus cleared the channels of promotion for the scientists who, decades later, were to begin to move up in the civil service. The frontier radicalism of the day distrusted all forms of Establishment; this was the era in which state constitutions forbade ministers

5. McCrensky, Edward, *Scientific manpower in Europe*, 27–29, New York, 1958, gives the general picture with respect to salaries and personnel policy. As for the classic attitude of the Administrative Class regarding its relation to the scientific civil service, see the testimony of Sir Warren Fisher, Permanent Secretary of the Treasury, before the Royal Commission on the Civil Service, 1929–1930, *Minutes of evidence*, 1276, 1282. For its contemporary attitude, see Sisson, C. H., *The spirit of British Administration*, London, 1959.

to hold public office and prohibited educational qualifications for admission to the bar. But as the business of government got more complicated, the frontier had to admit that certain skills were necessary. Its essentially pragmatic temper insisted, as it became necessary to hire civil servants for merit rather than patronage, that the requirements be defined in terms of the needs of the specific jobs, rather than by general educational status. It was easiest to prove the need for special skills, of course, in technical fields, partly on account of the objective nature of the problem, partly because scientific societies were determined to raise and maintain their professional standards in the civil service as well as in private practice.[6]

As a result, it was in the scientific and professional fields that the career civil service system was first pushed up to the higher ranks. As we developed our top civil service, we made it something quite different from a career Administrative Class; most of its members are not only nonpolitical, but nonadministrative as well, and they are not career officials in the same sense as a U. S. Navy officer or a British Civil Servant.

In recent years, scientists and engineers, while certainly rare among those in high political office, have done reasonably well in the civil service. The positions of administrative continuity and bureaucratic power in Washington are, in the civil service departments, the bureau chiefs. A study in 1958 of the 63 bureau chiefs showed that 9 of them had advanced degrees in the natural sciences, and 17 others had been trained in lesser ways as engineers or technicians. By comparison with these 26 from various branches of technology, there were 9 economists and only 8 lawyers, and 20 from miscellaneous administrative or business careers.[7] Aside from the positions of bureau chief, the top career positions are the so-called "super-grades," which were added above the regular civil service grades to let the government compete for scarce talent.[8] The favorite justification for these positions is the need to employ capable scientists and

6. As A. Lawrence Lowell put it, "The great professions, which have secured general recognition in the community, have been strong enough to insist that strictly professional work must not be intrusted to men who have had no professional training or experience" (*Public opinion and popular government,* 274, New York, 1926). Detailed illustrations for specifically scientific fields may be found in the series of "Service Monographs of the United States Government" published by the Institute for Government Research, notably those on the Steamboat Inspection Service, the Office of Experiment Stations, the General Land Office, and the Public Health Service. See also Lewis Mayers, *The federal service,* Institute for Government Research, 21, 1922, and Lewis Meriam, *Public personnel problems,* 317.

7. Smith, Michael E., Bureau chiefs in the federal government, 1958, in *Public Policy,* the Yearbook of the Graduate School of Public Administration, Harvard University 10: 62, 1960.

8. United States Civil Service Commission, *The federal top salary network,* Washington, 1960.

engineers, notably in the technical branches of the Defense Department and the National Aeronautics and Space Agency. Administrators have ridden along to higher salaries on the political coattails of scientists.

Scientists who become bureau chiefs are, of course, no longer practicing scientists; they are doing work that in the United Kingdom would be done by a member of the Administrative Class educated in history or the classics. But when they are good at their jobs, as some of them are, it is for a reason that would have appealed to Macaulay, who used to argue that he wanted to recruit university graduates in the classics not because they had been studying the classics, but because the classics attracted the best minds, which could adapt themselves to anything.[9] And the American scientist who turns administrator is the equal of his English humanist counterpart in at least one respect: his lack of interest in management as a science, or sometimes at all.

But while the scientists in top civil service posts have not been deeply interested in administration, they have been interested in policy. What chance do they have to make their policy views prevail?

In their influence on policy, as in their advancement in the hierarchy, the scientists in American government had a special opportunity because they did not have to work under a tightly organized governing elite. After the Civil War, there was no strong conservative tradition based on a landed interest, and no national party with a coherent ideology, to take control.

As a result, policy tended to develop separately in every field. There was no one to tell the scientific experts that they were on tap but not on top; indeed, they were listened to all the more readily because they were usually not thought of as bureaucrats. There was no one from whom Congress wanted advice less than from the regular career service. But each group of scientists had one foot in government, so to speak, and one outside, and the policy views that the insiders developed would come back to the Congress from the National Academy or the scientific societies.[10] In a

9. He put it more pointedly in 1833: "If astrology were taught at our universities, the young man who cast nativities best would generally turn out a superior man." Royal Commission on The Civil Service, *Fourth report,* Cd. 7338, 1914.

10. ". . . from the beginning the membership of the Academy included many officers of the Government. . . . On one occasion at least this led to some embarrassment, for the reason that through this double relationship it was thought that the view of subordinate officers might control the action of those higher in authority" (True, Frederick W., *A history of the first half-century of the National Academy of Sciences,* 202, Washington, 1913). The same fear, or hope, exists in the present relationship between the Academy and the Federal Council for Science and Technology. True's history of the Academy, and his *History of agricultural experimentation and research in the United States* (Misc. Pub. No. 251, U. S. Department of Agriculture,

government of limited constitutional powers, a research program could be justified in a given field when an action program could not. But the research ultimately seemed to lead to action, in spite of the lawyers' scruples and the lack of interest of the party machines. This was only in part because the politicians were persuaded by objective data; it may have been even more because scientists (and in some fields, the economists) were the major organized communities of professional opinion with a continuous interest in specific public programs. This is a summary of the development of many new federal programs: you can trace it in agriculture, in natural resources, in the regulation of business, in labor and welfare, and we now see its beginnings in the support of education.

The most influential pattern was set in agriculture. Washington and Jefferson had been interested in fostering scientific improvements in agriculture, and in federal support of a national university. They were blocked by the lawyers' scruples about states' rights, until the agricultural scientists found a way to get there by a different route—one that evaded constitutional barriers by merging federal and state interests through the device of federal grants to states in either land or money, and by building a program up on scientific and educational bases. The foundation was, of course, the land grant college; from it grew the experiment station, the extension program, and the whole system of policy which has let the federal government play a more effective role in the agricultural economy than the government of any supposedly socialized state. In all this development, the land grant colleges and the associations of various kinds of agricultural scientists maintained an important influence on the Department of Agriculture, supplied most of its career personnel, and generally provided the intellectual leadership for national agricultural policy. They thus in effect greatly weakened the old constitutional distinction between state and federal functions, but without subjecting the field of agriculture to the control of a centralized bureaucracy.

The pattern of grants in aid, with its new set of administrative relationships, met two cardinal needs: to provide money, as well as national policy direction, from Washington, and to maintain the autonomy of the states. It accordingly became the basis on which new programs were developed—highways, public health, social security, welfare, housing, and others. This was what political scientists came to call the "New Federalism," which has given the scientists and specialists in each field of policy a chance to work out programs without too much constraint by any party doctrine.

An elite administrative corps may look on scientists as properly subor-

Washington, 1937) tell a great deal about the role of scientific societies in the development of new Federal programs.

dinate, and science as a way of thinking that should deal with the means to support a policy, a tradition, or an ideology, rather than an end in itself. We can understand this relationship in other countries if we recall how until recent years our military services thought that civilian scientists in military laboratories should conduct their research only pursuant to "requirements" defined by military staff work. This notion was exploded as it became apparent that what scientists discovered by unrestricted research might be of greater military importance than the things the military officers thought they wanted—in short, that the means might determine the ends.

This example provides the extreme (and almost the only conspicuous) example in American politics in which scientists have been faced with difficulties in getting a direct political hearing for their policy ideas. The typical editorial writer may still think in terms borrowed from the experience of parliamentary constitutions with tightly knit administrative elites, but all the habits of American public life run on a different pattern.

Its constitutional peculiarities are typified in one trivial incident: in a recent Congressional hearing, a friendly Representative addressed the newly appointed political head of the National Aeronautics and Space Administration, to his mild embarrassment, as "Doctor." In a legislature that is supposed to distrust eggheads, a Congressman often wants his advice on a specific program undiluted by either party doctrine or the policy views of general administrators; he is so conditioned to go directly to the scientific expert whenever he can that he sometimes treats his witnesses as experts even when they are not. This constitutional model is worth looking at with more critical sympathy. Its essential parts—none of which exists in the classic parliamentary system—are the standing Congressional committee that considers policies without being bound by party doctrine; a chief executive who is elected independently of the legislature on a non-ideological platform so that he can tolerate loose coordination and experimentation in policy matters; and a civil service which lets scientists move freely up into top administrative positions, and in and out of government, thus maintaining a continuous interchange of men and ideas between the government and universities. This system makes it impossible to maintain an institutional distinction between ends and means, between policy decisions on the one hand, and on the other hand scientific research or administration. Hence it makes party responsibility in the parliamentary sense impossible, and it greatly complicates the task of coordinating either policy or administration.

On the other hand, to deny the distinction between ends and means is a part of the scientific approach: no scientist likes to feel that his basic values and objectives have been set by others so rigidly that he cannot follow where his research leads him. It was, after all, the purpose of the Enlightenment to free both politics and science from the monarchical and ecclesiastical institutions that defined traditional values.[11] It may be even more necessary to deny the distinction between ends and means, in an institutional sense, in the twentieth century, when it is the requirements of new ideology, rather than old orthodoxy, that threaten freedom. For science itself, by introducing so many complexities into public policy, destroyed the comfortable nineteenth-century notion that public issues could really be determined by the parliamentary competition of two opposing doctrines. At the same time, it made possible, by the development of new techniques of mass communication, the means for producing disciplined support of authoritarian government. If the structure of political institutions does not specifically encourage some social experimentation based on scientific initiative, with some degree of deliberate freedom from the constraints of policy as determined by either partisan theorists or an administrative elite, it will narrow the range of free scientific and political development. Perhaps our eighteenth-century Constitution, with its implied distrust of party discipline, will yet prove to be more adaptable to our scientific era than the classic nineteenth-century parliamentary model of Walter Bagehot or Woodrow Wilson.[12]

At any rate, it is easy to guess why large groups among American scientists—especially in the agricultural sciences—were less pessimistic in the period after the First World War than their European colleagues with respect to the role of science in democratic politics. In two very practical ways their situation was entirely different; in civil service, their advancement was not blocked by a career bureaucracy, and the constitutional system gave them a chance to advocate policies in comparative freedom from administrative or political discipline. It was no wonder that they had not lost faith in the political approach of the Enlightenment, for they had made it work.

Nevertheless, by the time of the Great Depression this naive faith was least prevalent in the most important universities and the most advanced

11. Frankel, Charles, *The case for modern man,* 58, Boston, 1955. Ernst Cassirer noted "the almost unlimited power which scientific knowledge gains over all the thought of the Enlightenment. . . . A . . . deeper insight into the spirit of laws, of society, of politics, and even of poetry, seems impossible unless it is pursued in the light of the great model of the natural sciences" (*The philosophy of the enlightenment,* 45–46, Boston, 1955).

12. Bagehot, Walter, *The English Constitution,* and Wilson, Thomas Woodrow, Cabinet government in the United States, *The International Review,* August, 1879 (reprinted 1947 by the Overbrook Press, Stamford). By the turn of the twentieth century, Wilson had apparently changed his mind, in view of the new role of the presidency, especially in international affairs: *Congressional government,* Preface to 15th edition, 1900.

fields of science. In them, science was supported more by private corporations and foundations than by government, and its leaders in newer fields like nuclear physics and biochemistry had closer intellectual ties with their European counterparts than with the agronomists or engineers of the land-grant colleges. For the loose American constitutional system had worked best in those aspects of public affairs in which the power of government and the power of the great industrial corporations were not in rivalry. The scientists in institutions that derived their support from industrial wealth and were interested in problems of the industrial urban economy saw the constitutional model in a different political perspective. Among them, accordingly, were to be found both those conservative scientists who were most distrustful of government, and those radicals who tended to take a Marxist view of the role of science in society.

The Depression had thus made it impossible for the American scientist to avoid the second challenge, explicit in Marxism, with respect to the significance of his role in society: does science as it grows in importance lead us away from constitutional liberalism, and require party dictatorship? In a society of growing complexity, is not an increase in the role of government inevitable, and does not that inevitably lead to a centralization of power that will destroy democratic freedom?

These are still troublesome questions, but they are being discussed on a somewhat higher level of sophistication than three decades ago. The change has come about partly because scientists, under the pressure of the Second World War, worked out a new type of contractual relationship that has brought private scientific institutions into a connection with the federal government as intimate and active as that of any land-grant college. And the extension of this system to industrial corporations may now be bringing about a new relationship between government and business following the quarrels of the Depression era, much as the grant-in-aid system transformed federal-state relations after the Civil War.

Before going into the nature of this new system, let us note two peculiarities of American politics that made it possible.

The first was the assumption that it was just as appropriate for the voters and legislators to control the administrative organization and procedures of government as its policies, that is to say, the means as well as the ends. This was a radical departure from British or European assumptions. The political progression from conservatives to liberals to socialists never changed the fundamental European assumption that, while governments might be responsible to legislatures for the substance of their policies, it was better for politics and legislation not to meddle with internal administrative organization, or the management of the bureaucracy. The socialist political leaders took the unity of the state and its bureaucracy for granted. If anything, they tended to make it all the more monolithic, and to push to its logical conclusion the tendency of Benthamite liberalism to abolish the privileges of guilds and public corporations. But in the United States the current of radicalism ran in the opposite direction; after the age of Jackson, lobbyists and legislators were likely to concern themselves at least as much with the details of administrative organization as with major policies, generally with the purpose of creating centers of independence within government. This tendency was pushed so far that it destroyed the unity of administration, and had disastrous effects on the competence and the political responsibility of government. But it also made it a mistake to assume—as was often assumed both by those who admired and those who feared socialism—that an extension in the scope of governmental business in the United States would automatically involve a corresponding centralization of power.

The second peculiarity of American politics was the extent to which universities and private foundations had a hand in the initiation of new public policies. Private universities as well as the land-grant colleges were drawn into public service functions, partly because they were, in the absence of a career bureaucracy, the main reservoir of expertise on which politicians could draw for advice, and partly in response to the influence of the philanthropic foundations.

By the 1920's, some of the major foundations had lost interest in the charitable alleviation of social problems, and began to hope that science might solve them. This idea led to a strategy of supporting both scientific research and demonstration projects to test the application of such research, which could then be extended by the greater resources of government. Their aid to scientific education and research is a familiar story, in almost every branch of science. But equally important, they went on to help strengthen the professional organizations of scientists,[13] and to pay for the efforts of governments to improve their organization and administration, and to make use of research and research institutions as they did so. By the time of the Second World War, the leading scientists knew that a grant-making agency like a foundation could initiate nationwide programs by working with independent universities and governmental agencies, as the stories of hookworm control, the foundation of public libraries, and the reform of medical education all suggested. And political leaders were inclined to turn to private funds to help them explore future

13. The National Research Council, created by President Wilson to do in the First World War (in a rudimentary way) what the Office of Scientific Research and Development did in the Second, was supported not by appropriations but by the Rockefeller and Carnegie foundations (Axt, Richard G., *The federal government and financing higher education*, 78, New York, 1952).

policy opportunities, or experiment with them, as when President Hoover sought foundation financing for his Committee on Social Trends and for a National Science Fund, and the Public Administration Clearing House provided the initial administrative costs for President Roosevelt's Science Advisory Board.[14]

As scientists learned that the organization of government was something that could be influenced from the outside, and that universities and foundations could have a substantial influence on public policy, they were in effect freeing themselves from the assumption that government and private institutions were sharply different in nature. They were accordingly ready, at the outset of the Second World War, to work out a thoroughly pragmatic set of arrangements for the conduct of weapons research. The approach that they adopted was simply to enlist institutions rather than individuals in the two great scientific programs of the war: the Office of Scientific Research and Development (OSRD), and the Manhattan Project of the Army Engineers.

To those who expect wartime crises and military authority to produce a centralization of authority, this approach must have been as surprising as if the Army had used the war as an excuse to increase, rather than decrease, its reliance on the state militias. But in the hands of Vannevar Bush, James B. Conant, and Karl T. Compton, the government contract became a new type of federalism. Under the OSRD, the Massachusetts Institute of Technology took on the responsibility for developing radar, and California Institute of Technology rockets, and under the Manhattan District, the University of Chicago set up the first sustained nuclear reaction and the University of California fabricated the first atomic bomb, while du Pont, General Electric, Union Carbide, and other industrial giants built the facilities to produce the fissionable materials.[15]

The postwar sequel is a well-known story. Through a continuation of this system of administering research and development programs by grant or contract, the Atomic Energy Commission, which was hailed by the draftsmen of the Atomic Energy Act as a triumph of socialism,[16] sup-

14. *Report of the Science Advisory Board,* 15, Washington, D. C., Sept. 20, 1934.
15. See the first volume of the forthcoming official history of the Atomic Energy Commission, Hewlett, Richard G., and Oscar E. Anderson, Jr., *The new world,* to be published in 1962.
16. "The field of atomic energy is made an island of socialism in the midst of a free enterprise economy" (Newman, James R., and Byron S. Miller, *The control of atomic energy,* 4, New York, 1948). Mr. Newman, writing a preface to this book a year after the text was completed, noted that "Only one major policy formulation, the decision by the Atomic Energy Commission not to conduct research in its own laboratories, departs sharply from the interpretations of the Act set forth in these pages" (p. xi).

ports a program in which some nine-tenths of the employees work for private corporations. The adamant argument of many scientific leaders of the 1930's against federal support of science now seem as ancient and irrelevant as debates over infra- or supra-lapsarianism; no major university today could carry on its research program without federal money. The Massachusetts Institute of Technology, California Institute of Technology, Chicago, and Johns Hopkins, of course, all administer special military or atomic energy programs and consequently draw from three-fifths to five-sixths of their budgets from government, while Harvard, Yale, and Princeton now get a larger proportion of their operating revenues from federal funds than do land-grant colleges like Illinois, Kentucky, and Maryland.[17]

In dollar volume, the biggest contracts are between the military services and industrial corporations; while most of this money goes for procurement, much of it goes for research and development, and for the kind of systems analysis and the direction and supervision of subcontractors that in a simpler age would have been done by the technical services of the Army and Navy. And even in the business of procurement, the contractual relation is not the traditional market affair: the contract is not let on competitive bids, the product cannot be specified, the price is not fixed, the government supplies much of the plant and capital, and the government may determine or approve the letting of subcontracts, the salaries of key executives, and a host of other managerial matters. A sizable proportion of the government's (and nation's) business is done this way; any one of six industrial corporations spends more federal tax dollars than any of the four smallest executive departments.[18]

But the significance of this development does not turn on the sheer quantity of money, but on the possibilities of institutional development: if a contract can be made with an established academic or industrial corporation, why cannot a new one be set up for the purpose, and if the system will work for scientists and engineers, why not for others? Accordingly, we have been seeing not only the splitting off of certain functions that government might have operated directly and their administrative fusion with private institutions, but the creation of entirely new private corporate

17. See the forthcoming study, to be published by the Carnegie Foundation for the Advancement of Teaching in 1962, on the relationship of American universities to the federal government.

18. For a general discussion of this problem from the legal point of view, see Miller, Arthur S., Administration by contact: a new concern for the administrative lawyer, *New York University Law Review* **36:** 957–990, 1961. The economic aspects are discussed in a study by Carl Kaysen, *Improving the efficiency of military research and development,* to be published in 1962 by the Committee for Economic Development; and the general problems of weapons development and procurement programs in a study, to be published by the Harvard Business School in 1962: Peck, Merton J., and Frederic M. Scherer, *The weapons acquisition process: an economic analysis.*

entities (e.g., the RAND Corporation, the Institute for Defense Analyses, the Aerospace Corporation) for the performance of government business.

As for the kinds of business that can be done under this system, Sir Henry Maine, who believed that progress was measured by the change from status to contract, would be intrigued to note that private corporations have contracts to maintain the Air Force's bombers and its missile ranges, private institutions make strategic studies for the Joint Chiefs of Staff and foreign policy studies for the Senate Foreign Relations Committee, universities administer technical-assistance programs for the State Department all over the world, and telephone and radio companies are about to help the National Aeronautics and Space Administration carry our messages through outer space.

This new system is doubtless breaking down the political opposition to federal programs even more effectively than did the system of grants to the states. State and local governments and private corporations used to join in their jealousy of purely federal activities, any extension of which was considered socialistic. The federal grants to states in the field of agriculture, however, were no longer socialistic in the eyes of the governors and the farm bloc; they were a defense of the American way of life, even though they involved more government controls than some avowedly socialistic states have ever managed. And now that the atomic energy and space and military programs support such a large share of the nation's business, and so much of its enterprise and innovation come from research and development financed by federal funds, and so much of that innovation and enterprise spills over quite naturally and properly into related commercial fields, it is no wonder that private business corporations are less jealous of government. More accurately, their jealousy no longer takes the form of fighting socialism, but of haggling over the administrative provisions of contracts. A great deal of private enterprise is now secreted in the interstices of government contracts. In short, what the grant-in-aid programs did to the arguments for states' rights, the new contractual systems are doing to those for pure private enterprise.

But the argument for a measure of independence from central authority still remains valid in either case, and so does the need to recognize that the fundamental responsibility of government cannot be delegated. In a proper sense of the term, "sovereignty" is, of course, not affected by this type of delegation. Policy decisions remain the responsibility of government. But "policy" here means simply those aspects of the business that government authorities consider it important enough to warrant controlling, either because they think them of major importance, or because they realize that voters or Congressmen think so.

This means that they will consider as policy certain aspects of management (for example, fair employment practices or prevailing wage rates). But, as long as they retain ultimate control, they may act on the advice of contractors with respect to the most momentous new issues, or delegate major segments of the business whenever they can specify the purposes to be accomplished: the complex and costly nature of certain types of military studies, and the sophistication of the new techniques of operations research, make the possibility of such delegation very broad indeed. There is nothing in the nature of the contract itself (or the grant, which differs from it only symbolically and in technical detail) to determine whether in this relationship a central bureaucracy will control every detail of the contractor's management, or will leave him free to decide matters in secret that ought to be determined by the President and Congress.

But the general effect of this new system is clear: it has destroyed the notion that the future growth in the functions and expenditures of government, which seems to be made inevitable by the increase in the technological complexity of our civilization, would necessarily take the form of a vast bureaucracy, organized on Max Weber's hierarchical principles, and using the processes of science as Julian Huxley predicted to answer policy questions.[19] To the considerable extent that scientists have shaped this development, its political and administrative patterns have reflected the way scientists actually behave rather than the way science fiction or Marxist theory would have them behave: they have introduced into the stodgy and responsible channels of bureaucracy the amiable disorder of a university faculty meeting.

Compare, for example, our oldest and least scientific federal agency with a large operational mission with the newest and most scientific—the Post Office with the Air Force or the Space Administration. The Post Office is a relatively self-contained hierarchy. The Air Force develops its policies and runs its program with the advice and cooperation of several dozen of the most influential universities and industrial corporations of the country, whose executives and faculty members consequently have independent bases from which to criticize any policies, strategic plans, or administrative arrangements they dislike—and they can always find a Congressional committee to listen to them.

I do not think the role of science in this difference is entirely accidental. This is in part because the pursuit of science itself is a nonhierarchical affair; the best scientists either personally prefer, or are taught by their guilds that they should prefer, the university's combination of research, teaching, and irresponsible administration, and to get the best scientists

19. Huxley, Julian, *Man in the modern world,* **120–121,** New York, 1948. See also his *Religion without revelation,* **4,** New York, 1957.

the government took them on their own terms. But more important, I believe, is the long-range and indirect connection: when the Revolution of the Enlightenment proposed that the organization and procedures of government as well as its policies should be open to scientific inquiry and independent criticism, they started a process which has had deep effects on the constitutional system. These effects showed first in the relation of scientific administrators to their executive superiors and to Congressional committees, and later in the new structure of federalism, and in the new contractual relationships between the federal government and private institutions.

As the story of the President's Science Advisory Committee illustrates, to say nothing of the similar advisory groups to the military services and the Atomic Energy Commission, this type of relationship very greatly reduces the possibility that great issues will be decided by closed scientific politics, or that the increase in importance of scientific staff work will reduce the free play of policy debate. For the institutional bases from which advisers operate give them a measure of independence as public critics, and thus provide something of a counterbalance to the centralizing pressures of wars and rumors of wars.

American scientists, who have tended to be a little disillusioned about their relationship with politicians ever since the Jacksonian period, are now entitled to look with somewhat greater satisfaction on the domestic Establishment that they have helped set up. For to some small extent science has helped the political system of the United States develop along lines quite different from the classic patterns of either parliamentary government and laissez-faire economics on the one hand, or socialism and one-party rule on the other. Among its essential institutional features are universities that are concerned with applied as well as basic sciences, and continuously exchange personnel with the government at all age levels; a personnel system which puts up no barrier against the administrative promotion of men with scientific training; and grants-in-aid and contracts through which federal agencies may influence or guide the policies, but not direct the detailed management, of certain aspects of local governments, business corporations, and universities. Among these institutions, the connecting links are strongest in scientific and technical fields. And the peculiar looseness of the constitutional system enables the scientists in each field to take the initiative in developing policies—just as their innovations are providing the greatest impetus to industrial enterprise. Most important, science is not restrained in its impact on policy by any rigid distinction between ends and means, imposed by institutionalized systems of traditional or ideological values. The key to this is the freedom to influence or determine the organization and procedures of government from the outside, not conceding control over them to professional administrators or party leaders.

But there are some good reasons why scientists should not be too self-satisfied about their new status. A good many of them already think that science has been corrupted by this new system, and the wealth that it has brought.[20] They tend to look back on pre-war science as the Reformers looked back to the Primitive Church: a period of austere purity, an era in which no vows were needed to guarantee the poverty of the professor, no scientist was seduced by a government contract, and teaching fellows were obedient. One may well be a little skeptical about this point of view, and suspect that poverty probably brought its distractions no less troublesome than those of riches. But even if we discount such dangers so far, the worst may be yet to come. The public and members of Appropriations Committees are being led to think of science in terms of spectacular results like a space satellite or a cancer cure, and the political pressure to pass miracles may lead to some major distortions in our national policy, and put some uncomfortable pressures on the independence of scientific institutions. We probably have less reason to fear that major governmental decisions involving science will be secret than that they will be popular.

For while our new system of administration by contract temporarily avoids the political problems that come with the growth of bureaucracy, it encounters them again in more subtle and difficult forms. We do well to recognize that a government bureau is tempted to be more concerned with its own status and power than with the purposes of national policy. But if we entrust those purposes to industrialists or even scientists, we do not sterilize that political temptation. We only let it begin to work directly on the industrialists and scientists. If public ownership is no guarantee of unselfishness, neither is private ownership. And it is ironic, in view of the general public image of his political ideas, that it was President Eisenhower who presented most forcefully to the country the danger that, having hired private corporations to further specific public ends, we will see them use the public means for private profit, or even in political efforts to control the policy decisions of the government.

Government policy, like science itself, needs to be conceived and pursued with some regard for its totality as well as its parts. By giving priority to the parts—by turning over the administration of public functions to private institutions—we have strengthened our ability to do a great many separate things, but not our ability to give integrity and discipline and direction to our total effort. Indeed, by relying too much on the contracting method we have probably weakened the quality of the scientists within the

20. Tuve, Merle A., Basic research in private research institutes, in Dael Wolfle, Ed. *Symposium on basic research*, **178**, Washington, 1959.

civil service, whose help is needed by the executive who seeks to manage our scientific programs as a coherent system.[21]

In the dimensions of its financial support and in the breadth of its influence, science has indeed become a national Establishment. Politicians are more likely to abuse it by calling on it to advance their special causes than they are to ignore it. In this predicament, scientists cannot protect their essential interests in government by setting themselves apart in a separate status or separate department. They used to be content with the control of particular bureaus or programs. Today, in the White House Office or the lobbies of the Capitol, they are obliged by the nature of the system they helped create to play a responsible role in all aspects of national policy, and in the development of a new pattern of relationships between public and private institutions in our society.

CHARLES V. KIDD

The Growth of Science and the Distribution of Scientists among Nations

'A law of acceleration, definite and constant as any law of mechanics, cannot be supposed to release its energy to suit the convenience of man. In every age man has bitterly and justly complained that Nature hurried and hustled him, for inertia almost invariably has ended in tragedy. During a million or two of years, every generation in turn has toiled with endless agony to attain and apply power, all the while betraying the deepest alarm and horror at the power they created.' [Henry Adams, *The Education of Henry Adams*, Chapter XXXIV (1904).]

EXPONENTIAL GROWTH

The poetic insight of perceptive philosophers into the rate of growth of science, and the stresses that this growth generates, has been supplemented by studies which reduce to numbers the 'law of acceleration' in science.[1] The exponential growth of science is now a well-documented

21. Brown, Harold, *Research and engineering in the defense laboratories* (An address by the Director of Defense Research and Engineering), Washington, October 19, 1961.
1. The observations in this article, which is simply a preliminary sketch of the nature of the problems and of the steps which might be taken to deal with them, are

From *Impact of Science on Society*, 14, No. 1 (1964). Reprinted by permission.

phenomenon. The regularity with which the intensity of science—measured in terms of published papers, numbers of scientists, investment in physical facilities and other plausible indices—has increased is remarkable. In Europe, scientific effort has doubled about every fifteen years since the mid-seventeenth century.[2] Beginning later, the scientific effort of the United States of America has doubled every ten years. The pool of trained people required to staff this effort has grown at approximately the same rate. In the United States, for example, the number of persons with a Ph.D. degree in science has doubled every ten years during the twentieth century.[3]

The growth rate of science in different countries and cultures lies at the root of the problem to which this article is directed—the migration of scientists, to and from less and more developed countries and among developed countries. Permanent migration is the focus of the article. The important subject of short-term visits of students and mature scientists is not dealt with.

Some interesting generalizations emerge when differential growth rates are examined. First, the fact that the countries with large scientific establishments will, in terms of absolute size, not only stay ahead of those with smaller establishments but will in all probability forge even further ahead. This growth will both contribute to the production of scientists and technicians and generate an insatiable demand. Every advanced nation faces a shortage of highly qualified scientists for the indefinite future. They will exert strenuous efforts to educate more scientists and to educate them better. They will tend to attract scientists from other countries. And they will still have a scarcity. Accordingly, it is realistic to expect that competition for talent will continue among advanced nations, and that this competition will generate strains among nations. This competition may take the form of 'functional' as well as 'physical' migration through purchase of the services of scientists under industrial or governmental contracts. Scientists who work for other nations, in the sense of producing information which is by the terms of contracts available only to the government or industry of a country other than their own, have in a sense and to a degree migrated. This kind of competition for brains can generate as much strain among countries as physical migration.[4]

in part derived from a note published in the United States papers prepared for the United Nations Conference on the Application of Science and Technology for the Benefit of the Less Developed Areas, Volume IX, *Scientific Technological Policy, Planning and Organization,* Washington, D.C., Government Printing Office, 1963.

2. Derek Price, *Little Science Big Science,* Columbia University Press, 1963.

3. Scates, Murdock and Yeomans, *The Production of Doctorates in the Sciences, 1936–1948,* Washington, D.C., American Council on Education, 1951.

4. See, for example, a form letter of 11 December 1962, sent by the Association of Chemical Industries (chairman O. Bayer) to German professors: 'We have on a

In many less advanced countries, the rate of growth of science may well be greater than the rate of growth in more advanced countries. Beginning at a low level, relatively small increments to the pool of manpower and physical resources can produce remarkable growth rates. In this situation, the demand for scientific manpower in less advanced countries will be high. Their ability to fulfill this demand will depend to a substantial degree not only upon their ability to educate scientists, at home or abroad, but also upon their ability to keep them at home. They will have to produce and keep scientific talent in the face of high and growing rewards of all kinds for scientists in more advanced nations.

The loss of people from less developed to more developed areas occurs not only among countries but also within all countries which have relatively rich and relatively poor areas. Areas with relatively low *per capita* income typically lose talent to areas with higher *per capita* income. Dr. Lloyd V. Berkner, director of the Graduate Research Center of the Southwest, has succinctly stated a plausible general prophecy: 'Only those regions will be economically healthy that have the intellectual power to exploit the new science and the consequent industry. Most certainly, those regions that fail intellectually will fail economically and become chronically poor and colonial to the intellectually advanced regions. This is the social certainty that the technological revolution of our century has made clear.' [5] All nations containing areas with wide economic and cultural differences face this problem.

NATIONAL AND INTERNATIONAL SCIENCE

Despite the strain generated by movement of scientists to and from more and less advanced countries and areas, migration of substantial numbers of scientists is useful in a number of ways. Science in many countries, including the United States, has been invigorated by migration of scientists from Europe. Science itself, apart from the status of any country, is stimulated by movement of people. Indeed, the only reference to movement of scientists in a recent study of ways to strengthen Western science was a set of recommendations designed to stimulate movement. 'Science in the

---

number of occasions expressed the wish to university professors not to enter into research agreements with foreign industrial concerns. The financial means which serve to support university research derive from the taxation of the German people and therefore in the last analysis from German business. In addition, substantial financial assistance and materials are provided by the chemical industry. In our opinion, recipients of such foreign aid at German universities carry a moral obligation that what is investigated and accomplished thereby does not serve to reduce the sources of tax income.'

5. L. V. Berkner, 'Renaissance in the Southwest', *The Saturday Review*, 3 June 1961.

Western world suffers, as we have seen, from the handicaps of language barriers and the disadvantages of some local traditions and customs which impede the circulation of students and scientists. Hence, it is all the more important that artificial barriers should be removed. These include restrictions on the granting of visas to scientists, inadequate budgets for international travel, and the restriction of permanent university posts to nationals of the country concerned. Delays in the acquisition or replacement of essential equipment which arise from customs and currency barriers stifle research and should be eliminated.' [6]

Migration is sometimes defended on general philosophical grounds. Thus, many people believe passionately that science is not political, that the pursuit of science is an activity transcending national boundaries. They believe that the primary ethical and intellectual obligation of the scientist is to work as hard as he can under the conditions that permit him to advance his work most effectively. If this view is essentially correct and complete, then it would be wrong to attempt to keep scientists in an environment where their science would be handicapped. But this is clearly only part of the story. Science, engineering, and technology contribute to national culture, and are essential to economic development. These activities cannot exist without professional practitioners. Acceptance of the need to import talent of this sort as a permanent condition is acceptance of low intellectual status and of a kind of scientific or intellectual colonialism.

In reality, science is not in all respects international, even though the substance of science is international. Neither are scientists as people international, even though their work is in large part international and even though they have close colleagues and friends in many other nations. Conflicting demands are often placed upon scientists by national States and by the values of the international community of science.

As in many other matters, the rights of the individual must be balanced against the needs of the State. This balance is set at different points by different nations. The individual has some right to the pursuit of his career under satisfactory conditions, and the claims of the State are not absolute and overriding in every circumstance. By one means or another the State must persuade rather than direct, because people cannot be ordered to be intellectually productive.

THE UNIQUE MOBILITY OF SCIENTISTS

While forces that tend to make people migrate affect all occupational, social, and economic groups, scientists and engineers are particularly mobile. They are highly educated, and sensitive to opportunities. They are

6. Science Committee of the North Atlantic Treaty Organization, *Increasing the Effectiveness of Western Science*, p. 6. (Fondation Universitaire, Brussels, 1960.)

highly oriented towards their professions. Many of them have lived in other countries, often under living and working conditions much better than they could expect upon return to their native countries. But these circumstances accurately characterize the experience of many professional groups, and the question whether engineers and scientists are more mobile than other professional groups arises. The propensity of engineers and scientists to migrate may be greater than that of other professional persons such as lawyers or physicians, although the case cannot be proved.[7] But of all occupations, the work of the scientist and engineer is the least culture-bound, and science is less so than engineering. While all people must live and adjust to some degree to alien cultures when they migrate, the strain is less on scientists and engineers because their work is little affected by national customs. Even so, scientists cannot be viewed as a single homogeneous group in relation to their propensity to migrate. 'Experimental scientists, even of the purest variety, are materially affected by the facilities that a strong industry or technology can provide.' [8] This sets up forces leading to migration. Such forces are not as strong in such fields as agriculture, botany, and geology which are to a degree 'place bound'.

A corollary of the proposition that scientists and engineers are particularly mobile is the proposition that the propensity to migrate is strongly affected by changes either in the homeland or in countries to which they might migrate. For example, relative changes in opportunities for engineers and scientists in Canada and the United States have recently reduced migration from Canada to the United States from about 1,300 to about 800 per year.[9] As a further example, the movement of scientists to and from Argentina has been quite sensitive over the past few years to shifts in the economic and political situation in Argentina. The conclusion to be drawn from these rapid changes in the flow of scientists and engineers is that policies designed either to keep or to attract scientific talent may well be quite effective.

THE ONE-WAY FILTER—LESS TO MORE ADVANCED COUNTRIES

The world has long been familiar with the migration of talent from less developed to more developed areas.[10] From the early days of recorded

7. For example, more physicians than scientists migrate to the United States. About 1,500 physicians per year enter the United States from other countries, and few leave.
8. David Tabor, 'Science and Research, Problems of Small States', *Physics Today*, August 1963, p. 39.
9. *Winnipeg Free Press*, 29 August 1963; interview with Neil A. McDougall, general manager of the Technical Service Council.
10. Stevan Dedijer, 'Why did Daedalus leave?' *Science*, No. 133, 30 June 1961, pp. 2047–52. Dr. Dedijer, an outstanding student of the development of science policy,

history, centres of wealth and culture have drawn people of talent, and nurtured them. The phenomenon is not essentially one concerned with national States. It arose before national States, or even city-states, existed. It exists now where differential opportunities—cultural, material, or scientific—are available to talented people.

Production of an adequate supply of scientists, engineers, and technicians is a basic problem in the application of science and technology in developing areas. Indeed, the strategy of manpower development is as significant as any other facet of policy for science and technology in developing areas.[11] Within this broad complex of manpower development, the migration of highly trained scientists from developing nations is in a sense a national catastrophe. This movement constitutes, in effect, an irreplaceable loss of a most valuable resource available to developing nations—scientific and technological brain power. Not only are the talents of the individuals as scientists lost, but the nucleus of people who alone can build an indigenous base for science is dissipated. The bare statistics of migration do not illuminate problems such as this.

The migration of scientists from less to more developed areas poses a continuing threat to the growth of indigenous science and technology in developing areas. During the second half of the twentieth century, and perhaps for a long time thereafter, the development of the poorer countries must encompass the establishment and growth of an indigenous structure and policy for science and technology. This can be done only if people from those countries are capable of planning for science and technology and of staffing growing national efforts. In few countries will this be possible without aid from more advanced countries, and particularly aid in the form of help from scientists. In the light of these needs, the inherent pressures towards the migration of scientists and engineers from less developed countries assume special significance. This threat is not an episode, but rather a continuing condition generated by the fundamentals of the development process itself. Substantial numbers of scientists and engineers have migrated to the United States from South America and Asia. While they have, as will be shown in the following section, comprised a small proportion of the total migrants, the absolute numbers have been substantial, particularly in view of the relatively small number of engineers and scientists in the countries which they left. These figures from

is engaged in further serious studies of this question and of the movement of scientists among nations. His paper, *Migration of Scientists,* presented at the First National Institutes of Health Symposium on International Biomedical Research (Bethesda, Maryland, 1–2 November 1963) will be published in the proceedings of that symposium.

11. Frederick Harbison, 'Education for Development', *The Scientific American,* September 1963, p. 140.

selected fields are indicative of the absolute volume of migration over the period 1957–61.[12]

Field	South America	Asia
Engineers	1556	1810
Chemists	213	231
Physicists	21	61
Biologists	47	40
	1837	2142

While these statistics are interesting, they do not measure either the contribution which the immigrants make to the United States, nor the loss which their departure imposes upon their country of origin.

As is true in all phases of national development, it is a gross and misleading oversimplification to speak of 'less' and 'more' developed nations. With respect to any index of development, nations are spread across a spectrum. They do not cluster in a clearly defined way at opposite ends of a scale. And the relative position of a nation may shift depending upon the index of development that is used—gross national product, *per capita* income, proportion of relevant age groups in elementary, secondary, or advanced education, life expectancy, proportion of population engaged in agriculture, etc. Nevertheless, nations can be grouped in a useful way for study, and one of the most appropriate schemes of classification is one elaborated by Walter Rostow of the United States.[13] It distinguishes, to oversimplify the classification, between those which have not and those which have attained the capacity to develop their economies at a rapid rate without reliance upon outside aid—the so-called 'take-off' stage. This concept is also useful in the more limited context of the capacity of a nation to train its own scientific manpower, and more work on the stages of development of manpower resources is needed.

It is certain that less developed nations will discover and nurture scientists at an increasing rate. The distribution of innate capacity to excel in science is probably roughly equal among the people of the world. Individuals with high talent for science will emerge in any society as soon as the structure of secondary education becomes broad enough to expose a large group to elementary science, and the general cultural climate permits scientists to emerge. This has been true in the past, and it will no doubt be

12. *Scientific Manpower from Abroad, United States Scientists and Engineers of Foreign Birth and Training,* Washington, D.C., National Science Foundation, Publication NSF 62-24 (1962).
13. Walter Rostow, *The Stages of Economic Growth,* Cambridge, Mass., Cambridge University Press, 1961.

true in the future as secondary education is extended to additional hundreds of millions of people in developing nations.

Poor countries generally do not have the scientific structure required for advanced training of younger scientists. They therefore must offer opportunities for advanced study abroad. When students from poor countries study abroad, their personal standards of living generally rise, and they carry on their work amid stimulating colleagues and with good facilities. Many of them choose not to return to their native lands. Losses of promising students are usually more serious for poorer countries than are losses of fully trained scientists. This is true, for example, of India.

The extent to which developing nations must depend upon provision of advanced study abroad is related to their stage of development. Countries without universities or other possibilities for scientific research and training must simultaneously import scientific talent and export students for advanced training. In countries with a university, or a structure of universities, both the problems and the opportunities are more complex. Opportunities to train people to high levels in national universities expand, eventually reaching the stage at which the country 'takes off' by becoming substantially self-sufficient. At the same time, the very quality of indigenous education and training produces a cadre of scientists sought after by many more advanced countries.

CROSS-MOVEMENT AMONG ADVANCED NATIONS

The attainment of a 'take-off' stage or even 'maturity' in the development of scientists, engineers, and mathematicians does not lift a nation above the competition for talent. Indeed, the most extensive tides of migration are among advanced nations. Their problems of national policy and action are fully as acute as those of less developed nations. They are, as will be pointed out below, simply different.

The movement of scientists and engineers is predominantly among advanced countries rather than from less to more advanced countries; and, of all advanced countries, the United States predominates as the country of destination. This statement can be confidently made even though statistics on the subject are scarce. One comprehensive (though not fully accurate) set relates to the United States, and some facts and observations based on them follow.[14]

1. Over the thirteen years from 1949 to 1961, 43,500 scientists and engineers, or an average of about 3,350 per year, have immigrated to the United States. Of these, about 33,000 have been engineers, 10,000 have been scientists, and 500 have been professors and instructors. The loss

14. *Scientific Manpower from Abroad* . . . , op. cit.

to other countries, and the gain to the United States is equivalent to the training provided by several large universities.

2. The number of immigrants rose steadily from about 1,200 in 1949 to about 5,800 in 1957 and declined to about 4,000 in 1961.
3. Immigrants have added about 3.2 per cent to the output of scientists and engineers from universities in the United States over the period 1949–61.
4. About 2,000 of all immigrants were political refugees.
5. Seventy per cent of all immigrants came from: Europe (32 per cent), Canada (25 per cent), and the United Kingdom (13 per cent).

The fact that the largest proportion of the immigrants are from countries with relatively high levels of living and highly developed structures for science underscores the observation that relative rather than absolute forces affect migration. In current studies that will be published, Dedijer presents data emphasizing the complexity of the currents of migration, and he particularly emphasizes the fact that about 60 per cent of all migrating scientists go to countries other than the United States.[15]

While the migration of scientists and engineers among advanced nations does not seem to be catastrophic it can jeopardize the timely attainment of the goals of nations which lose manpower, particularly if the migrants include scientific leaders. The problems can be serious and they can generate a substantial amount of political heat. One of the most serious of these tides of movement, and one of the best publicized, is the migration of scientists from the United Kingdom to the United States. In February 1963, the Royal Society issued a factual report on the emigration of scientists from the United Kingdom.[16] The facts were disturbing. About 12 per cent of the total output of Ph.D.s in science and engineering were migrating permanently, and 7 per cent of the total output has been migrating to the United States. The number of permanent emigrants with a recent Ph.D. increased by a factor of ten over the decade ending in 1961. 'Moreover, the country has in the last five years lost a number of outstanding scientists to the United States, including nine fellows of the Royal Society. The gaps created by their departure have caused difficulties in certain important fields of scientific research in this country.' While deploring the loss represented by expenditures on the education of migrants, the report concluded by noting that, 'We regard as much more serious the economic consequences of the loss to this country of the leadership and the creative

15. S. Dedijer, op. cit.
16. The Royal Society, *Emigration of Scientists from the United Kingdom*, report of a committee appointed by the Council of the Royal Society. Royal Society, Burlington House, Piccadilly, London, W.1., February 1963. A full report of articles, letters to newspapers, and so forth, relating to this question was published in *Minerva*, Spring 1963.

contributions to science and technology which they would have made in their working lives.'

The report of the Royal Society provoked a pronounced reaction, beginning with a speech by Lord Hailsham in the House of Lords on 27 February 1963.[17]

Lord Hailsham's vigorous statement brought forth equally vigorous responses. The most significant reaction was a widespread feeling among the university community that fewer people would migrate if the government had invested more heavily in science and in the development of universities. One of the most articulate and positive expressions of this view was from the physicists.[18] A report of their society said that 'Conditions in America are generally better simply because the Americans appreciate the importance of science more than we do in Britain. The scale and balance of activity in higher education has been badly mismatched in Britain to the needs of a technological civilization.' This example is given to make explicit the fact that the migration of scientists is a matter intimately intertwined with national science policy and with broader national political and economic issues.

MEASURES TO KEEP SCIENTISTS AT HOME

Despite the inherent handicaps faced by many countries in retaining scientists, they are far from helpless. There are conditions, policies and actions which tend to keep scientists in their homelands; other circumstances tend to accentuate the pressures for migration.

Foremost among the conditions tending to stabilize the scientific group are patriotism and cultural ties. Simple love of country and desire to aid in the development of one's homeland are powerful forces that can hold scientists against the powerful attractions of other countries. However, persistent political instability, or denial of equitable professional opportunity through discrimination based upon race, religion, wealth, family or political views, tend to force people to migrate in spite of the basic desire to stay at home. Chronic inflation, typically a consequence of deeper political problems, can discourage scientists earning fixed salaries which lag behind price increases. Not only professional careers but family life, and the welfare and education of children, must be taken into account. The problems faced by those who must decide to stay or go are not scientific but intensely personal and human. The general political and economic measures that nations can take to encourage scientists to stay are simply those designed to produce a decent way of life for all citizens.

17. *Parliamentary Debates* (Hansard), 27 February 1963, pp. 86–109.
18. Institute of Physics and the Physical Society, *Problems Facing University Physics Departments,* September 1963.

However, more specific actions can be helpful. The attention paid to science by national governments is significant. Throughout the world, the emergence of science and technology as a major influence on all aspects of national life is forcing the development of common policy towards science and technology, and of formal administrative structures for developing and executing science policy.[19] The place given to matters of science in the councils of state will influence the decisions of scientists to remain at home or to migrate. Tangible evidence that the activity in which they are engaged is worthy of specific attention by government tends to influence scientists, and this is true whether they are engaged in fundamental or applied research. Such actions as the establishment of a science section as part of a national planning body, or the establishment of a national research council, can symbolize the significance of science and tend to hold scientists at home.

Forms are significant, over the long run, only to the extent that the attention to science and scientists is followed by action. What specific measures are indicated? In general the line of policy directed at keeping scientists at home is simply the line of policy directed at strengthening science in a country. It is difficult to generalize because of the wide variation in problems and solutions among countries at roughly the same stage of development; the difficulty is intensified by the fact that patterns of problems change roughly in accordance with the state of development of a country. For example, the problems and potentialities of countries without a university, with a single university, and with a number of universities are typically quite distinct. Nevertheless, some general statements seem valid for all countries.

First, each country should endeavour to educate scientists to the highest level provided at home before sending them abroad for further training. This consideration is particularly important in those countries which have developed points of excellence in research and higher education, but which have gaps in their scientific structure. The earlier people leave their native country, the easier it is for them to become expatriates. The longer people remain in science at home, the more realistic are their expectations and the keener their perceptions of the work which they can carry on successfully at home. Accordingly, the general procedure should not be to send persons abroad for scientific training as early in their careers as possible, but rather to postpone such training until solid academic advancement at home is not possible without training abroad. This principle applies to regional as well as to national effort. Continuing exposure to higher education within the general cultural pattern to which students are

19. Stevan Dedijer, *Research Policy, Its Making and Measurement,* reprint of lecture before the Swedish Academy of Engineering, 7 November 1962.

accustomed is the important thing. In Latin America, for example, efforts are being made to send students to advanced laboratories in various Latin American countries before sending them to Western Europe or the United States.

Second, the home country should play a definite role in planning the strategy of training abroad. The numbers to be trained abroad, the broad fields of training, the length of training periods are all matters of national concern. These decisions are related to plans for economic development, and to plans for the import of scientific and other talent. The home country should participate appropriately in the selection of persons for study even if the training is financed from foreign sources. Highly trained scientific manpower is a scarce national resource, and effective use of the resource warrants national planning. The nature of the role of government and of planning will vary roughly in accordance with the stage of development as a nation. In general, the broader and deeper the scientific structure of a nation, the greater will be its dependence upon the creation of a favourable environment for science and the less its dependence upon direct influence over the choices of individuals.

Third, conscious attention should be paid to reconciling the need for national planning and direction with the need for scientific freedom. This is a pervasive and most complex problem which cannot be dealt with here, but some ways in which the nature of the reconciliation can affect migration of scientists might be mentioned. In most developing countries, the number of career opportunities open to scientists is heavily influenced if not entirely determined by national plans. National governments' cannot afford to have scarce talent trained along lines and in numbers that do not contribute to the attainment of national goals. It is possible, although difficult, to select and administer national research priorities in such a way that concentration upon the solution of indigenous economic problems through applied science and technology can simultaneously provide opportunities for free scientific inquiry into fundamental problems. For example, the problems involved in making the Brazilian *cerrado*—the immense high, dry, central plateau—productive can be solved only by a wide spectrum of practical studies in such fields as biology, geology, agronomy, hydrology, sociology. But an attack upon these problems both rests upon and generates another set of more fundamental studies. The task of administering a national scientific and technological programme in a way that contributes both to the solution of urgent practical problems and to the development of a more free-ranging intellectual effort is central to an effective science effort in developing countries and to retention of trained scientists.

In more advanced countries, the simple question of national budgetary priorities is critical. Some scientists leave their home countries because they become discouraged with the low levels of support for science provided by their national governments. For scientists in many fields, moderate expenditures suffice to provide the means required for work of Nobel Prize quality.

Fourth, before persons go abroad for study, attention should be paid to the conditions of their work on return. The adjustment of training to anticipated career opportunities is such a crucial factor that the home country should interest itself in the number trained to various levels, by field, in relation to prospective jobs. In medicine, for example, much expensive training has been wasted and many individuals have been frustrated, through provision of very advanced research training that could not be put to use at home. When foreign countries make training or educational opportunities available, the home country should exert efforts to retain substantial control over the opportunities for training in other countries which are typically made available in an unco-ordinated manner. The lack of co-ordination on the part of countries offering training opportunities is often the consequence of lack of organization in the home country.

Fifth, the training of scientists should be considered not only by the national groups concerned with science but also by those concerned with manpower planning. Those countries which have manpower planning councils, or similar groups, at the ministerial level should ensure that the supply of and demand for scientists and engineers is considered by these groups.

Sixth, considered, pointed efforts to provide satisfying careers in science should be made by countries which wish to retain trained scientists. Typically, the needs of scientists can be met without excessive expenditures, particularly if the country has undertaken to plan the broad strategy of education for science. Generally, the question of career for scientists is closely related to the provision of career opportunities in academic life. A number of countries have adopted specific plans for career support of scientists in universities. While many governments face difficult problems in singling out any occupational group for preferred treatment, the high value of trained scientists to their nations—and the negligible cost in terms of national budgets—argues for serious attention to the establishment of salary scales and other aspects of career development which will tend to keep this critical group of citizens at home. The career problem is not limited to poorer nations. In some countries with highly developed structures for science, the organization and traditions of universities are such that limited opportunities for scientists are provided in academic life. This tends to force the establishment of separate research institutes, or to lead to the migration of scientists. The tradition of separate faculties in Latin America, resulting in the dispersion and weakening of teaching and research, is a serious barrier to the advancement of careers in science. In Western Europe, the tradition of the single professor in each field has similarly tended to limit career opportunities and hence to generate pressures for migration.[20] These traditions are changing in both parts of the world.

Seventh, those advanced countries which have lost substantial numbers of scientists and which can offer conditions better than those existing when the migrants left, can aggressively recruit scientists who have left other countries. The British Government, particularly the Atomic Energy Commission, conducts an annual campaign in the United States aimed at bringing scientists home.

Eighth, concentration upon the substance as contrasted with the form of training is important. In some countries, lack of experience leads both students and governments to propose training on the basis of the prestige of the university providing the training. Universities such as the Sorbonne, Oxford or Harvard have such a degree of prestige that some students go to them as much to acquire status in their homelands as to acquire knowledge. The needs and capacity of the student, and the real needs of the nation, sometimes tend to be secondary.

Ninth, laboratories, or even one laboratory, properly and necessarily on a small scale in those countries with scientific efforts in the earliest stages of development, must be established if scientists are to remain in their homelands. Investments in the training of scientists and engineers are ineffective or wasted if adequate conditions for work are not provided. Ideally, construction of facilities and purchase of equipment should be guided by scientists. Without scientific advice, prestige rather than utility may be the primary guide to construction and acquisition of equipment. Indeed, this problem is not always resolved by reliance upon scientists.

Tenth, in many of the richer and technologically advanced countries, the simple matter of improved salaries and facilities would turn the tide. Some countries cannot afford the obvious remedy. 'For others, especially those of Western Europe, it is not necessarily impossible, and their governments would do well to ponder how their policy towards science and technology should be changed in order to avoid this steady and damaging drain of their ablest men.' [21]

Measures such as those outlined above will tend to reduce the migra-

20. N. Kaplan, 'The Western European Scientific Establishment in Transition', *The American Behavioral Scientist,* December 1962, p. 17.
21. 'Transatlantic Science Traffic' (editorial), *Endeavour,* Vol. XXII, No. 87, September 1963.

tion of scientists and engineers. But they will not, in the absence of absolute control of migration, halt the movement of people.

When the measures that countries can afford are not taken, loss of scientists must be expected. Advanced training is useful only if it is used. Migration of scientists who cannot function effectively as scientists in their homeland is not so much a loss of trained manpower as it is an indication of a nation's inability to use them.

MEASURES BY COUNTRIES IMPORTING SCIENTISTS

The migration of scientists and engineers generates a number of dilemmas for the countries to which scientists migrate. On the one hand, scientists and engineers are in chronically short supply in technologically advanced countries. Highly trained people are difficult to produce, and importation of brains is less expensive than the expansion of universities. The attainment of important national goals is made easier by immigration and it is not to be expected that countries will renounce this means of enriching their cultural and material resources.

On the other hand, the parts of the world with high standards of living have available to them fantastically productive systems of production built in large part upon continuing scientific and technological advances. It is quite possible, in the absence of deliberate efforts, that the gap in *per capita* incomes between the more and the less industrialized countries will become wider rather than narrower. If the gap does not narrow over the long run, the prospect for reduction of world tensions is dim. The richer nations must therefore commit themselves to an effort to aid poorer nations over a period of decades. This aid must encompass a gigantic export of capital, and the elements of 'know-how' necessary to make the capital productive. One key element of cultural independence is the establishment of indigenous technology and science. In turn, scientists, engineers, and technically trained people are the key to the establishment of a base of science and technology. Viewed in this perspective, the simultaneous export of capital from richer countries and import of scientists and engineers from poorer countries makes no sense. How is the dilemma to be resolved? Without pretending to answer this complex problem, some suggestions can be made.

First, minimum reliance should be placed upon direct prohibitions on the movement of people. To the extent that migration of scientists and engineers to advanced countries should be discouraged, the most productive approach is to take every step possible to make careers in less developed countries attractive. Some of these measures were suggested in the preceding section.

Second, the advanced countries should make strenuous efforts to make their universities available to students from less advanced nations. Large numbers of foreign nationals are brought to the United States for specialized education and training. 'In 1960, 6,275 trainees came to the United States from Africa, Europe, the Far East, Latin America, and the Near East, as follows: agriculture, 1,141 trainees; atomic energy, 205; commercial development, 60; education, 1,138; health, 428; housing, 66; industry, 1,577; labour, 680; public administration, 401; public safety, 323; social welfare, 7; other, 249. At least 25 per cent of the total, it is estimated, spent the principal portion of their time at educational institutes. Many of the others attended colleges and universities for refresher courses, seminars, or other short-term studies.' [22]

Third, in view of the attractiveness of life in advanced countries to many students, specific measures to ensure return to their homelands are indicated. The United States, for example, requires by law that students and trainees who come to the United States as exchange visitors must return abroad for a period of at least two years before applying for an immigrant visa. This is a compromise between absolute prohibition on migration of such people to the United States, and free movement of individuals. Another measure generally regarded as wise is a requirement that opportunities for study in advanced countries be made available only if plans are laid in advance for the careers of students upon their return home.

Fourth, advanced countries must export not only goods and money, but help in the form of advice. Many countries are in effect exporting brains on a large scale to aid less developed nations. This counter-flow tends to balance the importation of talent.

INTERNATIONAL ACTION

Apart from national action, international consideration of the questions relating to migration of scientists and engineers is indicated. For one thing, facts relating to migration of scientists are scarce and often of dubious validity. Uniformity of definition and a general consensus as to what should be measured would increase understanding of the magnitude and nature of the phenomenon of migration. International agreement on such matters would also encourage nations to begin the collection of more adequate information. Other kinds of facts are needed. For example, some countries have adopted specific measures designed to keep scientists at

22. *Scientific Manpower from Abroad* . . . , op. cit.

home or to attract them home after they have migrated. These facts could be collected and assessed by an international effort. As a third specific action, organized discussion of the phenomena of migration by informed and interested people from a number of nations should illuminate both the questions of migration and deeper questions of science policy to which migration of scientists and engineers is related. Why do some advanced countries lose scientists while others with lower levels of income do not? What significance is to be placed upon levels of national investment in science, and upon kinds of investment, as a factor affecting migration? What cultural and institutional factors, such as the structure of universities and the status of engineering as contrasted with science, appear to exercise substantial influence? It should be possible to discuss such questions as productively and dispassionately as other matters affecting the progress of science and technology among nations.

THE PROCESS OF CONTINUING ADJUSTMENT

There is no foreseeable solution of the problem of migration of scientists. Science and technology must be fostered and exploited by all nations in the process of development. Rates of advancement will differ. Restless and rapid change is inherent in development. The existence and creation of differential opportunities for scientists is an inherent consequence of the process of development itself. Coping with the problem of migration of scientists is simply one among many complex tasks to be faced as nations develop. Measures taken by some countries to keep their scientists and engineers, and by other countries to discourage immigration and to encourage repatriation are therefore best viewed not as attempts to reach a final solution but rather as part of a continuing, dynamic process of adaptation.

II

ORGANIZING FOR SCIENCE

With the dynamic growth of science in the United States came the need for structural adaptations in the federal government. New offices and agencies were established to marshal, co-ordinate, and direct the official portion of the scientific effort. At the very top level, within the Executive Office of the President, the Office of Science and Technology was created; and in the White House Office, the Special Assistant to the President for Science and Technology, the President's Science Advisory Committee, and the Federal Council for Science and Technology were set up with particular scientific responsibilities. As illustrated in the first essay, the science staff of the White House now represents the biggest single influence on national decisions affecting science and technology.

A different view of the effectiveness of the labyrinth of agencies, foundations, consultantships, academies, and committees that deal with science is provided by Meg Greenfield. With the Rube Goldberg institutional structure that has been created, no one can be sure "what a government scientist is or when he is acting as one." The role played by the several hundred "influentials," the scientists who repeatedly turn up as advisers and consultants, may be even more important than the daily contribution of the permanent members of the science staffs.

The phenomenal growth of science in the government has led to the establishment of several new agencies to administer specialized aspects of the burgeoning program. Most of these agencies have responsibilities to both the President and Congress, but they exist separately from the executive and legislative departments. There is every reason to believe that these independent agencies will be called upon more and more for functions requiring a special expertise to administer.

The diverse activities of the National Science Foundation are described in a general review of its first fifteen years, a special report submitted to the House Committee on Science and Astronautics. Of particular impor-

105

tance are the responsibilities of the Foundation in the support of basic research. The assistance rendered to the International Geophysical Year, the Antarctic research program, the weather modification program, Project Mohole, the International Indian Ocean Expedition, the United States–Japan co-operative science program, the ocean sediment coring program, and the International Upper Mantle Project is described in short résumés of each program.

In a case study of the legislative input to national science policy, James R. Kerr uses the controversy on the relative merits of solid and liquid propulsion systems for missiles to show that despite the involvement of Congress in the support of science, it still finds itself without adequate counsel on questions requiring technical judgment. The result is, as might be expected, that congressional attitudes are the product more of politics than of objective evaluation.

AMERICAN CHEMICAL SOCIETY
White House Superstructure for Science

Next month's Presidential election looms large in implications for science and technology. Not the least of these is the effect of the outcome on the growing movement toward direct White House control of the federal science establishment—a movement which has characterized the Kennedy-Johnson Administration. Whether this movement will continue and at what pace will depend largely on the will of the man who is elected President next month.

This movement, principally in just the past three years, has provided a tight new superstructure for federal science and technology. Its influence is international as well as national in scope. It weaves through our entire social fabric—political, industrial, educational. For it is this handful of people who to a lesser or greater degree hold sway over the Administration's plans in science and technology—plans which this year will mean a federal outlay probably in excess of $15 billion.

Dubbed by its critics as the Executive Branch "innersanctum for science," the White House science staff consists of the Special Assistant to the President for Science and Technology and his 19 aides. The degree of actual power which this group possesses and the manner in which it exercises it are topics of much controversy and confusion.

The controversy and confusion is due in no small measure to the self-generated aura of mystery that has surrounded the group and the way it operates. Aside from that of the Special Assistant to the President for Science and Technology, even the identity of the science staff of the White House is known to relatively few of the nation's scientists and engineers. Yet, working quietly behind the scenes, the group represents perhaps the biggest single influence on national decisions affecting science and technology.

The group's power—as well as much of the confusion surrounding the White House science structure—stems from the multiple roles and responsibilities of the Special Assistant to the President for Science and Technology (known informally as the Presidential science adviser). He is, at

From *Chemical and Engineering News,* Vol. 42, October 19, 1964, pp. 78–92. Copyright 1964 by the American Chemical Society; reprinted by permission of the copyright owner.

the same time, personal science adviser to the President, chairman of both the President's Science Advisory Committee and the Federal Council for Science and Technology, and director of the Office of Science and Technology.

Despite his multiplicity of titles, the Special Assistant to the President for Science and Technology actually has just two responsibilities. They are to advise and assist the President on all matters of national policy affected by or pertaining to science and technology and to evaluate and coordinate the total federal program in science and technology. All the various jobs he holds in addition to that of Special Assistant are tied directly to these two responsibilities.

Thus reduced to fundamentals, any real power of the Special Assistant to the President for Science and Technology, and consequently of his staff, is predicated to a very large extent upon his access to, and influence on, the President in determining who gets how many of the federal dollars for science and technology.

RAPID DEVELOPMENT

The evolution of this new superstructure for science in the Executive Branch has spanned just a short seven years from birth to full maturity. Prior to 1957, the only formal scientific body in the White House was a relatively obscure science advisory committee submerged in the old Office of Defense Mobilization (now the Office of Emergency Planning). In the period just prior to the launching of the first Sputnik, this committee— shortly to be vitalized into the powerful and prestigious President's Science Advisory Committee—was relegated to the role of advising the President through the director of ODM, not directly. It was concerned principally with scientific and technical aspects of defense mobilization and national security.

In the great scientific flap in this country following the Soviet's spectacular launching of the first man-made satellite, President Eisenhower hurriedly set about to equip the White House with some sort of scientific and technical competency. He created the top-level post of Presidential science adviser and assigned to it the primary task of taking stock of this country's scientific and technical resources and coming up with ways to best bolster and mobilize them to meet this new Soviet challenge.

To aid the Presidential science adviser in his job, President Eisenhower yanked the existing science advisory committee out of ODM and made it advisory to the President directly, thus greatly increasing its stature, powers, and, by the same token, its appeal to the scientific community. The

Presidential science adviser was made chairman of the revitalized committee.

The President's Science Advisory Committee (PSAC) is composed of 18 of the nation's most distinguished scientists and engineers drawn from industry, the universities, and from other nongovernment areas. The President appoints its members for four-year terms. PSAC meets on an average of two days a month and is concerned with major issues bearing on this country's scientific and technological posture. It undertakes studies both on its own initiative and in response to specific requests from the President. The White House describes a primary characteristic of PSAC as "the role it plays in blending and integrating governmental and nongovernmental views to achieve a total approach to problems involving science and Government."

In 1959 the mission of the Office of the Special Assistant to the President for Science and Technology was elaborated further by an executive order which created the Federal Council for Science and Technology. The council is composed of the top policy-level representative from each of the federal agencies involved in science and technology, and the Special Assistant is chairman. It was designed to provide a coordinating mechanism for the total federal effort in science and technology. In the process it also served to tighten White House control over scientific programs and policies of the federal agencies.

ESTABLISHMENT COMPLETE

The framework of this new White House superstructure for science was completed in 1962 by President Kennedy's Reorganization Act No. 2, which created the Office of Science and Technology (OST). The director of OST is charged generally with assisting the President in "coordinating federal science and technology functions." More specifically he is to "advise and assist" the President with respect to:

> Major policies, plans, and programs of science and technology of the various agencies of the Federal Government, giving appropriate emphasis to the relationship of science and technology to national security and foreign policy, and measures for furthering science and technology in the nation.
>
> Assessment of selected scientific and technical developments and programs in relation to their impact on national policies.
>
> Review, integration, and coordination of major federal activities in science and technology, giving due consideration to the effects of such activities on nonfederal resources and institutions.
>
> Assuring that good and close relations exist with the nation's

scientific and engineering communities so as to further in every appropriate way their participation in strengthening science and technology in the United States and Free World.

Such other matters consonant with law as may be assigned by the President to the office.

OST did not represent so much a new White House scientific function as it did a formalizing of already existing functions. It gives statutory permanence for continuing Presidential staff support to the Special Assistant to the President for Science and Technology, PSAC, and the Federal Council for Science and Technology. The creation of OST has more than tripled the number of permanent science staff members available to the President.

OST was the Kennedy Administration's answer to growing Congressional unrest over the lack of coordination and central control of the Federal Government's burgeoning research and development effort. Congress was also demanding a single authority it could call in to answer its questions on the Administration's plans and policies on matters dealing with federal science and technology.

Under its charter, the National Science Foundation had been charged with advising the President on coordination of federal research policies and evaluating the research programs of government agencies. But for a number of reasons, NSF had been unwilling or unable to exercise this authority, mainly because it is on the same organizational level as other agencies. Its management felt that the agencies would balk at having NSF, in essence a sister agency, ride herd on their R&D programs.

So the Administration felt it needed to create a new office at a higher level than the agencies themselves to review and evaluate the total federal R&D effort and to meet demands in Congress for a better source of information.

The kind of information Congress wanted had not been fully available to it in the past. Presidential science advisers, for example, on numerous occasions appeared before Congress to describe in a general way various Administration plans and programs. But they have refused to answer certain more specific Congressional inquiries on the grounds that to do so would violate the doctrine of executive privilege. This doctrine says in effect that communications between the President and his advisers shall remain confidential.

The creation of this new White House office, according to Administration spokesmen at the time OST was proposed, would reduce these pressures on the Presidential science adviser. Congress could instead call in the director of OST to testify for the Administration on matters dealing with science and technology. In this way, they explained, the confidential relationship that exists between the President and his science adviser would not be impaired.

This would seem to be an adequate solution to the problem were it not for the fact that, ever since the creation of OST, its director and the Presidential science adviser have been one and the same person.

KENNEDY-WIESNER

During the Kennedy Administration, with Dr. Jerome Wiesner as spearhead, White House control of federal science and technology reached a new high. Dr. Philip H. Abelson, editor of *Science* and probably the most vocal critic of the White House's power structure for science, remarked at the height of this regime shortly before Mr. Kennedy's assassination, "Dr. Wiesner has accumulated and exercised more visible and invisible power than any scientist in the peacetime history of this country."

It was also during the reign of Dr. Wiesner that the Presidential science adviser emerged for the first time as a prominent and influential figure in affairs of state.

To a large measure, this increase in the job's power and prominence can be attributed to the close, informal relationship that existed between the Chief Executive and his science adviser, a closeness and degree of influence which the two previous Presidential science advisers did not enjoy with their leader, Mr. Eisenhower. To some degree it stemmed from the way the late President operated—the relatively free hand Mr. Kennedy gave his top advisers as a show of his confidence in their abilities.

Another contributing factor to the new and larger scientific role of the White House under Dr. Wiesner—one that is sometimes overlooked by critics of the White House science movement—is that about that time the Government really began to broaden the scope of its involvement in science and technology. The two previous holders of the office under President Eisenhower, Dr. James R. Killian and Dr. George Kistiakowsky, had been largely preoccupied with the defense and space efforts. But as the Government began to move more heavily into support of other scientific and technical endeavors—oceanography, environmental health, consumer protection, and the like—the role of the Presidential science adviser correspondingly increased both in scope and in importance.

But a good deal of the credit (or blame, as you choose) for the office's new power went to Dr. Wiesner himself. Brilliant, ambitious, and tough, the MIT electronics whiz was the embodiment of the Kennedy kind of New Frontiersman.

Dr. Wiesner quickly adapted to the milieu of Washington and proved to be an eager and fairly adept performer in his own right in the political arena.

Forceful and confident yet with an easy, outgoing manner, Dr. Wiesner was regarded generally by both friend and foe alike as an articulate and effective salesman for Administration views relating to science and technology.

But trouble was brewing beneath the surface. Some scientists and others in Government complained privately about what they called Dr. Wiesner's "take charge" manner and "high-handed" methods. From agencies with scientific and technical programs came scattered rumblings of undue meddling in their affairs by Dr. Wiesner and his staff. The cry was taken up by a small but vocal sector. These critics accused Dr. Wiesner of attempting to mastermind and control the entire federal effort in science and technology. They labeled him the self-ordained "czar of American science."

This smoldering controversy flared into the open briefly, then died suddenly with Dr. Wiesner's decision last fall to return to academic life. The tragedy that followed shortly thereafter in Dallas put an end to the issue at least for a time.

WINDS OF CHANGE

In January of this year, Dr. Donald F. Hornig, a soft-spoken, 44-year-old physical chemist, took over as Special Assistant to the President for Science and Technology. Named as Dr. Wiesner's replacement by President Kennedy shortly before his death, Dr. Hornig assumed office at a time of change: change in the White House precipitated by the Kennedy tragedy and change in the political climate of the nation toward science and technology generally. Both Dr. Hornig and his office have been caught up in those changes.

Under President Johnson and with Dr. Hornig, the job of Presidential science adviser at first seemed to have taken a reverse turn to the more muted days of President Eisenhower. That is, it seemed to be more one of a behind-the-scenes adviser and less one of a direct participant in affairs of state. As one veteran Washington scientific observer remarked shortly after Dr. Hornig took office, "For better or for worse, the freewheeling days of the Kennedy-Wiesner regime—a period of unprecedented scientific influence in this country's affairs—have come to an end."

In truth, however, the apparent change did not represent a decrease in the powers or influence of the Presidential Science Adviser. It really reflected a change in the methods of operation both of the White House itself under President Johnson and of the new science adviser.

President Johnson brought to the White House his own methods of doing business which differ significantly from those of his predecessor. The casual, almost family-like relationship that existed between President Kennedy and his top White House aides was replaced to a large degree by a more formal business-like working environment.

This change in the internal workings of the White House had a direct bearing on the powers of the Presidential science adviser. Dr. Hornig still does not enjoy the close personal relationship with President Johnson that his predecessor, Dr. Wiesner, did with the late President. Prior to taking office, he had only a nodding acquaintance with President Johnson. And unlike Dr. Wiesner with President Kennedy, Dr. Hornig is not a member of President Johnson's select inner circle of confidants. While he thus may not make his voice heard on broad topics to the extent Dr. Wiesner did, when it comes to scientific and technological matters, the President turns to him first for advice. Thus, there has been no weakening of the Presidential science adviser's role in guiding the nation's overall plans for science.

The changing role of the Presidential science adviser from the overt and public display of power by Dr. Wiesner to the behind-the-scenes "persuasion" of Dr. Hornig is due in no small measure to the sharp differences in personal makeup between Dr. Hornig and his predecessor. A deliberate, somewhat reticent man, Dr. Hornig so far has succeeded in avoiding the hard glare of publicity which focused attention so often on the outspoken and often volatile Dr. Wiesner.

Dr. Hornig continues to align himself solely with the scientific community and has been well received generally by scientists both inside and outside the federal establishment. He is a scientist who has involved himself in Washington with only broad-scope scientific issues. He had judiciously avoided being drawn into the political arena—a jousting area Dr. Wiesner neither succeeded in skirting nor apparently attempted to skirt.

There is every indication that regardless of who is elected President next month the White House science organization will continue its dominant role. The level of federal spending for space and defense R&D appears to be reaching a plateau. The Democratic Administration now has turned more attention to long-standing problems of society—poverty, disease, environmental pollution, consumer protection, and the like—all of which have large scientific and technical components. Thus, its policy of increased federal involvement in science and technology, coupled with the building pressures from an ever-mounting federal budget, should demand firm White House control in all areas.

Senator Goldwater, on the other hand, deplores "big government." If elected President, he may work for a reduction in the Federal Government's participation in many areas in which he feels it has no business being involved. His philosophy of less, rather than more government, plus his call for more fiscal responsibility in Government, would seem to favor an overall reduction in federal spending for science and technology—with the one notable exception of that related to defense—and, correspondingly, a tighter White House grip on scientific expenditures.

One thing is certain, however. Should Senator Goldwater become President, there would be at least a few personnel changes in the White House science staff. The Special Assistant to the President for Science and Technology and probably his top aides would be replaced by people who more closely share Senator Goldwater's political views.

DR. HORNIG APPOINTED

A renowned scholar, scientist, and teacher, Dr. Hornig is a highly respected member of the scientific community who brought to the White House an intimate knowledge of the major scientific and technical issues that face this nation. The Harvard-educated (B.S. 1940, Ph.D. 1943), Milwaukee native came to the job from Princeton University where he is Donner Professor of Chemistry and chairman of the chemistry department.

During World War II he was research associate at the underwater explosives research laboratory at Woods Hole, Massachusetts. Later he served as group leader in the Manhattan Project at Los Alamos Scientific Laboratory.

After the war, Dr. Hornig joined the faculty of Brown University. He was director of the Metcalf Research Laboratory there from 1949–1957 when he moved to Princeton.

His research interests have included molecular and crystal structure, infrared and Raman spectra, shock and detonation waves, relaxation phenomena, and fast chemical reactions at high temperature. He has published about 70 scientific papers in these areas.

When the magazine *International Science and Technology* criticized the appointment of Dr. Hornig, labeling him "a virtual stranger to the Washington scene," an irate Chris Hornig, age 10, quickly rose to his father's defense. "My father has served for three Presidents," he informed the monthly's editor, "and is in Washington so much that by now he is a virtual stranger to me."

Dr. Hornig has been a member of the advisory panel for chemistry of the National Science Foundation, and from 1956 to 1961 served as a member of the physics advisory committee, Air Force Office of Scientific Research. In 1959 he was appointed to the Space Science Board of the National Academy of Sciences.

He was named to the President's Science Advisory Committee in 1960 by President Eisenhower and was later reappointed by President Kennedy. He was an adviser to the late President during the 1960 Presidential campaign and later served on the Kennedy Task Force on Space to help formulate policy in this field for the new Administration. In 1962–63, Dr. Hornig was a member of the delegation headed by National Aeronautics and Space Administration Deputy Director Dr. Hugh Dryden which negotiated the agreement with the U.S.S.R. for cooperation in certain space activities.

Dr. Hornig is a member of the American Chemical Society. He is also a Fellow of the American Physical Society, of the American Academy of Arts and Sciences, and of the Faraday Society, London. In 1957, he was elected to the National Academy of Sciences.

SCIENCE STAFF

The controversial Office of Science and Technology, which comprises the permanent science staff for the White House, is a generally loose-jointed organization, although more clearly defined areas of individual responsibilities are taking shape. For practical considerations, it is a two-tiered organization with the director, Dr. Hornig, and his deputy on one level and an 18-member professional staff strung out along a horizontal plane on the other. In a sense, these 18 people are junior staff officers to the President in their individual areas of responsibility and carry considerable weight in scientific and technical policy considerations. The entire operation is housed in the antiquated Executive Office Building near the White House on Pennsylvania Avenue.

The scope of individual responsibilities of the OST staff men is enormous. For example, some 28 federal agencies are involved in one way or another with water resources alone. Thus, the OST staff man charged with responsibilities for water resources must somehow keep track of all these goings on plus activities of state and local governments as well as industry—not to mention those of Congress.

The size and complexity of its job—coupled with Dr. Hornig's desire to keep the office a small, flexible, and highly mobile operation—forces OST to rely heavily on the use of consultants via the *ad hoc* committee approach and to borrow people with hard-to-find skills from within Government whenever they are needed and wherever they can be found (a fact OST tries to play down for fear some Congressmen may frown on this practice).

In practice, the *ad hoc* committee approach works like this: A problem is either identified within OST or PSAC, or perhaps referred to it by the President. A group of knowledgeable people is assembled, usually with a member of PSAC as chairman, to hear testimony, to analyze the problem, and to recommend actions to be taken. When the work of the panel is complete, usually within a few months to a year, the panel is dissolved.

OST has found from experience that specialists usually don't work out well as permanent staff members. In the first place, the jobs do not lend themselves to specialization. Individual responsibilities are usually too broad.

"It is difficult, if not impossible, to find a man who is a specialist in all the areas he may be called upon to cover," an OST official points out. "Even if you could find one, you probably couldn't get him. That kind of person is usually serving at the level of the President's Science Advisory Committee."

"The ivory tower scientist," he goes on, "finds himself in a different world in Washington. Many of them just can't seem to bridge the gap between the two. For the kind of work our staff has to do, we have found that it is better to have people who can understand both aspects of the job, the scientific and the political. They must be able to get at the heart of scientific problems and then recommend a course of action to chip away at them while keeping within the bounds of political reality. That is, they must chart some middle course that takes into account all those things it might be nice to do, the things that absolutely must be done, and the size of the program that Congress will stand still for."

Is the OST staff as big now as it is going to get? According to Dr. Hornig this is difficult to say. "Much of the past success of the office has been due to the policy of focusing on relatively few big issues and collecting expertise as it was needed," he explains. "The *ad hoc* panel with staffing from the office has been the most effective operating mechanism, and I for one wouldn't like to see a new bureaucratic superstructure grow here in the White House."

But, he points out, the problems on which he is experiencing more and more pressure are those of coordinating the science activities of the Federal Government and developing integrated approaches to problems. These, he says, are thorny problems because they are not particularly amenable to solution by outside consultants.

What happens in this regard will depend largely on how effective the various coordinating mechanisms such as the Federal Council and its committees can be made. Otherwise, "to do the job properly will require a considerably larger staff than we now have," Dr. Hornig says.

CRITICISM

The Presidential science adviser and his staff have been portrayed by some members of high standing in the scientific community as an unscrupulous, power-hungry band of scientific incompetents bent on complete domination of federal science activities at all levels. To get its way, one is led to believe, this group might resort to such sinister devices as budgetary blackmail, rigged agendas, and stacked committees.

Much of this criticism was laid at Dr. Wiesner's door. And his departure seems to have cleared the air somewhat. But despite the changes in leadership, the White House science complex is the same now as it was under Dr. Wiesner. Dr. Hornig has taken it upon himself to defend it against these charges, which he brands "ridiculous."

A close examination of the facts would tend to bear out Dr. Hornig on many points. For example, some critics would lead one to believe that agency officials sit quaking by the phone awaiting the next pronouncement from the White House.

True, at the policy-making level Dr. Hornig and Company have considerable say about the overall size and direction of an agency's R&D effort. But both from observation and private conversations with key agency personnel, C&EN can find little evidence that the White House science staff is pulling the strings for the day-to-day operation of the federal science establishment.

On this point, Dr. Hornig perhaps best sets the record straight when he says,

> There are competent, strong agencies administering scientific and technical programs. When our views differ from theirs, none of them simply give up their position and adopt ours.
>
> In many ways, our most important task is to provide alternative views to the President. Most things we deal with, incidentally, don't originate here. They would if this were a hierarchy as some people have branded the office.
>
> Our function tends to be more of a review body, encouraging some things and discouraging others which have been proposed elsewhere. The exceptions are those problems of very general significance that can't really be approached from any single agency because they straddle many—such things as the integration of the entire federal scientific effort, the determination of overall scientific and engineering manpower needs, and the coordination of scientific and technical information.

Admittedly, there is scattered resentment of the White House science staff within the agencies. This is understandable when a new office is created at a higher level to ride herd on agencies which previously were free of any such reins. Old empires go crashing. Toes are stepped on. Feathers are ruffled.

Some agency people are still nursing grievances from the early days of Dr. Wiesner's reign. In his zeal to carry out his duties during a period of rapid expansion in the scope of White House responsibilities for science and technology, Dr. Wiesner was sometimes guilty of neglecting the social amenities and protocol in his dealings with the agencies.

Dr. Wiesner is described by a number of his close associates as being "completely intolerant of mediocrity," and he generally made no pretense at hiding this fact.

The most vocal critics of science operations at the White House level are a relatively small group of scientists who for the most part have dedicated themselves to scholarly achievement and not to the hard realities of trying to run a $15 billion-a-year R&D enterprise subject to tremendous political, economic, and social pressures in addition to scientific ones.

They charge, among other things, that national goals in science and technology are set arbitrarily by the White House, without proper regard to whether they represent the thinking of the majority of the nation's scientists and engineers. They imply that the White House is not getting the best advice available on scientific and technical matters, that it is hand-picking its advisers from a small select group of scientists who are for some unexplained reasons favorites of the Administration or of the Presidential science adviser. And they don't think much of the caliber of the White House science staff in general.

The big controversy in recent times about national scientific goals is that raised over the late President Kennedy's decision in 1961 to make an all-out effort to land a man on the moon by 1970. As in any general policy decision of this magnitude, considerably more than just purely scientific considerations were behind the President's decision, factors which the Chief Executive should have been in the best position to know about. And even a number of the moon project's biggest critics today concede that despite the project's scientific shortcomings, it has provided a much-needed shot in the arm for U. S. science and technology in general and in scientific and engineering education in particular.

The criticism of the competence of the supporting White House science staff seems to be based in large part on its alleged lack of scientific stature. The critics resent appointment to important positions related to science of men who have risen by standards other than their own.

While generally displeased with the way scientific decisions are arrived at in the White House, critics do not advance any alternative systems they feel would be better suited to the country's needs. One is left with a decided impression, however, that they would prefer a more "democratic," or broader sampling, process. Perhaps they would favor some sort of national poll to assure that everyone concerned has a say in decisions involving science and technology.

Opponents of the present White House structure for science and technology also are not consistent in their arguments. For example, in one breath they express fear for what could happen by placing so much power in the hands of one man. And in the next they accuse the man of being largely ineffectual, leading one to believe that he is not using the power that has been given him.

POWER

How much actual power do the Presidential science adviser and his staff really have? Actually, the office has no intrinsic power at all. Dr. Hornig tries to clear up the power question in this way: "Any office connected with the White House does not have power as such. It has influence, which is not quite the same thing. This is to say that the commodity we deal with is advice, and advice can be taken or ignored. Our advisory role would imply strong power if there were not alternative sources of advice which, of course, there are."

Semantics aside, though, the office has the wherewithal to bring considerable pressure to bear in the determination of the size, scope, and direction of the federal effort in science and technology. It reviews all major federal programs and policies which have any scientific and technical content or implications and it convenes groups of experts to consider their merit. As chairman of the President's Science Advisory Committee and the man who is in the best overall position to keep abreast of emerging scientific trouble spots, the Presidential science adviser plays a dominant role in selecting the subject matter for PSAC's bimonthly meeting.

The major source of the office's strength is its voice in money matters. Critics have charged the office with exercising nearly absolute control over agency budgets for science and technology. They maintain that the Director of the OST has become, in effect, Director of the Budget where scientific matters are concerned.

Dr. Hornig calls these charges "highly exaggerated." The office does review the scientific and technical aspects of the budgets of all federal agencies. But, as Dr. Hornig points out, the thoroughness of his review is limited by the size of his staff. "It's not a detailed review of every entry," he explains. "We try to sort out what we call budgetary issues and subject them to varying degrees of analysis."

The situation is the same on budgetary matters as it is on general matters of advice, he claims. "We work closely with the Bureau of the Budget, true. And we present our views on programs; that is also quite correct. Our views are sometimes accepted; also true. But sometimes they're not."

Drawing up the federal budget, he explains, is not as simple or clear-cut a procedure as some people would make it out to be. "It isn't just an exercise of someone's proposing a program and someone else higher up accepting or vetoing it."

Here is Dr. Hornig's account of how the budget-making process works:

> An agency proposes a program. Say this office, for a number of reasons, doesn't like it—we don't think it is well advised. Or, and I think this point is often ignored, we think it ought to be much bigger. At any rate, the Bureau of the Budget takes an independent position: It knows our position and that of the agency, and it knows from its own budget analysis the overall budgetary restraints.
>
> At this point in the scheme of things, there is a discussion of the reasons on all sides. BOB tends to look at things in the overall budgetary context. We tend to look at them as to how they fit into the total scientific and technical picture. The agency is concerned with how to carry out its statutory mission.
>
> Usually these differences are resolved by talking them out, although from time to time we must take a strong position. But even if they cannot be resolved in conference, there is still no veto. If they are major issues, the President can make the decisions. Then one tries as carefully as possible to crystallize the issue and the alternative courses of action for him. But in relatively few cases where the issue is drawn is the decision made by the President.

IN ACTION

The office functions both on its own and at the request of the President. The series of studies on scientific manpower conducted by the office, for instance, were at the request of the President. The office's current study of the National Institutes of Health's extramural research program also originated with the President. These are just two of many jobs which the office has undertaken at the request of the President.

The majority of the time the office is a self-starter. As Dr. Hornig sees the office's role, "On most scientific matters, if we do our job well, it's up to us to anticipate problems before the President."

What spurs the White House organization into action? According to Dr. Hornig, it is nothing more complicated than the recognition of a problem. He uses the recent pesticide incident as a typical example of how these things get started.

We might as well face it squarely. Maybe we should have recognized the problem earlier, but Rachel Carson published a book that caused considerable public discussion and got members of the President's Science Advisory Committee to scratching their heads. Violent discussion followed in which a strong segment—in this case, many of the chemical people—said it was a scurrilous book and was not based on any sort of fact, and so on.

There was another equally strong set of voices, possibly not entirely rational in all cases, which said the situation was even worse than she portrayed it. As a result of this, PSAC decided there certainly was a problem that ought to be looked at.

That was step one, and certainly not uncharacteristic. We don't usually start from published books; in fact, it's the only case I know of. But in any event, the first step is always the recognition of a problem.

The second step was also characteristic. We selected what we considered a highly competent panel for the purpose. It went into the problem, produced a study, made some recommendations. Some of the recommendations involved actions by federal agencies, and to a considerable extent they have been put into effect. Some of them involved legislation. Bills containing most of those recommendations have been introduced, and some of them have been enacted into law.

Finally, some of those recommendations haven't yet been put into effect. We still do not have a completely unified policy on pesticides. This is partly a result of the fact that the problem comes up in agencies which are oriented entirely differently. The Department of Agriculture, for example, is interested in the production of crops and is interested in pesticides from that point of view. The Department of Health, Education, and Welfare is worried about the effects of pesticides on human health. Given these different points of view, it's a problem to get a really unified approach. But we're moving in that direction and have made a lot of progress.

LAURELS

Dr. Hornig feels that the White House science staff has made major contributions in a number of different problem areas. A good many of these achievements, he points out, have been in highly classified areas. And naturally they cannot be talked about openly today, which makes it impossible for those on the outside to get a true picture of the group's accomplishments.

But among the major ones that can be talked about, Dr. Hornig rates high the steady progress that has been made by this group in bringing some coherence into the federal system of supporting research. "The office," he points out, "has not tried to pull things together here in the White House, which would be the case if one were 'building an empire.' Instead, it promoted the idea of having assistant secretaries of research and development in all of the major agencies concerned. This has resulted in lifting the scientific competence to the policy-making level and in bringing a new and greater awareness of science in the agencies."

Congress' approval this year of the National Science Foundation's proposal to establish a "centers of excellence program" marked the successful climax of a hard uphill fight by both Dr. Hornig and his predecessor to increase the number of top-notch scientific and engineering schools in the country and thus provide new sources of advanced-degree personnel. The program is budgeted for $25 million this fiscal year. Maximum grants to individual schools will probaby be about $5 million.

The need to develop these centers of excellence stems from the fact that in the past the bulk of the Ph.D.'s in this country have been graduated from a small number of schools. These same schools have also provided the research leadership and attracted a major share of federal research funds. In fiscal 1962, for example, 10 universities accounted for nearly 40% of total funds.

Since 1940 the number of Ph.D.-producing schools has been expanding steadily, but as the need for more people with advanced training grows and as the have-not sections of the country look to universities as a means of invigorating their economies there has been increasing pressure to speed up the process.

Under the new program, NSF will make grants to institutions which, in its judgment, "have substantial potential for elevating the quality of their scientific activities."

Right now Dr. Hornig is trying to get federal agencies that support research in the universities to agree upon a plan to give the schools a freer hand in the way they can use this money.

He feels that the project system, by which grants are made to individual investigators or groups on the basis of proposals which are judged by juries of peers is a major strength of American science. However, the project system in practice tends to neglect support for instruments which are used generally rather than for a specific project or service facilities such as machine shops, computers, and libraries. It makes it hard to support beginning investigators who are not yet in a position to write convincing proposals.

To do these things he has proposed that a small part, perhaps 3%, of the money in each project be made available to local administrators so the pooled funds can be used in ways which would improve the performance of all projects and strengthen research groups as a whole.

TROUBLE SPOTS

Dr. Hornig sees a number of other pressing scientific trouble spots. Perhaps the most central one, he feels, is the need to establish a better rationale for the level and kind of federal support of fundamental science. This problem is brought into sharp focus by today's changing political climate toward science and technology generally. The Government's R&D programs and policies are being held up to the most searching analysis to date by an increasingly budget-conscious Congress alarmed at the snowballing of federal spending for research and development. Legislators no longer view science as a sacred cow. In short, the era of the blank check for R&D seems to have come to an end.

Up to now, the nation has based its support of fundamental science largely on national security arguments, except in the health field, Dr. Hornig points out. "If security demands should relax, we will have to face squarely the problems of a more general rationale for supporting science," he says. "I don't think this is a basic problem. It is just one that has to be faced."

"At this time more than ever before, the nation must weigh its scientific programs against their cost to acquire a better understanding of their importance in relation to national goals," he says. "In particular we must have a clearer view of the role of basic research."

Dr. Hornig thinks that basic research sometimes has been oversold on a pie-in-the-sky basis. "The public and the Congress are entitled to a more reasoned analysis of just what is the role of basic research," he feels.

Another pressing problem Dr. Hornig points to is the need to learn about the relationship of R&D to economic growth. "We simply don't understand it in quantitative terms," he says. "We need to have the answers to such questions as: How do you stimulate the growth of the economy? What, if anything, should the Federal Government do along this line, and how should it do it?"

MEG GREENFIELD
Science Goes to Washington

In the beginning, a current saying in Washington goes, were the lawyers; next came the economists; and then came the businessmen. Now it is the scientists' turn. This new breed, or more precisely, these new hybrids, who began their more or less reluctant ascent to power during the Second World War, are now so thoroughly enmeshed and infiltrated into every level of government that no one seems capable of stating with any precision just what their function is.

The role of the scientist-in-government as it has evolved in Washington in the past twenty years has been interpreted so loosely, by both the scientists and the administrations that have dealt with them, that each has inflicted punishment on the other, and neither, so far, seems to show any genuine understanding of the duties or requirements of the other. Invariably, science in Washington is science under pressure; it is science having to react to something, science having to hurry along, science having to worry about what the Russians might do, what the Congress may say, what Bertrand Russell is likely to think of next. The government in turn has yet to get accustomed to this strange community whose members are given in the best academic tradition to squabbling, back-scratching, and casting doubt on one another's competence—a community that cannot help being politically minded and yet cannot possibly resolve its dissensions according to majority principle.

It is a measure of the difficulty that nobody has—or could—come up with a readily comprehensible table of organization to explain the labyrinth of agencies, foundations, consultantships, academies, and committees that has grown up in Washington in recent years. A simpler guide might begin with the new Office of Science and Technology, created a year ago. The OST, which is directed by Jerome B. Wiesner, is part of the Executive Office and is accountable to Congress. It is charged, formally, with evaluating the programs of other agencies, and with helping to formulate national science policy.

Next, there would be the Federal Council for Science and Technology, a subcabinet group of which Wiesner is the chairman. The Federal Council is composed of a ranking member of each of eight government agencies along with a few official observers, and its purpose is to co-ordinate government programs in science. The task is a formidable one, since even such agencies of government as the Small Business Administration engage in some sort of scientific activity, while the giants such as the National Aeronautics and Space Administration (NASA), the Atomic Energy Commission, and the Department of Defense maintain their own laboratories, award their own contracts, and employ their own private armies of consultants. But the Federal Council's aims are modest. According to one staff aide, it is presently working against the day when ships from two of the twenty government agencies presumed to be involved in oceanography collide and sink while trying to take the same soundings.

In yet another of his capacities, that as Special Assistant to the President for Science and Technology, Wiesner and his staff of thirty-five function as personal advisers to the President. Here they work with the President's Science Advisory Committee (P-SAC), eighteen distinguished and more or less nongovernment scientists and engineers who meet monthly under their chairman, who, again, is Wiesner. P-SAC members are organized into standing committees and *ad hoc* panels, and for assistance they draw on a pool of around two hundred part-time panelists and consultants whose identity is kept secret. (Reportedly, about half the mystery guests come from private industry, and of these the largest single group is said to be from Bell Telephone Laboratories.) P-SAC may also receive what are known as "inputs" from committees of the National Science Foundation, which is concerned with the development of science and science education. Finally, the Foundation, P-SAC, the Federal Council, the individual agencies, and Wiesner in any of his multitudinous roles may request advice from the National Academy of Sciences, a quasi-official agency that has close ties to the Federal government.

One consequence of this chaotic institutional structure is that no one can be sure exactly what a government scientist is or, more to the point, when he is acting as one. It is not unusual to find a scientist like biologist H. Bentley Glass serving simultaneously as an adviser to the AEC on the effects of atomic radiation, as one of the independent experts selected by the National Academy to pronounce upon the same subject, and as a participant in such private groups as the Congress of Scientists on Survival and the Pugwash conferences, which on occasion deplore what the AEC is doing. One effect of the now-they-have-it-now-they-don't relationship many scientists enjoy with government has been to make remarkably vague the degree of their officialness at any given moment in terms of both their rights and their responsibilities.

THE STATUS OF SCIENCE

When is a government scientist speaking for government, and when is he speaking as a private citizen? Government has provided few guide lines, and those adopted by the scientists themselves have been, by and large, unsatisfactory. Last summer, for example, UCLA physicist Joseph Kaplan, who serves as an adviser to both the White House and the Air Force, was asked by a television interviewer for his opinion of the high-altitude nuclear test that had recently been conducted over Johnston Island. He emphatically regretted that the United States had been first to violate "an international agreement" to submit any such potentially harmful experiments in space to international scientific judgment. Yet questioning disclosed that the United States government was not a party to the agreement at all. The "agreement" had been subscribed to by official delegates of the semi-official National Academy at a conference of the International Council of Scientific Unions (ICSU), an organization that is remotely connected with the U.N.

When the scientists are unable to distinguish between their private and their public areas of responsibility, it frequently is government that ends up being embarrassed. Regularly, for example, members of P-SAC go off to the Pugwash conferences. There on occasion they have agreed to disarmament schemes less stringent than those they presumably support as members of government. In explanation of this practice, it has been said that they are acting in their capacity as private citizens, and no doubt they are. The problem has been the Russians' persistent refusal to take the disclaimer seriously, partly because the concept of "private capacity" is unfamiliar to them and partly because it is logical to expect that the views of the President's advisers—public or private—may ultimately carry some weight and even prevail. The effect has sometimes been confusion over U.S. policy, a fact that has begun to trouble even some former enthusiasts of Pugwash. "I think," I was told by one, a P-SAC member presently trying to devise a new format for the conferences, "that Khrushchev may have been misled by some things that were said in private on Berlin in 1961." Not long ago, in fact, Khrushchev, in a correspondence with President Kennedy, alluded to the views of U.S. scientists at Pugwash to bolster his own position on the monitoring of a test ban. In reply, the President was obliged to point out that the scientists "were speaking as individuals."

Painful as such effects of the scientists' irregular status may be, there is little that is likely to be done about it. For most attempts to bring scientists further within the framework of ordinary governmental procedures are suspected as attempts to compromise them; and many scientists who have no trouble understanding, say, the need to "muzzle" the military on subjects that may affect the conduct of foreign affairs consider a call for restraint on the part of government scientists an attack upon their intellectual freedom. This confusion, institutionally blessed, that characterizes their relationship to government in general, leaving them never quite free but never quite responsible either, also characterizes their manner of functioning within it.

"Who is providing the facts . . . ?" Representative Melvin Price (D., Illinois) demanded a while back. "By what authority do they act? . . . Are they qualified?" It was the familiar cry of a congressman who has learned that government scientists have lately put the kibosh on one of his favorite projects—the nuclear-powered aircraft in this instance—and who also knows that his questions will not be answered. For the system and its mode of operation are such that even well outside areas of security classification it is rarely possible to determine who has acted, for what reason, or even in what capacity.

What with everyone participating *ex officio* in everyone else's business and regularly exchanging an embarrassment of inputs, the point has finally been reached where it is no longer clear at a given meeting who is advising and who is consenting and, in either case, on behalf of whom. Thus physicist James A. Van Allen complained last winter that he had been "intimidated" by members of a P-SAC committee before which he twice appeared, only to learn that he had never appeared before a P-SAC committee. It turned out to have been an interagency group convened by Wiesner in P-SAC headquarters under the auspices of the OST. There were P-SAC members present in some capacity and outside consultants too, but they were agency advisers on this occasion. For having failed to grasp this distinction, Van Allen was later charged by one of Wiesner's aides with a lack of "sophistication." In other words, what began as a laudable exercise in co-ordination has ended by almost completely dissolving lines of responsibility in government science, a process that has been hastened by the informal out-of-channels way in which the Kennedy administration likes to operate. In contrast with the two Special Presidential Assistants who preceded him, for example, the somewhat stately James R. Killian, Jr., and the respected scholar George B. Kistiakowsky, Wiesner is widely and admiringly held to be "an operator" in Washington.

Whether or not, as it is claimed, Wiesner accomplishes more this way, there has been a further loss of visibility in an already dim area of activity, and government scientists themselves have begun to complain. What once might have been public reports, according to some consultants who prepare them, are nowadays treated as documents for Wiesner's own guidance, and panel findings that seem to be going the wrong way are apt to meet untimely and mysterious ends more often than was thought practical in the past. The secrecy of preparations for the Johnston Island shot, for instance, bothered many scientists more than the test itself. Joseph Kaplan, who thought the test a "very good experiment," claims to have written Weisner some "rather frank and strong letters" on the subject. "You were quoted . . . ," Kaplan's TV interviewer said apropos of his displeasure, "that the only way to get any information on what we're doing in the scientific space experiments was to sit around the Cosmos Club in Washington. Is that an accurate quote?" "No," said Kaplan, "that's simply one of the better ways. . . ."

For each of the factors that tend to put the scientists beyond accountability and their work beyond review—the maze at the working level, the fuzziness of authority at the middle and the top, and the unorthodoxy of present operations—good reasons and even necessity can sometimes be adduced. But taken together with the part-time nature of many scientists' employment, they have undeniably encouraged on more than one occasion a quick, casual, and even sloppy approach to problems, one that the scientists themselves would be the last to tolerate in their own laboratories. And, as is often the case, an inadequate system has begun to become a justification for its own inadequacies. For even though the government scientists' footlooseness and relative obscurity tend to promote careless work and to make its discovery by others difficult, the possibility of such work occurring has been offered by Wiesner and others as a reason for making their activities even more obscure. The point, as it is often argued in Washington, is that government simply could not get scientists to come down to perfunctory, accident-prone, potentially embarrassing work if even so much as their identity were revealed.

Partly on the basis of such unreassuring logic, a kind of secrecy has been maintained about government scientists that is practiced elsewhere in Washington only on behalf of intelligence agents. Not only are the names of some two hundred P-SAC consultants kept secret, but so are those of other paid scientific advisers to government. Spokesmen for both the Air Force and the Arms Control and Disarmament Agency recently refused to divulge the identity of certain of their scientific advisers on the grounds that to do so would (1) expose them to "pressure," (2) ensure that they would receive unwanted mail, and (3) put them under public scrutiny, which was exactly where they did not want to be.

Why shouldn't government scientists be under public scrutiny? The prevalent view seems to be that since science is more or less objective truth, scientists themselves are all but interchangeable, and their individual identity need not be a matter of concern. It is a view that, oddly enough, the public and the press seem to share. "A noted biologist," the New York *Post* declared not long ago, had made a certain comment about radioactive fallout. The *Post* quoted his comment and proceeded to base a passionate editorial upon it, never bothering to reveal which noted biologist he was, one presumably being as good as the next. The government scientists' exemption from public responsibility, in other words their relative freewheeling and remoteness, are more than side effects of the curious ways in which most of them have been organized into government; it is thought that they should be thus exempt, freewheeling, and remote.

Not long ago, a press officer of the Arms Control Agency informed me that the identity of ten scientists working full-time as civil servants *within* the agency could not be disclosed to the press. He reluctantly produced their names only when he had come to understand the difference between managing the news and managing civil-service regulations. "We claim Executive privilege," he said quite seriously at one point. And at another: "What good would it possibly do you? Why do you want to know who they are?"

THE INFLUENTIALS

Well, who are they? Who are the government scientists? One answer, of course, is practically everyone who has an advanced degree in science or engineering. For taking account of government contracts with universities, industry, and nonprofit organizations, it is estimated that between sixty per cent and seventy per cent of the nation's scientists and engineers are directly or indirectly employed by Washington. According to the Science Foundation, scientists and engineers account for 128,000 of the government's white-collar workers, or about eight per cent of the total. But in discussing those of their number whom they consider "politically relevant," scientists do not speak in thousands but in hundreds. One study, after investigating the subject, posited an "elite" of nine hundred and an "active elite" of 392. Killian reportedly has arrived at two hundred as the number of government scientists who are "consistently influential."

Because of the mystery in which they move and the frustration of those who have tried to find the locus of scientific decisions in Washington, the "active elite" has become subject to vague and contradictory accusations. Characteristically, suspicion on the Right and despair on the Left have produced two abiding myths about where the weight lies in government science and who the Influentials actually are. They are, to hear it told on Capitol Hill, the "fuzzy-wuzzies," by which is meant, roughly, the do-good, left-wing, academic basic-research set. "Like Rabi," they say to cover the other few hundred; ". . . like Bethe." At least, however, proponents of the fuzzy-wuzzy theory can produce a name or two upon request. The same cannot be said for the other side, the believers in the omnipotence of someone called the Military Scientist, a heartless, scheming, and above all irresponsible fellow who would just as soon blow up the Taj Mahal as look at it.

Neither of these devil theories makes much sense. For while it is true that military experiments often develop from recommendations made by the working scientists in the labs of the AEC and the armed services, higher approval has often come from none other than the so-called fuzzy-wuzzies. This was true, for example, of the two experiments most loudly denounced as Pentagon plots in recent years—the Johnston Island test and Project West Ford, a communications experiment that involved creating an orbital belt of copper needles around the earth.

Actually, the academic-military distinction is a false one, and not only because "fuzzy-wuzzies" may claim credit for having invented much of the infernal modern machinery of war. Most of the "active elite" could qualify either as military scientists *or* as fuzzy-wuzzies, whichever they themselves found less disturbing in terms of their personal politics. For the main thing to understand about the "active elite" is what makes it so active in the first place: there are many more influential jobs, it would seem, than there are influential scientists to fill them. Indeed, one reason all the institution-building and committee-creating of the past few years has brought relatively little order to science advising is that the new positions have gone, by and large, to the same old frantic, multi-hatted, over-worked, exclusive crew. There exists at the top in government science not an academic-military split but what political scientists have politely described as a "self-selecting group" that "intercommunicates," and what congressmen rather more bluntly have called a game of musical chairs. In part it exists by default, and in part it exists by design. "Only those who circulate . . . in the right circles," as an editorial in *Science* magazine puts it, "who have the right connections, are likely to be called on to give advice . . ." Not long ago a prominent government consultant with whom I was discussing the controversy about the effect of the Johnston Island test on the Van Allen Belt thought it relevant to point out that Van Allen was "just a little man from Iowa." The question I should have asked, he said, "was whether we would hire him at MIT."

The "right connections," by all accounts, were made during and shortly after the war. Those most multifariously involved in government science are likely to be wartime veterans (or students of the veterans) of one of two institutions: Los Alamos or the MIT Radiation Laboratory (Rad Lab), which was run by Lee DuBridge during the war. After the war there was further commingling on military projects and science advisory committees. According to one scrupulous historian of these matters, some time around 1954 the "core group of the Rad Lab and the old Los Alamos people seemed to merge." Los Alamos as an institution has declined since then. California, on the other hand, has gained ground. And people have moved from place to place. At the present time, government science advising might best be described as a sort of Harvard-MIT-Bell Telephone-

Caltech situation, with lines out to a few Eastern universities and to Palo Alto, Berkeley, and the RAND Corporation.

While the number of posts held simultaneously or in succession is one index of a government's scientist's influence, it doesn't tell the whole story. Being appointed is one thing; being listened to is another. Friendship, skill, chance, willingness to work, and a little bit of auld lang syne have combined in various ways to make some of the elite more elite than others. Certain members of P-SAC are called on for advice more often than is P-SAC itself—Edward Purcell, Wolfgang Panofsky, Jerrold Zacharias, George B. Kistiakowsky, Harvey Brooks, who is Dean of Engineering and Applied Physics at Harvard, and Paul Doty, a Harvard chemist who is a close friend of the President's special assistant, McGeorge Bundy, and who has taken an active interest in disarmament and the test ban. Also, government has its favored businessmen-scientists, such as James Fisk, president of Bell Telephone Laboratories, and Emmanuel Piore, who is vice-president for research and engineering at IBM. Similarly, the advice of certain lab directors in the field often carries more weight in Washington than that of their nominal superiors. One of these is Norris Bradbury, director of Los Alamos. Another is John S. Foster, Jr., who is director of the Lawrence Radiation Laboratory in California and who, along with Richard and Albert Latter of the RAND Corporation, John Wheeler of Princeton, and a few others, represents what has come to be thought of as the scientific shadow cabinet or loyal opposition on questions having to do with nuclear armament and disarmament.

From the days of the Manhattan District Project there has existed within the community of government science a political split over the proper use and control of atomic weapons, a split that was exacerbated by the Oppenheimer hearings and subsequent controversies over fallout and the technology of a test ban. For several years after the war, power shifted from side to side as scientists of opposing views swept in and out of control. The hegemony of the General Advisory Committee of the AEC (I. I. Rabi, DuBridge, Fisk, *et al.*) ended with the Oppenheimer hearings and was followed by a period of hegemony on the part of the Teller group. The ascent of Sputnik in 1957, and a new interest in a test ban on the part of the Eisenhower administration, combined to bring on Period 3. Killian became Eisenhower's Special Assistant for Science and Technology and P-SAC, formerly part of the Office of Defense Mobilization, was elevated to the White House. Its members included Fisk, Kistiakowsky, Rabi, Wiesner, and Zacharias, and for about two years they were again at the undisputed center of scientific power in Washington. The creation of other agencies and advisory groups in government—largely at their own recommendation—has dissipated P-SAC's power since then and given the loyal opposition at least a chance to speak if not always to be heard.

If most of those in the new positions have been around before, one reason may be lethargy and indifference on the part of the out-group scientists as well as finickiness and snobbery on the inside. "You sit on the sidelines and complain," Wiesner chided a convention of scientists in Washington recently. But, he added, it was "surprising" how many scientists when approached by the government made it plain that they only were willing "to come down and help out occasionally." Indeed, the chairmanship of the National Science Foundation went begging for nine months until Atomic Energy Commissioner Leland Haworth, still a member of the "in-group," finally took it this spring. And it took Wiesner more than a year after OST had been established by law to oversee all scientific operations in government to acquire the deputy director provided for in the act. Some people said he couldn't find one, others that he wouldn't; writ large, the argument was whether the dearth of government scientists was due to the fact that no one has been knocking at the door or to the fact that no one has been answering. But whatever has caused the scarcity, it still exists.

What has happened since Sputnik rattled the china in 1957 has been an elevation of scientists, who were for the most part already there, to posts of new responsibility with access to the top. P-SAC moved up to the White House; scientists were taken on by the departments for the first time at the secretariat level; advisory groups were established to communicate directly with Congress and with agency heads; a scientist, Glenn T. Seaborg, became chairman of the AEC. The movement has been upward, and the harassed few now constitute a new class in Washington. They are scientific upper-middlemen—translators, reviewers, communicators, monitors of what goes on below in the labs and agencies, as well as participants in what goes on above, namely policymaking.

THE NATURE OF SCIENCE ADVISING

In a series of Godkin Lectures delivered at Harvard a few years ago, C. P. Snow related a story of conflict between two British science advisers during the war, laying stress on the intractable mysteries of scientific knowledge and its inaccessibility to those in government who had to base decisions upon it. Though Snow's lectures were widely challenged, this chilling and romantic version of science advising dies hard. For the least argument, accident, or admission of uncertainty related to science these days continues to bring on that now familiar host of editorial warnings about how the nation and its leaders must learn science while there's time, or it's curtains for the democratic process. Are the warnings justified? Is radio-physics, like democracy, really everybody's job?

According to those who give and receive advice in Washington, the answer is "No." Wiesner, speaking of the President, and Harold Brown, Director of Defense Research and Engineering, speaking of Secretary McNamara, both concede that there have been times when they had trouble communicating information because of its technical complexity. But such trouble is said to be rare and relatively easy to overcome. "If you can't put it into English," as Jerrold Zacharias has summed up the prevailing view, "it means you don't understand it yourself." Far more troublesome to those who receive advice from Washington's new class of scientific watchdogs, consultants, and policymakers has been the seemingly simple matter of figuring out what is a scientific question in the first place, and what is a scientific answer.

No one was in a mood to make such discriminations in the period immediately following Sputnik I. "They gave us a flabbergasting array of responsibilities," Killian has recalled of those days in 1957 and 1958 when a kind of desperate blur characterized official thinking about the scientists' newly announced purpose of bringing their wisdom to bear on such policy matters as military security and the space race. They were looked upon by the White House and by many in Congress as saviors and miracle workers who could solve, rather than merely assist in, the problems of defense.

The problem of determining what exactly is a scientific question was nowhere so acute and is nowhere better illustrated than in the general field of disarmament and the test ban, largely because science slips so easily and imperceptibly into non-science at almost every point on both issues. Last spring, for example, the following statement was made before the Joint Committee on Atomic Energy by Air Force seismologist Carl F. Romney: "Based on all the information now available, we can conclude that it is feasible to design a detection system, based entirely outside the Soviet Union, which is capable of detecting explosions of about 1 kiloton in granite, 2–6 kilotons in tuff, and 10–20 kilotons in alluvium." As a statement of fact, it was agreed to by government scientists. Yet the old quarrel over our detection capabilities immediately broke out anew among them. Why? They were arguing about many things—whether the Soviet Union would go to the expense of developing weapons below that threshold of detection, whether such weapons would be worth not only the cost to them but the opprobrium of getting caught—whether, in fact, such weapons would have any decisive military value at all. In other words, they were arguing about Soviet intentions and Soviet strategy, not about science. Failing to appreciate the distinction, many people continue to in-

voke the scientist of their choice in support of their own test-ban and disarmament positions in the happy belief that they are citing unchallenge-
able scientific authority.

The associative process whereby a physicist's special knowledge of nuclear weapons is transformed into an equally special knowledge of all the
political, military, and diplomatic problems in which they figure has got
the government into trouble often enough now to be fairly widely recognized for what it is—though not by everybody. In one case, when I asked
a member of P-SAC not long ago if he could describe the extent to which
government scientists found themselves marshaling facts in support of decisions already taken, he replied with great feeling, though a little off the
point, "Never! Because we have always told them what's coming. *They*
ask *us*."

His subsequent account of the astuteness and foresight scientists have
displayed as instructed military thinkers has been challenged lately by a
number of non-scientists in and around government. Albert Wohlstetter,
formerly of RAND, in a recent speech presented an imposing collection of
mistaken predictions and judgments made by such scientists as Bethe,
Teller, and Rabi on such subjects as air defense, civil defense, Soviet behavior, and military strategy in general since the onset of the cold war. "I
believe neither Dr. Teller nor Dr. Bethe has done . . . systematic analysis of the military worth of these weapons they talk about," he said.
"Both are experts on the technology of bomb design. But that is quite another matter."

CONGRESS EYES THE 'EXPERTS'

Predictably, the newly gained insights into what is and what is not a scientific issue in government have suggested to some that time is ripe for that
classical counter-revolution against the government scientist—back to the
bevatron and speak only when spoken to. Something of the sort, for instance, was in the mind of Congressman Craig Hosmer (R., California)
last March when he demanded that a statement made before the Joint
Committee on Atomic Energy by scientist Jack Ruina be stricken from
the record since, even though Ruina had identified the statement as an
opinion, it dealt with aspects of a test ban that were outside his special
competence as an electrical engineer. "This witness is stating an opinion
in an area in which he is not an expert," as Congressman Hosmer
summed up the New Thinking, "and therefore it clutters the record."
Ruina, who was then Director of the Defense Department's Advanced Research Projects Agency, has probably been one of Washington's most
careful and sensitive scientists where infringements of this kind are con-

cerned. At the level of government where he operated, it would be highly impractical to try to keep science advisers in bottles. The genuinely scientific part of most issues in government is so thoroughly entwined with and dependent upon other considerations that it is at best an imperfect, partial science. Thus, Wiesner, at the time of the United States' resumption of atmospheric nuclear testing in 1962, was not called upon to deal absolutely with the question of how much radioactive fission release would be permissible or safe. Rather, he is said to have mediated a behind-the-scenes dispute on the matter between the Public Health Service on the one hand and the AEC and Defense on the other, balancing potential risks to health against potential risks to military security in the light of what the Russians were thought to have achieved in their tests.

The word "potential" was the key on both sides of the radiation dispute, since the ultimate effects of radioactive fallout were—and are—if anything more a subject of conjecture among scientists than the achievements of the Soviet test series. But the sacred distinctions that scientists normally make between scientific fact and scientific theory, or that which is known because it has been proved and that which is still a matter of speculation, have all but gone by the boards in government.

Even making allowance for the fact that government scientists are often pushed into making such premature judgments, however, too often they seem to volunteer them as well. Accordingly, some people have begun to speak wistfully of the need for some sort of self-enforced fair labeling practice among scientists, one that would require them to indicate (as Ruina, in fact, did) when they are departing scientific fact for scientific speculation and when they are departing science altogether. Take the affair of the "black boxes"—the unmanned detection stations that were set forth last winter as a means of policing a test-ban treaty. The scientists had said they were "safe," as people liked to point out. But what exactly had they meant by "safe"? "There never was much enthusiasm around here for the black-box concept," an Arms Control Agency scientist explained to me. "But after the Russians made it plain that they wouldn't take internationally manned stations, we began to find the idea more attractive. Black boxes aren't very reliable when you compare them with manned stations. But they are reliable when you compare them with nothing." So much for the policy judgment and the meaning of "safe." What precisely had the scientists meant by "black box"? There was and still is no such thing—except in theory. Understandably, this bit of news came as something of a shock to legislators who were pondering its place in our then current test-ban proposal last March. Was the black box real or was it "imaginary," as Senator John Pastore (D., Rhode Island) finally put the question to J. H. Hamilton, who is responsible for the project. "I think this system is essentially within the state of the art," Hamilton replied. ". . . I would say to assemble these components, to test, and be reasonably sure of yourself, we are talking about eighteen months."

Such canny questioning of scientists is a relatively new development on Capitol Hill, and its meaning has not been lost on the administration. The plummy days of the hushed hearing room and the reverential "Well, now, Doctor . . ." are becoming a thing of the past. And for once, the narrowing squint of Congress has been turned on the scientists' science rather than on their political upbringing. Consequently, not only have the President and his advisers themselves learned that the phrase "The scientists say . . ." may carry any number of meanings and degrees of authority; they have also learned that simply to quote them will no longer do to persuade Congress of the wisdom of a particular decision. For the Congress has learned that a scientist's own emotions and his personal politics may well affect the advice he gives.

The repugnance with which most people respond to the idea that a scientist may even have such things as emotions and politics, let alone that either might influence his work, is a tribute to the durability of some rather odd beliefs about both science and politics, and about any encounter that takes place between them. Science is the man in the white coat, the thinking goes, and politics is the man with the stale cigar, from which it follows that a politically motivated scientist must be a venal one, a passer along of equations that don't prove out. The truth is considerably less dramatic. P-SAC, for example, has a reputation for scientific rashness where the test ban is concerned and for scientific skepticism about proposed military weapons systems. Among Defense Department scientists, quite naturally, it has been the other way round. "It's hard to separate emotion from hard facts," an Arms Control Agency scientist explained. "We can get agreement on the facts, but not on what we could do on the basis of them. We can't get agreement on the scientific promise, on where it will lead."

He was talking about the test ban, and his first point was illustrated—and continues to be—in the scientists' quarrel over the meaning of the element of uncertainty in test detection. To those scientists, such as Teller, who oppose the ban, the uncertainty meant danger: we could not be sure of detecting Russian evasions. To those who favored the ban it meant increased safety: the Russians could not be sure of evading detection and therefore would be less apt to cheat.

The test ban serves equally to illustrate the way in which the scientists' political inclinations have affected their intuition and inventiveness—their actual scientific creativity. In Washington the process is known as "finding ways that things won't work." Both Teller and Bethe have proved masters of the art. Teller, as Wohlstetter has pointed out, has been particularly adept at imagining weapons that the United States could not develop under the terms of a test-ban treaty. Bethe, on the other hand, has generally responded to such imaginings with imaginings of his own—"enemy countermeasures which would reduce their military worth to zero." The scientists' advice has not only been affected by their political preference. Their curious status between and betwixt government and private roles has left room for any number of interests to inspire their advice in both areas. As presiders over the national science purse, are the scientists speaking in the interest of science or in the interest of government or in the interest of their own institutions? Is their policy advice, on the other hand, offered in furtherance of national objectives or agency objectives—or their own objectives based on their political thinking? It has begun to become apparent that wherever they have favored the more private aim over the more public one, they have not only limited their usefulness to government—except as checks and balances to each other—but undermined their own influence as well. The extent of the confusion that exists on the subject became apparent at a meeting of the Federation of American Scientists not long ago when Wiesner was asked rather imperiously from the floor how he could justify the way in which government annually disposed of its $12-billion budget for science when there were so many neglected projects more worthy of support. The funds, Wiesner pointed out, were not being spent *for* science but *on* it. They were being spent *for* government, he said.

SHOOTING THE MOON

Despite its many achievements, the present balancing act has proved inadequate for the chores the scientists in government set for themselves. It has not been possible to make even a start on the establishment of scientific priorities and long-range plans for science. Agency monitoring proceeds on a helter-skelter basis. And chaos and frenzy are at least as common to the process of advising as order. "Valuable as such [*ad hoc*] advice is," as Kistiakowsky has summed up the problem, "it does not fill today's requirements for a continuing and intimate involvement in the policymaking process of competent people who understand science and its significance to policy . . ." Indeed, six years after the ascent of Sputnik, what might be called the state of space in Washington is a fairly good index of what the scientists have and have not been able to achieve—and why.

"The scientists cringe when you call it science," a NASA administrator recently told me on the subject of Project Apollo, the moon-flight program. He added that of course it wasn't supposed to be "science"; science was only one part of the program. In return, many scientists have pointed out that while science is a relatively small part of the program, the program will still have an enormous impact, by reason of money spent and manpower committed, on the future of science itself.

But to some extent the fault was their own. The point has been made that the initial response of the newly elevated P-SAC and of other leaders of the scientific community in 1957 to the post-Sputnik space emergency was almost entirely geared to the interests of science—from the original proposal for a research-oriented space agency to the casual dismissal of both the military and diplomatic ramifications of a space program. "There is plenty to do without trying to nail the American flag on the whole solar system by next week," Lee DuBridge put it at the time. By speaking mainly for science conceived as basic research, P-SAC saw its power over the program diminish and with it the chance to influence the program's impact on science.

The moon program was worked out over a hectic weekend in May of 1961 at the Pentagon following Alan Shepard's successful suborbital flight. It was a political response to the Gagarin venture and to the Cuban disaster, among other things. Reportedly, Secretary McNamara, James Webb of NASA, and a few others met round the clock starting Friday evening and worked out the crash program that was presented to the President for a decision the following Monday. "We had been told," as one of the participants puts it, "not to fool around." What was Wiesner's role? "Jerry was associated with the decision. He was called in. He was there. He wanted everything to be done right by the administration. And he had his constituency of scientists he was worried about too. As I remember, he was torn."

In Washington these days, the definition of a truly hip science adviser is one who knows that the moon money could be better spent on other scientific projects and who also knows that Congress won't appropriate it for any of them. The kind of passive in-betweenness this suggests is more or less the state of science advising now. "The scientists think you are a tool of the administration," Wiesner told me in summing up the predicament not long ago, "and the administration thinks you are a tool of the scientists."

The National Science Foundation
A General Review of Its First Fifteen Years

Introduction

A. ORIGINS AND DEVELOPMENT OF THE
NATIONAL SCIENCE FOUNDATION

The National Science Foundation operates under a mandate from the Congress "to promote the progress of science; to advance the national health, prosperity, and welfare; to secure the national defense; and for other purposes." To fulfill this responsibility, this agency supports basic research in physical sciences, engineering, mathematical, biological, medical, and social sciences; funds education in these sciences and fosters the interchange of scientific information among scientists in the United States and foreign countries; maintains a register and provides a central clearinghouse of information concerning all scientific and technical personnel in the United States; and develops studies related to planning of science policy. Some 42 other technically oriented Federal agencies in some degree or other engage in similar functions when conducting research and development to carry out such explicit missions in the national interest as military security, agriculture, aviation, medicine, and meteorology.

But in its concept, in its development, in its problems, and in its emerging role, the Foundation represents a unique entity in the Federal panoply of technically based agencies. For in the Federal spectrum of research support, only the Foundation (and, in certain respects, the Smithsonian Institution) was established to sponsor scientific activity without any regard for practical application, and only the Foundation has the responsibility to consider policy related to and foster development of the total complex of research resources, including development of facilities and of trained manpower to help assure sustained U.S. leadership in the sciences and engineering, measured both by quality and size of effort.

The proposal for a National Science Foundation grew from a World War II-induced shortage both of scientific research and of scientists. Education of young scientists and engineers had been seriously interrupted; private sources of grant money had significantly evaporated; and the stock of scientific discoveries that are produced by research had been systematically drained by technological demands of World War II.

Even before the war ended, President Roosevelt wrote Dr. Vannevar Bush, then the director of the Office of Scientific Research and Development, to request preparation of a study on various aspects of postwar sci-

From *Report on the National Science Foundation,* House Committee on Science and Astronautics, 89th Cong., 1st Sess., 1965.

ence. With the aid of four special committees, Dr. Bush submitted his report entitled "Science, the Endless Frontier," to President Truman in July 1945. A principal recommendation in that report was that a new agency, then called the National Research Foundation, be established with broad powers and functions to advance American science. Intensive congressional action followed release of that report, but initial legislation was vetoed by President Truman because the authority vested in a part-time board appeared to violate the President's constitutional duties. It was not until May 10, 1950, that Public Law 81–507 was enacted to establish a new agency. During the interim, the Office of Naval Research, the new Atomic Energy Commission, and the National Institutes of Health became leading Federal sponsors of basic research. The NSF legislation, however, symbolized an intent as a matter of public purpose that the Nation support whatever activities were necessary to sustain world leadership in science, a position to which the United States unexpectedly fell heir at the end of World War II.

Science was not new to this Nation. A keen appreciation by early statesmen of the potential of science and the industrial arts is reflected in the Constitution. Industrial progress in the 19th century and the very winning of a continent were manifested largely through American engineering and technology. This advance was based on native invention and innovation. After World War I, this advance depended more on exploitation of science. But this was science largely of foreign origin, for the maturing of science in this country was conspicuously a product of scientists who were either born or trained abroad.

The lesson of World War II dramatized the potency of science to generate a new style of warfare in which technological superiority of weapons greatly outweighed superiority in numbers of men and even skill in tactics. Successful development of the atomic bomb catalyzed a national purpose to maintain a sharp scientific cutting edge to this country's future military apparatus. To do so would also require a hospitable peacetime environment for the continued preeminence of a domestic scientific establishment, productive both of knowledge and of trained manpower. A Government-university partnership had been swiftly assembled during the war under an alert, effective Office of Scientific Research and Development. And this successful utilization of scientific talent for development of a variety of such new weapons as radar led the Federal Government to assume a major role as the sponsor of peacetime science.

The birth of the National Science Foundation entailed much controversy both within the Congress and with the executive branch. Questions arose regarding the necessity of Federal aid to science. Even more intensively argued was the question of whether Federal support for research and graduate education would inadvertently bring Federal control that could stifle the creative forces that thrive best in academic freedom. The proposed structure of the organization was contested, especially on means of insuring guidance from responsible leaders in science, education, and public affairs, while insulating them as far as practicable from politics. How to treat patents arising from public support was at issue as were questions on whether to include the social sciences within NSF jurisdiction. In light of contemporary concerns, it is interesting to note the debate at that time on whether funds for scientific research should be distributed partially on a geographical basis, and how a central responsibility for Government-wide policy planning for science should be assigned. . . . Although NSF is often thought of as a public foundation that functionally imitates historic support of worthy research by private foundations, the legislation provided a far broader concept, power and responsibility.

Immediately after its establishment, the Foundation encountered effects of an economy drive and then the diversion of the Korean war that limited its ability to carry out its extensive responsibilities. At least as measured by funds, the sponsorship of project research to refill the reservoir of basic knowledge and to strengthen U.S. science in terms of facilities and faculty continued to be far more a matter of support by the Department of Defense and the Atomic Energy Commission than by the National Science Foundation, whose mission it was to fulfill this national need. (That fundamental research should be supported by mission-oriented agencies may seem contradictory; for, in contrast to applied research, basic research implies a quest for scientific understanding without explicit concern for the ultimate use of results. Such support by mission-oriented agencies was justified by the need to sustain and nurture a national scientific capability which could be tapped for applied purposes in times of future emergency. Equally important was the recognition that, as in the case of the atomic bomb, many discoveries of military significance could and would evolve unpredictably from basic research motivated only by the uncommitted curiosity of a qualified investigator. This rationale for diversity of support by agencies with explicit public purposes continues.)

NSF's early years are thus marked by a disparity between goals and resources. By virtue of its broad, comprehensive legislation assigning responsibility "to develop and encourage the pursuit of a national policy for the promotion of basic research and education in the sciences," and the desire by its first Director to adhere to congressional intent, planning and some programs were undertaken by the Foundation in support of the three primary components of a scientific capability: Research, manpower development, and communication. From a variety of options, the Foundation chose to support research through grants for individual projects rather

than for programs or general institutional support. Grantees have been selected on the basis of merit of research proposals by review panels comprising the Nation's leading experts in the respective field. But certain special areas were also selected for emphasis; that is, sciences encompassed
by the International Geophysical Year program. The Foundation began to
support both small- and large-scale facilities in universities to meet growing enrollments and changing needs of science. Support for students was
undertaken at a relatively high level, focused on graduate and postdoc-
toral fellowships awarded through competitive examination rather than
undergraduate scholarships. In recognizing that science majors poorly
prepared at high school levels could not meet college scholastic standards,
the Foundation initiated support for improved science teaching in primary
and secondary schools and at college levels, as well as for studies to improve curriculum at pre- and post-college levels. There was concern for
providing information to the general public to foster an improved scientific literacy of the Nation as a whole. Finally, support was instituted to
facilitate effective dissemination of scientific results, including international
communications, to match the growing pace of scientific publication, need
for interdisciplinary communication, abstract services and verbal modes of
information transfer.

With these enormous tasks, but with limited funds, it is clear that during its early years only a start could be made. Yet, a start was made in all
of these areas, and the pattern of subsequent growth, in recent years when
funding has approached the half-billion-dollar level, reflects more an expansion in size and scope of existing program elements than the creation
or addition of new ones. The fraction of the total budget for basic research and supporting facilities, for example, has been constant since
1957.

Since its establishment in 1950, the authority of the Foundation has
undergone but few amendments. To some extent, this may reflect the
breadth and flexibility of the original enabling act. The most significant
and far-reaching change occurred in 1962 when, under Reorganization
Plan No. 2, certain elements of Government-wide policymaking and coordination were transferred to a new Presidential Office of Science and
Technology. Implications of this transfer are elaborated on subsequently.
Prior to that action, however, the initial limitation of $15 million on an-
nual appropriations was removed in August 1953. And, in 1958, responsibilities were added for development of Federal efforts in weather modification. Responsibilities in the science-information area were added in
1958, by law, and Government-wide coordinating responsibility in 1959
by Executive order. . . .

Although differing in subject areas, mode, and level of support, it should be clear that numerous Federal agencies, in addition to the NSF, sponsor basic research. In fiscal year 1966 proposals, for example, the Foundation budget represents only $357 million out of $16.2 billion estimated obligations for research, development, and construction of related facilities. The Foundation's share of support for basic research is $290 million out of a Federal total of $2.27 billion. Other agencies support students at all levels, through a variety of subventions; and, finally, all agencies engaged in the research and development enterprise assume as part of their responsibilities steps to assure effective dissemination of scientific information. Numerous agencies also have responsibilities for gathering and analyzing manpower statistics.

The Foundation thus shares with other agencies a responsibility in every field for which it has programs. But from its founding, the agency has been given an additional, unique role—that of providing orientation for the entire Government-wide enterprise.

In its initial act, the Congress assigned to the Foundation responsibility "to develop and encourage the pursuit of a national policy for the promotion of basic research and education in the sciences." The Congress also initially authorized the Foundation "to evaluate scientific research programs undertaken by agencies of the Federal Government and to correlate the Foundation's scientific research programs with those undertaken by individuals and by public and private research groups." Finally, in establishing the dual administrative structure, the Congress provided both for a Director, who is chief executive of the Foundation, and a National Science Board consisting of 24 members appointed by the President, with implications—if not instructions—that the Board should not be limited to advising on internal Foundation operations but would contribute to the development of a national science policy.

What is meant, incidentally, by a national science policy is ambiguous, and subject to a variety of interpretations. These range from a "unified, comprehensive, coherent national statement of goals and methods for science" to simply the composite of separate policies of the Congress and various agencies of the executive branch related to science. A third interpretation of the phrase would broaden it to include not only policy concerning needs of science per se, but also a full spectrum of disparate science-based public policies related to technologies of agriculture, defense, civil aviation, resources development, urban transportation, and so forth.

Regardless of definition, the Foundation was uniquely assigned in its organic act the responsibility for whatever policymaking would be rationalized in this area. Many observers of NSF development, however, have noted that the Foundation moved cautiously in this area. As one author has noted, "the Foundation is not the only Federal agency that supports research. The potential friction and jealousies confronting a fledgling agency that tried to evaluate the programs of other and frequently much larger Federal agencies are obvious."

Regardless of motivation, there was comparatively little emphasis on policy matters by the Foundation during its early years. Rather, it devoted its energies to development of its own operations. In 1954, however, the need was identified for some Government-wide influence to develop unity in Federal goals and consistency in Federal processes, although certainly not a master policy for all of science. Executive Order 10521 explicitly instructed the Foundation "to recommend to the President policies for the Federal Government which will strengthen the national scientific effort and furnish guidance toward defining the responsibility of the Federal Government in the conduct and support of Federal research." The Executive order also called on the Foundation to make comprehensive studies and to make recommendations regarding the Nation's scientific research effort and its resource needs; to review scientific research programs and activities of the Federal Government to strengthen program administration; to be increasingly responsible for providing support for general-purpose research; to study the effects upon educational institutions of Federal policies and administration of grants and contracts for research and development.

Two congressional actions in 1958 and Executive Order 10807 in 1959 assigned additional coordinating or evaluation responsibilities to the Foundation for weather modification and for science information services. Moreover, during this interval, the Foundation provided support for the Secretariat of the Interdepartmental Committee for Scientific Research and Development that had been previously established in 1947 to coordinate Government-wide science programs (superseded in 1959 by the Federal Council for Science and Technology).

Notwithstanding these instructions, the Foundation was faced with the politically arduous responsibility to coordinate activities of sister agencies which were organizationally coequal or had Cabinet rank and frequently were more affluent.

With the global reaction in 1957 to Soviet achievements in space and the associated concern over relative United States-Soviet strength in missile technology, President Eisenhower acted to accommodate the growing breadth and complexity of Federal programs in science and technology, and to improve organizational arrangements and policy planning in the executive branch. Virtually all of the steps taken impinged on national policy responsibilities of NSF which had been assigned by the Congress, but which it could not or would not implement.

In 1957, he established the White House Office of the Special Assistant to the President for Science and Technology; and reconstituted the 17-man Science Advisory Committee in the Office of Defense Mobilization as a Presidential advisory panel. In 1959, he established the Federal Council for Science and Technology, through Executive Order 10807, as a "science cabinet" of senior policy officials.

The special assistant, incidentally, serves as Chairman, both of the President's Science Advisory Committee (by Committee election) and of the Federal Council for Science and Technology (by designation of the President). This composite of executive activities in a single office then was designated as the focal point for construction of science policy as well as for science monitoring.

The Congress was not satisfied with this policymaking machinery; and based on recommendations by a Senate subcommittee, President Kennedy proposed, under Reorganization Plan No. 2 of 1962, additional major steps to strengthen science organization at the Presidential level. With congressional approval, a new Office of Science and Technology was established in the Executive Office of the President through transfer of the NSF authority to develop national policy and evaluate Federal programs. Science policy transcending agency lines would thus be shaped at the level of the Executive Office of the President, and difficulties under which NSF had operated from its establishment would be corrected. Moreover, through the device of a legislatively based coordinating agency, the Congress would have access to information and advice on Government-wide plans and programs which heretofore the Director of NSF would have found awkward to present.

In transmitting this proposed reorganization plan, however, the President stated that "The Foundation will continue to originate policy proposals and recommendations concerning the support of basic research and education in the sciences and the new Office will look to the Foundation to provide studies and information on which sound policies in science and technology can be based."

It is important to note that the primary change in NSF function was the transfer to the new Office of Science and Technology of authority "to develop and encourage the pursuit of a national policy for the promotion of basic research and education in the sciences" and "to evaluate scientific research programs undertaken by agencies of the Federal Government." NSF's gap-filling responsibility to correlate its programs with those sponsored by both public and private groups was unchanged.

Thus the authority of the Foundation to engage in basic research, support of education, etc., would continue, but the responsibility for setting Government-wide goals, establishing balance, etc., which went unimplemented from 1950 to 1957, then established in the White House at an appropriate level but operationally shielded, would now be shared by OST and NSF.

It is interesting to note that in his first annual report for 1950–51, the NSF Director stated that among the questions which needed to be answered in developing a national policy are the following:

What is the total financial support now being provided for scientific research?

What is the distribution of this support among the three major sources —Government, industry, and educational institutions?

What amount of financial support can and should be provided and what is the most desirable distribution from among the available sources of support?

What is the division of research effort among the various natural sciences?

What areas need greater emphasis and what less?

What means can be developed to shorten the period between discovery and practical application?

What are the present and future needs for trained scientific manpower?

What is the impact of Government support of research programs on the educational process in universities and colleges?

What is the effect of Federal research programs on the financial stability of universities?

Most of these questions remain unanswered; others are only partially answered. Several, in fact, have been recently posed by the House Committee on Science and Astronautics in its March 1964 request for advice from the National Academy of Sciences:

I. What level of Federal support is needed to maintain for the United States a position of leadership through basic research in the advancement of science and technology and their economic, cultural, and military applications?

II. What judgment can be reached on the balance of support now being given by the Federal Government to various fields of scientific endeavor, and on adjustments that should be considered, either within existing levels of overall support or under conditions of increased or decreased overall support?

A number of related questions have been posed by Federal officials, by Congress, by scientists, and by students of public administration, whose answers are essential to the fashioning of national science policies—as significant guidelines both for the functioning of Government and of universities that depend so critically on Federal support for scientific research, facilities, and graduate education.

To develop such policies in the first instance requires information—data and analysis—regarding manpower, facilities and funds; regarding their distribution by performer groups, by geography, by level of fundamentality, by field of science. The NSF was given statutory responsibility for the maintenance of a manpower register as the first element of a capability which would assist the Foundation in its own internal operations, but also as an adjunct to the forging of a national science policy. Such data were especially required if the Foundation were to fulfill its crucial role of maintaining a balance in science, considering that the preponderance of Federal support arose from mission-oriented sponsors who neither individually nor collectively could maintain a concern for the balance of science as a whole. Steps could then be taken to compensate for fads in science, or to meet emerging technological needs for which the necessary scientific base required stimulation.

To meet all of these questions involves an activity that has frequently been designated science policy planning: To set goals; to identify national needs for the support of basic research in order that the United States maintain its leadership; to identify the Federal responsibility; to establish criteria and techniques for balance of support as between different fields of science and between basic and applied research; to meet growing research requirements in engineering and behavioral sciences; to establish criteria for distribution of research support as between universities, Government, and industry; to prevent distortion of the university aims and structure; to assess adequacy of manpower resources and scientific facilities; to meet expensive facility requirements such as in high energy physics; to maintain quality of research activities; to accommodate diversity of support by different Federal agencies and delineate responsibility for funding; to coordinate Federal planning and programs; to meet international needs and opportunities involving science; to assure adequate communication of scientific results and their transfer to meet applied needs.

In its early years the Foundation considered science policy planning primarily as data gathering. Subsequently, after Executive Order No. 10521, it established a Program Analysis Office, later an Office of Special Studies, then an Office of Economic and Statistical Studies; in 1961 a Science Resources Planning Office; and in 1964 a Division of Planning, with a number of supporting branches.

The national policy formulating roles of the Foundation are not clear in relation to the National Science Board, the Office of Science and Technology, the Office of the Special Assistant to the President for Science and Technology, the President's Science Advisory Committee, the Federal Council for Science and Technology, the National Academy of Sciences, and the new National Academy of Engineering.

In its 1962 annual report, the Federal Council for Science and Technology noted that a new long-range planning committee had been appointed with responsibilities to—

a. Identify and coordinate long-range goals of Federal agencies in science and technology;

b. Foster preparation of an inventory of research resources—manpower and facilities;

c. Project future demands for resources and funding;

d. Develop techniques for Government-wide planning to minimize gaps and redundancies, and to achieve maximum utilization of resources;

e. Formulate recommendations for program emphasis and allocation of resources;

f. Function as a clearinghouse of information on planning techniques, to aid departments and agencies in formulating their individual plans and programs.

The Committee obtains staff assistance from various offices of the National Science Foundation, and as its first major assignment requested the Foundation to survey projections of all Federal agency plans for research and development to 1970. . . .

This general discussion of the framework of science and of the Federal organization in which the NSF operates would not be complete without some statement of accomplishments. In the first instance, the fact that the United States has sustained its World War II preeminence in science is now universally accepted. Credit for this accomplishment has been attributed to the competence and leadership of the scientific community. But where the health and growth has been so much a consequence of Federal funding, the wisdom of Federal executives and in all agencies and in the Congress must be acknowledged. It is also generally believed that the influence of the Foundation was far out of proportion to its budget. This agency has no mission other than to advance science. Since it operates no laboratories of its own, the focus of its activity has been extramural research through project grants and student support. Judging from annual reports of Dr. Alan T. Waterman, its first Director, it is clear that he saw the role of the Foundation as one of setting the tone and national standards, and serving as a catalytic agent without undue interference, to assure the quality of U.S. science while other agencies assumed more the role of massive support. Assessment of the Foundation's contribution cannot be measured by numbers of scientific papers, or numbers of students supported. But the present strength of U.S. science speaks to the overall accomplishment.

During this era of early growth, the Foundation has not been immune from criticism. Mostly this has been focused on what it failed to do, rather than what it did. It was criticized for not exercising Federal policy leadership when it had authority, and for mismanagement of those large projects for which it assumed responsibility; i.e., Mohole, and delays in construction of the Green Bank radio telescope. Most recent criticism has been directed toward problems in statistics gathering and resources analysis, lack of support in engineering and behavioral science, and retarded action in providing for additional and better distribution of centers of excellence. Significantly, when the Foundation had authority to establish a balance, it lacked funds. With its growing budgets that permit the filling of gaps and the redress of balance, the responsibility for policy setting now substantially resides in the Office of Science and Technology.

B. THE FUTURE ROLE OF THE FOUNDATION

The potential of science to serve society appears to be widely accepted—not only for military security, but to meet domestic and global economic and social needs. It is important not only to its participants but to the general population. Yet, a number of new circumstances now have been manifested which are bound to exercise a critical influence on the course, direction, and rate of future growth of the Foundation, and for which policy planning is essential:

1. The need for goal identification and deliberate allocation of resources was far less developed in the 1960–64 era when Federal R. & D. budgets were growing sharply and a variety of competing interests could be partially or completely satisfied. Because of Federal budget constraints, this growth has been arrested and with the public interest in broad educational needs, medical care for the aged, antipoverty measures and support for the arts and humanities, the competition for scarce funds now involves the making of unprecedented hard choices.

2. The R. & D. budgets of mission-oriented agencies are leveling off even more sharply. Although for purposes of decisionmaking the "R" category of activities has been separated from the "D" category, and subject to milder deceleration, the responsibility for any expanding Federal support of basic research may increasingly be thrust upon non-mission-oriented agencies.

3. At the same time, the national needs for support of research in the universities continue to rise—as a consequence of increasing college enrollments and the increasing fraction of college graduates who go on to graduate study (even though the percentage of those entering science and engineering remains about the same as it has through the first half of this century)—and the costs of conducting fundamental research continues to rise as a result both of inflation and increased complexity of required facilities.

4. The potential of science to contribute to economic and social needs has illuminated the heavy localization of Federal support both in universities and in industry, and has brought about a sharper inquiry by the Congress on the manner in which science and technology contribute to local and regional activities and how, in combination with special local attributes, a different geographical distribution of Federal support would contribute increasingly to the national welfare.

5. Although the apprehensions about manpower shortages fluctuate, there is widespread agreement that certain categories of technical manpower are in continuing short supply, especially for university faculty to meet growing needs in higher education, and for technical managers.

6. Imbalances continue to arise between different scientific fields, partly as a consequence of unequal leadership and opportunities in science, and partly as a consequence of the stimulation of certain fields in the national interest. Detecting and redressing these imbalances is a matter of national concern in which all institutional entities must participate, and information concerning the present state of activity is needed by all such participants so that decisions can be made at all levels.

7. The Federal support for research in the universities constitutes a very substantial fraction of the universities' total income, such that more explicit statement of national policy is necessary for institutions to plan for stability and future growth.

8. At the same time, passage of the education legislation by the 88th Congress is expected to meet national needs more completely and should assist the universities so that the NSF may not have to shoulder the same burden of responsibility for science education as it has done heretofore.

9. Insofar as the balance between scientific fields is concerned, the scientific community, particularly through the National Academy of Sciences, continues to give careful study and publicize needs and opportunities in special fields of science. Any Federal reaction to such proposals inevitably requires consideration of these specific needs against the spectrum of total needs. The same type of evaluation appears necessary in the light, for example, of demands for "big science" such as high energy physics and the space sciences.

10. Attention is being increasingly drawn to the potential of science to alleviate domestic and international economic and social problems. Because of the structure of Federal organization and the interdisciplinary nature of the problems, research sponsorship by present mission-oriented agencies may not meet needs and a general purpose source may be required to support interdisciplinary natural and social sciences research.

11. Finally, Federal organization for science is likely to undergo review and possible metamorphosis. A bill for a Commission on Science and

Technology has been reintroduced in the 89th Congress and problems it addresses may receive more attention as congressional review of present Federal organization and decisionmaking apparatus intensifies. Any reshaping of Federal organization would require a review of both national and Government-wide goals and Government-wide capabilities.

The future role of the Foundation was a major subject for comment in the April 26, 1965, response by the National Academy of Sciences to the House Committee on Science and Astronautics' request for advice as to level and balance of Federal support for basic research, needed to maintain U.S. scientific leadership.

Although the study was conducted by a special 15-man panel that did not seek consensus, two major conclusions emerged:

> The first is that Government should recognize that, on the whole, science in the United States today enjoys a preeminence, and that what is done in the future should be based on expanding and improving the present situation. . . . The second essential point that runs through at least half the papers (of the 15 panel members) is the belief, stated either explicitly or implicitly, that the role of the National Science Foundation during the next decade should become much greater than it has in the past, especially in the physical sciences. . . . Two courses for providing increased support to the physical sciences are open, and probably both should be followed. The first, recommended by several panelists, is that mission-oriented agencies, at times such as this when budgets are rather stationary, should devote a larger fraction of their budgets to basic research. . . . The second course, which by no means excludes the first, is to make the National Science Foundation a much larger agency than it now is—so large that it can eventually become the "balance wheel," or even the main "umbrella" for the support of basic research—especially in the physical sciences—that is too remote to merit support from the mission-oriented agencies.

All of these considerations reflect the characteristic of science as a national resource—a renewable resource, one that is vital to the public welfare. At one time, the Director of the Foundation observed that "in its broadest sense, national policy for science is a matter primarily to be determined by the scientists themselves. The scientists of the country are unquestionably the ones most capable of deciding what is best for progress in science, in the true meaning of the word." Since that statement was made in 1960, many circumstances have changed. Science as science policy may be increasingly separated from science as public policy. . . .

The text that follows is intended primarily to set forth facts on the Foundation's status today and how it developed. Details have been classified to fit NSF program descriptions. But wherever possible, these have been placed in the context of the total Government-wide activity, as measured both by funds and by responsibilities. For it is only in this perspective of "Federal science" that the Foundation's future role can be evaluated in support of basic research, facilities, graduate education, curriculum revision and teacher training, science information activities, and science policy planning.

Authority, Organization, and Funding

• • •

A. A REVIEW OF THE ORGANIZATIONAL STRUCTURE

1. Director

The Director is the chief executive officer of the National Science Foundation. He is appointed by the President, by and with the advice and consent of the Senate. He is appointed for a 6-year term, unless sooner removed by the President. He may not engage in any business, vocation or employment other than as Director, and he may not, except with the approval of the National Science Board, hold any office in or act for any organization, agency or institution with which the Foundation makes any contract or other arrangement. Following the Federal Salary Act of 1964, his annual salary was increased to $28,500.

The National Science Foundation Act of 1950, as amended, cites the general authority of the Director as follows:

> (*a*) The Foundation shall consist of a National Science Board and a Director. . . .
>
> (*b*) The Director shall serve as a voting ex officio member of the Board. In addition thereto he shall be the chief executive officer of the Foundation. . . .
>
> (*c*) In addition to the powers and duties specifically vested in him by this Act, the Director shall, in accordance with the policies established by the Board, exercise the powers granted by sections 10 [award of fellowships] and 11 [do all things necessary to carry out the provisions of the Act] . . . together with such other powers and duties as may be delegated to him by the Board. . . .
>
> (*d*) . . . but no final action shall be taken by the Director in the exercise of any power granted by Section 10 [award of fellowship] or 11 (c) [award of contracts or other arrangements for the carrying on of (i) basic scientific research activities and (ii) specific scientific research activities at the request of the Secretary of Defense] unless in each instance the Board has reviewed and approved the action proposed to be taken, or such action is taken

pursuant to the terms of a delegation of authority from the Board or the Executive Committee to the Directors. . . .

* * *

Assisting the Director in the performance of his duties is a Deputy Director. This post, vacant since 1957, was filled during fiscal year 1964 by Dr. John T. Wilson, a former longtime NSF official who most recently held an administrative post at the University of Chicago.

There have been two directors of the National Science Foundation to date: Alan T. Waterman, who served from April 6, 1951, to June 30, 1963; and Leland J. Haworth, the present Director since July 1, 1963. A biographic statement on Dr. Leland John Haworth appears below:

Leland John Haworth became Director of the National Science Foundation on July 1, 1963, following Senate approval on May 9, 1963, of his nomination by President Kennedy. Dr. Haworth came to the Foundation from the Atomic Energy Commission, where he had served as Commissioner since April 1961.

Dr. Haworth began his career as a high school teacher in Indianapolis, Ind., in 1926–28, and then served as an instructor in physics at the University of Wisconsin, 1930–37. He was a Lalor fellow in physical chemistry at the Massachusetts Institute of Technology, 1937–38. At the University of Illinois, he was an associate, assistant professor, and professor of physics, 1938–47. From 1941 to 1946, Dr. Haworth was on leave from Illinois working on defense projects at the MIT Radiation Laboratory. He was appointed Assistant Director of Brookhaven National Laboratory in 1947 and Director of the Laboratory in 1948. In 1951, he was named vice president and in 1960 president of Associated Universities, Inc., while continuing as Laboratory Director.

From 1959 to 1961, Dr. Haworth was a member of the Board of Directors of the Oak Ridge Institute for Nuclear Studies. He became a member of the Atomic Energy Commission on April 17, 1961.

Dr. Haworth was born in Flint, Mich., on July 11, 1904. He received an A.B. in 1925 and an A.M. in 1926, both from the University of Indiana. He was awarded his doctorate in physics from the University of Wisconsin in 1931. Dr. Haworth was the recipient of D. Sc. degrees from Indiana and Bucknell and a D. Eng. degree from Stevens Institute of Technology in 1961. He was also awarded a D. Sc. by the University of Wisconson in 1962.

The list of special scientific committees and project groups that Dr. Haworth has served on include Project Vista, U.S. Army, 1961; the ad hoc Committee on Combat Developments, U.S. Army, 1954; Technological Capabilities Panel of the President's

Science Advisory Committee, 1954; member and Chairman of the
National Science Foundation Advisory Panel on High Energy Accelerators, 1954 to 1961; and Project Atlantis of the U.S. Navy,
1959. He was a member of the board of directors of the American
Nuclear Society, 1955–60, and president, 1957–58. He is a fellow
of the American Physical Society, American Nuclear Society, and
the New York Academy of Sciences. Dr. Haworth is also a member of the Cosmos Club, Sigma Xi, Gamma Alpha, Phi Beta Kap-
pa, and Lambda Chi Alpha. He received a certificate of merit from
the President of the United States for his World War II research.

2. National Science Board
a. Composition

The National Science Board is the policymaking body of the National Science foundation. As set forth in the enabling legislation, the Board shall
consist of 24 members who are appointed by the President, by and with
the advice and consent of the Senate, and of the Director of the Foundation. The persons nominated for appointment must be eminent in the
fields of the basic sciences, medical science, engineering, agriculture, education, or public affairs, and shall be selected solely on the basis of distinguished service records in their chosen fields. Recommendations for
nominations of Board members may be submitted to the President by the
National Academy of Sciences, the Association of Land Grant Colleges &
Universities, the National Association of State Universities, the Association of American Colleges, or by other scientific or educational organizations.

The term of office of each Board member shall be 6 years, unless appointed to fill the unexpired portion of the term of a predecessor. The an-
niversary of a Board member's term is May 10, the date of the approval of
the National Science Foundation Act of 1950. At that time, terms of the
first members were staggered, one-third each to end in 2 years, 4 years,
and 6 years respectively, so that at the present time the terms of one-third
of the Board members end on May 10 of every even-numbered year.
Members may be reappointed for a second term; however, after a person
has served for 12 consecutive years, he is ineligible for reappointment during the ensuing 2-year period.

Members of the Board receive compensation at the rate of $50 for each
day they are engaged in business of the Foundation and they are also allowed travel expenses.

b. Functions and operations

Concerning the general functions of the Board, Director Leland J. Haworth commented:

In addition to establishing general policies for the Foundation the Board must either approve, or delegate authority to the Director or Executive Committee to approve fellowships and grants or contracts for basic scientific research activities. As a practical matter, the Board has delegated to the Director authority to approve such actions except with respect to very large awards, or where policy issues are involved. Although the Board must also take action on such matters as setting up new divisions within the Foundation, it is not a day-to-day operating body.

An Executive Committee of five members, consisting of the Director ex officio and chairman, and four other members, elected by the Board from its membership, was established by Reorganization Plan No. 2 of 1962, which at the same time abolished the existing Executive Committee. The members serve for 2-year terms; after a member has served for 6 consecutive years, he is ineligible for reelection during the ensuing 2-year period. The Board may assign to the Executive Committee such of its powers and duties as it deems appropriate; except that the Board may not assign to the Executive Committee the function of establishing policies. The Executive Committee reports annually to the Board concerning its activities and concerning such recommendations as it feels are appropriate; minority views and recommendations are to be included.

The National Science Board must meet annually on the third Monday in May, unless another date in May has been agreed upon, and it may meet at such other times as the Chairman may determine, except that a request by one-third of the members for a meeting must be honored. In recent years the Board has been meeting about nine times a year.

The NSF program is directed to—

A. The support of basic research and research facilities, both to sustain momentum of U.S. scientific progress and to fund thesis research which is a necessary part of graduate education.

B. The support of science education to maintain a supply of scientists and engineers, adequate in quality as well as quantity to meet present and future national needs through stipends for students (especially graduate and postdoctorates); course content improvement and assistance to secondary school and college science teaching.

C. The support of institutions, to facilitate internal balance in those already achieving excellence, and to foster a growth and geographical distribution of additional centers of excellence.

D. The support of science information services, to foster effective dissemination and use of scientific results by other scientists, engineers, and administrators.

E. The support of science policy planning, to develop statistical information and studies as a basis for public policy decisions involving science and technology, as a guide both to NSF internal management and to policymaking at presidential and congressional levels.

For virtually all of the program components which the Foundation supports, other Federal agencies also provide support—often exceeding the NSF contribution. Data have thus been added wherever possible indicating the budget and functional relationships of such multiagency activities, and the coordinating agents established by the President to provide coherence in policy and program formulation.

A. SUPPORT OF BASIC RESEARCH AND SUPPORTING FACILITIES

Under this heading, which accounts for approximately 51 percent of the Foundation's total budget request of $530 million for fiscal year 1966 are grouped four major elements of research support:
1. Basic research project grants;
2. National research programs;
3. Specialized research facilities; and
4. National research centers.

Some of these programs have been part of the Foundation's activities from the beginning; others have been added from year to year as the need for supporting a particular kind of activity became apparent. From 1958, this component has ranged only from 49 to 51 percent of the total budget.

1. Basic research project grants
a. Authority for research grants and contracts
Section 3 (a) (2) of the National Science Foundation Act of 1950, as amended, authorizes and directs the Foundation—

(2) to initiate and support basic scientific research and programs to strengthen scientific research potential in the mathematical, physical, medical, biological, engineering, and other sciences, by making contracts or other arrangements (including grants, loans, and other forms of assistance) to support such scientific activities and to appraise the impact of research upon industrial development and upon the general welfare.

At the time the act was passed, it appeared that no other Government agency had discretionary authority to use funds for either grants or contracts, as was appropriate in each case. Most agencies had only contracting authority and a few like the Department of Agriculture and the Public Health Service had been given statutory authority to make grants. In this sense, therefore, the authority which was given to the Foundation upon its establishment of "making contracts or other arrangements" was unique.

Since 1958, all agencies who previously had contracting authority for basic scientific research have . . . been given authority also to make grants for the support of such basic scientific research. The Foundation took the view that the plural system would strengthen science as a whole, and supported the passage of the 1958 legislation to facilitate research arrangements.

Contracts have traditionally been used when the nature of the end product sought is known and requirements can be made the subject of negotiation between the Government and interested parties, normally through competitive bidding procedures with the contract being awarded to the lowest bidder. Contracts are widely utilized for sponsoring engineering development projects with private industry. In the case of scientific research, however, even where answers are sought to explicit scientific questions, the success and thus the cost of attaining it are uncertain, and applications are generally unknown. Contract procedures cannot be utilized in their usual form. Certain modifications have had to be made, leading to use of negotiated contracts for research, rather than those let by open competitive bidding, and to contracts at a cost-plus-fixed-fee where it is impossible to ascertain the cost in advance.

Grants have been defined as "essentially unilateral actions by the Government under which payments are made in advance of the investigations concerned for the purpose of encouraging, supporting, and stimulating the general research work of public and private institutions and individuals, based on a decision of Congress that the support of the work of such institutions and individuals will be of benefit to the public." Three types of grants have been identified: block grants, grants fixed by statute, and project grants.

Characteristics of the project grant are "specific objective or narrow field of inquiry, limited preliminary negotiation, predetermined budget, prepayment, administrative determination of audit, and evaluation of fulfillment based on degree of attainment of specific objective, or equivalent attainment of a collateral objective developed during the course of the investigation." In practice, distinctions between grant and contract instruments by various Federal agencies for support of basic research has been lost; both have been adjusted to meet needs.

· · ·

b. Policies and procedures for project grants

A major policy decision was made by the Foundation almost from its inception to support research mainly through grants to individual scientists on the basis of meritorious proposals for research projects rather than through grants to institutions.

Certain basic decisions concerning the grant process were also made early in the Foundation's history. These were enumerated in the Foundation's fifth annual report for fiscal year 1955:

> (a) Grants in support of basic research, declared meritorious following review by scientists in that scientific field, would be awarded to institutions on behalf of the principal investigator.
>
> (b) Grants would be made for the period of time required by the research project, up to a maximum of 5 years.
>
> (c) Grants would include a reasonable amount for indirect costs. As an interim policy, the Foundation determined that this amount may be up to 15 percent of the total direct costs in the grant request. * * *
>
> (d) Grants could include, as well, allowance for publication costs anticipated, including purchase of reprints.
>
> (e) Grants, under normal circumstances, would permit title to equipment purchased or constructed with grant funds to be vested in the grantee institution.

These basic criteria were valid in 1955 and they are still valid in 1965, from all available information, except that the allowance for indirect costs has been modified as discussed below.

Under the project system, individuals or groups of scientists submit research proposals through their institution to the Foundation. The proposals are reviewed by advisory panels and review groups, which the Foundation has set up, composed of persons who have intimate knowledge of the particular fields involved. These groups select and recommend for support those proposals for grants which are judged to have the greatest scientific merit. A grant usually provides support for one phase of a program which may continue for many years. Continuity of support is exceedingly important. Since the Foundation has "no-year" funds, money provided in grants may be used for an indefinite period beyond the current fiscal year; in practice, the maximum grant duration has been 5 years.

2. National research programs

Apart from its support of basic research through individual projects, the Foundation assumes responsibility for broad scientific programs in which a number of departments and agencies of the Federal Government participate, along with nongovernmental entities, and often in cooperation with other nations on an international basis. As the Federal agency uniquely concerned with basic research, the Foundation has come to be regarded as the most appropriate "delegated agent" to coordinate and handle the financial aspects of U.S. contributions to what NSF designates as "national research programs."

National research programs are usually undertaken at the initiative of the scientific community, who after reaching agreement on the desirability of U.S. participation in a project, request support from the Federal Government. The National Academy of Sciences has been an important intermediary between the scientific community and the Federal Government in such matters, and usually provides continuing guidance to the NSF after a national program is initiated. NSF often funds such advisory bodies.

National research programs usually have a limited budget and a definite scope. However, funds are disbursed primarily to academic institutions for use of scientists in the conduct of research in almost the same fashion as project funds. They may thus be considered supplementary to basic research project grants. Authority to participate in national research programs may arise from the broad authority of the NSF legislation, but more often participation stems from specific legislation or Executive orders, in particular for international programs.

The following programs have been so designated by NSF:

	Fiscal year
International Geophysical Year	1957–58
Antartic research program	1958–
Weather modification	1960–
Deep crustal studies of the earth (Project Mohole)	1961–
International Indian Ocean Expedition	1962–
United States–Japan cooperative science program	1963–
International Years of the Quiet Sun	1963–
Ocean sediment coring program	1966
International upper mantle project	[1]

Each of these programs is discussed briefly in sections that follow.

a. National programs of the Federal Council for Science and Technology

As noted above, the Foundation has been given responsibility for two general categories of national research programs:

1. Those programs in which the United States participates as a component of an international program under auspices of intergovernmental or multinational science organizations. Examples are the International Geophysical Year, the Antarctic research program, International Indian Ocean Expedition, United States–Japan cooperative science program, and the International Years of the Quiet Sun program.

2. Those programs which are entirely domestic and of a nonmission-

[1] Not yet formally recognized as a national research program.

oriented basic research nature, such as Project Mohole, the ocean sediment coring program, and weather modification.

There is a third category of national research program designated by the Federal Council for Science and Technology comprising those scientific fields that depend substantially on Federal support, are not the primary responsibility of any one agency, and whose scientific merits or promise in relation to public interest warrant acceleration. Among this category of national research programs are the following:

Atmospheric sciences.

High-energy physics.

Materials research.

Oceanography.

Water resources research.

• • •

Several of these were designated by President Kennedy as warranting this status; others were selected by the Council. The National Science Foundation participates in all of these programs but only as one among the several agencies with primary interests. The development of Government-wide goals and programs, and the designation of agency responsibilities including that of the National Science Foundation, is thus established through appropriate interagency committees operating under the aegis of the Federal Council for Science and Technology.

NSF participation in national programs of the Federal Council for Science and Technology

OBLIGATIONS OF FEDERAL AGENCIES
FOR ATMOSPHERIC SCIENCES
[IN MILLIONS OF DOLLARS]

Department or Agency	1964 actual	1965 estimate	1966 estimate
Department of—			
Agriculture	0.5	0.5	0.7
Commerce	15.1	13.9	17.1
Defense	70.5	72.2	79.9
Health, Education, and Welfare	1.6	2.0	2.2
Interior	1.0	1.9	1.7
Atomic Energy Commission	6.2	7.0	7.9
Federal Aviation Agency	.9	2.2	2.4
National Aeronautics and Space Administration	106.5	74.5	81.4
National Science Foundation	22.7	20.2	26.2
TOTAL	225.0	194.4	219.5

OBLIGATIONS OF FEDERAL AGENCIES
FOR OCEANOGRAPHY

Department of—			
Commerce	23.3	19.9	13.3
Defense	54.6	65.1	68.0
Health, Education, and Welfare	2.9	3.5	4.4
Interior	16.5	20.0	16.9
State	.6	.6	.6
Treasury	1.2	1.8	2.1
Atomic Energy Commission	3.8	4.0	4.6
National Science Foundation	19.6	19.3	30.0
Smithsonian Institution	.6	.9	1.7
TOTAL	123.1	135.1	141.6

OBLIGATIONS OF FEDERAL AGENCIES
FOR WATER RESEARCH AND SURVEYS

Departments of—			
Agriculture	11.0	13.0	14.5
Commerce	1.2	1.2	1.5
Defense	3.4	3.5	4.0
Health, Education, and Welfare	13.2	13.1	17.7
Interior	30.1	39.3	58.0
Atomic Energy Commission	3.1	2.3	2.5
National Science Foundation	1.7	1.8	2.1
Tennessee Valley Authority	.9	1.1	1.2
TOTAL	64.7	75.3	101.5

b. International Geophysical Year

During 1957–58, for the third time in a century, scientists in the United States joined with scientists in many other countries to make certain observations and synchronize measurements as part of a world-wide study of the planet Earth. The resulting project—the International Geophysical Year—involved 66 nations and embraced many fields of the earth sciences including astrogeophysical measurements, meteorology, oceanography, glaciology, ionospheric physics, aurora and airglow, geomagnetism, cosmic rays, and rocket exploration of the upper atmosphere. From 20,000 to 30,000 scientists and technicians are estimated to have made observations at more than 4,000 stations. Three World Data Centers were established to acquire complete sets of all IGY data: In the United States, in the U.S.S.R., and a third operated by Western European and Pacific nations. A part of the U.S. contribution to the program was the plan, announced July 29, 1955, by the White House, to design and launch small, unmanned earth-circling satellites which were intended to represent a pioneer effort in this area. A successful launching of the first U.S. earth satellite was made on January 31, 1958. In the meantime, however, the Soviet Union surprised world scientists as well as laymen by orbiting a much larger satellite on October 4, 1957. The geopolitical as well as scientific repercussions of this achievement are still being felt—and perhaps more than any other single event furnished impetus to U.S. interests in basic research and in development of scientific manpower reflected in the recent growth of the NSF, which is described in this report.

Background.—Earlier international undertakings of this scope had been organized in 1882–83, when the First Polar Year was launched, and in 1932–33, during the Second Polar Year. As their names suggest, the regions about the North Pole were the subject of these earlier inquiries.

In 1950 a proposal was made for another international research effort on the scale of the two earlier ones, to be scheduled for 1957–58 during which a period of maximum solar disturbances was predicted. A U.S. National Committee for the International Geophysical Year was established by the National Academy of Sciences in 1952 to represent the United States in the International Council of Scientific Unions and to coordinate the U.S. effort. In March 1953 a grant of $5,000 to support the Committee was made by the National Science Foundation; later that year the Foundation made another grant for $22,000 to continue the support of the Committee through 1954.

NSF direct involvement in the IGY came about as the result of a formal request in December 1953 from the National Academy of Sciences-National Research Council to the National Science Board requesting that the NSF accept responsibility for obtaining and administering Government funds for the Federal participation in this effort. At the request of the Foundation, Congress subsequently appropriated funds totaling $43.5 million. About $100 million of additional funds were appropriated for other Federal agencies to participate in IGY, provide logistic support, and launch the Vanguard satellite.

The Foundation's role in IGY appears to have been primarily that of providing funds. Scientific planning and coordination was undertaken by a special committee of the National Academy of Sciences.

Post-IGY activities.—The IGY has been considered an unqualified success, measured both by advances in scientific knowledge and by continuing international cooperation in science. This latter achievement has in turn had a salutary effect on communication both between scientists and between participating nations, and has established a durable pattern that has been considered a contribution to world understanding. In October 1958 the International Council of Scientific Unions met in Washington to formulate plans for post-IGY activities. Among the new committees established at that time to continue international collaboration in various fields, were the Special Committee on Oceanic Research (SCOR), the Special

Committee on Atmospheric Research (SCAR), and the Committee on Space Research (COSPAR).

c. U.S. Antarctic research program

The Antarctic research program is a continuation in the Antarctic regions of the research in the several fields of the earth sciences on which observations, research, and data collections were made during the International Geophysical Year, 1957–58. Almost all the nations which had conducted research in this region during the IGY continued their programs. On December 1,1959, the 12 nations that took an active part in Antarctic research during the IGY signed the Antarctic Treaty, which guarantees free access to the entire continent, and provides for unlimited inspection of all installations.

As a result of a U.S. Government policy decision to continue operations in the Antarctic on a basis consistent with the U.S. national interest, the National Science Foundation was assigned responsibility for planning, coordinating, managing, and funding the U.S. scientific programs in the field, and the Department of Defense was named the agency to budget for and provide logistic support to such programs; the Department of State is responsible for assuming overall coordination.

The program is directed by an Office of Antarctic Programs under the Associate Director for Research. NSF coordination with the Navy Department, which is handling the logistic support, was explained by the head of the Office during 1964 House appropriation hearings:

> The Foundation develops the scientific plans, which are outlined for 5 or 6 years in advance; this includes the probable experiments that will develop, the needs of the scientific program, and what our men would like to do. We also prepare an annual short-range scientific program. These requirements are transmitted to the Navy for their consideration, for their criticism as to whether it can be done within the available facilities they have. When it appears they can support this work, we sit down with the Navy officials and discuss it. Other matters are coordinated in a group under the chairmanship of the Department of State. We sit down together and come up with what we can both support.

The Committee on Polar Research of the National Academy of Sciences, the Foundation's predecessor as coordinating agent, provides broad program recommendations and indicates new areas of research to which attention might be given.

The Foundation maintains a 266-foot research vessel *Eltanin* as a floating mobile station for U.S. Antarctic research. There are four mainland stations: McMurdo, Pole, Byrd, and Eights, and a number of inland regions.

The Antarctic research program enables scientists from colleges, universities, Government laboratories, and other research centers to carry out a wide variety of basic scientific investigations in Antarctica.

Funds obligated or requested for the program by the National Science Foundation from fiscal years 1958 to 1966 are as follows:

Fiscal year 1958	$446,000
Fiscal year 1959	2,306,000
Fiscal year 1960	6,180,000
Fiscal year 1961	5,461,000
Fiscal year 1962	7,188,000
Fiscal year 1963	6,359,000
Fiscal year 1964	7,145,000
Fiscal year 1965 estimate	7,500,000
Fiscal year 1966 amount requested	8,600,000

Logistic support of the program is considerably higther than the cost of the research program. In fiscal year 1964, for example, the Navy requested $20 million for its part in the program, as compared to the $9 million which the Foundation requested.

The Congress has raised questions concerning this program especially over the lack of "coordinated, continuing, and consistent interest in the Antarctic," and over the logistic support of the program.

d. Weather modification

Public Law 85–510 of July 11, 1958, amended the National Science Foundation Act by adding to the functions of the Foundation under section 3 (a) a new paragraph (9)—

> SEC. 3. (a) The Foundation is authorized and directed—
>
> • • •
>
> (9) to initiate and support a program of study, research, and evaluation in the field of weather modification, giving particular attention to areas that have experienced floods, drought, hail, lightning, fog, tornadoes, hurricanes, or other weather phenomena, and to report annually to the President and the Congress thereon.
>
> • • •

Delegation to the Foundation of this responsibility was the culmination of an investigation which had been made by an Advisory Committee on Weather Control which was established by Congress in 1953 to study and evaluate public and private experiments in weather modification. During the next 4 years the Advisory Committee and two other organizations—the American Meteorological Society and the Committee on Meteorology of the National Academy of Sciences—made an extensive survey of cloud-seeding operations in the United States and also gathered data on activities abroad. The three groups published comprehensive reports at about the same time and all the reports reached essentially the same conclusions.

In its final report published in December 1957, the Advisory Committee on Weather Control made the following recommendations:

1. Encouragement be given for the widest possible competent research in meteorology and related fields.

2. The Government sponsor meteorological research more vigorously than at present.

3. The administration of Government-sponsored research provide freedom and latitude in choosing methods and goals, with emphasis on encouraging talented men as well as their specific projects.

4. An agency—the National Science Foundation—be designated to promote and support research in the needed fields, and to coordinate research projects.

5. Facilities required to achieve a research project should be provided by the appropriate agency whenever the project has the endorsement of the National Science Foundation.

The act of July 11, 1958, cited above, was the congressional response to the need to designate some agency to promote and support research in weather modification. The Foundation promptly established a new program, and expended $1,141,000 during fiscal year 1959 for research and evaluation in weather modification.

When Foundation officials appeared before the House Independent Offices Appropriations Subcommittee to request $2 million for fiscal year 1960 for the program, discussion ensued as to why and how the Foundation had become involved. The chairman of the subcommittee questioned the advisability of the Foundation's becoming involved in specific research projects:

> Mr. THOMAS. If we started giving you specific research projects to perform where will you be at the end of 5 years? You are not set up to do specific jobs and yet here is one dumped on you.
>
> Dr. WATERMAN. The history of course is that when the President's Committee on Weather Control finished its job the decision had to be made as to who would carry on.
>
> • • •
>
> Mr. THOMAS. Why should the National Science Foundation do it? I will ask you my original question. If we enlarge your juris-

diction with specific enactments, commanding you to do specific research in this field, that field or the other field, what will happen to you 4 or 5 years from now? You are not set up to do a specific job on anything in the way of research, and yet here is a specific job dumped on you.

After a continued discussion of various aspects of the Foundation's responsibility for the program, and with respect to other agencies, the chairman again voiced his apprehension:

> Dr. WATERMAN. It seems this is a critical area in science and we believe that the Foundation ought to take charge in such critical areas. I would hope in years to come we would not have many of these.
>
> Mr. THOMAS. If you want to change this basic act and get yourself in the research business proper this is a good way to start. You have done a good job and now they are going to tie you down to a specific job, and the first thing they will ask, "Well, you have had the job 5 years and you haven't come up with an answer."

Administratively, the program is operated through awarding of grants and contracts with university and other research groups for investigations of various aspects of this broad field. An advisory panel for weather modification, similar to other advisory panels which the Foundation utilizes, provides advice and assistance concerning the program to be supported.

Three main goals for the program have been set forth:

1. Continue to attract new, creative talent to weather modification research, and to the atmospheric sciences as a whole. . . .

2. Broaden the attack on weather modification research by supporting theoretical and field research into potential new methods of weather modification or control, with new emphasis on the long-range investigations of weather and climate modification on regional or continental scales.

3. Shorten the time gap between the development of theory and the start of field research so that new techniques may be tested as soon as a sound theoretical basis is established.

An annual survey of weather modification issued by the Foundation reports on the activities of other Federal agencies who also have responsibilities in this field. Approximately $1.5 million has been obligated annually by the Foundation for the weather modification program from fiscal year 1960 onward; $2 million has been requested for fiscal year 1966.

e. Deep crustal studies of the earth (*Project Mohole*)

By virtue of its scientific importance, funding level, organizational novelty, and degree of public controversy over NSF management, this program might well be the subject of an entire treatise. This presentation must of necessity sketch only the barest detail of those aspects which characterize Project Mohole as unique among Foundation activities.

Project Mohole is the name given to a research project whose objective is to penetrate into the earth's outermost crust in order to remove samples of the underlying mantle of rocks which make up an estimated 80 percent of the earth's volume and which surround the inner core. While it has often been contended that part of the mantle is exposed at places on the earth's surface, this assertion has not yet been proved. To retrieve specimens from the mantle, it is necessary to drill through the earth's crust. And the sites have been selected in the ocean where the crust is much thinner than has been found on exposed land areas. Drilling is anticipated through a crust 20,000 feet thick, under approximately 15,000 feet of water.

The scientific interests center around the nature of the lesser density of the earth's crust as compared to that of the mantle. This change is known by a sharp discontinuity in velocity of elastic wave propagation. The interface is called the Mohorovicic Discontinuity after its discoverer, from which the name for these studies—Project Mohole—was derived.

Among the scientific benefits which it is hoped to obtain from the project are a better determination of the age of the earth and of the amounts and distribution of its elements, and the proving or disproving of the theories of continental drift.

The project is a pioneering effort in two respects: From the scientific point of view, Mohole offers unprecedented opportunity for scientific discovery and confirmation of geophysical theories. From the engineering point of view, the project introduces enormously difficult problems which must be resolved in order to drill into the earth through the deep ocean.

(1) *Historical sketch of the project*—(*a*) *Phase I of the Project Mohole: Role of AMSOC—NAS.*—The idea for the project is credited to a group of individuals, mainly geologists and oceanographers, who in 1957 joined together in an informal unit, calling themselves the American Miscellaneous Society. By the end of 1957, this group had sought and obtained an affiliation with the National Academy of Sciences, and was designated as the AMSOC Committee. Financial support for their effort was obtained from the National Science Foundation in the form of project grants totaling $1.8 million between 1958 and 1961.

The AMSOC Committee carried the research on Project Mohole through phase I, the preliminary phase in which in the early part of 1961 they proved the feasibility of stabilizing a floating vessel sufficiently to carry out experimental oceanic drilling at two sites—through depths of water of 3,000 and 11,700 feet respectively at La Jolla and at Guadalupe

Island off the coast of California. In the latter attempt, maximum drilling into the second layer of the earth's crust to a depth of 601 feet was accomplished, and a core sample which was found to be basalt was retrieved.

(b) *Phase II of the Project Mohole: How the NSF became directly involved.*—At the completion of phase I, the AMSOC Committee and the National Academy of Sciences concluded that the operational aspects of phase II, leading up to actually drilling through to the mantle, should be turned over to a prime contractor. This is the stage where the National Science Foundation began to play a leading role in lieu of the backstage indirect support it had been giving to the project through provision of project grant money, during the previous 3 years.

By letter of June 23, 1961, the president of the Academy, Dr. Detlev W. Bronk, transmitted to Dr. Waterman, Director, National Science Foundation, the report of the AMSOC Committee which summarized the views of the committee with regard to the objectives of the Mohole project, the functions and responsibilities of the committee with respect thereto, organizational and operational arrangements for completing the project within the next 3 fiscal years, and the budget for fiscal 1962. The letter concluded, "We shall be glad to cooperate with the Foundation in every possible way in the completion of arrangements for the expeditious continuation of the Mohole project."

(i) *Initial AMSOC–NSF agreement on scientific objectives of the project.*—The report made clear that the AMSOC committee sought to turn over the operational aspects of the project, but wished to retain for itself "matters of scientific policy, engineering review, and budget." The recommendations concerning scientific policy are excerpted to delineate the project objectives as seen by the AMSOC committee:

SCIENTIFIC POLICY

1. We are agreed that the major scientific objective of Project Mohole is to drill to the earth's mantle through a deep ocean basin to core as much of the section as possible, and to make pertinent geophysical measurements in the hole.

2. Our immediate objectives are:

(a) To sample through the second layer and determine its thickness and characteristics.

(b) To sample the characteristics of the top of the third layer.

3. Also exciting, and of prime scientific importance is the fact that we now have a new tool, the floating drilling vessel, with which to explore thoroughly the sediments and upper crustal layers of the ocean basins. We find, however, that the major objective of the committee will entail work enough, and that we must recommend this possible exploration program to you for separate scien-

tific and financial consideration. We expect the initiative for general ocean basin exploration to come from the large oceanographic institutions, and we heartily endorse the importance of the work.

4. The committee finds, upon recommendation from our site selection panel, that we need additional geophysical information to help select a suitable drilling site for carrying out our major objective. We require further geophysical research at sea, both of a reconnaissance nature and in detail, to locate possible Mohole sites.

Dr. Haworth testified on November 1, 1963, that the Foundation was in full agreement with AMSOC concerning these objectives.

(ii) *Summary of major decisions, 1961–65.*—In the summer of 1961 the National Science Foundation took over responsibility for phase II of the Mohole project. Throughout the remainder of that year the Foundation was involved in a search for a prime contractor for engineering and operations. That the Foundation was also seeking full-time scientific guidance for the project during this period other than from AMSOC also was evident from a letter of February 7, 1962, from the NSF Assistant Director for Mathematical, Physical, and Engineering Sciences to the chairman of the AMSOC committee asking for recommendations for a scientific director for the project. On February 28, 1962, the search for a prime contractor was culminated with an announcement that Brown & Root, Inc., of Houston, Tex., had been chosen. The contract which was signed on June 20, 1962, was on a cost-plus-fixed-fee of $1.8 million basis. Questions about the suitability of this contractor and NSF procedures for his selection were raised by the Congress and professional groups, and were pivotal in the controversy over Mohole that raged for several years.

The contractor assembled a project staff and began work on the design of a platform from which the drilling will be done. Concurrently, subcontracts were let for design and construction of requisite positioning equipment for the platform, to hold it steady at sea, and for the drilling equipment, taking into consideration the necessity to use material in the drilling string which will withstand the unusual dynamic and fatigue loadings that result from wave- and wind-induced motions of the drilling platform.

On January 21, 1964, the Foundation announced "a technical and operating plan for Project Mohole, involving design and construction of a large [buoyant] drilling platform, equipped initially to carry out developmental and scientific drilling programs at intermediate depths prior to its use for the deep hole through the earth's crust to the mantle."

When completed, the platform will be equipped initially with equipment designed to carry out intermediate developmental and scientific drilling programs at depths of 20,000 to 24,000 feet below the ocean's surface. In this choice of technique, the Foundation emerged from a second major

controversy on whether to use a conventional ship or an oil-drilling platform type of vehicle on which drilling equipment would be mounted. In
deciding to proceed with a large drilling platform rather than an "intermediate" conventional vessel, the Foundation explained:

> The possibility of using an "intermediate" conventional vessel
> for testing equipment and gaining drilling experience—as had been
> recommended by some scientists and engineers associated with the
> project—was rejected partly because of additional cost but pri-
> marily because the platform with its greater inherent stability is a
> better base for carrying out the necessary drilling system devel-
> opments. Attempts to compensate for the effects of motions in a
> smaller conventional vessel that would not be present in a large
> platform would be both costly and time consuming. Furthermore,
> operational use of a conventional vessel would have little impact
> on the problem of design and construction of the platform itself,
> which most engineers agree is the proper choice for deep drilling.
> Experience gained by intermediate drilling will have its greatest en-
> gineering impact on drilling equipment and techniques rather than
> on the vessel.

f. International Indian Ocean Expedition.—The International Indian
Ocean Expedition (IIOE) is a continuation of the international cooperative research programs which began with the International Geophysical
Year. Responsibility for coordinating Federal support for U.S. participation in the Indian Ocean Expedition, including financial support, was assigned to the National Science Foundation by President Eisenhower in an
announcement of June 13, 1960. President Kennedy endorsed the expedition in his message to Congress of March 29, 1961.

The purpose of the IIOE is to learn more about the Indian Ocean
whose 28 million square miles cover over 14 percent of the earth's surface. The several aspects of the program include research into the ocean's
topography, circulation, and the distribution of living organisms, both
plant and animal, in it. Both scientific and long-range economic benefits
are expected to be realized from the program.

Nations participating with the United States include Australia, France,
Germany, India, Indonesia, Japan, Pakistan, Portugal, South Africa, Thai-
land, and the United Kingdom. Nearly 40 ships in all are taking part. The
United States has 14 ships and 5 aircraft engaged in the program.

Four Federal agencies are participating in the International Indian
Ocean Expedition: the Department of the Navy, the Coast and Geodetic
Survey of the Department of Commerce, the Bureau of Commercial Fisheries of the Department of the Interior, and the National Science Foundation.

International planning by scientist-participants has been undertaken through the Special Committee for Oceanic Research (SCOR) and intergovernmental planning through UNESCO's Intergovernmental Oceanographic Commission (IOC). The National Academy of Sciences serves as a communication medium with SCOR. The State Department that has responsibility for developing a U.S. position in the IOC has delegated that function to an international panel of the Federal Council's Interagency Committee on Oceanography.

As reported in annual reports of the Interagency Committee on Oceanography of the Federal Council for Science and Technology, the funding of the IIOE by the participating agencies has been as follows:

[In thousands of dollars]

	Actual, fiscal year 1962	Actual, fiscal year 1963	Actual, fiscal year 1964	Estimated, fiscal year 1965	Estimated, fiscal year 1966
Department of the Navy	580	1,300	803	250	—
Coast and Geodetic Survey, Department of Commerce	—	—	125	75	—
Bureau of Commercial Fisheries, Department of the Interior	—	102	154	154	125
National Science Foundation	1,394	4,400	4,900	3,500	1,400
International Indian Ocean Expedition total	1,974	5,802	5,982	3,979	1,525

The U.S. contribution amounts to approximately one-third of the total and has entailed approximately 14 cruises to the area; $550,000 of the $1.4 million budgeted by the National Science Foundation for fiscal year 1966 is for air-sea interaction and is also reported to the Interdepartmental Committee on Atmospheric Sciences for inclusion in the national atmospheric sciences program. The NSF also requested and received approval to activate and refit the mothballed Presidential yacht *Williamsburg*, with operations through a contract with Woods Hole Oceanographic Institution. Renamed *Anton Brun*, the ship served mainly as a center for biological research during IIOE; its future disposition is as yet undetermined.

Just how the Foundation coordinates the efforts of the various agencies involved in the program is not clear from the record. Nor is it clear what the coordinating function is of the Interagency Committee on Oceanography which has been assigned the responsibility for coordinating the entire Federal oceanographic effort—one aspect of which is the International Indian Ocean Expedition.

Field operations for the expedition are expected to be phased out in fiscal year 1966; subsequent activity will involve processing the vast amount of data obtained. Scientists participating in the program, however, are expected to seek support for continuation of their research programs through NSF project grants or contracts with other Federal agencies. How such a transition is effected is not clear.

g. *United States Japan cooperative science program*

The United States–Japan cooperative science program was established in fiscal year 1963 in response to agreements reached between President Kennedy and Premier Hayato Ikeda in June 1961 for increased cooperation between the two countries. The agreements were announced in a joint communique of June 22, 1961, following talks between the two leaders during a visit of the Japanese Premier to the United States. According to the agreement,

> . . . The President and the Prime Minister also recognized the importance of broadening educational, cultural, and scientific cooperation between the two countries. They therefore agreed to form two United States-Japan committees, one to study expanded cultural and educational cooperation between the two countries, and the other to seek ways to strengthen scientific cooperation.

Under this program, recommendations for cooperative projects to be undertaken are made by a United States–Japan Committee on Scientific Cooperation established by the Secretary of State of the United States and the Foreign Minister of Japan. Because the joint Committee is not an administrative body, the Department of State requested the National Science Foundation to coordinate the scientific interests of the United States toward implementation of recommended research projects. As coordinator, the Foundation (1) evaluates and verifies the desirability and practicality of U.S. participation in proposed projects; (2) provides funds for support of projects which fall within its jurisdiction; and (3) provides funds to support projects in which other Federal agencies have an interest until they can assume the costs out of their own budgets.

The Pacific Science Board of the National Academy of Sciences and a number of individual Academy members have been associated with different panels that provided advice on various aspects of the program.

Cooperative projects are being supported in the following areas as recommended by the Joint Committee:

1. Exchange of scholars in the sciences;
2. Exchange of scientific and technical information and materials;
3. Earth sciences of the Pacific area;

4. Animal and plant geography and ecology of the Pacific area;

5. Medical sciences;

6. Education in the sciences;

7. Hurricanes and typhoons.

As agreed by the administering agencies in both countries, the following criteria shall be applied to all proposals:

1. Program areas shall be those identified and recommended by the United States—Japan Committee on Scientific Cooperation, and projects selected for activation shall be confined to those areas;

2. The activity must be of high scientific quality and beneficial to science both in Japan and the United States, and the results available for general publication;

3. There will be participation by both Japanese and United States scientists, and each country will support the costs of its participants.

4. Cooperative projects should provide an effective and efficient mechanism for advancing science in both countries.

In calculating the contributions of each nation, items other than funds, such as equipment, apparatus, materials, outstanding research, or teaching ability, et cetera, may be considered. While contributions need not be equal for each specific project, the overall contribution by each country is expected to be equitable.

Obligations for the program to date are:

Fiscal year

1963	$717,000
1964	708,000
1965 (estimated)	700,000
1966 (estimated)	700,000

h. International Years of the Quiet Sun

On September 14, 1962, President Kennedy authorized U.S. participation in the International Year of the Quiet Sun and designated the National Science Foundation as the coordinating and funding agency. The program is an international cooperative effort in which scientists from more than 60 nations are studying aspects of the geophysical environment during a time of minimum solar disturbance. The data gathered are expected to be complementary to that gathered during the International Geophysical Year when there was unusually intense solar activity. It was agreed that the observation period would extend from January, 1964, through December 31, 1964. This has now been extended to 1967.

The IQSY program originated in a statement formulated by the NAS Geophysics Research Board's Panel for IQSY in February 1962 and transmitted to the National Science Foundation with the request that the Foundation seek approval of U.S. participation and develop fiscal support for the program within the Foundation.

During the summer of 1962 the Foundation began to receive specific proposals for suitable projects. A total of $1,021,000 was obligated for the program in fiscal year 1963; $3,665,000 in 1964; $3,500,000 was the estimated figure for 1965; $2,500,000 has been requested for fiscal year 1966 to be used for the final 6 months of the observations, for costs of terminating operations, and for data reduction and analysis. The final year of the program will be 1967; funding at the 1966 level will be required for completion of analysis and publication of results.

The U.S. program includes observations in the fields of meteorology, geomagnetism, aurora, airglow, ionospheric physics, solar physics, cosmic rays, and aeronomy. Stations of the Weather Bureau, the Central Radio Propagation Laboratory of the National Bureau of Standards, and the U.S. Coast and Geodetic Survey are involved in network activities. These agencies together with NASA, and Department of Defense research laboratories also undertake or sponsor research programs of relevance to the IQSY.

The year following the observation period, will be devoted to interpretation and evaluation of the observations secured.

i. Ocean sediment coring program (proposed fiscal year 1966)

The ocean sediment coring program is a new line item in the fiscal year 1966 budget for the National Science Foundation. A program extending over about 20 months is planned during which core samples from the sediments which comprise the upper part of the oceanic crust will be taken from various locations for study. It is hoped that the data will yield information concerning such scientific questions as the age of the ocean basins, a long record of the earth's climatic history, the origin, history, and structure of the Continental Shelf, and possibly the discovery of new mineral and petroleum resources. It appears that scientists proposing this activity anticipate that chartering and modifying an existing drilling vessel might be the best course of action, in the interest of speed and flexibility. While this program is now separate from Project Mohole, scientific objectives, hardware, and participants historically maintained an identity with Mohole.

The total cost of the proposed program including the chartering of an existing drilling vessel, including demobilization costs at the completion of the program would be about $1 million; operational cost would be about $4 million, based on an estimated 400 days at $10,000 per day. Other logistic costs are estimated to total $400,000.

At the end of the 20-month program the work will be reevaluated to determine whether it should be continued and whether the character of the operation should be changed.

j. International Upper Mantle Project

Another international program in which the United States is participating, along with some 32 other countries, is the International Upper Mantle Project. As was the case with a number of other international programs which the Foundation is supporting, the overall plans for U.S. participation in the project were prepared by the National Academy of Sciences-National Research Council, which then asked the National Science Foundation to obtain endorsement of the program.

The National Science Foundation in a letter of January 29, 1963, from the Director to the Special Assistant to the President for Science and Technology reviewed the project and recommended endorsement of U.S. participation in the program. The letter continued:

> . . . With such endorsement, and subject to appropriate program and budget review, the Foundation stands ready to support in fiscal year 1964 the estimated funds required for the university and non-profit laboratory effort in this program (up to $3 million), and to make arrangements with other appropriate agencies and the National Academy of Sciences for carrying out this program. It is proposed that other Government agencies participating in the program will provide within their own budget requests for the cost of agency activities which contribute to the program's objectives.

The Special Assistant to the President for Science and Technology, in a letter of April 17, 1963, to the Director of the National Science Foundation endorsed the "principle of U.S. participation in the upper mantle project because of its importance to worldwide advance in the field of geophysics" and named four agencies of the U.S. Government as having primary responsibility: "the Department of Interior through the Geological Survey, the Department of Commerce, through the Coast and Geodetic Survey, the Department of Defense, through the Advanced Research Projects Agency; and the National Science Foundation, through its extramural support of scientific research." He concluded:

> . . . I would appreciate your [National Science Foundation] taking the lead to set up a committee of representatives of these agencies to work out a coordinated interagency program and to serve as a focal point within the Government for discussion with the Geophysics Research Board.

The cost of the 3-year program for all agencies was estimated by the Foundation in January 1963 to be approximately $31 million. Foundation support for the project is derived from grant funds for basic research.

The Foundation's 14th annual report for 1964 discussed the International Upper Mantle Project along with other national research programs, at the same time pointing out that the project has not been formally recognized as a national research program.

> The international upper mantle project has most of the characteristics of a national research program although it has not been formally recognized as such. Its purpose is to determine the composition, structure, and dynamics of the crust and upper 1,000 kilometers of the mantle of the earth. It is an important region in that it presumably holds the secrets of mountain building, the origin of continents and oceans, the source of the earth's internal heat, the driving force for continental drift, and the causes of volcanoes and earthquakes; many primary ore deposits also originate here. The project includes the study of seismic waves generated by earthquakes and explosions, the variations of heat flow from the earth, the interpretation of the record of ancient magnetic fields as recorded in the rocks, the systematic study of the magnetic and gravity fields of the earth in special regions, the direct evidence from deep drilling, and the determination of the characteristics of earth materials under laboratory conditions simulating the high pressures and temperatures presumed to exist in the earth. This concerted worldwide field and laboratory attack on the largely unsolved fundamental problems in the earth sciences will extend through 1967. . . .

JAMES R. KERR

Congress and Space: Overview or Oversight?

Science and technology have been a concern of the federal government since the founding of the Republic. Government sponsored scientific re-

From *Public Administration Review*, vol. 25, no. 3 (September 1965), pp.185–92. Reprinted by permission of the publisher.

(The author wishes to acknowledge financial support from the Committee on Research in Public Affairs, Stanford University. This article is the outgrowth of research conducted during participation in the American Political Science Association's Congressional Fellowship Program, 1961–62.)

search, moreover, has increased tremendously to keep pace with the expansion of government functions. Government relied heavily upon the applied sciences in the development of the continent in the nineteenth century when national associations and organizations of scientists, not the federal government, provided the most dynamic initiative.[1] World War II changed this pattern drastically. Not only was the influence of private scientists upon national policy making greatly accelerated, but scientific and technical experts also began to fill roles in the highest circles of government. In the post-war world, the government continues to have a major responsibility for science and technology, becoming the primary direct and indirect user of scientific talent.[2]

The placing of scientists on important national advisory boards and within the Executive Branch is another significant trend since World War II. The dependence of government officials upon scientists, in fact, has made it impossible for the scientist in Washington to claim insulation from politics. Glenn T. Seaborg, Chairman of the Atomic Energy Commission, has written:

> The government has become increasingly dependent upon scientists for advice. This is true not only in the sphere of the administration of government science, but in a much more comprehensive way. Any evaluation of the future of the economy must embrace scientific and technological knowledge. Decisions in military matters are intimately involved with science and technology. And any commitment of portions of our national resources for science and technology themselves must be decided with the help of men of wide knowledge in these fields.[3]

Involvement of scientists in national policy making is not intrinsically different from the participation of other experts in the policy making process. Scientists, like other experts, will not always agree with one another and the non-expert official may have to choose between conflicting scientific or technical advice. Like all experts, scientists will have predispositions about the solution of policy problems. Thus the individual seeking advice will have to identify consciously and guard against the intrusion of scientific biases and predilections. Assuming that administrators and scientists both want to enhance the role of scientific counsel, the major problem is developing the most advantageous arrangements for integrating the

1. Don K. Price, *Government and Science* (New York: New York University Press, 1954), p. 18.
2. Carl F. Stover, *The Government of Science* (Santa Barbara, California: Center for the Study of Democratic Institutions, 1962), pp. 13–14.
3. Glenn T. Seaborg, "Science and Freedom," *Air Force and Space Digest*, XLV, No. 3 (March, 1962), 56.

scientist into the policy making machinery as consultant, advisor, or official without debasing the coinage of his own expertise.[4]

POLICY INVOLVEMENT OF SCIENTISTS

The degree of involvement of scientists in the policy process can be divided into four levels of participation. First level: the scientist may identify, define, and collect the facts for the solution of a technical problem. Second level: he can provide habits of orderly thought and appreciation of variables which will produce comprehensive answers to technical problems. Third level: he can use scientific research to improve the process of decision making. Fourth level: he may actively and sympathetically participate in the political, that is, policy-making process.

Scientists now participate at all four levels. While their participation is prominent and straight-forward at the first level through membership on advisory panels, it is somewhat ambiguous at the fourth level. American teams negotiating for the nuclear test ban, for example, have been composed of both scientists and diplomats. Until scientists reached agreement on certain technical matters, the diplomats could not even begin useful talks. Thus, scientists involved in high policy making cannot restrict themselves to providing technical information. They will take part in the discussion and debate of policy issues and will take sides on these issues. The scientist, on his part, must make clear when he speaks as a concerned private citizen and when he speaks as a technical expert. The Pauling-Teller debates over nuclear testing clearly indicate that when scientists give way to special pleading, they tend to abandon scientific reserve and suspended judgment. Non-scientists, by the same token, must recognize that scientists cannot be expected to be politically indifferent to the policy issues with which they are concerned. Many scientists appreciate these realities and urge all scientists to be aware of the role and limitations of the advisor.[5]

CAN CONGRESS BE BOSS?

The U.S. Congress has not remained unaffected by the growth and importance of government science. Congressional interest in science on a somewhat regularized basis is reflected by the creation of the House Committee on Science and Astronautics, the Senate Committee on Aeronautical and

4. See particularly Warner R. Schilling, "Scientists, Foreign Policy, and Politics," *American Political Science Review*, LVI, No. 2 (June, 1962), 287–300.
5. Bentley Glass, "Scientists in Politics," *Bulletin of the Atomic Scientists*, XVIII, No. 5 (May, 1962), 6.

Space Sciences, and the Joint Committee on Atomic Energy. Yet despite the growth of government involvement and support of science activities, Congress finds itself conspicuously lacking in counsel on questions requiring scientific or technical judgment. Though the Soviet Union's satellite Sputnik brought science into the inner councils of the President, through the creation of the post of Special Assistant for Science and Technology, no comparable staff aid was created for Congress.

Executive privilege has made it difficult if not impossible for congressional committees to get comprehensive testimony from government science advisors on national science policies. Since this information is possessed by officials in the Executive Office of the President or by presidential advisory panels, Congress is denied the benefit of their advice. The President's science advisors, no matter how well qualified, cannot establish or conduct programs to coordinate federal science activities. This responsibility rests with Congress. Yet Congress finds itself unable to get comprehensive testimony in order to evaluate the organization, scope, and direction of government science.[6]

The establishment of the national space program was initially a problem of governmental organization. Formulation of the broad policy goals and administrative set-up was the product of elected officials aided by their staffs, lawyers, and government scientists. The heavily funded space program not only competes with other federal programs for appropriations and scientific talent, it also has important ramifications upon international relations, arms control, and the national economy. What role can Congress play in evaluating and reviewing the space program?

One of the facts of contemporary legislative policy making is that Congress relies more and more upon the advice and testimony of political executives and their expert advisors. The space program is an excellent example. Faced with the rapid expansion, the breadth and technicality of the program, it is a question whether the Congressman actually exercises meaningful scrutiny over the experts. Many members of the House Space Committee, in fact, admit that to a great extent they accept space programs at face value or even on faith.

James Burnham asserts that in cases like defense and space Congress cannot comprehend the myriad technical problems involved and thus cannot control their solution. Votes on the array of military and astronautical equipment are necessarily blind.[7] This does not mean that Congress has no viable role to play in reviewing technical programs. Burnham

6. U.S., *Congressional Record*, 87th Cong., 2d Sess., March 12, 1962, CVIII, 3517 (daily ed.).
7. James Burnham, *Congress and the American Tradition* (Chicago: Henry Regnery Co., 1959), p. 348.

suggests that Congress does have a real, albeit limited, role to play in passing judgment on the race to the moon:

> Congress as a collective body cannot possibly understand the detailed technical problems of setting up installations on the moon . . . But . . . literate adults should be able to form a reasonably qualified opinion on the desirability of a moon installation in terms of the nation's needs, security, and resources; on the cost range, and the nation's ability to pay costs of that order; and what sort of agency—military, civilian, international—ought to carry the project out, if it is attempted.[8]

How can Congress prove that it is boss? The power of the purse immediately comes to mind. Yet since its creation, the National Aeronautics and Space Administration (NASA) has been authorized and appropriated virtually all the funds it has requested.[9]

In the House, the role of "watchdog" of the space program is assigned to the Committee on Science and Astronautics, commonly called the Space Committee. This committee exercises the most continuous and detailed review of the space program of any committee in Congress. One basis of the committee's authority stems from a congressional distinction between authorization of funds and appropriation of funds. A statutory provision requires that no appropriation to NASA be made without prior legislative authorization. This requirement means that *every year* NASA must defend its budget before both authorizing and appropriating committees in House and Senate. Only a very few other federal programs, notably foreign aid and procurement of aircraft, missiles, and naval vessels, require annual authorization.

ASKING THE RIGHT QUESTIONS

There are three principal types of questions which can be raised in considering the space budget. First, there are questions of policy which concern how far and how fast the United States wishes to commit itself to the exploration of space. Second, there are administrative or organizational questions relating to what agencies should contribute to accomplishment of the space goals and how heavy and how broad their respective responsibilities should be. A third group of questions is concerned with technical matters, such as the physical equipment and techniques employed to carry out specific programs.

The most basic policy question is why the United States wants to place

8. *Ibid.*, 190.
9. See James R. Kerr, *Congressmen as Overseers: Surveilance of the Space Program.* Unpublished Ph.D. dissertation, Stanford University, 1963, pp. 371–420.

a man on the moon. Since President Kennedy committed the nation to accomplishing this objective by 1970, the question really becomes—do we want to reach the moon before the Russians? The answer is yes since we feel that our reputation for leadership in science and technology and national prestige is at stake.[10] A sticky policy question concerns the possibility of exploration of space for strictly peaceful purposes. Another major policy question asks how broad and deep the government's responsibility for scientific research and development should be and what priorities should exist among government programs.

The second category of questions concerns administrative problems. As the space program broadens, more agencies have participated in space activities. Is the United States making optimum use of the resources of corporations, universities, and government agencies? A further question is what role, if any, the Department of Defense ought to play in the exploration of space.

A third group of questions raises technical issues. In the spring of 1962, there were several lively technical issues. It had not been resolved whether the astronauts would use a huge rocket to reach the moon by direct ascent or would attempt rendezvous, the joining of two orbiting satellites before flight to the moon. Another technical issue was whether the U.S. should build an orbiting manned space platform before attempting manned lunar exploration. Still another issue concerned the need for expediting nuclear propulsion research as opposed to more conventional forms of space propulsion.

Liquid v. Solid Fuel, 1962—A Balanced Research Program?
The technical issue which the Space Committee showed greatest interest in, however, was whether NASA was carrying out a balanced program of liquid and solid propulsion research and development. The committee asked NASA to conduct parallel programs so that it could resolve conclusively the dispute over the potential of the two kinds of fuel for extended space missions. There was no consensus within the committee on this question in mid-1962. Of seventeen members questioned, eight felt that more attention should be given to solids.[11] Seven members felt that

10. See Vernon Van Dyke, *Pride and Power: The Rationale of the Space Program* (Urbana, Illinois: University of Illinois Press, 1964) and Gabriel A. Almond, "Public Opinion and the Development of Space Technology: 1957–60," in Joseph M. Goldsen, ed., *Outer Space in World Politics* (New York: Frederick A. Praeger, 1963), pp. 71–96.
11. Interviews with members and staff of the House Committee on Science and Astronautics and NASA officials were conducted during spring and summer 1962. One of the ground rules was that quotations would not be attributed directly to the speaker.

the space agency programs were balanced and two were undecided. Partisan affiliation had no bearing on the division. The strongest indictment of NASA's failure to explore solid propulsion came from a Democrat:

> I must confess that I am sorry that NASA has not moved into the solid field because I'd prefer to see NASA do it rather than the Air Force. But NASA's dominated by liquid fuel people . . . An Agency may get a program to which it is not psychologically oriented, like the solid booster program, and then it will not develop it properly.

Another Democrat stressed that in spite of the committee's directive that NASA explore solid propulsion more fully, NASA would spend its money as it wanted to:

> I wasn't a solid booster enthusiast at first. Last year we increased the solid budget considerably. But you can't make the boys do it; they have their minds made up and that's it. You can't make them spend it as the committee may want it spent.

Committee interest in solid propulsion was aroused in the spring of 1961. Several industry witnesses expressed the belief that the potential of solid fuels had been only incompletely explored by NASA. Dr. Arch C. Scurlock, President of Atlantic Research Corporation, reported:

> Solid propellant systems offer tremendous potential toward achieving low cost, high reliability, and unmatched simplicity for first stage propulsion of space vehicles." [12]

The upshot of the testimony was that solid propulsion offered a cheaper, simpler, and faster means of getting to the moon than the liquid propulsion system which NASA planned to use. Solids, the witnesses claimed, could cut *two years* off the liquid propulsion time schedule for Project Apollo!

Since NASA had initially requested only $3 million for Fiscal Year (FY) 1962 and later said it could use $15 million more, stepping up solid funding to $50 million might be excessive although several witnesses had recommended that sum. That sum, nevertheless, would have been far less than the $130 million which NASA had allocated for liquid fuel research.

The result of committee study was an increase of solid research funds from $3.1 million to $18 million. The Senate authorized only the initial

12. U.S., Congress, House, Committee on Science and Astronautics, *Hearings, on H.R. 3238 & H.R. 6029, 1962 NASA Authorization*, Part 2, 87th Cong., 1st Sess., 1961, p. 769.

$3.1 million but in conference this sum was raised to $10.2 million.[13] A committee report expressed the conviction that these funds would enable the United States to make use of:

> . . . the high reliability, simplicity, and economy which are intrinsic to solid-propellant engines . . . The proposed program will aim at improvement in the general state of the art of solid rockets with emphasis on application of the performance, reliability, and logistic advantages of solid rockets for NASA missions.[14]

The committee hoped that NASA could resolve the controversy over the potential of solids during the following year. Yet a year later, testimony revealed that NASA had transferred its $10 million for solid research to the Air Force. Still more disconcerting was the fact that evaluation of solids was still indefinite, tentative, and unresolved!

Liquid v. Solid Fuel, 1963—Uncertainties Prolonged, Predilections Reinforced

During the authorization hearings on the FY 1963 budget, the Subcommittee on Advanced Research and Technology gathered extensive testimony in order to determine what had been learned about solid versus liquid propulsion. Whether a NASA official, an Air Force general, a university professor, or an industry scientist, each witness was asked for his opinion on the relative merits of the two kinds of rocket fuel. Usually, the subcommittee received tentative or qualified answers since most witnesses felt that the optimum combination of fuels could only be determined in specific cases, not in the abstract.[15]

Congressman Corman (Dem-Calif) feared that the committee was hearing testimony from witnesses who were either biased for or against solids.[16] Chairman Anfuso (Dem-NY) suggested that Dr. Maurice Zucrow, a propulsion expert from Purdue University, would provide a disinterested evaluation. Zucrow thought that the liquid booster had an inherent advantage because it could be brought back to earth and reused repeatedly.[17] Later he pointed out several drawbacks of solids.

13. U.S., Congress, Committee of Conference, *Authorizing Appropriations to the National Aeronautics and Space Administration,* 87th Cong., 1st Sess., 1961, H. Rept. 742, p. 4.
14. U.S., Congress, House Committee on Science and Astronautics, *Authorizing Appropriations to the National Aeronautics and Space Administration,* 87th Cong., 1st Sess., 1961, H. Rept. 391, p. 38.
15. U.S., Congress, House Subcommittee on Advanced Research and Technology of the Committee on Science and Astronautics, *Hearings on H.R. 10100, 1963 NASA Authorization,* Part 3, 87th Cong., 2d Sess., 1962, p. 1294.
16. *Ibid.,* 1305.
17. *Ibid.,* 1554.

> . . . a solid propellant rocket engine has two serious drawbacks.
> First, you can stop it, but you can't restart it. Second, it gives one
> burning rate at one temperature and a different burning rate at a
> different temperature . . .[18]

He also felt that it would take at least three years to produce a solid
motor producing twenty million pounds of thrust—one should discount
the optimism of the industrial protagonists. Cost estimates of developing
such a rocket were misleading since they did not necessarily include the
expense of building large propellant mixing plants and testing facilities.

A NASA witness compounded the uncertainty when he observed:

> Development of flight stages with either solid or liquid motors are
> certainly on comparable time scales and when laid side by side, the
> uncertainties of program timing of either the solid or liquid stages
> overlap.[19]

Congressman King (Dem-Utah) strenuously objected, pointing out that
leading scientists at the Jet Propulsion Laboratory had recommended
greater emphasis on solid fuels. Asked King: "Certainly it is no secret that
many of them are completely sold on solid fuel. Do they see in the development of solid fuel a promise of a great new horizon?" [20] The NASA
official answered: "Yes; I think some of them do." [21]

While NASA witnesses continued to question the exaggerated optimism
about solids, the subcommittee called upon a number of industry witnesses to present their case. Each indicated his disappointment at the failure to explore solid propulsion fully. Dr. Lyman G. Bonner, Hercules
Powder Company, said that current knowledge of the burning rate of solid
propellants made them just as desirable as liquid propellants for any space
mission.[22] When Anfuso raised the question of vector control, Bonner
assured him that this problem had been solved. Solid rockets could be
steered by means of the injection of fluid into the nozzle from the throat
of the rocket. He was more tentative about cost estimates:

> The funding requirements are, of course, difficult to imagine . . .
> We can estimate . . . the cost of development assuming that we
> have defined correctly the mission . . . what we do have trouble
> estimating is the cost of the qualifications testing since it is not
> clearly defined . . . our current estimate . . . is approximately
> $275 million.[23]

18. *Ibid.,* 1558.
19. *Ibid.,* 1305.
20. *Ibid.,* 1306.
21. *Ibid.*
22. *Ibid.,* 1659.
23. *Ibid.,* 1656–7.

Testimony of G. P. Sutton, North American Aviation, was particularly interesting since its Rocketdyne division was involved in both liquid and solid propulsion. Sutton commended NASA's decision to use liquids:

> I furthermore believe that it provides a very timely course of action by which our Nation can meet its space goals within this decade at a reasonable cost with a high degree of safety for launching of manned spacecraft. I think even if we started another engine program today we probably couldn't overtake the F-1, which is pretty far along.[24]

What level of funding would be necessary to develop a parallel solid booster program? Sutton replied: ". . . roughly comparable." [25]

What did the committee learn from this testimony? Government and industry scientists presented conflicting evaluations of the potential of solids. NASA remained skeptical of solids while stoutly defending its commitment to liquid propulsion. Industrial witnesses who had a direct interest in promoting solids decried the failure to develop them. They did not simply make unsupported assertions but were armed with the results of actual demonstrations and testing of solid rocket motors. The testimony largely repeated what the committee had heard a year earlier. The uncertainties of committee members were prolonged and their predilections reinforced. Members who favored more solid research still believed that they deserved further study; those who were indifferent to the issue remained so; members who felt NASA was conducting a balanced program maintained that opinion. A staff member concluded:

> The committee goes over and over this question. What have you learned, they ask. What is new? But they don't really know what to do on liquids and solids. Both views continue to be expressed. The committee doesn't agree.

Technicalities, Attitudes, and Rational Considerations

Many problems complicate congressional review of propulsion technology in particular and the space program in general. Members frequently complained that they lacked guidelines or experience with the space program since it was a new, uncharted field. NASA officials, moreover, could often provide only informed guesses rather than firm estimates of program costs. The "homework" problem was mentioned repeatedly. Congressmen, after all, have many competing claims on their time and are only part-time overseers. The space program taxes the most conscientious. They are deluged with information about space activities, yet are lacking in concise, critical information on these programs.

24. *Ibid.*, 1723.
25. *Ibid.*, 1724.

The technicality of the subject matter often proved a barrier to understanding. Lack of technical staff assistance in making an initial review was sorely felt. When scientific experts disagreed on a course of action, the plight of the committee became still more difficult. Members could resort to common sense evaluation or simply support the witness whom they intuitively had confidence in. Since there were no adversary proceedings, it was not a matter of choosing between conflicting viewpoints. Witnesses were not objective. Virtually all were committed to an expanding program—their testimony always had a "pitch." How could the committee reconcile the over-enthusiasm of industry witnesses and the conservatism of NASA officials and arrive at a fair evaluation of the potential of solid fuels? The difficulty of weighing the testimony and discounting bias is illustrated by the thoughtful remarks of one member:

> Something we must consider is the pressure, the economic interests, the commercial giants . . . The committee must see through the power struggle in the missiles industry, through the competition of interests because congressmen are also subject to these pressures . . . We are both partisan (for our districts) and judge (for the nation) at the same time . . . Maybe this is inconsistent but that's the way it is. We must see through the pressures, pressures that exist even in NASA too. We have to discount partisanship and get testimony from other witnesses, balance it, and then evaluate conflicting testimony.

Committee interest in solid propulsion did enable industry to present its case before a national forum. It required NASA to make a detailed justification of its commitment to liquids. Committee interest was triggered largely by Congressman King. The role of advocate for local industry enabled him to represent his district's industries aggressively and, more importantly, bring the issue out into the open. An official suggested that the committee's attention caused an Executive Branch study group to expand its review of liquid and solid propulsion from two to seven months. A NASA official remarked: "King reflects strong lobbying by several contractors but this does not do any harm." Congressman Corman offered this frank analysis:

> . . . all members of the . . .committee are trained scientists.
> . . . we use our training to formulate . . . new scientific theory.
> . . . I have developed the theory that liquid propellants are the best bet for our rockets. . . . the people of my district agree with my theory, and they know something about this matter because there is a large liquid propellant . . . plant in my district.
> . . . David King . . . has developed a theory that solid propellants are the answer. . . . the people of his district agree with his

theory, possibly because there is a large solid propellant research . . . operation . . . there. Because . . . the answer is not certain . . . the Space Committee has done the wise thing by authorizing money for further studies of both. . . . Just the other day, however, a man . . . showed us some propellant . . . about the consistency of toothpaste, sort of halfway between liquid and solid. . . . it was very fortunate for the taxpayers. . . . that this man did not come from the district of any member of the committee, because all of us theoretical scientists were able to see immediately that his project was not really scientifically workable.[26]

Clearly, congressional attitudes toward the space program are influenced more by politics and conventional interpretations of reality than by engineering facts.

The committee has not resolved the issue which it raised. It showed that the liquid-solid propulsion decision is not simply a technical matter, but requires compromise in terms of time, money, scientific and engineering resources, and unanswered technical problems.

NASA did not pursue parallel programs.[27] Concerning the purported transfer of $10 million for solid propulsion from NASA to the Air Force, no transfer occurred. While $10 million was *authorized* for this purpose, somewhat less was appropriated. "Accordingly one of the budget reductions made was the elimination of the additional $10 million for solid rockets," NASA reported.[28] NASA also delegated responsibility for developing large solid rocket motors to the Air Force which had spent only $18 million of $50 million earmarked for solid propulsion in FY 1962.[29]

One might surmise that the Bureau of the Budget would be better equipped than the committee to determine how much should be spent on space propulsion. The responsibility of putting together the President's budget is staggering and perplexing not only because of its size and complexity but also because of the fact that dollar allocations reflect priorities among federal programs where no objective method of comparison is possible. Aaron Wildavsky reports that "Some officials do not deal with complexity at all; they are just overwhelmed and never quite recover. Others work terribly hard at mastering their subjects." [30]

Agencies would be more likely to deal candidly with the Budget Bureau

26. *The Washington Post,* April 1, 1962, p. E1.
27. NASA requested $163,100,000 for liquid propulsion and $7,900,000 for solid propulsion technology for FY 1963.
28. Subcommittee on Advanced Research and Technology of the Committee on Science and Astronautics, *Hearings,* 1962, p. 1264.
29. *Ibid.,* 1507.
30. Aaron Wildavsky, *The Politics of the Budgetary Process* (Boston: Little, Brown & Co., 1964), p. 11.

if they were certain to receive the amount recommended by the Bureau. Three quarters of the time, however, Budget Bureau estimates are reduced by Congress.[31] The Budget Bureau, therefore, usually recommends the upper limit of what Congress will accept.

Lacking presidential concern, the Bureau does attempt to determine how desirable a program is on the basis of intrinsic merit, yet objective rational criteria often cannot be used. In many cases, work load analyses and cost-benefit ratios do not exist. Judgment is not based on reasonable evaluation because political actualities intrude upon the process. Congressional predisposition, historical development, stress on agreement, even arbitrary ceilings all limit rational calculation.[32]

PRESENT EFFICACY OF LEGISLATIVE REVIEW

In trying to resolve the liquid-solid controversy, the committee labored under particularly acute handicaps. At times, the committee was constrained to admit the difficulty of understanding technical presentations. During a discussion of wind tunnels, Congressman Mosher (Rep-Ohio) confessed: "I don't feel I can ask an intelligent question because I am beyond my depth." [33] Congressman Corman later remarked:

> I am overwhelmed by the large figures we go through in the budget. I wonder . . . how much detailed analysis goes into arriving at figures . . . We might take a relatively small and simple one . . . For instance . . . you are asking for $25,000 for grading, parking lots, and roads . . . I am wondering how much effort you have to put into it to arrive at these figures . . .[34]

If comprehensive understanding is impossible, it seems entirely rational for members to seek refuge in evaluating the simple which is within their grasp. It is no surprise, therefore, that simple items are more difficult to justify than much larger, complex ones.

The efficacy of legislative review of technical programs such as space propulsion is very limited. Congress is confronted with the overwhelming superiority of the Executive Branch in the compilation and assessment of information about these programs. Without an expert staff to act as a counterforce or interpretative data to reassess executive decisions, the committee had to accept much on faith and had to bow to the priority of liquid over solid propulsion. Clearly (1) an expert staff, (2) a system of

31. *Ibid.,* 40.
32. *Ibid.,* 47.
33. Subcommittee on Advanced Research and Technology of the Committee on Science and Astronautics, *Hearings,* 1962, p. 1587.
34. *Ibid.,* 1588.

consultants, or (3) contract research studies would enhance congressional appraisal of scientific programs. The committee could make use of a "devil's advocate" who would be responsible for preparing a reasoned case against new programs. This would sharpen many facets of the programs, balance out prejudices of the witnesses, and prevent waste of public funds.[35]

The role of the congressman as judge is difficult, if not impossible, to perform. A member's viewpoint is determined by a complex of testimony, intuition, and predisposition. The liquid-solid debate demonstrated that NASA may refuse to comply with a committee recommendation on a technical question because NASA believes it is better qualified to pass judgment on such matters.

35. See especially James B. Conant, *Modern Science and Modern Man* (New York: Doubleday & Co., 1952), pp. 115–18.

III
THE MANAGEMENT OF RESEARCH
AND DEVELOPMENT

The advent of the scientific revolution has been accompanied by the general acceptance in the United States of a new concept of the appropriate role of government in society. This acceptance has been reflected in the significant expansion of the peacetime budget from prewar levels. Part of the expansion, of course, is attributable to the influence of the Cold War on governmental spending, but it would be a mistake to explain the extension of public services in this country solely as a reaction to international tensions.

Federal government appropriations for research and development have reached 15 per cent of the annual budget. Completely new systems of allocation and control have been instituted in an endeavor to make the most effective use of these funds; and yet budgeting and contracting for science remains one of the most criticized functions in the entire political process.

A review undertaken at the request of President Kennedy by the Bureau of the Budget, with the participation of the Secretary of Defense, the Chairman of the Atomic Energy Commission, the Chairman of the Civil Service Commission, the Administrator of the National Aeronautics and Space Administration, the Director of the National Science Foundation, and the Special Assistant to the President for Science and Technology, provides an enlightening view of the highly complex partnership that has developed between public and private segments of our society. It is this type of arrangement that prompted President Eisenhower to warn of the potential power of a vast military-industrial coalition. The special problems of possible conflicts of interests, arising from the government's relying on various advisers and consultants, are especially pronounced with decisions that are scientific and technological.

191

In examining the science and development programs administered by the Department of Defense, which account for the largest single portion of the federal research budget, Burton H. Klein finds the policy considerations involved to be not only complex but often contradictory. One of the questions he raises is whether the incentives provided in defense contracts are strong enough to make a real difference in the way contractors behave. In fact, the entire set of long-established rules of the research and development game in the Department of Defense, which Klein describes with some dismay, make the reader wonder how it is ever possible to arrive at an objective decision.

Klaus Knorr and Oskar Morgenstern pursue the inquiry further by questioning the basic management policies of military research and development. The military services do not give adequate inspiration and direction to the scientists and engineers working on government projects, they observe, and an even more serious problem exists in that the over-all organization is not sufficiently conducive to the assertion and survival of new ideas. The authors of this essay call for the defense establishment to raise its sights and include political, sociological, and psychological elements in military research, so that it may include the examination of how wars can be avoided as well as won.

Report to the President on Government Contracting for Research and Development

This report has been prepared in response to the President's letter of July 31, 1961, to the Director of the Bureau of the Budget, asking for a review of the use of Government contracts with private institutions and enterprises to obtain scientific and technical work needed for public purposes.

Such contracts have been used extensively since the end of World War II to provide for the operation and management of research and development facilities and programs, for analytical studies and advisory services, and for technical supervision of complex systems, as well as for the conduct of research and development projects.

As the President noted in his letter, there is a consensus that the use of contracts is appropriate in many cases. At the same time, a number of important issues have been raised, including the appropriate extent of reliance on contractors, the comparative salaries paid by contractors and the Government, the effect of extensive contracting on the Government's own research and development capabilities, and the extent to which contracts may have been used to avoid limitations which exist on direct Federal operations.

Accordingly, the President asked that the review focus on:

> criteria that should be used in determining whether to perform a function through a contractor or through direct Federal operations;

> actions needed to increase the Government's ability to review contractor operations and to perform scientific and technical work; and

> policies which should be followed by the Government in obtaining maximum efficiency from contractor operations and in reviewing contractor performance and costs (including standards for salaries, fees, and other items).

· · ·

From *Hearings on Systems Development and Management,* House Committee on Government Operations, 87th Cong., 2d Sess., 1962.

Part 1
Statement of Major Issues

Policy questions relating to Government contracting for research and development must be considered in the perspective of the phenomenal growth, diversity, and change in Federal activities in this field.

FEDERAL RESEARCH AND DEVELOPMENT ACTIVITIES AND THEIR
IMPACT

Prior to World War II, the total Federal research and development program is estimated to have cost annually about 100 million dollars. In the fiscal year 1950, total Federal research and development expenditures were about 1.1 billion dollars. In the fiscal year 1963, the total is expected to reach 12.4 billion dollars.

The fundamental reason for this growth in expenditures has been the importance of scientific and technical work to the achievement of major public purposes. Since World War II the national defense effort has rested more and more on the search for new technology. Our military posture has come to depend less on production capacity in being and more on the race for shorter lead times in the development and deployment of new weapons systems and of counter-measures against similar systems in the hands of potential enemies. The Defense Department alone is expected to spend 7.1 billion dollars on research and development in fiscal 1963, and the Atomic Energy Commission another 1.4 billion dollars.

Aside from the national defense, science and technology are of increasing significance to many other Federal programs. The Nation's effort in non-military space exploration—which is virtually entirely a research and development effort—is growing extremely rapidly; the National Aeronautics and Space Administration is expected to spend 2.4 billion dollars in fiscal 1963, and additional sums related to the national space program will be spent by the Department of Commerce and other agencies. Moreover, scientific and technological efforts are of major significance in agriculture, health, natural resources, and many other Federal programs.

The end of this period of rapid growth is not yet in sight. Public purposes will continue to require larger and larger scientific and technological efforts for as far ahead as we can see.

The increase in Federal expenditures for research and development has had an enormous impact on the Nation's scientific and technical resources. It is not too much to say that the major initiative and responsibility for promoting and financing research and development have in many important areas been shifted from private enterprise (including academic as well as business institutions) to the Federal Government. Prior to World War II, the great bulk of the Nation's research achievements occurred with little support from Federal funds—although there were notable exceptions, such as in the field of agriculture. Today it is estimated by the National Science Foundation that the Federal Budget finances about 65 per cent of the total national expenditure for research and development. Moreover, the Federal share is rising.

Federal financing, however, does not necessarily imply Federal operation. As the Federal research and development effort has risen, there has been a steady reduction in the proportion conducted through direct Federal operations. Today about 80 per cent of Federal expenditures for research and development are made through non-Federal institutions. Furthermore, while a major finding of this report is that the Government's capabilities for direct operations in research and development need to be substantially strengthened, there is no doubt that the Government must continue to rely on the private sector for the major share of the scientific and technical work which it requires.

The effects of the extraordinary increase in Federal expenditures for research and development, and the increasing reliance on the private sector to perform such work, have been very far reaching.

The impact on private industry has been striking. In the past the Government utilized profit-making industry mainly for production engineering and the manufacture of final products—not for research and development. Industries with which it dealt in securing the bulk of its equipment were primarily the traditional large manufacturers for the civilian economy —such as the automotive, machinery, shipbuilding, steel, and oil industries—which relied on the Government for only a portion, usually a minority, of their sales and revenues. In the current scientific age, the old industries have declined in prominence in the advanced equipment area and newer research and development-oriented industries have come to the fore—such as those dealing in aircraft, rockets, electronics, and atomic energy.

There are significant differences between these newer industries and others. While the older industries were organized along mass-production principles, and used large numbers of production workers, the newer ones show roughly a one-to-one ration between production workers and scientist-engineers. Moreover, the proportion of production workers is steadily declining. Between 1954 and 1959, production workers in the aircraft industry declined 17 per cent while engineers and scientists increased 96 per cent. Also, while the average ratio of research and development expenditures to sales in all industry is about 3 per cent, the advanced weapons industry averages about 20 per cent and the aerospace industry averages about 31 per cent.

But the most striking difference is the reliance of the newer industries almost entirely on Government sales for their business. In 1958, a reasonably representative year, in an older industry, the automotive industry, military sales ranged from 5 per cent for General Motors to 15 per cent for Chrysler. In the same year in the aircraft industry, military sales ranged from a low of 67 per cent for Beech Aircraft to a high of 99.2 per cent for The Martin Company.

The present situation, therefore, is one in which a large group of economically significant and technologically advanced industries depend for their existence and growth not on the open competitive market of traditional economic theory, but on sales only to the United States Government. And, moreover, companies in these industries have the strongest incentives to seek contracts for research and development work which will give them both the know-how and the preferred position to seek later follow-on production contracts.

The rapid increase in Federal research and development expenditures has had striking effects on other institutions in our society apart from private industry.

There has been a major impact on the universities. The Nation has always depended largely on the universities for carrying out fundamental research. As such work has become more important to Government and more expensive, an increasing share—particularly in the physical and life sciences and engineering—has been supported by Federal funds. The total impact on a university can be sizeable. Well over half of the research budgets of such universities as Harvard, Brown, Columbia, Massachusetts Institute of Technology, Stanford, California Institute of Technology, University of Illinois, New York University, and Princeton, for illustration, are supported by Federal funds.

New institutional arrangements have been established in many cases, related to but organized separately from the universities, in order to respond to the needs of the Federal Government. Thus, the Lincoln Laboratory of the Massachusetts Institute of Technology was established by contract with the Air Force to supply research and development services and to establish systems concepts for the continental air defense, and similarly the Jet Propulsion Laboratory was established at the California Institute of Technology to conduct research on rocket propulsion for the Department of the Army and later to supply space craft design and systems engineering services to the National Aeronautics and Space Administration. In addition, other research institutions—such as the Stanford Research Institute—which were established to conduct research on contract for private or public customers, now do a major share of their business with the Federal Government.

In addition to altering the traditional patterns of organization of private industry and the universities, the rise in Federal research and development expenditures has resulted in the creation of entirely new kinds of organizations.

One kind of organization is typified by the RAND Corporation, established immediately after World War II, to provide operations research and other analytical services by contract to the Air Force. A number of similar organizations have been established since, more or less modeled on RAND, to provide similar services to other governmental agencies.

A second new kind of organization is the private corporation, generally not-for-profit but sometimes profit, created to furnish the Government with "systems engineering and technical direction" and other professional services. The Aerospace Corporation, the MITRE Corporation, the Systems Development Corporation, and the Planning Research Corporation are illustrations.

A third new organizational arrangement was pioneered by the Office of Scientific Research and Development during World War II and used by the Atomic Energy Commission, which took over the war-time atomic energy laboratories and added others—all consisting of facilities and equipment owned by the Government but operated under contract by private organizations, either industrial companies or universities.

Apart from their impact on the institutions of our society, Federal needs in research and development are placing critical demands on the national pool of scientific and engineering talent. The National Science Foundation points out that the country's supply of scientists and engineers is increasing at the fairly stable rate of 6 per cent annually, while the number engaged in research and development activities is growing at about 10 per cent each year. Accordingly, the task of developing our manpower resources in sufficient quality and quantity to keep pace with the expanding research and development effort is a matter of great urgency. The competition for scientists and engineers is becoming keener all the time and requires urgent attention to the expansion of education and training, and to the efficient use of the scientific and technical personnel we have now.

QUESTIONS AND ISSUES CONSIDERED IN THIS REPORT

The dynamic character of the Nation's research and development efforts, as summarized in the preceding paragraphs, has given rise to a number of criticisms and points of concern. For example, concern has been expressed that the Government's ability to perform essential management functions has diminished because of an increasing dependence on contractors to determine policies of a technical nature and to exercise the type of management functions which Government itself should perform. Some have criticized the new not-for-profit contractors, performing systems engineering and technical direction work for the Government, on the grounds that they are intruding on traditional functions performed by competitive industry. Some concern has been expressed that universities are undertaking research and development programs of a nature and size which may interfere with their traditional educational functions. The cost-reimbursement type of contracts the Government uses, particularly with respect to research and development work on weapons and space systems, has been criticized as providing insufficient incentives to keep costs down and insure effective performance. Criticism has been leveled against relying so heavily on contractors to perform research and development work as simply a device for circumventing civil service rules and regulations.

Finally, the developments of recent years have inevitably blurred the traditional dividing lines between the public and private sectors of our Nation. A number of profound questions affecting the structure of our society are raised by our inability to apply the classical distinctions between what is public and what is private. For example, should a corporation created to provide services to Government and receiving 100 per cent of its financial support from Government be considered a "public" or a "private" agency? In what sense is a business corporation doing nearly 100 per cent of its business with the Government engaged in "free enterprise"?

In light of these criticisms and concerns, an appraisal of the experience in using contracts to accomplish the Government's research and development purposes is evidently timely. We have not, however, in the course of the present review attempted to treat the fundamental philosophical issues indicated in the preceding paragraph. We accept as desirable the present high degree of interdependence and collaboration between Government and private institutions. We believe the present intermingling of the public and private sectors is in the national interest because it affords the largest opportunity for initiative and the competition of ideas from all elements of the technical community. Consequently, it is our judgment that the present complex partnership between Government and private institutions should continue.

On these assumptions, the present report is intended to deal with the practical question: what should the Government do to make the partnership work better in the public interest and with maximum effectiveness and economy?

We deal principally with three aspects of this main question.

There is first the question, what aspects of the research and development effort should be contracted out? This question falls into two parts. One part relates to those crucial powers to manage and control governmental activities which must be retained in the hands of public officials directly answerable to the President and Congress. Are we in danger of contracting out such powers to private orgnizations? If so, what should be done about it?

The other part of this question relates to activities which do not have to be carried out by Government officials, but on which there is an option: they may be accomplished either by direct Government operations or by contract with non-Federal institutions. What are the criteria that should guide this choice? And if a private institution is chosen, what are the criteria for choice as among universities, not-for-profit corporations, profit corporations, or other possible contractors?

The second question we deal with is what standards and criteria should govern contract terms in cases where research and development is contracted out. For example, to what extent is competition effective in ensuring efficient performance at low cost, and when—if at all—must special rules be established to control fees, salaries paid, and other elements of contractor cost?

The third question we deal with is how we can maintain strong research and development institutions as direct Government operations. How can we prevent the best of the Government's research scientists, engineers, and administrators from being drained off to private institutions as a result of higher private salaries and superior private working environments, and how can we attract an adequate number of the most talented new college graduates to a career in Government service?

These questions are treated in the sections which follow.

Part 2
Considerations in Deciding Whether to Contract Out
Research and Development Work

Generalizations about criteria for contracting out research and development work must be reached with caution, in view of the wide variety of different circumstances which must be covered.

A great many Government agencies are involved. The Department of Defense, the National Aeronautics and Space Administration, and the

Atomic Energy Commission provide the bulk of Federal financing, but a dozen or more agencies also pay significant roles.

Most Federal research and development work is closely related to the specific purpose of the agency concerned—to the creation of new weapons systems for the Department of Defense, for example, or the exploration of new types of atomic power reactors for the Atomic Energy Commission. But a significant portion of the research financed by the Federal Government is aimed at more general targets: to enlarge the national supply of highly trained scientists, for example, as is the case with some programs of the National Science Foundation. And even the most "mission-oriented" agencies have often found it desirable to make funds available for basic research to advance the fundamental state of knowledge in fields that are relevant to their missions. Both the Department of Defense and the AEC, for example, make substantial funds available for fundamental research, not related to any specific item of equipment or other end product.

A great many different kinds of activity are involved, which have been classified by some under five headings:

(1) fundamental research
(2) supporting research or exploratory development
(3) feasibility studies, operations analysis, and technical advice
(4) development and engineering of products, processes, or systems
(5) test and evaluation activities.

The lines between many of the activities listed are necessarily uncertain. Nevertheless, it is clear that "research and development" is a phrase that covers a considerable number of different kinds of activity.

Finally, there have been distinct historical developments affecting the different Government agencies. Some agencies, for example, have a tradition of relying primarily on direct Government operations of laboratories —others have precisely the opposite tradition of relying primarily on contracting for the operations of such installations.

Against this background of diversity in several dimensions we have asked what criteria should be used in deciding whether or not to contract out any given research and development task? In outline, our judgment on this question runs as follows:

There are certain functions which should under no circumstances be contracted out. The management and control of the Federal research and development effort must be firmly in the hands of full-time Government officials clearly responsible to the President and the Congress.

Subject to this principle, many kinds of arrangements—including both direct Federal operations and the various patterns of contracting now in use—can and should be used to mobilize the talent and facilities needed to carry out the Federal research and development effort. Not all arrangements however are equally suitable for all purposes and under all circumstances, and discriminating choices must be made among them by the Government agencies having research and development responsibilities. These choices should be based primarily on two considerations:

(1) Getting the job done effectively and efficiently, with due regard to the long-term strength of the Nation's scientific and technical resources, and

(2) Avoiding assignments of work which would create inherent conflicts of interest.

Each of these judgments is elaborated below:

STRENGTHENING THE ABILITY OF THE GOVERNMENT TO MANAGE AND CONTROL RESEARCH AND DEVELOPMENT PROGRAMS

We regard it as axiomatic that policy decisions respecting the Government's research and development programs—decisions concerning the types of work to be undertaken, when, by whom, and at what cost—must be made by full-time Government officials clearly responsible to the President and to the Congress. Furthermore, such officials must be in a position to supervise the execution of work undertaken, and to evaluate the results. These are basic functions of management which cannot be transferred to any contractor if we are to have proper accountability for the performance of public functions and for the use of public funds.

To say this does not imply that detailed administration of each research and development task must be kept in the hands of top public officials. Indeed, quite the contrary is true, and an appropriate delegation of responsibility——either to subordinate public officials or by contract to private persons or organizations—for the detailed administration of research and development work is essential to its efficient execution.

It is not always easy to draw the line distinguishing essential management and control responsibilities which should not be delegated to private contractors (or, indeed, to governmental research organizations such as laboratories) from those which can and should be so assigned. Recognizing this difficulty, it nevertheless seems to be the case that in recent years there have been instances—particularly in the Department of Defense—where we have come dangerously close to permitting contract employees to exercise functions which belong with top Government management officials. Insofar as this has been true, we believe it is being rectified. Gov-

ernment agencies are now keenly aware of this problem and have taken
steps to retain functions essential to the performance of their responsibility under the law.

It is not enough, of course, to recognize that governmental managers
must retain top management functions and not contract them out. In order to perform those functions effectively, they must be themselves competent to make the required management decisions and, in addition, have
access to all necessary technical advice. Three conclusions follow:

First, where management decisions are based substantially on technical
judgments, qualified executives, who can properly utilize the advice of
technical consultants, from both inside and outside the Government, are
needed to perform them. There must be sufficient technical competence
within the Government so that outside technical advice does not become
de facto technical decision-making. In many instances the executives making the decisions can and should have strong scientific backgrounds. In
others, it is possible to have non-scientists so long as they are capable of
understanding the technical issues involved and have otherwise appropriate administrative experience.

By and large, we believe it is necessary for the agencies concerned to
give increased stress to the need to bring into governmental service as administrators men with scientific or engineering understanding, and during
the development of Government career executives, to give many of them
the opportunity, through appropriate training and experience, to
strengthen their appreciation and understanding of scientific and technical
matters. Correspondingly, scientists and engineers should be encouraged
and guided to obtain, through appropriate training and experience, a
broader understanding of management and public policy matters. The
average governmental administrator in the years to come will be dealing
with issues having larger and larger scientific and technical content, and
his training and experience, both before he enters Government service and
after he has joined, should reflect this fact.

At the present time, we are strongly persuaded that one of the most
serious obstacles to acquiring and maintaining the managerial competence
which the Government needs for its research and development programs is
the discrepancy between governmental and private compensation for comparable work. This obstacle has been growing increasingly serious in recent years as increases in Federal pay have been concentrated primarily at
the lower end of the pay scale—resulting in the anomalous situation that
many officials of Government responsible for administering major elements of Federal research and development programs are paid substantially smaller salaries than personnel of universities, of business corporations, or of not-for-profit organizations who carry out subordinate aspects

of those research and development programs. We cannot stress too strongly the importance of rectifying this situation, and hope the Congress will take at this session the action which the President has recommended to reform Federal civilian pay scales.

Second, it is necessary for even the best qualified governmental managers to obtain technical advice from specialists. Such technical advice can be obtained from men within the Government or those outside. When it is obtained from persons outside of Government, special problems of potential conflict of interest are raised. . . .

We believe it highly important for the Government to be able to turn to technical advice from its own establishment as well as from outside sources. One major source of this technical knowledge is the Government-operated laboratory or research installation and, as is made clear later in this report, we believe major improvements are needed at the present time in the management and staffing of these installations. A strong base of technical knowledge should be continually maintained within the Government service and available for advice to top management.

Third, we need to be particularly sensitive to the cumulative effects of contracting out Government work. A series of actions to contract out important activities, each wholly justified when considered on its own merits, may when taken together begin to erode the Government's ability to manage its research and development programs. There must be a high degree of awareness of this danger on the part of all governmental officials concerned. Particular attention must be given to strengthening the Government's ability to provide effective technical supervision in the letting and carrying out of contracts, and to developing more adequate measures for performance evaluation.

DETERMINING THE ASSIGNMENT OF RESEARCH AND DEVELOPMENT WORK

As indicated above, we consider it necessary and desirable to use a variety of arrangements to obtain the scientific and technical services needed to accomplish public purposes. Such arrangements include: direct governmental operations through laboratories or other installations; operation of Government-owned facilities by contractors; grants and contracts with universities and entities associated with universities; contracts with not-for-profit corporations wholly or largely devoted to performing work for Government; and contracts with private business corporations. We also feel that innovation is still needed in these matters, and each agency should be encouraged to seek new and better arrangements to accomplish its purposes. Choices among available arrangements should be based primarily on two factors:

> relative effectiveness and efficiency, and avoidance of conflicts of interest.

Relative effectiveness and efficiency

In selecting recipients, whether public or private, for research and development assignments, the basic rule (apart from the conflict-of-interest problem); should be to assign the job where it can be done most effectively and efficiently, with due regard to the strengthening of institutional resources as well as to the immediate execution of projects. This criterion does not, in our judgment, lead to a conclusion that certain kinds of work should be assigned *only* to certain kinds of institutions. Too much depends on individual competence, historical evolution, and other special circumstances to permit any such simple rule to hold. However, it seems clear that some types of facilities have natural advantages which should be made use of. Thus:

Direct Federal operations, such as the governmental laboratory, enjoy a close and continuing relationship to the agency they serve which permits maximum responsiveness to the needs of that agency and a maximum sense of sharing the mission of the agency. Such operations accordingly have a natural advantage in conducting research, feasibility studies, developmental and analytical work, user tests and evaluations which directly support the management functions of the agency. Furthermore, an agency-operated research and development installation may provide a useful source of technical management personnel for its sponsor.

At the present time we consider that the laboratories and other facilities available to Government are operating under certain important handicaps which should be removed if these facilities are to support properly the Federal research and development effort. . . .

Colleges and universities have a long tradition in basic research. The processes of graduate education and basic research have long been closely associated, and reinforce each other in many ways. This unique intellectual environment has proven to be highly conducive to successful undirected and creative research by highly skilled specialists. Such research is not amenable to management control by adherence to firm schedules, well-defined objectives, or pre-determined methods of work. In the colleges and universities graduate education and basic research constitute an effective means of introducing future research workers to their fields in direct association with experienced people in those fields, and in an atmosphere of active research work. Applied research appropriate to the universities is that which broadly advances the state of the art.

University-associated research centers are well suited to basic or applied research for which the facilities are so large and expensive that the research acquires the character of a major program best carried out in an entity apart from the regular academic organization. Research in such centers often benefits from the active participation of university scientists. At the same time the sponsoring university (and sometimes other, cooperating universities) benefits from increased opportunities for research by its faculties and graduate students.

Not-for-profit organizations (other than universities and contractor-operated Government facilities), if strongly led, can provide a degree of independence, both from Government and from the commercial market, which may make them particularly useful as a source of objective analytical advice and technical services. These organizations have on occasion provided an important means for establishing a competent research organization for a particular task more rapidly than could have been possible within the less flexible administrative requirements of the Government.

Contractor-operated Government facilities appear to be effective, in some instances, in securing competent scientific and technical personnel to perform research and development work where very complex and costly facilities are required and the Government desires to maintain control of those facilities. Under such arrangements, it has been possible for the Government to retain most of the controls inherent in direct Federal operations, while at the same time gaining many of the advantages of flexibility with respect to staffing, organization, and management, which are inherent in university and industrial operations.

Operations in the profit sector of the economy have special advantages when large and complex arrays of resources needed for advanced development and pre-production work must be marshalled quickly. If the contracting system is such as to provide appropriate incentives, operations for profit can have advantages in spurring efficiency, reducing costs, and speeding accomplishments. . . . Contractors in the profit sector may have the advantage of drawing on resources developed to satisfy commercial as well as governmental customers which adds to the flexibility of procurement, and may permit resources to be phased in and out of Government work on demand.

The preceding paragraphs have stressed the advantages of these different types of organization. There are disadvantages relating to each type which must also be taken into account. Universities, for example, are not ordinarily qualified—nor would they wish—to undertake major systems engineering contracts.

We repeat that the advantages—and disadvantages—noted above do not mean that these different types or arrangements should be given areas of monopoly on different kinds of work. There are, by common agreement, considerable advantages derived from the present diversity of operations. It permits great flexibility in establishing and directing different kinds of facilities and units, and in meeting the need for managing different kinds of jobs. Comparison of operations among these various types of organizations helps provide yardsticks for evaluating performance.

Moreover, this diversity helps provide many sources of ideas and of the critical analysis of ideas, on which scientific and technical progress depend. Indeed, we believe that some research (in contrast to development) should be undertaken by most types of organizations. Basic and applied research activities related to the mission of the organization help to provide a better intellectual environment in which to carry out development work. They also assist greatly in recruiting high quality research staff.

In addition to the desirability of making use of the natural areas of advantage within this diversity of arrangements, there is one additional point we would stress. Activities closely related to governmental managerial decisions (such as those in support of contractor selection), or to activities inherently governmental, (such as regulatory functions, or technical activities directly bound up with military operations), are likely to call for a direct Federal capability and to be less successfully handled by contract.

Conflicts of interest

There are at least three aspects of the conflict-of-interest problem which arise in connection with governmental research and development work.

First, there are problems relating to private individuals who serve simultaneously as governmental consultants and as officers, directors, or employees of private organizations with which the Government has a contractual relationship. Many of these individuals are among the Nation's most capable people in the research and development field, and can be of very great assistance to Government agencies.

. . . No individual serving as an adviser or consultant should render advice on an issue whose outcome would have a direct and predictable effect on the interests of the private organization which he serves. To this end the President asked that arrangements be made whereby each adviser and consultant would disclose the full extent of his private interests, and the responsible Government officials would undertake to make sure that conflict-of-interest situations are avoided.

Second, there is a significant tendency to have on the boards of trustees and directors of the major universities, not-for-profit and profit establishments engaged in Federal research and development work, representatives of other institutions involved in such work. Such interlocking directorships may serve to reinforce and strengthen the overall management of private organizations which are heavily financed by the Government. Certainly it is in the public interest that organizations on whom so much reliance is placed for accomplishing public purposes, should be controlled by the most responsible, mature, and knowledgeable men available in the Nation. However, we see the clear possibility of conflict-of-interest situations developing through such common directorships that might be harmful to the public interest. Members of governing boards of private business enterprises, universities, or other organizations which advise the Government with respect to research and development activities are often simultaneously members of governing boards of organizations which receive or may receive contracts or grants from the Government for research, development, or production work. Unless these board members also serve as consultants to the Government, present conflict-of-interest laws do not apply. . . .

Beyond this, however, there is a third type of problem which requires consideration: this might be described as potential conflicts of interest relating to organizations rather than to individuals. It arises in several forms—not all of which by any means are yet fully understood. Indeed, in this area of potential conflicts of interest relating to individuals and organizations in the research and development field, we are in an early stage of developing accepted standards for conduct—unlike other fields, such as the law or medicine, where there are long-established standards of conduct.

One form of organizational conflict of interest relates to the distinction between organizations providing professional services (e.g., technical advice) and those providing manufactured products. A conflict of interest could arise, for example, if a private corporation received a contract to provide technical advice and guidance with respect to a weapons system for which that same private corporation later sought a development or production contract, or for which it sought to develop or supply a key subsystem or component. It is clear that such conflict-of-interest situations can arise whether or not the profit motive is present. The managers of the not-for-profit institutions have necessarily a strong interest in the continuation and success of such institutions, and it is part of good management of Federal research and development programs to avoid placing any contractor—whether profit or nonprofit—in a position where a conflict of interest could clearly exist.

Another kind of issue is raised by the question whether an organization which has been established to provide services to a Government agency should be permitted to seek contracts with other Government agencies —or with non-Government customers. The question has arisen particularly with respect to not-for-profit organizations established to provide professional services.

There is not a clear consensus on this question among Government officials and officers of the organizations in question. We have considered the question far enough to have the following tentative views:

In the case of organizations in the area of operations and policy research (such, for example, as the RAND Corporation), the principal advantages they have to offer are the detached quality and objectivity of their work. Here, too close control by any Government agency may tend to limit objectivity. Organizations of this kind should not be discouraged from dealing with a variety of clients, both in and out of Government.

On the other hand, a number of the organizations which have been established to provide systems engineering and technical direction (such, for example, as Aerospace Corporation) are at least for the time being of value principally as they act as agents of a single client. In time, as programs change and new requirements arise, it may be possible and desirable for such organizations also to achieve a fully independent financial basis, resting on multiple clients, but this would seem more likely to be a later rather than an earlier development.

Enough has been said to indicate that this general area of conflict of interest with respect to research and development work is turning up new kinds of questions and all the answers have not yet been found. . . . We recommend that the President instruct each department and agency head, in consultation with the Attorney General, to proceed to develop as much of a code of conduct for individuals and organizations in the research and development field as circumstances now permit.

Finally, we would note that beyond any formal standards, we cannot escape the necessity of relying on the sensitive conscience of officials in the Government and in private organizations to make sure that appropriate standards are continually maintained.

Part 3

Proposals for Improving Policies and Practices Applying to Research and Development Contracting

During the course of this review, a number of suggestions arose which we believe to indicate desirable improvements in the Government's policies and practices applying to research and development contracting.

IMPROVING THE GOVERNMENT'S COMPETENCE AS A "SOPHISTICATED BUYER"

In order for the contracting system to work effectively, the first requirement is for the Government to be a sophisticated buyer—that is, to know what it wants and how to get it. Mention has already been made of the requirements this places on governmental management officials. At this point four additional suggestions are made.

1. In the case of many large systems development projects, it has been the practice to invite private corporations to submit proposals to undertake research and development work—relating to a new missile system, for example, or a new aircraft system. Such proposals are often invited before usable and realistic specifications of the system have been worked out in sufficient detail. As a consequence, highly elaborate, independent, and expensive studies are often undertaken by the would-be contractors in the course of submitting their proposals. This is a very costly method of obtaining competitive proposals, and it unnecessarily consumes large amounts of the best creative talent this country possesses, both on the preparation of the proposals and their evaluation. Delivery time pressures may necessitate inviting proposals before specifications are completed, but we believe this practice can and should be substantially curtailed.

This would mean, in many instances, improving the Government's ability to accomplish feasibility studies, or letting special contracts for that purpose, before inviting proposals. In either event, it would require the acceptance of a greater degree of responsibility by Government managers for making preliminary decisions prior to inviting private proposals. We believe the gains from such a change would be substantial in the avoidance of unnecessary and wasteful use of scarce scientific and technical personnel as well as heavy costs to the private contractors concerned—costs which in most cases are passed on to the Government.

2. We believe there is a great deal of work to be done to improve the Government's ability to supervise and to evaluate the conduct of research and development efforts—whether undertaken through public or private facilities. We do not have nearly enough understanding as yet of how to know whether we are getting a good product for our money, whether research and development work is being competently managed, or how to select the more competent from the less competent as between research and development establishments.

When inadequate technical criteria exist, there is a tendency to substitute conformity with administrative and fiscal procedures for evaluation of substantive performance. What is required is more exchange of information between agencies on their practices in contractor evaluation and on their experience with these practices. A continuing forum should be provided for such exchange. It is possible also that some central and fairly formal means of reporting methods and experience and recording them permanently should be established. We recommend that the Director of the new Office of Science and Technology, when established, be asked to study the possibility of establishing such a forum and the best means for providing information regarding evaluation practices.

3. With the tremendous proliferation of research and development operations and associated facilities in recent years, it has become difficult for the Government officials who arrange for such work to be done to be aware of all the facilities and manpower that are available. To maintain a complete and continuous roster of manpower, equipment, and organizations, sensitive to month-by-month changes, would undoubtedly be too costly in terms of its value.

Nevertheless, we believe that an organized attempt should be made to improve the current inventory of information on the scientific and technical resources of the country. We recommend that the National Science Foundation consider ways and means of improving the availability of such information for use by all concerned in public and private activities.

4. In addition, the expansion of the Nation's research and development effort has multiplied the difficulties of communication among researchers engaged on related projects at separate facilities, both public and private. It is clear that additional steps should be taken to further efforts to improve the system for the exchange of information in the field of science and technology.

•   •   •

IMPROVING ARRANGEMENTS WITH THE PRIVATE SECTOR TYPES OF CONTRACTS

The principal type of contract for research and development work which is made with private industry is the cost-plus-fixed-fee contract. Such contracts have been used in this area because of the inherent difficulty of establishing precise objectives for the work to be done and of making costs estimates ahead of time.

At the same time, this type of contract has well-known disadvantages. It provides little or no incentive for private managers to reduce costs or otherwise increase efficiency. Indeed, the cost-plus-fixed-fee contract, in combination with strong pressures from governmental managers to accomplish work on a rapid time schedule, probably provides incentives for raising rather than for reducing costs. If a corporation is judged in terms of whether it accomplishes a result by a given deadline rather than by whether it accomplishes that result at minimum cost, it will naturally pay less attention to costs and more attention to speed of accomplishment. On the other hand, where there is no given deadline, the cost-plus-fixed-fee contract may serve to prolong the research and development work and induce the contractor to delay completion.

Consequently, we believe it to be desirable to replace cost-plus-fixed-fee contracting with fixed-price contracting wherever that is feasible—as it should be in the procurement of some late-stage development, test work, and services. Where it is judged that cost reimbursement must be retained as the contracting principle, it should be possible in many instances to include an incentive arrangement under which the fee would not be fixed, but would vary according to a predetermined standard which would relate larger fees to lower costs, superior performance, and shorter delivery times. There is ample evidence to prove that if adequate incentives are given by rewards for outstanding performance, both time and money can be saved. Where the nature of the task permits, it may be desirable to include in the contract penalty provisions for inadequate performance.

Finally, if neither fixed-price nor incentive-type contracts are possible, it is still necessary for Government managers to insist on consideration being given to lower cost, as well as better products and shorter delivery times—and to include previous performance as one element in evaluating different contractors and the desirability of awarding them subsequent contracts.

Contract administration

The written contract itself, however well done, is only one aspect of the situation. The administration of a contract requires as much care and effort as the preparation of the contract itself. This is particularly important with respect to changes in system characteristics, for these changes often become the mechanism for justifying cost overruns. Other factors of importance in contract administration are fixing authority and responsibility in both Government and industry, excessive reporting requirements, and an all-too-frequent lack of prearranged milestones for auditing purposes.

Reimbursable costs

Concern has been expressed because of significant differences among the various agencies in policies regarding which costs are eligible for reimbursement—notably with respect to some of the indirect costs. These differences are now being reviewed by the Bureau of the Budget with the cooperation of the Department of Defense, the National Aeronautics and Space Administration, the Atomic Energy Commission, and the General Services Administration.

Arrangements with universities

With respect to universities, Government agencies share responsibility for seeing that research and development financed at universities does not weaken these institutions or distort their functions which are so vital to the national interest.

Government agencies use both grants and contracts in financing research at universities, but in our judgment the grant has proved to be a simpler and more desirable device for Federal financing of fundamental research, where it is in the interest of the Government not to exercise close control over the objectives and direction of research. Since all relevant Government agencies are now empowered to use grants instead of contracts in supporting basic research, the wider use of this authority should be encouraged.

Apart from this matter, three others seem worthy of comment.

One arises from the extensive use of contracts (or grants) for specific and precisely identified projects. Often there is a tendency to believe that in providing support for a single specific project the chance of finding a solution to a problem is being maximized. In reality, however, less specific support often would permit more effective research in broad areas of science, or in interdisciplinary fields, and provide greater freedom in drawing in more scientists to participate in the work that is undertaken. Universities, too, often find project support cumbersome and awkward. A particular professor may be working on several projects financed by several Government agencies and must make arbitrary decisions in allocating expenses to a particular project. It thus appears both possible and desirable to move in the direction of using grants to support broader programs, or to support the more general activities of an institution, rather than to tie each allocation of funds to a specific project. A number of Government agencies have been moving in this direction and it would be desirable to expand the use of such forms of support as experience warrants.

At the same time, it would not, in our judgment, be appropriate to place major reliance on the institutional grant, since the major purpose of making grants in most cases is to assure that the university personnel and facilities concerned will be devoted to pursuing specific courses of inquiry.

A second problem associated with the support of research at universities is whether the Government should pay all costs, including indirect expenses or "overhead", associated with work financed by the Government. We believe this matter involves two related but distinct questions, which should be separated in considering the appropriate policy to be followed.

1. We believe there is no question that, in those cases in which it is desirable for the Government to pay the entire cost of work done at a university, the Government should pay for allowable indirect as well as direct

costs. To do otherwise would be discriminatory against universities in comparison with other kinds of institutions. For purposes of financial and accounting simplicity, in those cases where grants are used, and it is desirable for the Government to pay all allowable costs, it may be possible to work out a uniform or average percentage figure which could be regarded as covering indirect costs.

2. We believe there are many cases in which it is neither necessary nor desirable for the Government to pay all the costs of the work to be done. In many fields of research, a university may gain a great deal from having the research in question done on its campus, with the participation of its faculty and students, and may be able and willing to share in the costs, either through its regular funds or through raising additional funds from foundations, alumni, or by other means. The extent and degree of cost-sharing can and should vary among different agencies and programs, and we are not prepared at this time to suggest any uniform standards—except the negative one that it would be plainly illogical to require that the university uniformly provide its share through the payment of all or a part of the indirect costs. Only in the exceptional case would this turn out to be the best basis for determining the appropriate sharing of costs.

A third problem relates to the means for furnishing major capital assets for research at universities (such as a major building or a major piece of equipment such as a linear accelerator, synchrotron, or large computer). In most cases, it will be preferable to finance such facilities by a separate grant (or contract), which will ensure that careful attention is given to the long-term value of the asset and to the establishment of appropriate arrangements for managing and maintaining it.

Arrangements with respect to not-for-profit organizations other than universities

It has been the practice in contracting for research and development work with such organizations to cover all allowable costs and, in addition, to provide what is commonly called a "fee." The reason for paying a "fee" to not-for-profit organizations is quite different from the reason for paying a fee to profit-making contractors and therefore the term "fee" is misleading. The profit-making contractor is engaged in business for profit. His profit and the return to his shareholders or investors can only come from the fee. In the case of the not-for-profit organizations, there are no shareholders, but there are two sound reasons to justify payment of a "development" or "general support" allowance to such organizations.

One is that such allowances provide some degree of operational stability and flexibility to organizations which otherwise would be very tightly bound to the precise limitations of cost financing of specific tasks; the al-

214 THE POLITICS OF SCIENCE

lowances can be used to even out variations in the income of the organization resulting from variations in the level of contract work. A second justification is that most not-for-profit organizations must conduct some independent, self-initiated research if they are to obtain and hold highly competent scientists and engineers. Such staff members, it is argued, will only be attracted if they can share, to some extent, in independently directed research efforts.

We consider that both of these arguments have merit and, in consequence, support the continuation of these payments. Both arguments represent incentives to maintain the cohesiveness and the quality of the organization, which is in the interest of the Government. They should underlie the thinking of the Government representatives who negotiate contracts with not-for-profit organizations. But the amount of the "fee" or allowance in each instance must still be determined by bargaining between Government and contractor, in accordance with the independent relationship that is essential to successful contracting.

An important question relating to not-for-profit organizations other than universities, concerns facilities and equipment. In our judgment, the normal rule should be that where facilities and equipment are required to perform research and development work desired by the Government, the Government should either provide the facilities and equipment, or cover their cost as part of the contract. This is the rule relating to profit organizations and would hold in general for not-for-profit organizations—but there are two special problems with respect to the latter.

First, we believe it is generally not desirable to furnish funds through "fees" for the purpose of enabling a contractor to acquire major capital assets. On the other hand, the Government should not attempt to dictate what a contractor does with his "fee," provided it has been established on a sound and equitable basis, and if a contractor chooses to use part of his "fee" to acquire facilities for use in his self-initiated research, we would see no objection.

Second, we would think it equitable, where the Government has provided facilities, funds to obtain facilities, substantial working capital, or other resources to a contractor, it should, upon dissolution of the organization, be entitled to a first claim upon such resources. This would seem to be a matter which should be governed, insofar as possible, by the terms of the contract—or in the case of any newly established organizations, should be provided in the provisions of its charter.

Salaries and related benefits
In addition to the question of fees and allowances, there has been a great deal of concern over the salaries and related benefits received by persons

employed on federally financed research and development work in private institutions, particularly persons employed in not-for-profit establishments doing work exclusively for the Government. Controls have been suggested or urged by congressional committees and others to make sure that there is no excessive expenditure of public funds and to minimize the undesirable competitive effect on the Federal career service.

We agree that where the contracting system does not provide built-in controls, (for example, through competitive bidding), attention should be paid to the reasonableness of contractors' salaries and related benefits, and contractors should be reimbursed only for reasonable compensation costs.

The key question is how to decide what is reasonable and appropriate compensation. We believe the basic standard for reimbursement of salaries and related benefits should be one of comparability to compensation of persons doing similar work in the private economy. The President recently proposed to the Congress that the pay for Federal civilian employees should be based on the concept of reasonable comparability with employees doing similar work in the private economy. We believe this to be a sound principle which can be applied in the present circumstances as well.

Application of this comparability principle may require some special compensation surveys (perhaps made by the Bureau of Labor Statistics), which can and should be arranged for as necessary. Furthermore, there will undoubtedly be cases in which comparable data are difficult to obtain—as, for example, with respect to top management jobs. In such cases the specific approval of the head of the Government contracting agency or his designee should be required.

In view of the inherent complexity and sensitivity of this subject, we suggest that special administrative arrangements should be established in each agency. Contract policies respecting salaries and related benefits in each contracting agency should be controlled by an official reporting directly to the head of the agency (in the Department of Defense, to assure uniformity of treatment, by an official reporting directly to the Secretary of Defense), and salaries above a certain level—say $25,000—should require the personal approval of that official.

Part 4
Proposals for Improving the Government's Ability To
Carry Out Research and Development Activities Directly

Based on the evidence acquired in the course of this review, we believe there is no doubt that the effects of the substantial increase in contracting out Federal research and development work on the Government's own ability to execute research and development work have been deleterious.

The effects of the sharp rise in contracting out have included the following. First, contractors have often been able to provide a superior working environment for their scientists and engineers—better salaries, better facilities, better administrative support—making contracting operations attractive alternatives to Federal work. Second, it has often seemed that contractors have been given the more significant and more interesting work assignments, leaving Government research and development establishments with routine missions and static programs which do not attract the best talent. Third, additional burdens have often been placed on Government research establishments to assist in evaluating the work of increasing numbers of contractors and to train and educate less skilled contractor personnel—without adding to the total staff and thus detracting from the direct research work which appeals to the most competent personnel. Fourth, scientists in contracting institutions have often had freedom to move "outside of channels" in the Government hierarchy and to participate in program determination and technical advice at the highest levels—freedom frequently not available to the Government's own scientists. Finally, one of the most serious aspects of the contracting out process has been that it has provided an alternative to correcting the deficiencies in the Government's own operations.

In consequence, for some time there has been a serious trend toward the reduction of the competence of Government research and development establishments. Recently a number of significant actions have been started which are intended to reverse this trend. We point particularly to the strong leadership being given within the Defense Department by the Director of Defense Research and Engineering, in striving to raise the capabilities of the Department's laboratories and other research and development facilities.

Nevertheless, we believe the situation is still serious and that major efforts are required.

We consider it a most important objective for the Government to maintain first-class facilities and equipment of its own to carry out research and development work. This observation applies not only to the newer research and development agencies but equally to the older agencies such as Commerce, Interior and Agriculture.

No matter how heavily the Government relies on private contracting, it should never lose a strong internal competence in research and development. By maintaining such competence it can be sure of being able to make the difficult but extraordinarily important program decisions which rest on scientific and technical judgments. Moreover, the Government's research facilities are a significant source of management personnel.

Major steps seem to us to be necessary in the following matters:

1. It is generally recognized that having significant and challenging work to do is the most important element in establishing a successful research and development organization. It is suggested that responsibility should be assigned in each department and agency to the Assistant Secretary for Research and Development or his equivalent to make sure that assignments to governmental research facilities are such as to attract and hold first-class men. Furthermore, arrangements should be made to call on Government laboratory and development center personnel to a larger extent for technical advice and participation in broad program and management decisions—in contrast to the predominant use of outside advisers.

2. The evidence is compelling that managerial arrangements for many Government-operated research and development facilities are cumbersome and awkward. Several improvements are needed in many instances, including

> delegating to research laboratory directors more authority to make program and personnel decisions, to control funds, and otherwise to command the resources which are necessary to carry out the mission of the installation.

> providing the research laboratory director a discretionary allotment of funds, to be available for projects of his choosing, and for the results of which he is to be responsible;

> eliminating where possible excess layers or echelons of supervisory management, and insuring that technical, administrative, and fiscal reviews be conducted concurrently and in coordinated fashion; and

> making laboratory research assignments in the form of a few major items with a reasonable degree of continuity rather than a multiplicity of small narrowly specified tasks; this will put responsibility for detailed definition of the work to be done at the laboratory level where it belongs.

To carry out these improvements will require careful and detailed analysis of the different situations in different agencies. Above all, it will require the energetic direction of top officials in each agency.

• • •

3. Salary limitations, as already mentioned, in our opinion play a major role in preventing the Government from obtaining or retaining highly

competent men and women. Largely because of the lack of comparable salaries, the Government is not now and has not for at least the past 10 years been able to attract or retain its share of such critically necessary people as: recently graduated, highly recommended Ph. D's in mathematics and physics; recent B.S./M.S. scientific and engineering graduates in the upper 25 percent of their classes at top-ranked universities; good experienced, weapons systems engineers and missile, space, and electronic specialists at intermediate and senior levels; and senior-level laboratory directors, scientific managers, and administrators. This obstacle will be substantially overcome if the Congress approves the President's recommendation to establish a standard of comparability with private pay levels for higher professional and technical jobs in the Federal service.

4. A special problem in the Defense Department is the relationship between uniformed and civilian personnel. This is a difficult and sensitive problem of which the Department of Defense is well aware. We do not attempt in this report to propose detailed solutions, but we do suggest that certain principles are becoming evident as a result of the experience of recent years.

It seems clear, for example, that the military services will have increasing need for substantial numbers of officers who have extensive scientific and technical training and experience. Such officers bring first-hand knowledge of operational conditions and requirements to research and development installations and, in turn, learn about the state of the art and the feasible applications of technology to military operations. The military officer is needed to communicate the needs of the user, to prepare the operational forces for new equipment, to plan for the use of developing equipment, and later to install it and supervise its use.

All of the above roles suggest that when military personnel are used in research and development activities, they should perform as "technical men" rather than "military men" except when there is a need for their military skills. Military command and direction become important only as one moves from the research end of the spectrum into the area where operational considerations predominate. Both at middle management and policy levels, a well-balanced mixture of military and civilian personnel may be most advantageous in programs designed to meet military needs.

In research, there are many instances in which the existence of military supervision, and the decreased opportunities for advancement because of military occupancy of top jobs, are among the principal reasons why the Defense Department has had difficulty in attracting outstanding civilian scientists and engineers. On the other hand, there are examples within the Department of cases in which enlightened policies of civil-military relationships have drawn on the strengths of each and produced excellent results. In such instances, the military head of the laboratory has usually concentrated on administrative problems and the civilian technical director has had complete control of technical programs.

Military officers should not be substituted for civilians in the direction and management of research and development unless they are technically qualified and their military background is directly needed and applicable.

* * *

5. In addition to the recommendations above, we have given consideration to the possible establishment of a new kind of Government research and development establishment, which might be called a Government Institute. Such an Institute would provide a means for reproducing within the Government structure some of the more positive attributes of the nonprofit corporation. Each Institute would be created pursuant to authority granted by the Congress and be subject to the supervision of a Cabinet officer or agency head. It would, however, as a separate corporate entity directly managed by its own Board of Regents, enjoy a considerable degree of independence in the conduct of its internal affairs. An Institute would have authority to operate its own career merit system, as the Tennessee Valley Authority does, would be able to establish a compensation system based on the comparability principle, and would have broad authority to use funds and to acquire and dispose of property.

The objective of establishing such an instrumentality would be to achieve in the administration of certain research and development programs the kind of flexibility which has been obtained by Government corporations while retaining, as was done with the Government corporation, effective public accountability and control.

We regard the idea as promising and recommend that the Bureau of the Budget study it further, in cooperation with some of the agencies having major research and development programs. It may well prove to be a useful additional means for carrying out governmental research and development efforts.

6. It would seem, based on the results of this review, that it would be possible and desirable to make more use of existing governmental facilities and avoid the creation of duplicate facilities. This is not as easy a problem as it might seem. It is ordinarily necessary for a laboratory, if it is to provide strong and competent facilities, to have a major mission and a major source of funding. This will limit the extent to which it is possible to make such facilities available for the work of other agencies. Nevertheless, in some cases and to some extent it is clearly possible to do this and a continuing scrutiny is necessary in order to make sure that the facilities which the Government has are used to their fullest extent.

7. Finally, together with the better use of existing facilities, the Government must also make better use of its existing scientific and engineering personnel. This implies not only a careful watch over work assignments, but also a continual upgrading of the capabilities of Federal personnel through education and training. At the present time, technology is changing so rapidly that on-the-job scientists and engineers find themselves out of date after a decade or so out of the university. To remedy this, the Government must strengthen its educational program for its own personnel, to the extent of sending them back to the university for about an academic year every decade. This program, necessary as it is, will only become attractive if the employee is ensured job security on his return from school and if his parent organization is allowed to carry him on its personnel roster.

BURTON H. KLEIN

Policy Issues Involved in the Conduct of Military Development Programs

The main purpose of this paper is to discuss some of the issues involved in the conduct of military research and development. But before turning to policy matters, it may be a good idea to spend some time asking ourselves "What is the essential nature of this activity?" Unless people who are interested in policy matters can come to some agreement on the kinds of uncertainties that underlie R and D decisions and therefore on the environment in which these decisions have to be made, discussion of policy matters hardly can be very fruitful.

But while we can agree that the nature of an activity ought to be taken into account in devising policies for its effective conduct, it unfortunately is not easy to characterize this activity—"military development"—in a meaningful way. To be sure, development can be defined in terms such as "the identification, modification, and combination of feasible components and devices to provide a distinctly new application practical in terms of

From RAND paper P-2648, October 1962. Reprinted by permission of the RAND Corporation.
(Any views expressed in this paper are those of the author. They should not be interpreted as reflecting the views of The RAND Corporation or the official opinion or policy of any of its governmental or private research sponsors.)

performance, reliability, and cost." But such a definition does not provide much of a flavor as to what development is all about. However, while frankly admitting that there is a good deal of room for disagreement on what are the essential characteristics of this activity—just as there is plenty of room for disagreement in saying what women really are like, leave alone how to deal with them—I want to give you my own impressions of what they are.

The one characteristic that is most common to military development projects, I have no doubt, is the sharp changes in the attitudes taken towards their outcome as they progress through various stages toward completion. To illustrate this point let me quote from a talk given by General Clifton Von Kann, Director of Army Aviation. He says:

> Let's examine the typical peaks of joy and valleys of depression in the life of an ordinary helicopter.
>
> First, the highest peak. It is hot out of the design concept stage and into the cocktail brochure. It will never be as good again. It is the finest thing since Coca-Cola and is a panacea for any problem you care to mention.
>
> Then comes the first valley. The engine that was to power this dream ship is found to be made of metal, weighs a few pounds, and burns fuel. The original concept did not take this into active consideration. Obviously, performance will suffer.
>
> Next peak—the mock-up. Now we can show something. You can just see by looking at it that here is a real machine. Potential customers seem to come from everywhere to take a look, make a few sage remarks, and leave the impression that they're ready to buy a thousand.
>
> Valley—slippage. If the target date for first flight were met, it would mean taking off without rotor blades or engine installed. Careful engineering department types are mad at sales-happy promotion types in front office for setting such an impossible goal. Front office types are mad at foot-dragging, super-meticulous engineers who want to turn this stage into a lifetime project.
>
> Peak—first flight. There will always be a great number of people who do not understand why a helicopter flies. This includes many helicopter engineers. So naturally they are elated and fascinated when a new one actually gets airborne.
>
> Then the lowest valley. Sometime in the testing stage, just as real production is being geared up, there is bound to be full panic. It may stem from anything—paint peeling near the exhaust—seat covers not holding up—the horrible realization that the engine life is not eternal—anything can trigger it. But the conclusion is always the same. "Let's stop this thing now and not throw good money after bad!"

The next peak is perhaps not very high in the terms of absolute altitude, but looking back into the very low valley we have just left, it is very impressive and gratifying. A couple of our potential owners have actually bought a few articles and are trying them out. Preliminary reports indicate a few 'bugs' but generally they are satisfied and pleased. There is every indication that they will order more and that the helicopter will join the ranks of the accepted standard family.

The only thing I find wrong with General Von Kann's story is that it ends a little bit too abruptly—he fails to mention the trough that often comes after the operational organization in question has bought a few of the articles, and has tried them out. Sometimes this is the lowest valley in the entire scenario, and not seldom a very large development effort indeed is required to get out of this valley. Assuming that a development program ends as of the time a new capability is initially introduced into operational use can lead to some very mistaken ideas as to how long it actually took to complete a program, and how much money was actually involved.

General Von Kann's illustration also brings out another much more significant characteristic of military development projects. You noticed, I'm sure, that not only were the attitudes taken toward his helicopter constantly changing, but so was the helicopter itself. Though the tendency depends somewhat on the ambitiousness of the advances being sought, all of the evidence I have examined strongly suggests that it is seldom indeed that the differences between the system as it was initially conceived and as it emerges from development are only of a minor sort. For example, by perusing the Congressional Hearings on the missile programs you can find that almost all the major subsystems now being used in the Atlas missiles are of a different kind from those initially planned. And when I say the present system is different from the one initially planned, I don't have in mind such minor differences as exist between, say, Boeing's 707 and Douglas' DC-8. The Atlas is not, of course, a unique example among missile systems. Others also have displayed a considerable tendency to end up with technological ingredients not initially intended for them. In fact, if you want a reasonable operational definition of a missile system I'd say that it is a system mainly made up of components and subsystems initially developed for other missile systems.

That pronounced changes in characteristics occur even when the advances sought are not so ambitious as they have been in some of our missile programs is indicated by a study we did at RAND of six fighter plane development projects.

All of these planes were designed for some particular mission—all-weather interception, or ground support, for example. All of the aircraft manufacturers based their airframe design on some particular engine design furnished by one of the engine manufacturers. In almost all of these cases, there were also programs for developing specialized electronic, as well as other, kinds of equipment. To what extent did these plans materialize? Four out of the six planes ended up with different engines, three with different electronic systems. In order to make them satisfactory flying machines, five of the airframes had to be extensively modified; three of the fighters came out of development essentially different airplanes. Of the six airplanes, three ended up by having quite different operational roles from what was originally planned for them. Only one of the airplanes possessed the same technological ingredients and had the same kind of operational role that had been initially planned for it. This plane, however, will have a much less important role than it was intended to have, in part because another fighter, whose development was started for a very different kind of role, has already provided quite as good a capability.

• • •

I could give many more such examples, but if you are willing to assume that weapon systems do undergo pronounced changes in the course of development, I would now like to take up a much more interesting question: Why? One of the main causes, we are often told, is the compulsion that engineers have for squeezing the last ounce of performance out of their systems. If anyone wants to study this tendency, a good place to look, I suggest, is the space business. Here, almost every space vehicle is specially tailored to take utmost advantage of its inherent payload lifting capability right through the development process, sometimes up to and including the day of launch. With regard to most of the military development projects I have looked into, however, I notice no substantial propensity to add refinements for performance after the system is in active development. In military programs the tendency to ask for everything usually gets so adequately expressed in the initial planning and design work that in development there is no longer a question as to whether further performance-oriented improvements ought to be added. One of the main problems in military development, then, and one of the main reasons for modifications, is simply that of getting a system into tolerable working order. To do that, often some performance has to be given up.

Another cause of the many changes in configuration that occur after development starts, I am sure you have heard again and again, is that the initial planning was poorly done—for if it wasn't, why, then, the many changes? If there is anything in this allegation one might expect to find a high degree of correlation between those projects that received the most attention in the initial planning stage of development and those that turned out to be most successful. But all the evidence that I have examined indicates that the correlation, if anything, is negative. For example, if you look into the field of radar development you will find that those radars that were most meticulously designed were almost invariably those radars that took the longest time to get into tolerable working order and whose development cost the most; measured either in terms of time or dollars, the differences were of the order of 2 or 3 to 1.

To continue along this line of thought, we all know that the scientific basis for radar was established before World War II, and if that is so, one wonders why it hasn't been possible for radar experts to sit down and figure out just what kind of radar would be most useful for some particular purpose, and to proceed forthwith to build it. To illustrate why it hasn't been possible, let's consider for a few minutes a radar known as side-looking radar, and more specifically one that operates at a very short-wave length frequency, say, .86 centimeters. The main virtue of this kind of radar over the conventional scanning radar is that it provides fantastically good resolution, almost approaching that of photographs. Scientists were aware that such a radar could provide much better resolution during World War II. It was known that exploitation of the shorter wave length bands would result in improved resolution; it was also known resolution could be improved by using longer antennas. And, as a matter of fact, there were some experimental attempts during the war to develop a radar which utilized instead of the conventional scanning antenna, long antennas mounted on the side of an airplane—hence the term side-looking radar.

But why then didn't the people at the Radiation Laboratory go ahead and build a practical device that would exploit the potentialities of side-looking, very short-wave radar? Let's ask first why they didn't develop a side-looking radar with the short wave length characteristic of present day side-looking radars. The answer is this: While it was believed that such a radar would have very good resolution, it also was believed—on the basis of experimental evidence—that such a radar would have extremely limited range. An experimental 1.25 centimeter radar had been developed towards the end of the war which, while it gave quite remarkable resolution, had a range of only several miles. And it was generally concluded that a radar with a wave length less than 2.0 centimeters would have no military utility.

Had it not been for some experiments conducted by British scientists this probably would have remained the general conclusion for some time. What their experiments proved was that the choice of 1.25 centimeters as a radar frequency was a very unfortunate choice indeed, for at frequencies slightly higher (1.8 centimeters) and slightly lower (.86 centimeters), atmospheric attenuation was far less serious than at 1.25 centimeters and other neighboring frequencies. In other words, these experiments proved that the function was not a monotonic one. You can say, of course, that the scientists who were responsible for the decision to develop the 1.25 centimeter radar should have known more about atmospheric attenuation, but that doesn't prove very much. I can assure you that more than routine engineering talent was devoted to the selection of that frequency, that, in short, a side-looking radar such as the kind we have today wasn't built during the war simply because the necessary knowledge didn't exist.

You might say to me, "Sure, but all that your example proves is that the science of radar wasn't very well known as of the outset of the war." All that I can reply is that in the sense of being able to predict the performance of a particular configuration of a missile, rocket engine, airplane, or almost anything you care to mention, science still has an awful long way to go. For example, in order to understand better the potentialities of some new-fangled airplanes, people at RAND tell me that it's imperative that we learn more about propellers. And although I am sure that a high-brow physicist would not regard the learning involved as science, it nonetheless would be very desirable to learn more about making items like valves for rocket engines work as well as do the valves in our automobile engines. Contrary to all the allegations that have been made, I don't think that the lack of larger rocket engines has been entirely responsible for holding up our space program. What has been at least as responsible is all that has had to be discovered about making a variety of components and subsystems perform reliably.

There is, of course, one significant difference between the discoveries made as a result of scientific inquiries, and those made in the course of development: In the case of a scientific discovery you aren't apt to find the same idea in a previous issue of the *Physical Review;* otherwise it wouldn't be a scientific discovery. (By the way, when I say "scientific discoveries" I want you to note that I am not talking about the discoveries of economists—they can get along very well, indeed, rediscovering each other's discoveries.) On the other hand, when things are learned the hard way in development, almost invariably someone will find an obscure article and say, "If those engineers only had read that, the entire difficulty could have been avoided."

In one sense, the radar example just quoted is not typical of the problems that come up in development; that is, whereas in the case of short wave length radar the "windows" came out in the form of "peaks," it is more usual for them to come out as "troughs." It is more usual for them to come out this way because no matter how many factors you take into account in your design study, there will invariably be some reactions that you failed to take into account, and sometimes they may be very important. Because such reactions are not taken into account, radars can turn out to have very bad antenna patterns, airplanes can be prone to structural fatigue, and space vehicles to blowing up.

It is true, of course, that none of these kinds of problems is insurmountable—true, that given enough time and effort any system can be developed to have more or less the performance characteristics it was predicted it would have. In other words, when someone tells you that this or that is in the state-of-the-art, you can be fairly sure that at some finite cost, or in some finite period of time, something more or less like the specified article can be developed. The only hitch is that you, the practical decision maker, might be somewhat concerned whether the device in question will take 3 years to develop, or whether it will be 8 years from now before the thing is finally made to work. It might make some difference to you whether a missile you are considering will cost you to develop no more than a medium-range bomber you recently developed, or ten times as much. And you may worry that the missile, when it is finally developed, will turn out to cost not a mere 50 per cent more than you were advised it would cost, but, instead, five times as much.

To minimize the chance of being grossly misled you can, of course, consult a wide number of experts, and—believe me—you usually do. However, even in those rare instances that there is a wide measure of agreement among them, you still can't be sure that their advice will turn out to be good advice, or their experience relevant experience. Just consider a few of the cases in which it didn't.

Since we were talking about radars, let me illustrate this point by the case of a radar whose design was laid down during the last part of the war, and whose development became a very high priority matter right after the war. It was generally agreed that this radar would take no longer than two or three years to develop. The advances that it incorporated were regarded as being less ambitious than those incorporated in the wartime radars; and the same organization that had developed several radars during the war to the point of an airborne reliability of greater than 90 per cent in less than two years worked on this new radar. But a host of unanticipated problems came up, and it was much longer than the entire period of World War II before the new radar was made into a reasonably reliable instrument.

To turn to a different field: Some years ago it was believed that ramjet engines were wonderfully simple things, and even though no large ramjet engines had ever been developed, no more than a simple scaling job seemed to be involved. On this premise the Navaho missile project was started. But I can tell you that today the "Navahoes" certainly do not believe that the development of large ramjet engines is a simple, straightforward undertaking.

Or we might consider the case of titanium, which contrary to all the prophesies has not been extensively used in airplanes and missiles. The fortunate aspect of this story is that although its weight-saving characteristics have not proved nearly as useful as was initially contemplated, titanium's non-corrosive qualities will lead to a series of applications that hardly anyone foresaw—from marine vessels to ordinary kitchen utensils.

Here is one final example of the experts' consensus being slightly off the mark. Right after the war, it was widely believed that the turboprop engine would be far better for bomber aircraft and transport airplane applications than the ordinary jet engine, and that the development of such an engine would not be a much more difficult task than the development of an ordinary jet, because after all, the difference between the two engines was only some gears, a propeller, and a few other "simple" items. Because it was believed that the turboprop offered the only way of getting the required range, the B-52 was initially designed as a turboprop airplane. It is fortunate indeed that before development work got actively underway, a jet was substituted, for the development of the turboprop engine took years longer than it was generally supposed it would take, in part because the darned propeller mechanism turned out to be a very nasty bottleneck. On the other hand, progress in reducing the fuel consumption of the jets was much more rapid than a lot of engineers thought it would be. (I might add that I am very well acquainted with some of the experts who had these ideas on the turboprop and the turbojet engines, because they work at RAND.)

Let me summarize all these examples by commenting that each of them, in its way, illustrates the point that development is not only a business in which you have to expect rather substantial changes in a system between its inception and the time when it can be called a useful device, but also a business in which you have to be prepared to make some pretty substantial revisions in the time you think it might take to get something developed, in what it will cost you to develop, and in what it will cost you to procure after it is developed. In other words, development is a business in which errors of 30 or 40 per cent can hardly be regarded as errors.

It is true, of course, that if military planners had been willing to settle for the kinds of advances that have typified commercial projects, the outcome of military development projects would be far more predictable than it has been. All that I am pointing out is that highly predictable kinds of advances and highly rapid advances are not the same thing.

• • •

Now let me turn to a somewhat different question: "When in the development process can you tell if the thing is going to work more or less as well as you hope it will, how much it will really cost, and when you really can expect to have it?"

It is fairly obvious from the examples I have been citing that when the thing is in the design stage of development, the range of uncertainty is very large: If you are very lucky, you could get the thing in three years; on the other hand, if events go as badly as they did on that other project, it could be as many as six or seven. You hope it will only cost two million dollars, but you would be more than willing to sign a fixed price contract right now for three millions, because something deep down inside of you tells you that you may end up with a five million dollar item.

If I may digress for a moment, one of the things that remains a continuous source of puzzlement to me is how people can know full well that a number of very unexpected things have occurred in every single program they have been acquainted with and yet believe that nothing of the sort is going to be true of this next one. It's positively amazing how, when the thing is in the design stage, arguments will go on almost endlessly about details of the design that have nothing whatsoever to do with the fundamental technological problems. In estimating the procurement cost, extreme care is taken to make sure that no item, however small, is left out of account—for example, the cost of the fence that is to enclose the missile site is estimated down to a gnat's eyelash. Kill probabilities are spoken of in terms such as 83 per cent, missile accuracies in numbers more precise than measurement techniques can provide. The development schedules are so meticulously worked out that you might have the feeling the development itself is no more than a routine process of confirming them. I say that I wonder how people can become so absorbed in pretending they know things that they really don't know. I often wonder how *I myself* can become so absorbed in a study involving some new kinds of missiles, say, that the computations become the reality, and all that's happened to past estimates becomes as unreal as something that might have happened two hundred years ago.

Sharp improvements in estimates begin to occur only after the missile, radar, or engine is in test. This is not to say that after an aircraft engine has been first put on the test stand, or after the first three shots of a new missile, you suddenly can make estimates of cost, performance, and development that will be accurate within a margin of error of 2 per cent. You can't. And some terrible mistakes have been made by concluding on the basis of the first few tests that something was practically developed. On the other hand, it is often true that some pretty impressive things are learned as the result of the initial tests. For example, if you're developing an engine based on a new compressor design—even if the engine tested is far from a complete aircraft engine—its initial tests can tell you whether you're likely to come within shooting distance of getting the performance you expected. For example, we at RAND tried to find out why the predictions that Pratt and Whitney made for its engines almost invariably turned out to be better than the predictions made by the other engine companies. One of the reasons, we discovered, is that unlike the other companies, they almost always had a preliminary model of the engine in test before they made the prediction. Earlier, I talked about side-looking radar. When an experimental side-looking .86 centimeter side-looking radar finally was put into development, it took just ninety days to get it ready to be tested, and the cost of finding out what resolution it actually would provide came to some three million dollars. As it turned out, this was actually a much smaller amount than the Government had spent on past studies.

Sometime ago we looked into the accuracy of the estimates of production costs for a number of missiles and aircraft as a function of the phase of development the system had reached when the estimates were made. What we found was that when about half of the development time has elapsed in a missile or aircraft development program, you can be, roughly speaking, nearly twice as confident of your estimates as you were at the beginning of the program. What it cost to get this improvement in the estimates will ordinarily be a good deal less than half of the total development cost, since the amount spent until half of the development period has elapsed is ordinarily a good deal less than half of the total development cost.

I might point out that the evidence that I have cited reflects, among other things, the kinds of development practices that were used in the programs we studied. I myself am convinced that if the major aim in the programs had been to find out as quickly and cheaply as possible what would be involved in getting a satisfactory capability, the improvement in the estimates would have been much more rapid. In a few of the programs this was the major aim. But in the vast majority of others it wasn't.

So far I have been talking about the conditions under which new weapon systems are supplied. One of the two main points I have been trying to make is that initial estimates of a system's performance, reliability, and cost are subject to very large errors—errors that can be substantially eliminated only by developing systems that incorporate more modest advances than have typified military development projects. The other is that there are ways of reducing the risks involved in relying on initial estimates. Short of making a major decision to develop an entire system there are commonly many kinds of tests and experiments which, if conducted, will result in decided improvements in the estimates. In short, whether or not it is so regarded, development is essentially a process of learning.

Now I would like to say something about the demand uncertainties that underlie development decisions. These are quite as important as the supply uncertainties, although my discussion of them will be much briefer and much more in the way of generalizations.

One of the factors that is important in determining the demand for particular weapon systems is the rate of progress in related technologies. The extraordinary progress that has been made in reducing the weight of fission and fusion weapons, for example, has had a very considerable influence in determining the preferred kinds of missiles. Progress that was made some years ago in overcoming the problems associated with large solid fuel motors also has had a good deal of influence. Development of vertical take-off airplanes could have a good deal to do with the kinds of naval forces we will have in the future. But though developments in related fields may be very important in determining the demand for particular kinds of systems, predicting the course of these technologies is subject to the same kinds of difficulties I already have discussed. If people had been able to foresee some of these things better, some major decisions on the development of production of weapon systems would have been very different from what they were.

Another factor of obvious importance in making decisions on weapon systems is a knowledge of the demands imposed by our actual or potential enemies—of what Russia, for example, is up to in her own military programs. Once having determined who our enemies are now or might be (and a brief glance at the alliances of World War II will reveal that this itself is not always easy), it would be nice if we could plan our own military procurement programs so that the actions we took were not sensitive to those taken by them. To a certain extent we do this, but to carry this idea very far would require a much higher level of military spending than we now have. Within anything like the current budget level, the programs for our strategic forces have to be premised on some kind of projection of Russian capabilities. In other words, what I am saying is that we cannot hope to build enough flexibility into our own forces so that their effectiveness is not affected by whatever course of action other nations may take.

However, it should not be necessary for me to belabor the point that there is a very wide range of uncertainties, indeed, in projecting opposing forces over a period of five, ten, or fifteen years. Besides the ordinary kinds of problems involved in making intelligence estimates and intelligence projections, there are, in the case of Russia, some very special problems: Contrary to what is often assumed, the Russians, in fact, do not give the impression of a highly rational set of decision makers, carefully using the country's resources to maximize some well-thought-out set of objectives. The strategic notions in back of their planning are at best often very difficult to understand, as are many of their weapon systems choices.

All these things considered, you can see why the factors influencing the demand for new weapon systems are no easier to predict than those influencing the conditions on which they will be supplied.

• • •

Thus far I have been talking about the general nature of the problems underlying R and D decisions. What about their implications for research and development policies—which is, after all, the principal subject matter of this paper? There are, I think, two main implications. I will summarize my views on them very briefly and then, before concluding this already too long paper, I shall say something about the obstacles in the way of better policies.

The first implication of the nature of military R and D for policy is that the Government should be devoting a very significant proportion of its R and D expenditures to research and development activities falling outside the major weapon systems programs. I have in mind here expenditures not only on basic research, but also on those activities directed to experimenting with new techniques and to obtaining measurements. I stress experimental activities because one of the most important prerequisites to rapid technological progress is a very considerable willingness to try out new ideas. Very seldom indeed have studies alone led to the decision to go ahead with the development of a major technological advance. In fact, in many cases the effect of conducting long, drawn-out "scientific" investigations has been to dampen enthusiasm for trying out a really good idea.

Beginning in the late 1920s, for example, almost every study that was made of the jet engine came to dimmer conclusions on the feasibility and value of a jet engine than the study preceding it. Shortly before World War II, a study group composed of some very distinguished American scientists proved more conclusively than anyone had before that the idea didn't make any sense. Shortly after that, the British let us in on their wartime secrets, and one of the U. S. engine companies that had earlier debunked the idea became the leader in developing the jet engine in this country. An experimental engine had been developed in Britain only because a British investment company decided a jet-powered airplane would have an enormous advantage for carrying airmail. It is of interest to note that the amount the company risked in demonstrating the feasibility of the jet engine came to something like twenty or twenty-five thousand dollars. This, essentially, is the amount scientific committees spent nearly ten years arguing about.

I don't regard the only purpose of a large program in basic research and exploratory development to be the discovery of exotic new techniques. As I tried to point out earlier, the strategic uncertainties facing this country are so large that it would be extremely costly indeed to insure ourselves against all reasonable contingencies in our weapon systems programs. A much less expensive method of buying flexibility—of buying a capability to adapt our weapons programs to the actual strategic situation quickly—is to develop a large menu of technology. In saying this I am not suggesting that we should attempt to carry the development of components so far that weapon systems could be assembled from previously developed components with no technical risks involved. It is true that experimental projects often have been carried too far—that too much money has been spent on them before deciding which, if any, systems will use them. But one of the often-suggested cures for that problem—making decisions on the basis of paper studies—is not a well-advised cure.

If one of the main purposes of these research and development activities is to insure against strategic uncertainties, a very significant part of the research effort should *not* be directed to work which is ordinarily regarded as extending the frontiers of technology. In fact, I personally believe that this country is not doing nearly enough R and D work on kinds of techniques that do not get into the headlines. But even though the less exotic techniques often promise to be of very considerable military value, it's hard to drum up any enthusiasm for them.

Now let me tell you what experience strongly suggests—at least to me —as the second major implication of the nature of military R and D, which concerns the kind of strategy that should be pursued in weapon systems programs. What it suggests is that approach taken in systems development projects should be a frankly experimental approach. Initially the requirements for the system should be stated in very broad terms, and considerable emphasis should be placed on keeping the system very flexible until the major technological difficulties have been resolved. To expedite their resolution, equipment should be gotten into test as rapidly as possible. Decisions on the best set of compromises should not be made until there is some basis for making them; specifically, these decisions should not be made until a preliminary version of the system is in test.

I would also urge that parallel approaches be taken in attempting to overcome difficult technological problems. Part of the reason for this is implicit in what I have already said: Carrying, say, three component development projects into the initial stages of development is often likely to cost a good deal less in terms of both time and money than selecting the wrong approach initially and proceeding into a full-scale development program on the basis of that approach. Another part of the reason is that the return from putting more and more engineers on the same project or subproject is apt to be rapidly diminishing. Typically, the success of any particular subproject will depend almost entirely on a relatively few individuals. Give these individuals more and more people to supervise, and all that you will have accomplished is to substitute complexity for ingenuity. Once you have three hundred instead of fifty engineers on a fighter plane project, for example, a devilishly complicated device is the price that you have to pay in order to allow all those people to express themselves.

Finally, I want to say something about the obstacles in getting R and D policies more oriented in the directions I have indicated. The one that has been given most publicity is the extensive review process that projects must go through before they are approved. Committees often impose elaborate requirements on weapon systems long before such requirements should be imposed, and in the course of satisfying all the committee members, systems are often made much more complex than they need to be. Committees also constitute an enormous obstacle when it comes to getting action on any really new ideas.

But we all know that all this reviewing is not going to be stopped, or even substantially curtailed. I think that a good deal could be accomplished, however, by making the reviewing process reflect the kind of decision being reviewed: The kind of review that is appropriate before a weapon system project is started is very different from the kind required when development has been carried far enough that detailed considerations are really worth arguing about. And the kind of review that is appropriate for experimental projects not likely to cost more than a few million dollars is certainly very different from that appropriate for major systems projects likely to cost hundreds of millions. But the way the decision-making machinery works at present, low- and high-cost risks are often regarded in the same way.

A second major obstacle to getting policies that will make for more rapid progress in R and D is, I think, the widespread belief that in minimizing the total amount of time required to get a system ready for operational use, production problems are likely to prove a more serious constraint than research and development problems. The belief that production problems are likely to be the dominant problems leads to the initiation of large-scale production preparation early in a development program, even at the expense of minimizing the program's flexibility. Moreover, initiating programs in this way is so costly that the number of options that can be carried into development is substantially smaller than it could be if the programs were initiated on a different basis.

As I have said, this belief is very widely accepted; I myself, however, have seen very little evidence that production problems are a serious constraint on the time required to get a system into operational use. An examination that we made of some twenty development programs failed to disclose that those begun on the basis of very large production preparations furnished operational systems sooner than those that were not so begun. Moreover, I don't know of a single program in which the dominant problems turned out to be production, not technical problems.

But there is a much more fundamental objection to making minimal procurement lead times a dominant objective in research and development policies. It is simply that given the uncertainties that exist both in the supply and in the demand conditions, such a policy will not lead to an efficient allocation of the research and development budget. If the military research and development programs had been entirely concentrated on those systems that were regarded as the favorite choices ten years ago, I can assure you that we would not be in a very good strategic position today.

Now I would like to turn to a much more deep-rooted obstacle. I am referring here to the tendency present not only in the Defense Department, but also, I suspect, in all large organizations, to overestimate the costs of flexibility and to underestimate its benefits.

Perhaps I had better make clear what kind of flexibility I have in mind, since I can identify at least two kinds that are relevant here. First, there is the type of flexibility that is built into military forces so they can handle a wide range of contingencies—Type I Flexibility, if you will. There are many matters likely to remain just as uncertain after the forces are built —for example, how a war might get started—as they are today, and Type I Flexibility buys insurance against the kinds of uncertainties that are likely to remain uncertainties. It is the type of flexibility that Stigler had in mind as he wrote his famous article on what kind of a plant to build when the demand for a product is very uncertain.

Type II Flexibility, on the other hand, attempts to reduce the uncertainties confronting the decision maker by buying information on competing development alternatives. It is premised on the assumption that some of our resources can be used to reduce these uncertainties before military forces are actually procured and put on the line, that the greater knowledge attained by comparing development alternatives will contribute directly to widening the range of alternatives available to and reducing the number of uncertainties confronting those responsible for using our Type I Flexibility. Recently, increasing attention has been focussed on measures that would result in more Type I Flexibility, but I have the feeling that still far too little attention is being given to flexibility in the development process itself.

The reasons why far too little Type II Flexibility is purchased—aside from a development philosophy which results in large technical as well as financial commitments very early in the game—are, as I have suggested, that its costs are typically overestimated (in time as well as dollars), and that its benefits are typically underestimated. While lower echelon organizations sometimes underestimate the costs of program changes, my observations indicate that upper echelons almost invariably overestimate them. Often the costs of making any changes in a particular configuration are made to seem astronomical, even before a single piece of metal has been bent. The benefits of flexibility are underestimated typically because the range of contingencies the decision makers regard as reasonable is much smaller than the range that should be taken into account. People will argue incessantly whether an engine will finally turn out to have this set of performance characteristics or that set, for example, when the real thing to worry about is whether even the engine with the less desirable characteristics might be three or four years longer in development than you were counting on. The range of weapon systems alternatives that might be available to our main opponents in this business is frequently assumed to be no larger than the range available to us. In short, whether or not large size itself makes the tendency inevitable, I suggest that large organizations are commonly highly intolerant of ambiguity.

Finally, another major obstacle to the conditions that would make for more rapid progress in our military capabilities is our system of incentives. In the past, the method used for rewarding defense contractors has made the reward more or less independent of their performance. At the present time, incentive contracts are being substituted for cost-plus contracts in an attempt to rectify this situation. But I wonder whether the incentives embodied in these contracts will be strong enough to make a real difference in contractors' behavior. If the Government wants to impose a much stronger system of incentives, it should insist that prototype models be built before full-scale development contracts are awarded, and that production contracts will not be let until the system in question is well in hand. In other words, I suggest that winning or losing a 500 million dollar contract might prove a stronger incentive to most contractors than a possible variation of from 4 to 10 percent in the profit rate of that contract.

Quite as serious a problem as that of the sellers' incentives is the lack of a much better system of incentives on the *buyers'* side of the market. Long established rules of the game within the Defense Department often lead to types of behavior which the uninformed may find hard to understand. I don't mean to imply that these rules are unique to Defense, for they prevail in many other public organizations and agencies, and are not unknown within the business and academic worlds. But to give you a little better idea of what I am talking about in the context of military R and D decision making, let's say that you are a military decision maker and that someone has given you an idea for a new system that not only looks good, but that might provide a clinching argument in the continuing interservice debate on roles and missions. What are some of the pressures and incentives that will affect the way in which you proceed to sell your idea to the highest defense echelons? In the first place, under the rules of the game as I understand them, until you've sold your system you should not direct undue attention to any other system that might conceivably be regarded as an alternative, even though it might be available only in a much later time period. In other words, there is great pressure on you to suppress alternatives, because they may be used against you in the higher courts. Secondly, after you have drawn up your plans and submitted them to the higher echelon agencies, it will be difficult for you to force yourself to change them; since changes might well be regarded as a sign of weakness in plan and uncertainty of will, your incentive is heavily on the side of preserving the *status quo* of your scheme. Third, if you finally do get the program started, the rules as they exist reward your getting it underway with sufficient steam that it will be terribly difficult to stop. Economists can iterate and reiterate that past investments should not be considered in making future decisions, but you know they will be.

You can say, of course, that people who obey these unwritten rules of the game act irresponsibly. To do so indicates a willingness to judge them that implies the game itself is poorly understood: no individual in the organization is more responsible for the kinds of rules of the game that result in such behavior than is an individual in a corporation whose rules result in other kinds of strange behavior.

Some people argue that the only way to get around these problems is to set up a centralized system for both procurement and research and development. But I myself would not want to see such a solution adopted. Without attempting to go into the reasons, let me only say that one thing that weighs very heavily in my judgment is the experience of the British Ministry of Supply. Though the Ministry did very well during World War II—when there apparently was not time to get things really well organized—in the postwar period what the Ministry did to improve efficiency in the small was far overshadowed by the conservative influence it had on military research and development as a whole.

To date, very little work has been done by social scientists on the crucial problem of getting better rules of the game. But there is no problem facing the Defense Department that is more important—or more challenging— than removing these and other obstacles to a more effective set of R and D policies.

KLAUS KNORR AND OSKAR MORGENSTERN

Science and Defense: Some Critical Thoughts on Military Research and Development

I. Introduction

This memorandum expresses the authors' belief that the management of military Research and Development (R & D) in the United States is wanting in some important respects—namely:

(1) that the present organization of R & D is not sufficiently conducive to the assertion and survival of new ideas;

(2) that we fail to give proper nurture to the nation's great R & D assets;

(3) that the military do not give adequate inspiration and direction to the scientists and engineers;

(4) that the concept of R & D is too narrowly confined to military weapons; and

(5) that this narrow concept neglects invention and innovation in military doctrine and in associated political strategy.

Although our analysis indicates various approaches toward remedying these deficiencies, the main task of this memorandum is to identify and evaluate the weaknesses we detect in R & D management. Once these are recognized and understood, we are sure, specific ways and means can be found to infuse our R & D effort with an improved sense of direction.

In raising certain questions about U.S. management of military R & D, we are not implying that the U.S. performance is unsatisfactory. Indeed, we know of no reliable criteria for making such a judgment. All we ask is whether on some particular scores this performance could not be better.

We also realize that it is very hard for the outsider to raise critical questions. As is usually with the executive branch of government, the defense-related departments—and, in this case, the armed services as well—deal with concrete problems about which they possess a wealth of information, and are able to draw upon a vast range of know-how that cannot begin to be matched outside the government. The information released by the government to the public at large is, in the military area, limited by the requirements of secrecy; and the public justification of government policies naturally emphasizes the merits of the decisions made, while de-emphasizing or ignoring the comparative merits of the choices that were forgone.

From Policy Memorandum No. 32, February 18, 1965. Reprinted by permission of the Center of International Studies, Woodrow Wilson School of Public and International Affairs, Princeton University.

This state of affairs does not absolve members of the public at large from posing questions, even critical questions, as long as they do so with a sense of responsibility. To ask such questions, is possible because a great deal about the management of R & D can usually be correctly inferred from what gets into the public domain. And to raise these questions is important inasmuch as foresight is at a premium in military R & D because of the long lead-time characterizing the development of new systems and doctrines, and flexibility is an asset because of the inevitable shortcomings of foresight in matters so much obscured by various uncertainties. Yet large bureaucracies find it hard to operate by procedures that cultivate and heed the imaginative long view, and that escape the drag of inertia. The searching question from outside—whether inspired by worry or curiosity—is therefore not a luxury. It is a challenge that may keep the respondent in trim.

II. Two Basic Questions on Current R & D

People who, in various capacities, have the opportunity to observe the current R & D effort of the United States in the military area often raise two central questions. First, is the current R & D output satisfactory, or is it stagnating or lacking in proper direction? Second, do we give proper nurture to the institutional complexes on which, over the long run, we must rely for imaginative military R & D?

These related questions are basic because they result from less than satisfactory answers to numerous more specific questions. But they usually lack a sharp cutting edge; they are of a generality difficult to translate into the kind of operational meaning that encourages and commands clear-cut answers. This is so partly because they deal with intrinsically difficult problems, partly because they suffer from unfamiliarity with the entire body of officially known facts—a circumstance that is not rarely used as a shield behind which the official world withdraws—and partly because they are frequently fathered by an ill-defined worry and a questioning mood rather than by incontrovertible demonstrations of poor R & D results.

STAGNATION OR PROGRESS?

If there are qualified observers who express concern over the present U.S. effort in military R & D, who suspect that it is suffering from a dearth of significant innovation or, in other words, from stagnation, they have not posed the issue in a way permitting their suspicion to be either confirmed or disproved. But neither have those who do not share these anxieties, and who roundly deny the presence of stagnation and defend or extol the current R & D effort. The facts are that both sets of responses rest largely on hunch, and that it is not easy to give these hunches proper definition and provide them with a rigorous analysis of observable phenomena.

If the present U.S. effort in military R & D is characterized as stagnating, it is usually implied that it compares unfavorably with some previous period, or with comparable activities elsewhere, especially in the Soviet Union. Those subscribing to this view feel that the last few years have been comparatively poor in terms of military innovation. However, others protest that one can hardly speak of stagnation in view of the broad push for major improvements in various weapons systems currently under way. This disagreement suggests the difficulty of giving the term "stagnation" operational meaning. It is implicit in the controversy that those apprehensive of stagnation refer to the relative absence, at present, of distinctly *new* weapons ideas—ideas that represent a *discrete* improvement on previous technology. But they do not suggest how discrete a change must be to rank as a truly innovative act. There are obvious choices, but there is no single obvious choice in this matter. Were one extremely demanding, perhaps only the nuclear bomb would rank as a true innovation in recent decades; in which case, the idea of steady innovative progress would be exceedingly dubious. Were one extremely generous, on the other hand, the number of observed innovations would be correspondingly very large. We must be careful not to identify as evidence of lack of progress the absence of spectacular events which impress themselves upon the mind of the public. Indeed, without an operational concept of either stagnation or its opposite—progress—different observers with equal knowledge and acumen could look at the same reality and characterize it as either stagnating or progressing. Under these circumstances, one's affiliation with either group is likely to be affected, if not determined, by the precise role one is performing in connection with military R & D; thus the "ins" (i.e., those in some manner responsible for R & D) will be inclined to reject the stagnation thesis, while the "outs" will be more likely to support it, or at least to entertain it.

It may be impossible to reach agreement on where and how the dividing line between stagnation and progress should be drawn. It may be suggested, however, that although any comparison of the current with some previous R & D performance may be instructive for purposes of remedial action, it is otherwise of only academic interest. Even if, by some sort of definition, we could be said now to be stagnating in comparison with a preceding period of military R & D, this change may be inevitable because the course of R & D is subject to fluctuations that are difficult, or impossible, to control. There are some observers of military R & D—but few scientists and engineers involved in weapons development—who maintain

that we, and presumably other countries as well, are moving on a technological "plateau," in the sense that no major breakthroughs in military
technology are now in sight, perhaps because another revolutionary advance must await the cumulation of new basic knowledge in the sciences.
It may also turn out that we can afford relative stagnation—indeed, that a
degree of stagnation is at this time economical *if we can be sure* that no
potential opponent will offer us a new challenge.

However, the only reference with regard to which stagnation—or, to
dismiss this dubious term, an unsatisfactory R & D performance—matters
concerns not past but future military needs and the comparable R & D
performance of the Soviet Union. We certainly do not want to fall behind
potential opponents in military technology, and we should prefer a degree
of technological superiority over them. In fact, even superiority would not
be satisfactory as long as it left the United States vulnerable. If it were
feasible, we should want a military technology, complete with appropriate
doctrine, affording military security at minimal risk of destruction and defeat. Given the objectives of national security, our military needs are
dictated not only by the Soviet performance. Indeed, our attention may be
riveted too exclusively on this one source of potential danger. The United
States has now, and will continue to have, military requirements involving
other potential adversaries, ranging from spear-throwing cannibals to large
countries possessing mass armies and, as a recent example shows, capable
of acquiring nuclear weapons of some sort.

But if the sufficiency of military R & D is to be measured in terms of
future needs and, to an important though limited extent, in terms of the
Soviet performance, then our yardstick is obscured by the veil of Soviet
secrecy and the opaqueness of the future. Even though our intelligence resources—themselves an important area for R & D—have recently improved, we are unlikely to gather full knowledge of the R & D effort of the
Soviet Union and other potential opponents; and, even if we did, we could
not be sure about the operational military capabilities to which their
efforts might lead some years hence. Indeed, our capacity to foresee future
contingencies is inevitably frail. All we can do is to perfect our intelligence resources as best we can and try to anticipate the kinds of conflicts
to which the United States might be a party in the future, and the conditions, including the military conditions, under which they might take
place. Inescapably confronting great uncertainties, there is one recourse,
however, which we can hardly afford to neglect. This is to maintain an
unremitting search for new military technologies, if only on the assumption that a resourceful or lucky opponent might be capable of making any
discovery *we* are able to discern at the technological frontier.

NURTURING OUR R & D ASSETS

Until the day arrives when military power is no longer organized on a national basis, another task we cannot afford to slight is to maintain our capacity for military R & D—and especially our great laboratories—at a high level of performance. It is these resources that have been advancing the technological frontier and provided us with a stream of new choices of military power.

The fact that scientific discoveries with unpredictable military implications may occur here or elsewhere, and that international political developments bring frequent shifts in alignment involving new and unexpected areas of conflict, makes it clear that the worst thing we can do is to rest content even for the briefest time, believing that our situation is safe, stable, and incapable of improvement.

We might neglect to nurture the national assets represented by our great laboratories for a number of reasons. We might subject them to various forms of maladministration; starve them of funds for reasons of economy; reduce them because we feel that we have forged ahead to our opponents or because of a belief that, moving on a technological "plateau," no exciting prospects are within reach. (This belief, incidentally, implies that we can determine unambiguously that such a "plateau" exists—obviously a very difficult matter to prove.) We might retrench in order to encourage our opponents to follow suit, and thereby abate the arms race and foster the prospects of international disarmament.

Much as we must welcome a beginning of effective arms control, which so far has only led to an agreement forbidding air and underwater nuclear tests, mere moves in that direction may have a retarding effect on development work. Because of it, the great government laboratories are made uncertain of their mission and have difficulty in holding and recruiting scientific and engineering talent. If we could be sure that the same effect is obtained elsewhere in the world, we might be justified in taking this as a revolutionary turn in the perennial, pernicious human tendency to degrade virtually every scientific discovery into a tool of war. But can we be sure?

Whatever the reason, to diminish our resources for military R & D is unsafe as long as international disarmament is not a dependable reality. It is these precious assets that help us to minimize the danger of technological surprise achieved by a potential enemy, and give us flexibility for adjusting our means to security in a dynamic world. To maintain these resources as a proper pitch requires their continuous exercise.

It is, of course, very difficult to maintain a perpetual sense of "urgency" in any organization. SAC has this problem as an operating unit. Business enterprise also faces it but is kept on the *qui vive* by competition. The problem is much less tractable in the case of government-organized research. Here also applied science responds to outside stimulus, even if it does not take a competitive form. But the guiding spirit of a government laboratory or other research organization is more dependent on the presence of eminent minds, on the phase of discovery in which a particular science finds itself, and on a host of other circumstances which cannot be predicted. If a laboratory shows signs of ossification, it is desirable to reorganize it. On the other hand, a great research tradition, if it can be kept alive, is a powerful magnet, as anyone knows who is familiar with the history of the Cavendish Laboratory at Cambridge or of Niels Bohr's Institute at Copenhagen. As far as government weapons laboratories are concerned, the difficulties are compounded by the need for secrecy and the difficulty which their scientists and engineers experience in receiving proper recognition individually or collectively, except for purely scientific work. Here the government has the important, but as yet unfulfilled, task of providing a solution. In addition, however, the academic scientific community, which normally awards accolades to members on the basis of published work, will have to find ways to express esteem for those members who in the interest of the nation devote their lives to work that for a long time must remain shrouded in secrecy. Only if this is assured will the government succeed in attracting and retaining the first-class talent it needs.

III. Invention and Innovation

Several problems of definition are encountered as one attempts to scrutinize the record of military R & D. Although a great deal of R & D is naturally undertaken for the improvement of existing weapons systems— undoubtedly an important function—its most interesting object, in an age of rapid and accelerating scientific and technological knowledge, is the generation of new systems.

The concept of a "weapons system" presents the first problem of definition. This concept should not, in our opinion, be limited to mere hardware, as is still often done, but should be understood to comprise a man-machine system, frequently of great complexity. Indeed, it should even be extended to new strategic, tactical, and logistical concepts of which new hardware is an integral part, or with which hardware is closely associated. For reasons spelled out below, thinking in terms of the larger configuration and context should offer more initiating points in the conception and development of new systems. The reader should note that, in the following, we apply the concept of R & D not only to military hardware, as is customary, but to the entire complex of military power and its components.

Another problem of definition, already noted, concerns the "newness" of a weapons system. When we talk of a *new* system, we exclude the improvement, no matter how substantial, of an established one and refer instead to a system based on a radically new idea, representing a discrete forward step. Thus the increase in speed, firepower, and range of tanks and airplanes is a highly desirable development of the capabilities of these weapons. But the associated extensions of their uses occur within an established pattern which changes only gradually and the defenses against these weapons require no basically new ideas or principles.

The dividing line between new and improved systems is not always easy to draw. Thus, the idea of the ballistic missile was no longer new when the POLARIS system was developed. But the system was fundamentally new in that it broke with the classical target of the submarine—the ship at sea—and made the submarine a strategic weapon against land-based targets deep in the interior of continents. Other illustrations are in order to show the difficulty of classifying progress: The invention of a multiple nuclear warhead for missiles could confound any contemplated anti-missile defense and also make hardened missiles easy targets. Yet a multiple warhead represents nothing but a step in the linear development of reduced weight and volume of nuclear weapons. Indeed, improved accuracy alone can be had by perfecting gyroscopes marginally. But the consequences are devastating for the strategy which still assumes that fixed bases have a future. In combination, these effects on present weapons systems and their related strategies are tremendous. It is clear that these developments are under way and that this must be true of both big nuclear powers. The changes are "small," but they are highly upsetting in effect.

Finally, there is the difficult problem of defining the birth of a new system. Its genesis, of course, begins when the underlying idea is first conceived. But in this sense the number of ideas conceived and broached is very large indeed; most of them are poor ideas, and many are premature, lingering for long periods of time before they arouse interest. It would seem useful to apply here the economist's distinction between "invention" and "innovation." The inventor has the idea; the innovator decides whether it is a "useful" idea, and organizes its development and application. The innovator assumes the risk of development and gives the "go ahead" sign. Without invention, the field of innovation lies fallow; and without the innovator, invention is barren. Both invention and innovation are creative acts, but they differ in the creative resources they call for.

It is generally agreed that ideas for new weapons systems have in the past usually come from the scientists and engineers, and only rarely from the military. The major exceptions are inspired on the battlefield, or by an arms race to the extent that it is qualitative rather than quantitative. On the battlefield, the military may conceive of new requirements under the stress of adverse circumstance, and a qualitative arms race will make the military want to acquire a system already developed by the potential opponent (in which case, the opponent is the "inventor"), or a new system to counter one of the opponent's. But in general it has been the scientists and engineers who have acted as the "inventors" and, with the large resources recently allocated for this purpose, they have fed a stream of new ideas to the military (and the civilians in the defense establishment), who must perforce act as the "innovators."

INVENTORS AND INNOVATORS

This distinction immediately suggests three questions: How good are the scientists and engineers as "inventors"? How good are the military as "innovators"? Has the relationship between these two groups been structured in a way to produce a satisfactory innovational output?

If we are interested in military R & D in the United States since World War II, the absence of any suitable basis for comparison makes it next to impossible to give a rigorous answer to the first two questions. Yet there seems to be widespread consensus among qualified observers that a rich technological menu has been offered to the military by the scientists and engineers—although, as far as the United States is concerned, it should be duly noted that many of those scientists and engineers, and many of their ideas, have come from abroad. There is appreciably less certainty that the military (and the civilians in the defense establishment) have, on the whole, performed the innovating function very well. This is perhaps not surprising, since innovation is a complex and difficult process, and a risky as well as expensive enterprise. When confronted with a new "invention," the innovator must evaluate it in terms of technological feasibility, economic feasibility, and military worth. All three tests require special resources and time, and are beset by various uncertainties.

If, on the whole, the military have done less well as innovators than the scientists and engineers have as inventors, one major reason for this difference in performance suggests itself immediately. By and large, the scientists and engineers engaged in military R & D have been recruited and, through experience, trained for the very business of invention. They tend to become specialists in the inventive process. The military, on the other hand, are recruited and trained primarily for the complicated— indeed, increasingly complex—business of waging war, and not for the equally complicated business of military innovation. Their main business is to use the equipment given to them under the most varying circumstances. Some of the military (and some of the associated civilians) no doubt become very good at the innovating business, especially in discovering optimal ways of employing hardware—in short, in developing "doctrine." They do so by dint of experience, inborn talent, and the ability to learn rapidly. But the majority hardly become specialists in military innovation and should not be expected to excel in this area. As one defense scientist put it to us: "It often seems to us that we must deal with layers and layers of people who have little or no technical competence, and hence possess only a limited ability to comprehend our statements."

Moreover, the business of military innovation has become far more difficult than it used to be. This is obvious as far as hardware is concerned. The military innovator must know enough science and engineering to deal with new inventions. What is less obvious is that a novel difficulty has arisen over the last few decades regarding the development of "doctrine." Doctrine is the selection of targets, the manner of deployment and use of weapons. Deterrence has appreciated, in comparison with defense, as a mainstay of security. Hence strategic targets must be chosen on political, psychological, and economic grounds, as well as on strictly military ones. The military can hardly determine them alone and their doctrine is thus constrained and formed by these other factors. Even in tactical situations, such views play an increasingly important role. One of the most formidable features is that ordinary military experience either does not exist (as is the case with nuclear weapons) or is inadequate because of the great complexity of present weapons systems. For instance, there is no intuitive way of optimally placing missiles, determining their firing rates, planning evasive and bluffing actions, etc. All this has now become subject to mathematical computation, to new scientific methods, and is thereby removed from mere experience. Maneuvers, which used to provide fundamental information, are either impossible or no longer as instructive as they formerly were. What is therefore needed is to train more officers scientifically so that they can preserve their influence upon the shaping of doctrine.

On the other hand, enthusiasm for computation and computers can easily get out of hand. There is no magic in statistics and computers. The value of statistics depends crucially on the quality of the assumptions on which they are selected and on the quality of the data that are procured. And the computer, no matter how "sophisticated," is merely a tool. Its output depends on the brain that uses it.

A vital part of doctrine is the *selection of targets*. In the past, this has been the undisputed province of the military. When fleets encountered each other, the target was the enemy vessel; when a landing had to be made, it was the coastal fortifications; heavy artillery fired to obliterate the enemy's heavy firepower and the machine gun was clearly an anti-personnel weapon. But with the advent of more modern weapons, old problems reappeared and new ones began to arise: To what extent should unarmed civilians be considered legitimate targets if they are caught in the field or working in arms factories, or even in factories several stages removed from weapon-making but indirectly vital to it? What does international law say about this? Which are vital targets from an economic point of view if one is faced with a prolonged conflict? Is a weapon that may be technically suited to destroy a given target also politically acceptable? If a weapon is to be fired only in order to demonstrate capability or resolve, will a target area do in which physical damage would be negligible or nil?

All these questions show that target selection, in many circumstances, is not simply a "military" matter. A military man cannot know where the enemy's economy is most vulnerable or why a certain target should at times be considered tabu. Targeting is a complex matter requiring the integration of many considerations. No simple military doctrine can be proposed or, if proposed, last long, since the value and meaning of all possible targets undergo constant fluctuations. New weapons may allow us to reach hitherto unattainable targets or, conversely, the realization that there are novel targets may call for the design of new weapons. This shows the manner in which the interplay between the military and the inventor has to be viewed. Closer cooperation is called for than is customary. There is clearly a wide area to be explored for novel ideas, such as points of vulnerability in machines and means of disabling them instead of killing soldiers and sailors; or devices or policies which will make the enemy unwilling to fight although he may have the physical equipment to do so, etc.

CONSTRAINTS ON INNOVATION

It is a different matter, however, that—with some notable exceptions—the military have been conservative in making their selections from the menu of radically new ideas proffered by the scientists and engineers. Relative lack of training for the innovative role may account for this conservative bent in considerable part. However, much of this conservatism may also be attributed to four intersecting sets of constraints on military innovation: economic, institutional, bureaucratic, and doctrinal.

Of course, there is no question but that there must be constraints in the form of checks. After all, not all new ideas, even if technologically feasible, can be adopted. The scarcity of financial resources and the need to maintain effectively organized and trained military forces call for an appreciable degree of stability, and hence of parsimony in the adoption of destabilizing systems. The real question is whether or not these constraints, as administered at any one time, are excessive, or applied in a manner tending to stultify innovation.

The need for and the impact of the *economic constraint* are obvious. Even though the United States has not, since the Korean War, denied defense a handsome share of the federal budget and the national income, the need for choices among innovations—and often painful choices—is inevitable. There is no doubt that innovation is expensive. Invariably it requires considerable expenditure even in its early phases. Some inventions may require very little, but the tendency is for basic discoveries to be made only in large, expensive laboratories as a by-product of continuing improvement work, often of a marginal character.

Two pertinent questions may be raised. First, it may be questioned whether, in their preoccupation with existing and ready capabilities and the funding of these capabilities, the military (with considerable assistance from Congress in many cases) have not been too slow in eliminating obsolete and truly redundant units, facilities, and supplies, thus unnecessarily denying resources to the innovating function. Holding on to existing weapons, bases, and doctrines is natural, especially when the new weapons and devices have never been used in earnest and when they become available only slowly. Because of this gradual replacement of the old by the new, outmoded and the most modern equipment will be on hand simultaneously. Besides, it is not obvious at which point some weapons become obsolete. When was the battleship doomed? The experiments made by General Mitchell foreshadowed the event, but they did not provide an immediately convincing argument and substitute. How definite can one be today in stating that the large aircraft carrier is finished, even though a few years hence it may appear that the answer should have been "obvious" to us at this present date? Considering that there are hundreds of interacting weapons systems, assigning a positive or negative *value* to each is indeed, even in the absence of new technology, a formidable task.

The second question worth raising is whether the recent emphasis on cost-effectiveness may not be too much of a good thing. Admittedly, sophisticated cost-effectiveness studies played too small a role until Mr. McNamara became Secretary of Defense. But there are fairly widespread feelings that its present role may be excessive and constitute an overreaction to the previous lack. Cost-effectiveness studies can obviously be valuable when one compares military systems with other systems producing similar specific outputs and manifesting a similar sensitivity to important environmental conditions—although even here various uncertainties may cause such studies to run the risk of a misleading dependence on pseudo-accuracy. In particular, the derivation of the numbers in terms of which "effectiveness" is measured is itself a far more delicate procedure than these studies reflect. The cost-effectiveness concept is less useful when it comes to choosing between systems with broadly dissimilar outputs, and this is precisely why, unless employed with intelligent regard for its necessary shortcomings, it may act as too sharp a brake on the innovating process that is concerned with radically new ideas. One might well ask whether the POLARIS system would have been developed if cost-effectiveness notions had been applied then as they are today. The reader will judge for himself what the right answer is. The authors have grave doubts that the POLARIS system would have been developed or, if introduced, have been pushed as hard as has been the case, to the benefit of the United States.

While economic constraint is important, it surely is not dominant, especially at the present time, when the wealth of the country is rising fast and a combination of easing of tensions and apparent absence of drastically novel technological moves by possible opponents gives this country a breathing spell. Should a reduction of defense expenditures prove possible, the best way to accomplish it would be by eliminating clearly obsolete bases and installations; and the worst way would be to cut down on basic research. Fortunately there is at present evidence of the former and, so far, none of the latter. But this danger always exists; it is an old experience that the economic ax as a rule falls first on research. In the present time of unparalleled broad scientific advance, for this to happen would be disastrous.

The *institutional constraint* interacts with the economic. Existing weapons systems, and their marginal improvement, have behind them very strong vested interests in the defense industry, in the Congress, and among the military themselves, many of whose skills and careers are tied to the operation and improvement of *existing* capabilities. Attention and spending may be biased in favor of the preservation and improvement of accepted systems, and thus make for a degreee of inertia inimical to enterprising innovation.

The *bureaucratic constraint* is perhaps more subtle. It resides in the power of inertia developed by all large bureaucracies, in a preference for doing accustomed things, for doing them in accustomed ways, and hence —without deliberation—for putting up undue resistance to innovation. Large bureaucracy necessarily means a large and layered structure of committees, and necessarily comes up against the familiar problems of centralization and decentralization. And there is the further well-known fact that there is safety in sticking to the familiar, and risk of making mistakes in backing the radically new.

A serious matter is the constant possibility that highly significant developments have occurred which have had no chance of being incorporated because they upset rather than support our current posture. The more basic the new idea, the more disturbing it is apt to be. It threatens to downgrade existing equipment, to disturb prevailing doctrine, and to divert money to new uses to the detriment of existing institutions. A monolithic control over the uses of new ideas works in the manner of all monopolies —i.e., they are essentially determined to fend off the new.

The final act of innovating in the military establishment requires that a new idea be transformed into, and authoritatively accepted as, a "military requirement." Within a large and complicated bureaucracy, this act demands a confluence of assent and support from many sections and layers. As experience shows, this is unlikely to happen unless the new idea succeeds in arousing a strong and pervasive feeling of enthusiasm and urgency. This collective endorsement is rarely created in a trice, and may be impossible to muster behind a very daring and unorthodox idea. It is clearly easier to persuade one man or a few that a new idea is a good idea than to persuade scores and hundreds of men to that effect. Within our context, numbers make for a conservative attitude—i.e., for risk aversion.

The *doctrinal constraint* likewise interacts with the others. Prevalent military strategy favors inventions that fit, and tends to resist ideas that clash with it and require its revision. The temptation is to evaluate new ideas in terms of old practices. The ideas that get the green light are not usually the ones threatening to unbalance strong doctrinal attachments. Military doctrine is distilled from experience and serves as a means to guide and coordinate the nation's military efforts. Its revision is a correspondingly serious matter. Yet, it is equally clear—especially in a world of accelerating change—that the orthodoxy of the day should be open to continuous challenge in the form of new information and new ideas. Too often, doctrines survive by inertia; good doctrines are only those that survive the test of challenge or are adapted in the light of challenges that, in turn, have survived the test of constructive criticism. The defense of established doctrine can be overdone; and it is overdone when it is allowed to rest on convenience rather than merit. Moreover, prevalent military doctrine tends to be preoccupied at best with *present* realities (more often, with those of the past) and is apt to discount to an excessive degree future requirements, which are often inevitably "iffy" and nebulous. Not rarely it is the chief potential user who is the last to get on the bandwagon. Doctrinal constraints are sometimes also of an ideological or political character. The uneasy feeling about the use of chemical and bacteriological weapons may be cited as an example.

All four constraints may not only join in resisting radical departures from existing systems, but also make it hard to kill R & D projects once

they have been accepted and have developed momentum, thus again denying resources and attention to novel alternatives that might turn out to be
superior. In the United States since 1954 about $6.8 billion was spent by
the Department of Defense and the Atomic Energy Commission on projects that were only abandoned after a long period of development (e.g.,
DYNO-SOAR, ANP, NAVAHO, SNARK).[1] This shows the difficulty of
recognizing obsolescence in a rapidly changing technological milieu, and
of acting accordingly.

At this point, however, we must mention one countervailing factor and
a few notable exceptions to the conservative bent of the military mind. Interservice rivalry has been an important factor in mitigating bureaucratic
inertia and the conservative bent. It can sharpen innovative alertness and
generate powerful motivation on behalf of change. For example, the main
force in moving the Navy to develop POLARIS was possibly the goal of
wresting part of the new missile technology from the Air Force. The
strong strategic rationale for the system was apparently a secondary and
later concern. Without it, however, the initial motivation would, of course,
not have been powerful enough to produce a strategic naval missile of
profound importance.

The chief exception to slowness in entering upon new ideas is the military eagerness to develop outer-space technology. Similarly, there was recently an overwhelming receptivity to the *laser*. No conservatism can be
detected in these two cases. In neither has there been, as yet, any significant military payoff. Technological opportunities connected with outer
space are met with what might be called innovational frenzy.

It is hard to understand why *some* novel technologies are able to stimulate such a sense of urgency in the military. (In the case of satellite technology, Soviet achievement no doubt prodded emulation and rivalry.) The
fact remains that these cases stand out as exceptions and do not necessarily compensate for undue conservatism in the development field as a
whole. On the contrary, once these exceptional areas have produced large
programs that have perhaps acquired some of the properties of romantic
fads, they may attract more attention, energy, brains, and money than
their military utility can justify, and thus act as barriers to the reception of
other, less glamorous "inventions."

These thoughts do not imply that the military (and the associated civilians) are not intelligent and conscientious, or that bright new ideas are rejected or shelved in favor of poor ideas. Rather, it is the *good* weapons

1. *Department of Defense Appropriations, 1965,* Hearings before the Subcommittee
on Department of Defense, Committee on Appropriations and Committee on Armed
Services, U.S. Senate, 88th Congress, 2nd Session, Washington, D.C., GPO, 1964,
Part I, pp. 178–79.

idea—an idea that has withstood protracted study and testing, and hence is relatively "safe"—that may be the enemy of the truly new and possibly brilliant invention. The latter has to be recognized as such and this is not a simple matter at the time when it appears on the scene. In scientific life, too, a new idea or principle usually has to fight hard before it is accepted, but its acceptance is speeded by the absence of monolithic organizations into which it has to be introduced and by which it has to be approved; rather, it encounters only diffuse opposition and can attract the ardent support of young scientists, uncommitted to the old.

IMPROVING INNOVATION

Some conclusions follow immediately from the foregoing. Clearly, military innovation will tend to flourish to the extent that the military are able to curb their conservative bent and are receptive to the consideration of new ideas, unsettling as they may be. This suggests a need for appropriate education and indoctrination. It likewise suggests the identification of military talent suitable for the innovational role, the assignment of identified talent to the innovating function, and perhaps even a modest acceptance of a degree of specialization by the military in different military roles and tasks. Our analysis also noted interservice (and perhaps even intraservice) rivalry as a spur to innovation. Such rivalry would seem to be an asset worth preserving. In fact, it might be useful to maintain a further rival or rivals in the civilian agencies of the defense establishment. Civilians, after all, are more easily recruited and trained for the innovational function, since, unlike the military, their principal role is not to man and operate weapons systems.

An outstanding example of imaginative rivalry is the foundation of the Livermore Laboratory of the AEC. While important work on nuclear warheads was done at the Commission's Los Alamos Laboratory, some scientists were dissatisfied with the speed of acceptance of new ideas there and organized the new laboratory in order to let their ideas have free play. Out of the ensuing rivalry came the speedy development of the hydrogen bomb and of many other devices which might have become available only after much longer time-intervals.

Having praised interservice and interinstitutional rivalry as a spur to efficient innovation, we must unfortunately observe that an overzealous Department of Defense has in recent years permitted less and less opportunity for healthy rivalry in activities pertaining to R & D. In an excessive and indiscriminate pursuit of economy (much of which may turn out to be illusory), it has acquired something close to a stranglehold on the military services and built a monolithic structure that—like all monolithic structures known in history—shackles rather than fosters the spirit of innovation.

The military may have to design new institutions and practices, and strengthen existing ones, such as the Office of Naval Research, by means of which to assure themselves of responding quickly to new ideas with military implications. To accomplish this is not primarily a matter of money; rather it is a matter of proper two-way information flow and evaluation of the new.

It also seems indicated that the four constraints we have discussed must be kept in check if innovation is to be given its full due. There is something to be said in favor or in defense of each constraint. As long as resources are scarce, economy is a legitimate social objective. But the military must make the claims; their economic evaluation—whether the country can "afford" all that is demanded—clearly belongs to the higher civilian levels of decision-making. The institutional, bureaucratic, and doctrinal constraints are in some measure inescapable, for in the modern world we cannot do without differentiated institutions, we must secure the great advantages of bureaucratic management, and we require doctrine for the guidance of behavior in the area of defense. The crucial question, as always, is one of proper balance. To decide on, and enforce, the right balance—"right" being a matter of politics as well as of administrative management—will always call for appreciation and alertness at the top level of the defense establishment, and of the government. There are no formulae for solving the problem in a mechanical manner. But there may well be new administrative devices for facilitating the enforcement of a proper balance.

We have noted above the need for curbing the bureaucratic constraints that militate against closer cooperation between scientists and engineers, on the one hand, and the military, on the other hand. There is no simple, administrative gimmick in sight for achieving better cooperation. One defense scientist told us: "When you put this problem to the military as individuals, they agree immediately and wholeheartedly that closer cooperation is needed. But when they act collectively, they always go the other way. Everybody agrees that closer cooperation is a good idea; yet practically nothing happens." This would seem to indicate that the military are in this respect slaves of institutions that they realize to be at fault; and that a new organizational idea—an important invention and far-reaching innovation —is needed to improve matters.

It also seems to us that it might be useful to introduce a measure of specialization in the evaluation of new ideas emanating from the scientists and engineers. Such evaluation is at the heart of the innovating process. To begin with a complete evaluation that brings all bases for evaluation to bear at once may cause a bottleneck and obstruct the imaginative application of any one basis for evaluation. This suggests experimentation with a scheme that would initially separate the evaluating function from making authoritative decisions in terms of budgetary requirements, and under the full weight of the other constraints. Of course, such specialization would work only if the decision-making authorities made full use of the evaluators' output—a condition that it would be admittedly hard to meet.

Another remedy for dealing with the more or less inescapable accretions of inertia and rigidity, and the drag of vested interest, is insertion in the innovative process of talented outsiders—that is, of people who are not a regular part of the bureaucratic structure. As American experience indicates, *ad hoc* groups of such people have been at various times very productive in handling major tasks of military R & D. In some important instances, they have been decisive. The difficulty lies in how to institutionalize the imaginative use of competent outsiders for this essentially non-routine purpose.

It is not even clear that any sensibly sharp line can be drawn between the "insiders" and "outsiders." Modern technology and science are so complex and so interrelated that even in the final stages of the development of a weapon there is no necessary concentration on a specific "military" technology. That is one reason why, on the one hand, the ostensibly strictly military laboratories often make important contributions to civilian technology, while on the other they are continuously drawing on an increasingly broad range of resources that seem to be fully divorced from everything military.

One classic case of outsiders intervening in a decisive way was the famous Von Neumann Committee, which was organized at John von Neumann's behest and without which the United States would not have embarked on a missile program at a time when its success was highly dubious, both from a technical and from a military point of view. Another concerned the POLARIS concept, which was made possible solely by the reduction of the weight of the warhead that could be put on a missile in a submarine, a fact that became known to its proponents only through the personal intervention of outsiders who realized what could be done. There was also Project MATTERHORN, set up by J. A. Wheeler on his own initiative; it was a critical element in initiating the invention of the hydrogen bomb. There are more such cases, though not all are as spectacular. But in their general effect they have been of very great significance.

A difficulty lies in how to institutionalize the imaginative use of competent outsiders for this essentially non-routine purpose. The chance factor connected with their activities is of great importance, as it is in the whole field of scientific work and discovery. One must never try to eliminate it.

On the contrary, devices favoring chance must be designed, but it does not make itself felt favorably unless invited by the proper environment. True research is simply not deterministic—a consequence of the stochastic nature of the world. In the ultimate analysis, excellent results are always the product of a single mind. Cooperation is also necessary, to be sure; but when the latter is overdone by insistence on too much teamwork, there is great danger that truly original thought cannot come to the fore quickly enough.

It is the essence of bureaucracy to organize human activity and it seems to be a law of bureaucratic life that anything made routine tends to develop the very propensities toward orthodoxy and inertia that must be kept in check. And yet the employment of outsiders to perform this initiating and checking function should be made a more frequent and important feature in producing and considering innovative choices. Perhaps, if this need were recognized as sufficiently urgent, the nation would muster the ingenuity to discover a reasonably promising solution to this problem. We have the feeling that over the last years there has been too much regimentation and rigidity in this area, a lack of free flow of people among the laboratories, the universities, the military, and the Department of Defense, and that this may account in part for the impression of stagnation which we have encountered in our studies and conferences.

THE "MILITARY REQUIREMENT" CONCEPT

Another precondition of vigorous invention is a deft handling of the requirement concept according to which an R & D project cannot be carried to an advanced stage unless there is a definite "military requirement" or mission for the hardware expected to result. The rather ill-defined military-requirement approach to authorizing an inventive effort has been reviewed and somewhat revised recently; but it is not yet clear whether these modifications go far enough toward ensuring against an excessive restraint on speculative exploration across the present boundaries of scientific and technological knowledge.[2] The scarcity of resources unquestionably demands some such procedure for selecting for development the most promising ideas and inventions, and for weeding out clearly disappointing projects after an early stage of development; and it is only reasonable to admit that the application of any procedure is itself costly, in terms not only of administrative resources but also of some margin of mistaken decisions.

2. See the searching paper by James T. Ramey, "The Requirements Merry-Go-Round: Must Need Precede Disarmament?" *Bulletin of the Atomic Scientists,* November 1964, pp. 12–15.

There are two entirely different reasons why some projects must be weeded out. The first, mentioned in the preceding paragraph, is disappointment regarding the military value of a new device. It may be found to be less than anticipated and the weeding out is in recognition of this disappointment. The second relates to the fact, not uncommon in a period of rapid technological advance, that, while a project is being carried out, a better idea, a superior device, or a technological move of the opponent appears, making an otherwise perfectly acceptable project obsolescent. Then a reappraisal has to take place. If it does not, we may be "throwing good money after bad" (as is frequently done in business) because a sizeable investment has already been made which supposedly is too valuable to be scrapped. But the logic and power of technological progress are inescapable. The DEW line, for example, which was a reasonable device as long as this country was exposed to aircraft attack, had to be abandoned because it became useless when missiles replaced airplanes, and the DYNO-SOAR never made much sense to begin with. Yet is was not abandoned until $411 million had been spent on it.[3]

Unless great care is taken, however, the military-requirement procedure may kill off too many new ideas *before* their value can be sufficiently established. This may happen as a result of fiscal overanxiousness in administering the economic constraint. If the military requirement must be very clearly elaborated before expenditures for the development of an idea or project are authorized, the economy ax may fall too readily in every case, or in most cases, of doubt. And if this happens, the procedure will favor conventional technology, for which the uses are obvious because they likewise are conventional, and will be inimical to novel ideas, whose specific military application is less immediately apparent or, more important, for which the specific application itself must be invented, together with the hardware. It is hard to see how blackboard demonstrations can be revealing enough in the case of many new ideas, especially radically new ideas. Often they must be pushed to the laboratory and demonstration stages before their potential is discovered; and it takes time and effort to discover the new uses and missions that a new technological idea opens up.

IV. Directing the Inventors

However, we must now turn to other, though related, aspects of the relationship between inventors and innovators. So far we have been discussing the stream of ideas moving from the inventors to the innovators—that is, from the scientists and engineers to the military and their civilian associates. Regarding *new* weapons ideas rather than the improvement of exist-

3. *Department of Defense Appropriations, 1965,* Part I, p. 179.

ing systems, this direction of flow seems indeed to have predominated. But this makes one wonder whether more of a feed-back flowing in both directions and initiated on either side would not enrich R & D results. Even as far as *new* weapons ideas are concerned, it is not clear that the inventors could not profit from some direction by the innovators. Why should the innovators not specify needs and the inventors try to meet them? Such a relationship should not be regarded as a substitute for, but rather as a supplement and stimulus to, the initiative of the inventor.

We are not saying that the inventors receive from the military innovators no direction whatever. The military ask for improvements of hardware all the time, and not rarely they approach the engineer with a specific concrete military problem. Moreover, the process of military R & D involves some sort of continuous dialogue between inventor and innovator and, provided it works well, the scientists and engineers cannot be unaware of the problems with which the military (and the Department of Defense) are preoccupied. The inventors, including those in defense industries, will have noted that the military tend to be preoccupied with the most destructive military contingencies—most destructive, that is, in terms of *physical* destruction; and that, offered a choice of new weapons, the military have a strong tendency to pick the most destructive one. In view of the training and indoctrination given to them, this is perhaps a natural inclination, even though, as we are at pains to demonstrate throughout this memorandum, the national interest would benefit from more versatility in this respect. At this point we only wish to note this fact. Inventors are apt to be responsive to this preoccupation of the military. In speaking of a relative lack of direction, we had in mind the endeavor of the innovator that is oriented to the imaginative solution of anticipated problems —whose recognition itself requires an act of imagination.

Indeed, it seems fair to ask whether U.S. weaponry (and hence military capabilities and doctrine) is not too much the result of new scientific progress and technological *opportunities,* and reflects to too small an extent anticipated security *needs* that might be derived from an imaginative identification of various future contingencies. There is no question that the exploitation of technological opportunities has proved extremely valuable in providing for U.S. security. But there is a question of whether we should not also encourage and organize, as a corrective and supplementary step, thinking that moves in the reverse direction—from contingencies to military choices and strategies to ideas for weapons systems— and to new tasks for the scientists and engineers. None of this should take the form of specific military requirements, the difficulties of which were discussed above. Rather the military should spell out frankly what their present and anticipated headaches are in order to stimulate thinking by the scientists.

As it is, the scientists and engineers will generate weapons ideas for which the military innovators see little or no use, or for which, though suspecting their usefulness, they find it hard to develop a doctrine. This sort of response is inevitable, and even necessary to some extent. But its extent might be diminished somewhat, perhaps even reduced to what is essential in terms of expected overall utility, if the military became more in the habit of trying to foresee military difficulties. A readiness to review and modify current strategies and doctrines would make them more receptive to new technologies, and, as we noted, would prevent the military-requirement approach to authorizing R & D from becoming dominated by conventional thinking. In addition, of course, the inventors would be encouraged to explore technological areas in which a military interest is already defined. It is largely for these reasons that we advocated at the outset an extension of R & D activities from hardware to doctrine.

CONJECTURING ABOUT FUTURE NEEDS

We have raised the question of whether the military establishment is adequately concerned with anticipating future military needs, and prepared, on the basis of such anticipation, to give the scientists and engineers fruitful directions. Beyond doubt, both the importance and the difficulty of applying imaginative foresight have increased with the pace of change in the modern world. As we look ahead, we must assume that the identity, capabilities, and behavior of potential opponents and present allies may change, and that the utility of employing military power in different forms is apt to increase or decrease in response to changing weapons technology or a changing political acceptance of the use of military force. Mutual apprehension over the risk of escalation, for example, has greatly narrowed the range of political issues justifying the use of certain kinds of force for certain kinds of purposes, at least at the present time. Similarly, the defiant behavior of militarily weak nations vis-à-vis great military powers— and the submission of the latter to such acts—indicates a much higher current discount on the sheer use of military force than prevailed in the past.

Any propensity to let technological opportunities govern military R & D to the exclusion of military and political desiderata would engender substantial and possibly fatal risks. If we permit technological opportunities, spontaneously developed, too strong an influence on the design of our military security posture, the latter may lack balance in terms of various contingencies. We would find ourselves ill-equipped for certain types of conflict that may arise, and that a clever opponent might choose to precipitate. On the other hand, we might condemn ourselves to wage wars for which we are superbly equipped but which, in many contingencies, are undesirable on other and compelling grounds. In order to minimize this risk, we should set out deliberately to promote the alternative approach to initiating invention as well.

An organization endowed with plentiful analytical resources should be able to subject the variable conditions determining the usefulness of military power to systematic and fairly continuous examination. It would not be difficult to design a conceptual structure to inform a systematic scanning of trends in the relevant military and political environment. Thus, we might formulate a typology and topology of potential military targets, of weapons capable of disabling targets temporarily or permanently, of various conflict situations, and of different military strategies and tactics.

The required enterprise is not directed to *predicting* the future. At no time is the future completely foreordained. It is not given in this sense, and hence it cannot be known in advance. On the contrary, it is to some extent subject to manipulation by men and governments, including our own. But if we are unable to predict the political and military future, we are able to conjecture about it; in fact, such conjecturing is inseparable from acting; and we can thus conjecture more or less well. On the basis of our discernment of relevant trends, and their evaluation in terms of our experience and preferences, we can project and evaluate hypothetical futures. Within limits, we are able to choose between hypothetical futures and try to bring about one rather than another—in other words, to make the future an object of our planning. The deeper our understanding of the present, the better we should be able to choose the future.

No matter how well conducted, such conjecturing enterprise will hardly reduce very appreciably the uncertainties that face us when we attempt to look and plan ahead; indeed, it may reveal further uncertainties that we would have ignored without it. But a better understanding of their nature puts us in a position to design our posture and policies in such a way that these uncertainties matter less, that we are better prepared to cope with them.

Conjecturing about the military and political future is really another area in which disciplined imagination, and indeed *inventiveness,* are patently needed; and—as we have already suggested—our R & D activities might well be extended to this problematical area. Several of our observations on the nature and management of military R & D apply also to invention and innovation (i.e., policy-making) in this area. For instance, intergroup rivalry should be a benefit, and a pluralistic structure for serving the conjecturing function would seem preferable to the single center. Likewise there is a useful role for outside talent in stimulating, challenging, and supplementing the insiders' performance; RAND, IDA, and other organizations serve this function to some extent but must guard against the inevitably strong forces which tend to make them insiders.

This requirement for conjecture about the future has not received adequate attention in the design of our military posture and in the guidance of military R & D. We do not, of course, pretend that better conjecturing is either a necessary or a sufficient condition for improving the R & D output. It would not be necessary if, without organized effort, the right kinds of hunches were somehow inserted into the process. But we have no evidence that this is so. It might not be a sufficient condition if we failed to let good conjectures influence policy. We do not know whether the integration of responsible conjecturing and planning would be hard or easy to ensure in our bureaucratic structure and within the context of established administrative practices. Finally, we realize that the conjecturing business is difficult to organize and to evaluate. But this is not a good reason for refusing to experiment and innovate in this perhaps crucial area of statesmanship.

In any case, the anticipation of future military needs—indicating the military choices of action that the United States should have in dealing with various conflicts apt to arise—is essential to basing R & D decisions (and many other defense decisions as well) on a proper appreciation of the interplay among developments in military needs, military doctrines, and military technology. Nobody will deny that these developments are interdependent. The question is whether we are imaginative in anticipating and in recognizing the new forms which this interdependency takes in a very dynamic world, and the reduction of these forms to specific new policies, doctrines, and hardware.

By way of illustration we will pose some questions of the kind we must ask if we want to mobilize whatever our potential may be as a nation for controlling the future.

TWO EXAMPLES: NUCLEAR AND NON-NUCLEAR FORCES

On the level of strategic deterrence, the general assumption at present is one of underlying stability. It is assumed that the strategic confrontation is overwhelmingly between the United States and the Soviet Union, that each is deterred from attacking the other because both populations are vulnerable to immense destruction at the start of an all-out war, and that the military technology exploited by both sides is basically stable—that is, that no upsetting breakthroughs are likely at present.

These assumptions may well hold true for some time to come. Yet we can scarcely afford to take this for granted. Even now, the invention of an anti-ballistic missile system cheap enough to place the protection of big cities within the realm of the economically feasible cannot be ruled out completely. More important, as already observed above, the development of multiple warheads and improved missile accuracies render missiles in fixed locations increasingly vulnerable to enemy strikes and, if this effect becomes important enough and greater resort to mobile and concealed systems seems desirable, technology might come up with countersystems that make mobile launchers less safe than they are now. How likely is it really that the POLARIS system will retain indefinitely the advantages at present attributed to it? We may judge the prospects of technological surprise in this area to be small; but, after all is it not in the nature of surprise that it is hard to anticipate?

Similar questions might be raised about the vulnerability of our system of command-and-control. This is perhaps the single most important complex of problems faced by the United States as far as its military power is concerned. Nor should the anticipatory worry focus solely on new engineering technology. Doctrine for the use of weapons is an important factor in the equation of security. The history of warfare is full of instances where success was achieved by using given hardware in surprising new ways. Classic cases occurred when Philip of Macedon organized his soldiers in phalanxes, when the English at the battle of Agincourt used dismounted bowmen in an unexpected manner, and when the Germans in World War II used the A-88 anti-aircraft gun against heavy fortifications or simply filled up their invading tanks at French gasoline stations instead of relying on their own logistic supply. Doctrine has a tendency to become rigid and ossified. While we concern ourselves much with research for new hardware, we make no remotely comparable effort to study new ways of using existing devices, of looking towards unconventional ways of waging —or avoiding—war.

The purpose of strategic nuclear forces is not exhausted by the deterrence of strategic attack by an opponent. The precise relationship between such forces organized on a national basis impinges on the behavior of states in various conflict situations, ranging from limited war to intense diplomatic crises. Strategic power, fundamental to military power as a whole, is an important means of communicating with an adversary, of making disclosures about one's resolve, contingent plans, and capabilities —in short, of influencing his behavior. The military system, therefore, needs to be judged not only in terms of its capacity for strategic reprisal or counterforce missions in the event of strategic war, but also as a system of communication. Indeed, fighting itself and the manner in which it is done are a communication. From this point of view, the hardware components and the doctrines require continuous review, within a framework of interaction with actual and potential opponents and allies. It would be surprising if this focus did not lead to innovative demands—that is, to demands for invention in the fields of hardware and doctrine. Invention in the latter area, the "soft" fields, is particularly difficult and ought therefore to be especially well supported. Of this there is little evidence. Yet it is precisely here that the most profound changes have occurred from time to time. They do not announce themselves dramatically like a nuclear explosion. They are suddenly with us, having come upon us silently and unheralded.

A searching review of strategic capabilities is also in order as major changes of the relevant environment take place, become imminent or—very important to preparedness based on anticipation—emerge as a distinct possibility. Major shifts in the patterns of alliances and international antagonisms may constitute a drastic change in the relevant environment. The gradual proliferation of national nuclear capabilities is another, and one where the United States may have been almost exclusively preoccupied with attempts to arrest it or slow it down. We have not concerned ourselves enough with anticipating ways of accommodating ourselves to this development by designing policies and means, including military means, to protect our security interests in the changing environment. To give an important example: drastic disarmament may be far less probable in the foreseeable future than nuclear proliferation. But if the prospects of disarmament should begin to increase, it will be late to begin studying its impact on our strategic power and capabilities. There is sure to be an appreciable impact on the delicate mix of weapons we are trying to maintain. Thus, the expected survivability of the remaining strategic forces might decline if numbers of strategic vehicles were greatly reduced or certain types of vehicles abolished entirely. Numbers and diversity have figured as an important way of ensuring adequate survivability of the strategic force. A reduction in the number of delivery vehicles would also affect the expected utility of active defenses against them, and hence their penetration and retaliatory power.

Arms control measures are easily affected by technological progress. The development of multiple warheads, for example, would make obsolete a well-thought-out arms control plan or agreement that rested on counting the number of missiles and equating these with the number of warheads (even if a fixed yield). It would become necessary to look into each warhead itself. And this might be an intolerable level of inspection to *both* sides. Nor is there any way of stopping this technological development unless laboratories were inspected and controlled. Whether this is feasible is another matter. What we want to show is merely that negotiators have to be aware of impending technological change and must understand its military consequences. For this, they must be assisted by properly supported research; a mere vague awareness of technological possibilities is insufficient, since their military implications may not be as transparent as in the above example. Otherwise the danger exists that negotiators might commit this country—with the best of intentions—to acts which conflict basically with its interests.

Even lesser measures of arms control—whether multilateral, bilateral, or unilateral—which are more likely to be adopted, are apt to influence the strategic balance. The need to anticipate such changes and their military consequences calls certainly for review of military hardware and doctrine, and possibly for an appropriate exercise of our capacity for invention and innovation.

Similar problems appear if one turns to so-called "non-strategic" military capabilities designed for more limited applications of force. Here one encounters evidence of great doctrinal uncertainty about the use of "tactical"—or, more correctly, low-yield—nuclear weapons. To develop suitable military doctrines for new arms is not an easy task in a world of rapid technological progress and political change. At present, we seem to be doctrinally at ease as far as strategic nuclear forces are concerned. But this feeling may be deceptive, and not necessarily long to endure, as the brief history of strategies for the employment of such systems clearly manifests. During the first few postwar years, when the United States enjoyed a monopoly of nuclear bombs, these were regarded as an uncertain adjunct to non-nuclear military power; and the last fifteen years have witnessed such frequent shifts in strategies for their employment that it does not seem absurd to ask: what next?

In the case of so-called tactical nuclear weapons, doctrinal uncertainty has been even more pronounced, with the most recent notable shift downgrading their utility in comparison with non-nuclear arms. The source of this change resides in the military and political disadvantages that the use of these weapons are surmised to entail. These disadvantages—though perhaps hard to anticipate in terms of concrete impact—loom so large that the *net* advantage of using these weapons is sharply called in question. Their presumed disadvantages derive primarily from anxiety lest their use involve a substantial risk of uncontrolled escalation, quick or gradual, to all-out strategic war. Hence the concept of safe "fire breaks." The political disadvantages of using tactical nuclear weapons are apt to arise primarily from their expected destructiveness in territories to be defended, and in the political and moral stigma that has attached itself to nuclear bombs, and that might be especially virulent if they were employed against an opponent not possessing such weapons.

These problems are exceedingly complex, and raise questions that apparently have failed to attract sufficient analysis and that have certainly not found answers in settled doctrine. A watchful public is left in a state of considerable uncertainty and anxiety. The problem of escalation and escalation management in particular calls for further study and decision. The basic dilemma is clear. In view of the enormous stakes involved, we must do everything to avoid uncontrolled escalation to the strategic level. On the other hand, although escalation to all-out nuclear war can hardly ever figure as a means of rational policy, the threat and risk of escalation from one to another of the lower steps of the escalation ladder may be a major means to conflict limitation or intra-conflict deterrence. This dilemma casts a dubious light on simple notions of the "firebreak" and shows again the need for research in this much neglected area. Clarification of these matters is more important than adding a new piece of hardware, but it is to hardware that we primarily look.

Another series of questions poses itself if we ask whether the military and political disadvantages anticipated from the use of non-strategic nuclear weapons are likely to materialize regardless of circumstances that are variable along several dimensions. For example, are all nuclear weapons equal in these respects? Or how do we have to distinguish among weapons of different yield, range, and accuracy; between defensive and offensive weapons (e.g., ASW vs. a PERSHING); and between the defensive and offensive use of one and the same weapon? In other words, do different nuclear weapons and different modes of employment vary in their escalation potential? And whatever the escalation potential inherent in a particular weapon or mode of employment, what can we do—for instance, by means of verbal communications to an opponent—to manipulate this potential? Similarly, does the escalatory potential of such weapons not also vary with kinds of conflicts, depending on the adversaries, the theater of war, the properties of the system of control, the severity of the provocation which led to the conflict, etc.? Turning to the political disadvantages, do they not differ with various conditions along the dimensions we have indicated? Thus, will not the devastation of territory to be defended vary greatly with the theater of employment; and may not the political onus of use against a non-nuclear power vary considerably, depending on whether or not non-strategic nuclear arms are used in the face of clear-cut aggression, and depending also on the kind of weapon employment, and on the scale of destruction caused?

If the results of such an exploration are confronted with existing military capabilities, it appears possible that—in terms of instruments capable of inflicting varying scales of destruction on an opponent—the United States is at present best equipped at the upper end of the spectrum, represented by means to inflict large-scale destruction. In contrast, it is probably less well equipped to deal with conflict situations in which capabilities represented at the lower end of the spectrum are called for; and are called for precisely because of the political and military consequences to be anticipated from the employment of highly destructive weapons. It is true that this lack of balance has been recognized by the Defense Department and that the buildup of non-nuclear capabilities has been accorded a high priority in recent years. It nevertheless remains a question whether corrective action has gone far enough. For instance, realistic anticipation of future conflict situations might suggest that the development of weapons of low lethality, or of wholly non-lethal systems, has been neglected, even though, in certain kinds of conflict, their use could achieve our military purpose exhaustively, and do so with minimum military and political disadvantages.

If an analysis recognized and used distinctions of the kind identified in the foregoing, we might find that U.S. weapons systems and use doctrines are adequate, and perhaps more than adequate, for coping with *some* kinds of conflicts, while they are quite inadequate, perhaps grossly so, for dealing with *other* kinds of emergencies. We might even conclude that the United States is not well equipped for asserting its interests in the *most likely* conflict situations. In any case, we are apt to discover that the United States is unlikely to be provided with satisfactory choices of action unless—on the basis of the kind of analysis suggested—it develops weaponry and doctrines to fill the gaps and repair weak spots in its armory. From such analysis, then, would come demands for military innovation and new inventions, a stream of instructions and inquiries addressed to the scientists and engineers, a new kind of activation of the nation's R & D resources. Indeed, a new role would be attributed to the importance of inventions in the field of political activity and, therefore, to political scientists, who would then be expected to turn inventors. For many of our problems, doctrines based solely on "military requirements" are too narrow, no matter how well developed in terms of traditional military competence. Unhappily, it cannot be said that the mere involvement of civilians from various government agencies provides a sure-fire remedy. Civilians, too, can be insensitive to the rapid change of political conditions and their military implications. They also need to become better "innovators" and to develop and use a corps of "inventors."

"TABU PROBLEMS"

The need to integrate the search for new devices with new uses of old and new weapons, the politico-psychological factors influencing target selection, the admissibility, or the lack of it, of certain weapons in various conflict situations, show that a broad area exists in which continuous study and review are needed. All these factors are subject to frequent variations whose influence upon defense policy is seldom, if ever, obvious. Moreover, these are inevitably delicate questions: they simultaneously involve the Department of Defense, the State Department, the Atomic Energy Commission, etc. Often no one department or office normally wishes to touch them for fear that the others will consider this an invasion of their rights. Nor do seemingly "independent" research organizations, working for particular government agencies and dependent on them for continuing financial support, dare to take up many of these questions—especially if they realize their political implications. The problem of escalation of nuclear conflict or of target selection is one illustration—although, of course, outsiders have written a fair amount at least about the first problem.

The fear of getting involved in difficulties of one kind or another keeps some of the most gifted and knowledgeable government employees from the frank and comprehensive study of these "tabu problems," to the detriment of the country. They are considered "political" and at that point the analysis normally stops and their resolution is left to the working of *ad hoc* political processes. The nation is, from time to time, openly confronted with such issues but no searching preparatory work has been done well in advance.

There ought to be no tabu problems in the military-political field. The issues involved are precisely the most vital for the nation. In science any question is admitted. The times are long past when non-scientific powers such as the churches could put a lid on the search for truth. This search always begins with asking questions, and does not become successful until the right questions start being asked. Finding the right question often takes a long time. But it is only in this manner that progress has been made.

It is even more difficult than that: before questions can be asked, facts have to be known. But there is also a tabu on looking for certain facts or mentioning them. Many relevant facts are uncomfortable to know and unpleasant to live with. They cannot even be stated without connecting them with other facts, beliefs, shibboleths, and this is undesirable. So in a spirit of pettiness or, worse, out of reluctance to face their fears, the powers that be do not like to hear that certain new powers are emerging, new attitudes exist, that projects have aborted and time limits been exceeded, that alliances have become brittle, etc., etc. Yet to know and to state this knowledge fearlessly wherever it is applicable is the fundamental preliminary condition for evaluating our situation.

Wherever administrations are involved, there is authority, obsolete tradition, stickiness of procedure—all detrimental to the exploration of the new, the unconventional. It will be a great day when a government office (or any other, for that matter) is organized with a built-in procedure to overcome precisely these obstacles to progress.

Here we note simply that a real, serious search should be made for devices whereby these vital "tabu problems" can be identified and thoroughly explored. The President's Scientific Advisory Committee (PSAC) would seem to be an ideal place, considering the delicacy and importance of these matters. Yet this committee does not have a single social or behavioral scientist as a member, although all these problems are overwhelmingly beyond the reach of "mere" natural scientists. (*Sit venia verbo.*) This in itself is a sad commentary on how limited is the appreciation of the situation. It is, of course, understandable that the "hard sciences" are held in higher regard than the "soft" social sciences. But we must realize that the greater apparent success of the former largely reflects two facts. They are dealing with essentially simpler problems than do the latter, and they have received far greater support than have the social sciences. Neither condition makes it reasonable to conclude that the social sciences cannot give greater assistance to statecraft—provided they are adequately nurtured.

THE VICE OF THINKING IN ABSOLUTES

The foregoing remarks have pointed up a vice from which some of our thinking on military problems has been suffering in the past and from which it seems hard to escape. This is the vice of thinking in terms of absolutes—by which we mean a tendency of thinking that something identified at a high level of generality is either this way or that way—for instance, unexceptionally good or unexceptionally bad—instead of allowing that consequences usually depend on a number of variable conditions. It is the tendency to think too much in terms of categories, as if its members contained wholly homogeneous rather than notably heterogeneous constituents; in other words, a tendency of not differentiating problems sufficiently, of shying away from their fine structure because taking this structure fully into account is difficult and speculative.

An example may indicate this tendency to think in simplistic terms. For several years, official spokesmen have laid down the categorical dictum that "nuclear proliferation" is bad and hence to be resisted. At this level of generality, we have no quarrel with the dictum, and we would not worry about its adequacy as a guide for action if the United States were in a position to put a stop to nuclear proliferation. But this is not within its power and, regarding the real world, the dictum is altogether too flat to serve as a good guide to realistic policy. As of the end of 1964, would the development of a national nuclear capability by India be as bad, from the viewpoint of U.S. interests, as was the explosion of a nuclear device by mainland China? Or would we be as worried if Sweden developed such a capability as we would be if the UAR did? Clearly, one can distinguish between *kinds* of nuclear proliferation in terms of the properties of the new nuclear capability involved, the system of command and control, the identity of the new recruit to the ranks of nuclear powers, the impingement of alliance structures, and so on. Surely, *some* kinds of proliferation are, from the viewpoint of our interests, worse than *others;* and it is not inconceivable that, under special circumstances, some cases would *in the net* not be bad at all. The inclination to deal in absolutes expresses itself not only in connection with the prospect of nuclear proliferation. We find its precipitations in much of current thinking on tactical nuclear weapons, the MLF, disarmament, bacteriological and chemical weapons, the concepts of "overkill" and "firebreaks," etc. It is a tendency in thinking about new weapons and doctrines, in military R & D, that we must begin to curb. When it comes to making policy, absolutist dicta are seldom very helpful.

V. A Conclusion

We cannot conclude this study without once more stating that any discussion of R & D for military purposes has to be widened to comprise political, sociological, and psychological elements. There are firm indications that warfare is assuming another face: though we possess infinitely more power than man has ever envisaged in his wildest dreams, the use of power—not only of the most brutal kind—is becoming an increasingly doubtful tool of international relations, even when they deteriorate to the most dangerous levels. This is more likely due precisely to the ease with which power could be used and to the danger of total annihilation with which the user is automatically threatened rather than to any new moral ideas—all other moral suasions having at any rate failed dismally in preventing war. It may be safer to rely on a new prudence than on a new morality. But our feeling that the recognition of immense danger to himself may prevent the potential aggressor from acting is after all only a feeling which may be disappointed at any moment. So the task is to search for new international systems, under which just peace can prevail and the changing aspirations of a world exposed to so many turbulent forces can be accommodated without disaster for any nation. Military force—as *one* basis of order—will have a firm place in such schemes, but its organization may radically differ from what we are accustomed to. It would therefore be fitting for the Defense Department to raise its sights and, besides supporting research for weapons and their use, also support and encourage research on how war may be avoided. Science can and should become primarily a tool for peaceful progress. This will mean that really bold, and yet tough, thoughts will have to be thought, far transcending anything that is now before the public eye—in this country or elsewhere.

IV

THE SCIENTIST AS A DECISION-MAKER

Along with the phenomenal growth of science in the United States has come an increased involvement of scientists and engineers in the decision-making process, and in politics in general. The scientists' new awareness of their societal responsibilities, both real and imaginary, and the concomitant desire to do something about these responsibilities, are natural reactions to the magnitude of the scientific programs which our government has undertaken. Even when scientists would have preferred to avoid the political thicket, they have been sought out to assist and advise the government on technical problems that involve contentious political considerations. A number of scientists have risen to top management positions in the executive departments and specialized agencies heavily involved in research and engineering programs. Even more important are the access and influence that scientists enjoy at multiple points in the government where policy is formulated.

Albert Wohlstetter, in the first article, points out that the scientists' potential contribution to resolving the problems that involve an interface of technology and politics is limited by the degree to which they fail to acknowledge the limits of their particular knowledge. The scientist who does not distinguish between scientifically derived judgment and "passionate opinion" can be more of a hindrance than a help to the public official charged with the responsibility of making a decision.

The participation of scientists in domestic politics is described in the articles by D. S. Greenberg and Donald R. Fleming. The political "baptism of fire" of scientists in the 1964 presidential election may presage a general political awakening to the potentialities of electioneering. Whether future campaigns will involve widespread co-ordinated action by groups of scientists and engineers probably will depend upon the appearance of a policy, or a candidate, that they especially dislike. Of more immediate concern to university scientists is the manner in which the federal govern-

269

ment distributes its funds for scientific research. Decisions on this distribution have brought the academicians into the high politics of science.

In an article analyzing the steps leading to the decision to build the H-bomb, Warner R. Schilling emphasizes the minimal character of the choices made by the President. With the Department of Defense and the Atomic Energy Commission divided about the advisability of undertaking the program, the State Department exerted the decisive influence in precipitating the decision.

The problem of conflicting scientific expertise, which is common to many national security decisions, is described by Robert Gilpin in connection with deliberations over a nuclear-test ban. He attributes much of this difficulty to the new social commitment of scientists which makes it hard to distinguish their advice on "what is" from "what ought to be."

ALBERT WOHLSTETTER
Scientists, Seers and Strategy

That scientists today crucially affect decisions on national and international security—and therefore the fate of us all—will come as no news. After radar and jets and the A-bomb and the H-bomb and intercontinental rockets, the statement surely is obvious enough. But what does it mean? Like much else that is obvious, it is not very clear. Just how do the results of scientific research and the methods of science and the scientists themselves actually figure in decisions on arms and arms control? And how is the role of the scientist in such matters related to the more familiar functions of the politician, the military man and the ordinary citizen? Above all, what does "scientist" mean in such statements?

Even partial answers to these hard questions might help us deal with some others that are even harder and trouble us more. If by "science" is meant a difficult and specialized discipline currently accessible only to the few, a trained minority, what does this do to the democratic process? At the end of his term in office, President Eisenhower spoke of the danger that "public policy could itself become the captive of a scientific-technological élite." On the other hand, scientists, it seems, might become the captives. When scientists are drawn into the pulling and hauling of "politics," what happens to the freedom and objectivity of science or scientists? Again, given the partially hostile world in which we live, defense decisions must sometimes be made in secret. Where scientists are involved in such decisions, what does this mean for the vital features of science as a fallible but open, verifiable and self-correcting enterprise?

Especially in the two years or so since Sir Charles Snow's Godkin Lectures, discussion of these and related issues has been intense, sometimes bitter, and I think on the whole useful. But the issues have provided matter for both of Sir Charles' renowned "Two Cultures": exciting literary material and a supply of blunt weapons for the factional quarrels and feuds

From *Foreign Affairs*, April 1963. Copyright by the Council on Foreign Relations, Inc., New York. Reprinted by special permission.

Note: This article is based on a longer monograph bearing the same title, presented at a conference of the Council of Atomic Age Studies at Columbia University, of which Mr. Christopher Wright is executive director.

271

among scientists. As a result, while there has been some light shed, there has also been much mystification.

The Godkin Lectures, delivered at Harvard in the fall of 1960, begin with the dark words:

> One of the most bizarre features of any advanced industrial society in our time is that the cardinal choices have to be made by a handful of men: in secret: and, at least in legal form, by men who cannot have a first-hand knowledge of what those choices depend upon or what their results may be.
>
> When I say "advanced industrial society" I am thinking in the first place of the three in which I am most interested—the United States, the Soviet Union, and my own country. And when I say the "cardinal choices," I mean those which determine in the crudest sense whether we live or die.[1]

This opening sets C. P. Snow's major theme. He illustrated it, of course, with a dramatic story of the two English scientists, Sir Henry Tizard and F. A. Lindemann, Lord Cherwell, and their role in relation to the vital decisions on air defense and strategic bombing in England just before and during World War II.

If Sir Charles is right, the cardinal choices of the United States, the United Kingdom and the Soviet Union can, it seems, be directly understood only by scientists and yet are and must be, "at least in legal form," made by non-scientists who are exposed to the advice of only a few. Sir Charles, who is at home in both the Scientific Culture and the Literary one, moves so easily from one to the other that we are never quite sure how to take lessons from what he calls his "cautionary" tales. Are they literally true? Or are they literature? The critical response to the Godkin Lectures by less partisan participants in the events they describe suggests that these stories may be fables. None the less, even a fable may contain a useful moral: the troubling questions remain.

In the limited sense of Snow's definition of "scientists," the cardinal choices referred to by Snow are not simply, as he suggests, a domain of "science." The decision at the start of World War II to develop a fission bomb, or the decision to use it against Japan, or the decision to develop an H-bomb, or to bomb German cities during World War II, called for much more than natural science and engineering. Such decisions have narrowly technological components, but they involve just as essentially a great many other elements: military operations and counter-operations by an enemy, the economies of industrial production, the social and political effects of

1. C. P. Snow, "Science and Government: The Godkin Lectures at Harvard, 1960." Cambridge: Harvard University Press, 1961, p. 1.

bombing on populations, and many others. Some of these other factors are qualitative. Many are quantitative, and in this very broad sense "technical." (They involve numbers and may be related in a numerical model.) However, even these do not fit into any of the traditional disciplines of natural science or engineering. They do not, for example, come under the head of electrical engineering or physical chemistry. And natural scientists and engineers do not normally acquire a professional acquaintance with subjects such as the cost of buying and operating a fighter bomber or the disaster behavior of urban populations. Nor do they ordinarily find these subjects essential in the course of engineering work in developing a bomb.

In fact, in addressing the complex cardinal choices, one of the inadequacies sometimes displayed by natural scientists is that they may ignore, or assume implicitly, or simply receive, or themselves casually estimate without enough study, the values of those variables that fall outside the traditional natural science disciplines. The cardinal choices, in Snow's sense, cannot be well made solely on estimates of the feasibility or infeasibility of some piece of hardware. They are political and military, strategic decisions. Technology is an important part, but very far from the whole of strategy.

Snow is not alone in creating this confusion. It is a very widespread practice among scientists concerned with public policy, and especially among those who direct urgent popular appeals. In the letter that Bertrand Russell sent in 1955 to heads of state enclosing a call for what later became the Pugwash Conferences, he began: "I enclose a statement, signed by some of the most eminent scientific authorities on nuclear warfare." The signers were indeed without exception eminent scientists, but among the ten physicists, chemists and a mathematical logician who were included, not one to my knowledge had done any empirical study of military operations likely in a nuclear war.

Similarly it is usual to find, at the head of petitions advocating some specific nuclear policy, sentences that run: "As scientists we have knowledge of the dangers involved," followed by the signatures of tens or even thousands of scientists, only a few of whom have examined the empirical evidence on more than one or two of the many alternative dangers involved in the policy choice. Simply as a scientist no one has a knowledge of these complex choices.

The bombing controversy in 1942, one of the "cardinal choices" recounted by Snow, was somewhat ill-defined, as is not unusual in such policy disputes. It had to do among other matters with the relative emphasis in air strategy on offense or defense—with how, for example, to allocate resources between the strategic bombing of German towns and the air defense of coastal shipping. This is hardly the sort of thing one would normally submit to a vote of the Fellows of the Royal Society, as Snow suggests, or to the "general population" of natural scientists and engineers. And not simply or in principle because of the difficulties of secrecy.

A good answer to the allocation question depended on a great many things, including, on the one hand, how rapidly bombers would be manufactured, how soon after manufacture they could be made an operational part of the military forces, losses that might be expected from enemy defenses, the expected number of sorties in the operational life of these bombers, the shape and population density of German cities, and the types of building in them, the efficiency of the German fire-fighting services, the reaction of populations to the stress of air raids; and, on the other hand, the effectiveness of these same bombers against enemy ships of war, the allied shipping and supplies likely to be saved, the military worth of these supplies, etc., etc. These are not matters found in physics textbooks. Nor could the Fellows of the Royal Society be expected to qualify for independent judgment on them in the course of a week.

Over a longer period, such questions are open to study, but—and this is a critical point—they are open to study and answer by a much wider group than engineers and natural scientists. And there is little evidence to suggest that at such study the technologists are signally best. Not only are some of the principal variables subject matter for the behavioral sciences rather than physics, but the appropriate methods of study also may be closer to the methods of some behavioral sciences. Blackett, writing in 1943, not long after the bombing controversy, pointed out that the mathematical methods he employed are in general use

> . . . in those branches of science whose subject matter has similar characteristics. These characteristics are that a limited amount of numerical data is ascertainable about phenomena of great complexity. The problems of analyzing war operations are almost all of this type and are therefore rather nearer, in general, to many problems, say, of biology or of economics, than to most problems of physics, where usually a great deal of numerical data is ascertainable about relatively simple phenomena.[2]

Perhaps even more important, while the job of gathering and examining relevant empirical data might be very laborious, the gist of the methods for using the data is quite generally accessible. The methods are within the grasp of an intelligent administrator, and, *given time,* open to his skeptical questioning.

I have stressed the phrase "given time." Without time on these complex questions, a government official is not likely to have a full understanding

2. "Operational Research," British Association for the Advancement of Science, Burlington House, Piccadilly, London. Reprinted from *The Advancement of Science,* v. 5, April 1948, p. 29. (Quarterly Journal of the British Association).

and may make some poor choices. This is also true, however, of the technologist or the analyst of tactics or strategies. One of the principal differences between our present situation and the circumstances in which decisions had to be made in World War II is that today we frequently have time. It is a salient difference bearing on the question of how technologists, strategists, military and political men may figure in cardinal choices. For the major peacetime decisions are seldom final. In short, given time, the decision-maker without a degree in physics, mathematics, or for that matter, mathematical economics, is quite capable of having a "first-hand knowledge of what those choices depend upon and what their result might be." [3] And he often will *have* time.

II

In the view of some scientists, it would appear that judgment does not really require time or a great deal of grubby work. It is, according to Snow, more a matter of intuition, an attribute of a few gifted men, a kind of "prescience." This quality evidently is present especially in scientists, who "have something to give which our kind of existential society is desperately short of: so short of, that it fails to recognise of what it is starved. That is foresight." [4] Foresight is "not quite knowledge," but "much more an expectation of knowledge to come . . . something that a scientist, if he has this kind of sensitivity latent in him, picks up during his scientific experience." [5] Some men other than natural scientists have this gift but, we gather, much more rarely and in a lesser degree.

The popular fantasies relating the pursuits of science to sorcery and an almost superhuman thaumaturgy make such a view of prescience rather widely credible. Not only may the layman talk in these terms of the mysteries of science, but also statesmen; the "Wizard War" Churchill called the technological race in World War II. We may not, as Mr. Eisenhower fears, become captive of a scientific élite, but it would seem that scientists, or at least the best scientists, may indeed be The Elect. And many of them have felt charged with a prodigious mission and a great moral urgency. Spurred by an apocalyptic vision of world annihilation, they urge a drastic transformation in the conduct of world affairs in the immediate future. They have been passionately sure that the choices are stark and clear: annihilation on the one hand or a paradise on earth. "Remember your humanity and forget the rest," read the invitation to the first Pugwash Conference.

3. "Science and Government," p. 1.
4. *Ibid.,* p. 81.
5. *Ibid.,* p. 82.

"If you can do so, the way lies open to a new Paradise; if you cannot, there lies before you the risk of universal death."

For many scientists there is very little time. C. P. Snow predicted at the end of 1960 that if events proceed on their present course, nuclear war is "a certainty . . . within at the most ten years." [6] Which does not leave much time. The clock on the cover of the *Bulletin of the Atomic Scientists* started so near twelve that a while ago it had to be set back.

In bringing about a new sort of world, the scientists feel that they have a special responsibility. They are free of the insincerities and dubious motives of the traditional actors on the political scene; they are interested only in clarification and truth. Furthermore the coöperative and potentially universal nature of the scientific enterprise is at hand as a model for a future world order, and the scientists can be vital agents in bringing that order about. "Scientists of the World, Unite!", the title of an article by a Princeton physicist appearing immediately after the war, sounds the right note.

This vision of the responsibility of the scientist—"a greater responsibility than is pressing on any other body of men," [7] according to Snow —puts him in a very different role from the scientist as technologist or the scientist dealing by tentative and empirical methods with broader questions or cardinal choices. It is fortified, however, by the confusion between technologist and strategist and by the related notion of the scientist as specially endowed—a seer or prophet.

The notion bears a strange resemblance to that of the prophets in the chiliastic and apocalyptic movements that swept Europe centuries ago in times of great disorientation, anxiety and instability. It has some inspirational uses, but a great many disabilities. Like past eschatology, it encourages schismatics, and the feuds among the scientists have been intolerant and implicitly rather bloody. Snow's tale of Lindemann and Tizard unconsciously illustrates the point: Lindemann is the dark angel, sadistic and violent, without the gift of foresight. And Blackett, a passionate battler against the forces of darkness, uses the story in his innumerable present feuds.

But most important, this urgent, tense feeling of mission can sometimes bias the technological studies and, even more, tends to discourage the use of the patient and tentative method of science, as distinct from the *authority* of science, in assisting the cardinal choices of which Snow speaks. It has led in some cases to a rather surprising anti-rationalism.

6. "The Moral Un-Neutrality of Science," Address to the 1960 meeting of the American Association for the Advancement of Science, reprinted in *Science,* Jan. 27, 1961, v. 133, p. 259.

7. *Ibid.,* p. 259. I have discussed this and related predictions by scientists in "Nuclear Sharing: NATO and the N + 1 Country," *Foreign Affairs,* April 1961.

III

Anyone who has searched diligently for a device, which in hostile hands might demolish what he had been building the previous year, is not likely to forget the sickening sensation of finding it. Yet that is the occupational hazard of a working strategist, a conscientious designer of what may be called "conflict-solving systems"—that is, systems for keeping the peace or fighting a war, where the opponents' countermeasures must be taken into account. Thus the honest strategist must wear two or more hats, and this can be something of a personal strain. It can actually lead to quarrels among friends and organizations. The inventor of an ingenious measure may come to regard the inventor of an even more ingenious counter-measure with some distaste or even detestation. Whose side does the fellow think he is on?

All of which is true enough for the design of some national or alliance weapon system for possible use in a war. The personal strain and the strain on friendship is likely to be even worse where the system to be designed is an international control system. For while with national defense measures the element of at least partial opposition by an enemy is, or always should be, as plain as can be, it is not so plain in the case of an international system. Here one has an agreement with an adversary, and it is tempting to believe that he will coöperate. A scientist who works on evasion schemes is almost certain to be regarded as a leper. Isn't he opposing the agreement and ruining the possibility of international control? This is a nearly universal attitude. It was frequently voiced in protest against studies of possible ways to evade the test ban. Now it may be that some of the men who find it easiest to work on evasion schemes are those who oppose the agreement. None the less, anyone who is soberly in favor of an agreement with adequate safeguards should systematically and seriously wear both hats all the time. Two illustrations will suffice to show how, in the case of the test ban, each of the two principal factions has found it hard to deal with countermeasures, except where these support a point of view it is propounding anyway.

First, Edward Teller: Dr. Teller in my view has performed an important service in helping to develop a test ban with adequate controls, by thinking ingeniously about the possibilities of evading the various control systems that have been proposed. On the other hand, when it has come to supporting his views on the importance of testing, he has argued that we would lose more than the Russians would if we both stopped testing. As the defender, in contrast to the aggressor, we have a harder job. Therefore, he reasons, testing will enable us to develop the more sophisticated weapons

we need for use in defense. However, in this argument he ignores the fact
that the Russians will also be developing their weapons of aggression as
counters to our defense, and there is no *a priori* reason for believing that
they won't make more rapid strides in their "easier" job than we in our
difficult one. In the past the development of nuclear weapons has favored
the offense. In short, when it comes to the exploitation of tests in the development of weapons, Dr. Teller ignores countermeasures; they do not suit
his argument. He has been extremely ingenious in considering enemy countermeasures to thwart control systems; these countermeasures do suit his
argument.

Next, Hans Bethe: Dr. Bethe has been the symmetrical opposite of Dr.
Teller on this matter as on others. As far as evasion schemes are concerned, he has said that he was embarrassed at presenting to the Russians
the possibility conjured up by another American because it "implied that
we considered the Russians capable of cheating on a massive scale. I think
that they would have been quite justified if they had considered this an insult." [8] This suggests that it is all right to set up a police system, but not
against potential crooks. His own energies in any case were devoted to the
measures rather than the countermeasures. On the other hand, when it
came to evaluating the military worth of weapons that might be developed
with the aid of testing, such as anti-missile missiles, Dr. Bethe could frequently think of nothing except enemy countermeasures that would reduce
their military worth nearly to zero. Dr. Bethe, like Blackett, is, without any
extensive study, quite certain that enemy countermeasures like decoys
would make a defense against ballistic missiles useless—or even harmful
—in any reasonably likely contingency.

There are two points which emerge from this discussion of countermeasures. First, most physical scientists and engineers find it hard to deal
with an enemy countermeasure, except where it spoils a system they themselves dislike on other grounds. This, I believe, is sometimes associated
with an aversion to putting the fact of hostility in the center of their attention. Many of the articulate scientists, especially when considering arms-
control agreements, prefer to think of harmony rather than conflict. The
difficulty they have in contemplating countermeasures stems from hostility
to the fact of hostility itself. In this way they slip more easily into the role
of prophet and agent of a perfectly peaceful world.

The second point is that the evaluation of countermeasures in military
conflict systems is likely to be very complicated, requiring painstaking
analysis, seldom undertaken by the technologists themselves. It involves for
one thing an extensive canvass of potential military operations on both

8. "The Case for Ending Nuclear Tests," *The Atlantic Monthly,* August 1960, p.
46.

sides and their possible interactions, and sometimes a consideration of allies and more than one adversary; I believe neither Dr. Teller nor Dr. Bethe has done this sort of systematic analysis of the military worth of the weapons they talk about. Both are experts in the basic technology of bomb design, but that is quite another matter.

Questions of military worth are broader than physics and in some ways harder. They of course are not purely military questions any more than they are purely technological. They may involve a forbidding nest of problems including political and economic, as well as military and technological, questions. However, on the questions that have called for systematic analysis, characteristically there has been no experience that was precisely relevant. For these questions relate to a near or distant future affected by novel techniques and political uncertainties. Experts are seldom "expert beyond experience," and analysis is needed, not to replace intuition, but to sharpen and supplement it, and to make it more public and verifiable.

The role of uncertainty in decision-making as well as in system studies to aid decision is so prominent that it is worth dwelling on, especially as it is related in several ways to some recent obscurantism. Attempts to prepare for anything other than the probable events are branded as "paranoid" by Erich Fromm. By this definition, all of us who live in normally fire-safe neighborhoods and houses and none the less take out fire insurance are paranoid. On the contrary, it would be simply irrational to stake everything on a "most likely" event where the uncertainties are so large and intrinsic. This would be true even if we were quite sure we knew which were the "most likely" events and could agree on what are useful objectives in these contingencies.

The scientists have been very far from agreement. In retrospect, their views since World War II on major strategic issues—the feasibility and usefulness, in deterring or fighting a war, of active or civil defense, of the ability to bomb enemy industry or cities or military forces, of tactical nuclear weapons, of restraint in nuclear war, and many others—show an extraordinary sequence of sudden and repeated reversals.[9] The principal factions of scientists have remained in opposition—sometimes, however, almost exactly changing place. Moreover, the thought devoted to defining these issues and the evidence gathered for resolving them in no case warranted the certainty with which opposing views were propounded. This is not to say, of course, that "the politicians and the generals," with whom the physical scientists are contrasted, have been right. It would be hard to show, however, that the scientists have been on the whole more realistic or more prescient. Moral certainty and feelings of prescience have been a

9. An account of this history is given in my monograph, previously referred to, which will be published in the fall.

pretty uncertain guide to the future—even to the immediately next future beliefs of the prophets.

The gift of prescience is not only hard to come by for oneself; it is difficult to identify in others. Snow, who should be a great connoisseur of prescience, has run into difficulties. He derides Lindemann for backing infrared detection: "This seemed wildly impracticable then. . . . It seems even more wildly impracticable now." [10] Chinese Communist pilots downed by Sidewinder missiles with infrared homing devices would disagree. This would appear to be a case, in short, where Lindemann's prescience exceeds Snow's present knowledge of what has long since happened. Snow—and Blackett—take much too literally one of the lessons Snow draws from his cautionary tale: "The prime importance, in any crisis of action, of being positive what you want to do. . . . It is not so relevant whether you are right or wrong." [11]

In fact, serious study of the large uncertainties in the major strategic choices we have had to make suggests the opposite. Bertrand Russell in a better day once said, perhaps overstating the matter a bit: "The opinions that are held with passion are always those for which no good ground exists; indeed the passion is the measure of the holder's lack of rational conviction." [12] Passionate assurance on these intrinsically uncertain matters is not justifiable on logical grounds. Some technologists who are most articulate on matters of public policy in the defense and arms-control field should worry us most in their moments of boundless conviction, when they assume the role of seers. The tentative and fallible methods they have used professionally seem even more appropriate in the complex and uncertain areas of cardinal choice.

Don Price, in a brilliant article, "The Scientific Establishment," has developed with admirable lucidity the difference between the role of the scientist in the United States and the picture that Snow attributes to the United States, the United Kingdom and the Soviet Union.[13] In the United States the scientists have had unmatched opportunities for getting a direct political hearing for their ideas on policy. On every one of the cardinal choices cited by Snow, scientists have been heard, and by top decision-makers. On the other hand, I know of no clear evidence that in the Soviet Union scientists have affected the cardinal choices either on the basis of their prescience or on the basis of systematic study of major alternatives.

In the United States the problem of scientists and strategists is, I think,

10. "Science and Government," *op. cit.,* p. 34.
11. *Ibid.,* p. 73.
12. Quoted by Charles Hussey in "Earl, Philosopher, Logician, Rebel," *New York Times Magazine,* May 13, 1962, p. 10.
13. *Science,* June 29, 1962, p. 1099–1106.

by and large not so much in being heard as in *saying* something, that is, saying something that is the result of thought and empirical study.

IV

It is high time that we recognized the extreme implausibility of the notion that war may become "impossible" in the next short space of time. On the other hand, neither is nuclear war inevitable in the next ten years, or many more. Since reducing the likelihood of war will preoccupy us for many years to come, it is appropriate to think of the probable consequences of this persisting preoccupation, some of which are already visible.

Decision-makers are likely to acquire a deep familiarity with these problems in the course of time, and to grow in professional competence in the continuing work on their solution. This is happening today, for example, in the Department of Defense. A year ago *The New York Times* published a statement of the Secretary on the issues in the choice of strategic bombardment vehicles for the late 1960s and after.[14] Whether or not we agree with the specific choice it explains, the document is an impressive one. In its thoughtful treatment of the uncertainties and the essential technological as well as operational and economic problems, it compares very favorably in sophistication with the analyses done by scientists to aid decision during World War II. Moreover, anyone who follows the Congressional Hearings will be quite convinced that such statements are comprehensively understood by a good many current decision-makers. These cardinal strategic decisions in general *are* made by them.

There is a good deal of hocus-pocus in Snow's pronouncement that the decision-makers "cannot have a first-hand knowledge of what those choices depend upon." [15] There is, of course, a sense in which nobody can have first-hand knowledge of *all* the things such decisions depend upon. They depend upon a great many things besides technology, in many fields. However, the choices that Snow dwells on, for example in his cautionary tales, are not all that obscure, and a first-rate Cabinet officer or military man can master the essentials of much more complicated matters, especially if they keep coming up. And they do.

The other side of this picture is that the natural and behavioral scientists, who offer advice or do analyses to assist decision, may experience a growth of professional competence too. Offhand judgments of individuals and crash studies by committees will always be with us and should. But expertise and committee activities have limitations. An expert on the whole range of problems involved in even one of these complicated choices is

14. *New York Times,* March 16, 1962, p. 1 and 12.
15. "Science and Government," *op. cit.,* p. 1.

hard to find, and if one is discovered, the way in which he reaches his conclusion may be difficult to reproduce and verify; this in turn affects whether his judgment will be subject to criticism by more than a "handful of men." Inexplicitness is likely to be even worse with committees, since they proceed frequently by bargaining rather than reason. But explicit statement of the way conclusions are reached and of the evidence is part of the normal method of science, and what I mean by "conflict-systems studies" is simply the application of the method of science to the analysis of political-military strategic alternatives.

This suggests a little of the answer to at least one of the large questions with which we began: Both the physical and the behavioral sciences have a role to play in component research on cardinal choices. And in the course of studying strategic alternatives the methods of science can be used to reach conclusions going beyond the skills of any of the individuals involved. The important point is that on these complex cardinal questions, answers are won precariously and intermittently, in the course of hard empirical inquiry into the major factors affecting choice. Intuition and intelligence help, but do not make superfluous the study not only of the vital technologies, but also of the behavior of men and nations using, and affected by the use of, such technologies. No one has the gift of reliable foresight on these cardinal choices. The primary thing, then, is *not* to be positive. The basic failure of the physical scientists and engineers in their turbulent history during the cold war is not their lack of prescience but their acting frequently as if they had it.

D. S. GREENBERG

Venture into Politics: Scientists and Engineers in the Election Campaign

One week before election day, Lyndon Johnson was campaigning in Albuquerque when he saw a sign that read, "New Mexico Scientists and Engineers Welcome LBJ." Pointing to the sign, the President declared that "about the best supporters I have are the scientists and engineers."

From *Science,* Vol. 146, pp. 1440–44, December 11, 1964, and pp. 1561–63, December 18, 1964. Copyright 1964 by the American Association for the Advancement of Science. Reprinted by permission.

Campaign hyperbole and the presence of a good number of people from nearby research facilities may have combined to inspire this compliment, but the fact is that the last political campaign energized the American scientific and engineering communities to a pitch of unprecedented political activity, virtually all of it in support of Lyndon Johnson. In 1956 and 1960, in what was the first conspicuous emergence of scientists and engineers into elective politics, a handful of them contributed their names and position papers and briefings to the presidential candidates, but the campaign that has just ended brought forth something altogether different: the establishment of a nationwide network of political action centers, organized, financed, and almost exclusively staffed by scientists and engineers, ranging from Nobel laureates and high-level administrators to undergraduate science majors and laboratory technicians.

In mid-July, when Senator Goldwater received the Republican nomination, these centers did not exist, and there was no plan to set them up. Within 45 days, headquarters, bearing "Scientists and Engineers for Johnson-Humphrey" signs, had sprung up in prominent downtown sections in all but two or three states; almost all employed at least one full-time executive or secretary and scores of volunteer workers, drawn from the scientific and engineering community, and they operated 7 days a week, 12 to 18 hours a day. Before the campaign was over they had listed over 50,000 scientists and engineers on their membership rolls; had raised some $500,000; had written and financed over 100 newspaper advertisements, 3000 spot radio broadcasts, and a half-hour nationwide TV show, and had elicited hundreds of column inches of newspaper notice. But, most important of all, by skillfully combining their energy and resources with deliberate exploitation of the prestige of science, engineering, and medicine, and the respect with which the public generally regards them, they contributed to burdening Senator Goldwater with the image that appears to have contributed most to his overwhelming defeat—namely, that he was unfit to control the nation's nuclear forces.

The electorate's repudiation of Goldwater was so overwhelming that it is impossible to establish that any one campaign effort, or that even the entire campaign, was of any sigificance in determining the outcome. But whether it was self-destruction or outside assault that did most to bring down the Senator, it is clear that the scientific and engineering communities brought remarkable political fervor to the campaign. And though it can be reasonably argued that this venture into political action did no more than add a few pebbles to a predestined national avalanche, it is clear also that, within the boundaries of science and engineering, the involvement in the campaign was an extraordinary event.

How and why was this activity organized, and what can be said of its significance as a phenomenon in the life of the American scientific and engineering communities? The answers, based on interviews throughout the country during the past few weeks, can perhaps best be developed by looking at the great network of institutions and individuals that comprise these communities, and tracing what happened when it became obvious that Senator Goldwater was unstoppable in his quest for the Republican presidential nomination.

Justifiably or not, a lot of people were profoundly disturbed by the prospect of the Senator's nomination and wanted to do something about it, and among them was a 33-year-old physical chemist, Donald M. MacArthur, who manages the chemical and life sciences research center at Melpar, Inc., in the Virginia suburbs of Washington. MacArthur, who holds a B.Sc. with honors from St. Andrews, in Scotland, where he was raised, and a doctorate from Edinburgh, had had no previous experience in elective politics; but he had two important things going for him in his desire to turn his concern about Goldwater into political action: he knows his way around the scientific community, and he is married to Mrs. Lyndon Johnson's niece, the former Diane Taylor—a relationship which gave him easy access not only to the upper echelons of the administration and the Democratic Party but also to the President himself.

A week after Goldwater's nomination, MacArthur spent 2 hours at the Pentagon with Harold Brown, Defense Director of Research and Engineering, seeking his opinion on whether scientists and engineers could be mobilized into a politically effective organization. Brown was confident that they could, and the next step was a call from Brown's office to Donald F. Hornig, the President's science adviser. Hornig reported that he had had several inquiries from scientists and engineers who wished to become involved in the campaign. Jerome B. Wiesner, M.I.T. dean of science who was Hornig's predecessor in the White House position, had indicated that he wanted to be active in support of Johnson, and so had two distinguished scientific figures with Republican affiliations: Detlev W. Bronk, president of the Rockefeller Institute, former president of the National Academy of Sciences, and long-time chairman of the National Science Board, and George B. Kistiakowsky, the Harvard chemist who served as President Eisenhower's science adviser.

WHITE HOUSE VISIT

Thus, MacArthur quickly found that support existed in the inner sanctum of the American scientific community, and that influential figures there shared his eagerness for activity against Goldwater, although it was not yet clear just what form this activity would take. It was at this point that

MacArthur's political connections proved immensely useful. MacArthur next went to the White House, admission to which was no problem for him, and told Jack Valenti, one of the President's personal staff members, that a group of scientists and engineers were organizing to work for Johnson's election. The visit to Valenti was ostensibly for information purposes only, but it also served to tie the organization directly to the White House, thus avoiding the great bureaucracy that was being put together for the campaign by the Democratic National Committee. Then he went to see one of the seemingly eternal behind-the-scenes powers of American politics, James H. Rowe, Jr., who came to Washington as a New Deal lawyer, served as secretary to Oliver Wendell Holmes, and stayed on to become an adviser and confidante in the upper echelons of the government and the party. Rowe, who is in Lyndon Johnson's inner circle, was to serve during the campaign as national coordinator of Citizens for Johnson-Humphrey, the grass roots effort to get out the vote. Thus, it would be necessary to get his support for the incipient organization, especially since he held the purse strings on the President's Club, a treasury of "seed money" initiated by the late President Kennedy to help citizens groups get organized in the early days of a campaign. Again, entree was no problem. MacArthur and Rowe were well acquainted socially. But Rowe wasn't to be easily infected by the enthusiasm that had enveloped MacArthur. The President was indulging in the fiction that he wasn't a candidate until the Democratic convention, scheduled for 24 August, had actually nominated him; until then, no citizens groups were to come into the open, and, furthermore, the party professionals, of whom Rowe is perhaps the epitome, didn't look too kindly on ebullient amateurs who wanted to plunge unguided into the serious business of national politics. Rowe advised MacArthur to hang on until the party chiefs had sketched out the strategy for the campaign. MacArthur, it appears, listened good-naturedly to the counsel of his friend and then hurried out to lay his hands on the lease for campaign headquarters that the defunct Rockefeller organization was vacating on Connecticut Avenue in downtown Washington. He wrote a personal check for $750 for one month's rent, plus another of $200 as deposit for a telephone. Said Rowe, in looking back: "They got off running hard, and there wasn't much we could do about them after that." A few days later the President's Club made $12,000 available to Scientists and Engineers for Johnson, and it became the first Democratic citizens group to make its appearance in the 1964 campaign.

At this point, then, the organization was in business, with an office, a telephone, a bank account, and the nucleus of a staff: MacArthur, who had taken leave from Melpar; his wife, who resigned from her position as head of the Peace Corps' programs for North Africa, the Near East, and South

Asia; and Rodney W. Nichols, a 27-year-old head of a systems analysis group in MacArthur's research center at Melpar. Nichols, who played a key role in formulating and carrying through the scientific community's first venture into large-scale political action, was joined by his wife, Carolyn, a sociologist, who, in effect, served as manager of what quickly was to become a frantic night-and-day, 7-day-a-week office operation from early August through 3 November.

Now during the first week in August, there actively began the effort to draw large numbers of scientists and engineers into the campaign for Johnson's election. And, as the effort proceeded, two things became plain: (i) Scientists and Engineers for Johnson had a latent constituency that was overwhelmingly eager for someone to come along to show the way to political action, and (ii) the American scientific and engineering communities are, in fact, communities so intimately linked across the nation by personal and professional relationships that a cause claiming any common denominator of appeal is swiftly communicated throughout the land—and, in this case, the appeal of anti-Goldwater activity seems to have been overwhelming.

FINDING SUPPORT

Wiesner, Kistiakowsky, and Bronk, who, through their long government advisory service and professional activities can probably claim at least one good acquaintance at virtually every university, major laboratory, and technologically-oriented firm in the country, got on the telephone and in short order had rounded up a 42-member national organizing committee that read like a house of representatives of American science, engineering, education, and industry. As word spread that the committee was being formed, they found themselves receiving requests from others wanting to serve.

In general, the requests were granted, but, after consultation with the President, it was decided that Wiesner alone of the members of the President's Science Advisory Committee (PSAC) would be permitted to serve on the national committee, a decision which was a hedge against the possibility that Goldwater might win. It was recalled that in 1961, when Kennedy succeeded Eisenhower, the apolitical nature of PSAC had made it possible for that body to continue without change under the new administration. In Wiesner's case, it was felt that he was publicly identified as a scientist with strong Democratic leanings, and, besides, his PSAC term would expire in a few months and he was so eager to get into the campaign that he offered to resign if Johnson desired. Thus, Wiesner stayed with PSAC and played an intensely active role in the campaign. But, for example, when Edward M. Purcell, the Harvard physicist who is a member of PSAC, sought membership on the founding committee, he was told that the White House felt it would be prudent for him and other PSAC members to play less conspicuous roles in the campaign. Purcell later served on the Executive Committee of the Massachusetts chapter.

GETTING ORGANIZED

The next few weeks brought such a rush of meetings and cross-country communications that it is difficult to sort out the sequence of events with any precision. But, in general, it appears that three closely connected developments of major significance began to occur: news of the existence of the organization was rapidly communicated throughout the scientific and engineering communities; operating guidelines were worked out on the basis of a planning paper by Nichols, and at a meeting in Washington, on 10 and 11 August, of about a dozen members of the national organizing committee; and money started to come in from the fledgling organization's constituency. For example, Milton Harris, vice president of the Gillette Company, contributed $1000. Edward U. Condon, former director of the National Bureau of Standards and now professor of physics at the University of Colorado, sent $150. And $100 each was contributed by Herbert S. Gutkowski, head of the division of physical chemistry, at the University of Illinois; Emmanuel R. Piore, vice president and director of research for IBM; and Peter C. Goldmark, president of CBS Laboratories. Wiesner later contributed $500, as well as taking on speaking engagements in California, Ohio, Illinois, New Hampshire, New York, Tennessee, Georgia, and Washington. A $500 contribution was also made by Roger Revelle, the oceanographer who recently became head of Harvard's newly established center of population studies.

In addition, according to campaign records filed with the clerk of the House of Representatives, many industrial executives and philanthropists listed large sums contributed to Scientists and Engineers for Johnson; but the intricacies of campaign bookkeeping make it difficult to determine whether the money actually went to that organization or was only nominally routed there to get around the legal limitation of no more than $5000 to any one campaign committee. Throughout the campaign there was a bewildering transfer of funds between Scientists and Engineers for Johnson national headquarters and the national party headquarters, part of it is repayment of what eventually added up to $25,000 from the President's Club.

In any case, the records list a contribution to Scientists and Engineers for Johnson of $5000 from Henry Ford, chairman of the Ford Motor

Company. And Thomas J. Watson, Jr., chairman of IBM, and Mary Lasker, the medical philanthropist, were each listed at $3000, the maximum, according to one interpretation of the tax laws, that may be given free of federal gift tax. Some party professionals dispute this interpretation, but it serves to keep many major contributors at the $3000 level.

GUIDELINES FOR ACTION

The guidelines for the organization leaned heavily on Nichols' paper, which stated that the basic goals should be to "influence opinion on science-related campaign issues through public pro-Administration statements from prominent spokesmen representing the scientific and engineering communities . . . (and to) stimulate and support scientists and engineers across the country to organize 'get out the vote for Johnson' groups." The paper also went into such practical political matters as the need to get "at least one woman and one Negro" to serve in positions of leadership. And it went on to advise that the organization should "assume . . . the role of a spontaneous citizens' surge for Johnson."

More specifically, at the 10–11 August meeting, and at several subsequent meetings, the following guidelines were worked out:

1. The primary objective was not to lobby in behalf of science and engineering; rather, it was to enlist these communities in behalf of Johnson and to turn their prestige against Goldwater.

2. Scientists and Engineers for Johnson would be a political action organization; it would not simply serve as a brain trust or a window-dressing for Johnson's candidacy. Immediate efforts were to be made to establish active chapters in every state; each was to be financially self-sustaining, with funds solicited from scientists, engineers, and the general public.

3. The organization was to be bipartisan and financially and operationally independent of other Democratic campaign groups. It was not to involve itself in any campaign issue but Johnson versus Goldwater. A conscious effort was to be made to provide a respectable political haven for Republican scientists and engineers opposed to Goldwater, particularly the engineers, whose political sympathies tended to be farther to the right than those of the scientists.

To cast the membership net as far as possible, the chapters were to remain aloof from local issues. This meant that, to the extreme annoyance of regular state and local Democratic organizations, the New York chapters were to avoid involvement in the hard-fought senatorial race between Robert Kennedy and Senator Kenneth Keating, and the California chapters were to stay out of the fight over the State's open-housing law and out of the senatorial contest between Pierre Salinger and George Murphy.

PUBLICITY PROBLEMS

With these principles agreed upon, work now began to bring into existence a nationwide organization that had not even been under discussion a few weeks before. And it was here that the staff which was to carry out this ambitious plan encountered a shock. The press release announcing the formation of the organization sank without a trace into the nation's news media. (Written in a clumsy style that resulted from many cautious revisions at Scientists and Engineers for Johnson headquarters, and at National Committee headquarters, where the professionals felt uneasy about the burgeoning organization, it managed to elicit no interest whatsoever.)

MacArthur and Nichols then quickly sought out professional help—at $1000 a week—in the form of David L. Garth, a New York producer who had won TV's Peabody Award and who had handled campaign publicity and organization for various political figures, including Adlai Stevenson, Representative John Lindsay, of New York, and Senator Abraham Ribicoff, of Connecticut. Garth arrived at the Washington headquarters 2½ hours after MacArthur called for his help, and thereafter he not only handled publicity, but rode the network of the scientific and engineering communities to provide the political and organizational know-how that were needed to turn enthusiasm into political action.

During 18 days Garth visited 30 states, to meet with scientists and engineers who had been drawn in by the founding group or who had independently called Washington for guidance. Actually, as Garth recalls it, the territory was immensely fertile, for word of this unprecedented political role for science and engineering had rapidly spread through an eager constituency.

SOUTHERN CALIFORNIA

For example, it was a call from Detlev Bronk that had brought Harrison Brown, professor of geochemistry at Cal Tech, onto the national organizing committee. Bronk and Brown had become well acquainted while both were serving as officers of the National Academy of Sciences. And, when the Southern California chapter of Scientists and Engineers for Johnson was being organized, it was Brown who brought in Bruce Murray, a 33-year-old associate professor of planetary sciences at Cal Tech, who completely left his research for 7 weeks to serve as executive director of the Southern California chapter. Murray and others met with Garth, who set out the rules: get a headquarters; put up a big sign reading "Scientists and Engineers for Johnson" (After the convention, this was changed to Johnson-

Humphrey, and, in many communities, the organizations were enlarged to encompass physicians.); prepare mailing lists from university and corporate directories, and start raising money through mail solicitations; use that money to solicit more money through newspaper ads (no funds were to be had from national headquarters); seek to inspire newspaper stories indicating that scientists and engineers of both parties are opposed to Goldwater. And stay out of local issues.

It was a call from the Defense Department's Harold Brown that brought John H. Rubel into organizing the Southern California chapter. And Rubel, a former Defense research and engineering administrator, who is now vice president of Litton Industries, soon enlisted the support of a life-long Republican, Clark B. Millikan, director of the Graduate Aeronautical Laboratories at Cal Tech. Millikan at first protested that he had never voted for a Democrat, but before the campaign was over he and Mrs. Millikan had solicited some $3000 from their friends to help finance the Southern California chapter. Eventually the chapter signed up over 2000 persons and raised about $22,000.

In Northern California, a call in the middle of the night from Wiesner brought into the organization Russel Lee, president of the Palo Alto Medical Research Foundation. Soon afterward, Garth arrived with organizational instructions. Lee made available $4000 of his own money to get the chapter going, and made contact with Rogers Cannell, a Stanford Research Institute engineer and economist who was to become director of the Northern California's chapter's two offices, in Menlo Park and Berkeley.

It was also a call from Wiesner that brought in Owen Chamberlain, a Nobel laureate in physics at the Berkeley campus of the University of California. Not long afterward, Chamberlain could be found addressing and licking envelopes at the Berkeley headquarters. By election day the Northern California chapter had raised $8700, sent out 60,000 mailings, put on 68 spot radio broadcasts, and financed a full-page color newspaper ad.

On the other side of the country, Kistiakowsky made at least 100 phone calls to colleagues and acquaintances throughout the country. And all 25 members of the Harvard chemistry department signed a letter which was sent to hundreds of persons, including former students. The letter stated, in part:

> The members of the Department . . . representing a wide range of political conviction, conservative through liberal, Republican, independent and Democratic are *unanimously* committed to the view that Senator Barry Goldwater and Congressman William E. Miller must be resoundingly defeated in their bid to take over the highest office in the land. We are convinced that our country would be presented with the clear prospect of disaster in the do-

main of foreign relations, and grave setbacks in economic, social, technological and political progress at home, under an administration led by these men.

Mrs. Frank Westheimer, wife of one of the chemistry department members, later became executive secretary of the Massachusetts chapter.

It was acquaintanceship with Wiesner that brought in Walter Rosenblith, an M.I.T. electrical engineer, who presided at the chapter's organizational meeting at the M.I.T. faculty club. Rosenblith became co-chairman, along with Arthur R. Kantrowitz, director of the Avco Everett Research Laboratory. The division of leadership between campus and industry was deliberately designed to cover the spectrum of the Cambridge area's science and technology. By election day the chapter had about 3000 members; it raised over $25,000, sent out 35,000 mailings, and financed a series of newspaper and radio advertisements.

AID FOR HEADQUARTERS

It was through Rosenblith that Paul A. Kolers, a 38-year-old research psychologist at M.I.T.'s research laboratory of electronics, came into the organization. Kolers was put in touch with Rosenblith when he told a colleague that he was interested in working in the campaign. And, when Washington headquarters indicated that it needed willing hands, Kolers took leave to spend most of September at the Connecticut Avenue office. There his duties involved making use of his knowledge of the scientific community to find contacts for Garth, the touring organizer.

For example, when it came to setting up a chapter in Alabama, Kolers thought of Leland Clark, professor of biochemistry at the University of Alabama. Kolers had never met Clark, but he knew of him professionally and, in addition, Clark's name was suggested by several persons. Clark agreed to set up an Alabama chapter, and he promptly called a meeting in Birmingham. In attendance were about 35 persons with whom Clark was acquainted personally or professionally at nearby Alabama institutions. Working in that troubled state, Clark and his colleagues signed up 200 members and raised about $400. For his efforts, Clark found himself the object of vile telephone calls, obscene letters, and midnight vandalism on the grounds of his home.

In St. Louis, a number of persons, including Peter Gaspar, assistant professor of chemistry at Washington University, had heard of the founding of Scientists and Engineers for Johnson. A call to Washington brought a visit from Garth. Between the beginning of October and election day the St. Louis chapter sent out 16,000 solicitations to scientists and engineers in Missouri, and raised $7500 for publicity of various kinds.

The North Carolina chapter signed up 550 members, ran quarter-page ads in six newspapers, covering an estimated 75 percent of the state's population. It sponsored 16 1-minute spot announcements and sent an airplane with a streamer, "We all win with Lyndon," over several football stadiums on the Saturday before the election.

The Southern Ohio chapter reported 500 members, a banquet at which Bronk was the principal speaker, numerous ads and newspaper reports of their activities. And it reported that its most active members were Republicans.

Throughout the country, these patterns were being repeated. And, at chapter after chapter, it turned out that many of the most active workers had previously taken no part whatsoever in political activity.

Thus, less than 6 weeks after MacArthur went to the Pentagon to seek Harold Brown's views on whether scientists and engineers could play a role in the campaign, Scientists and Engineers for Johnson had come into being. It was a thriving, nationwide organization, and with shrewdness and diligence it served, as much as anything else, to convince the American public that Senator Goldwater was a poor choice for the presidency. As Garth said, "By the time we were through, any guy in Pittsburgh in a T-shirt with a can of beer in his hand knew that the smartest people in this country considered Goldwater unfit."

On the Sunday before election day, Henry Fonda appeared on the television screens of 128 communities throughout the country and said, "now you are going to meet six of the most brilliant and able men this country has produced."

For the remainder of the half-hour broadcast, a physician and five scientists and engineers cited each other's professional experience, praised Lyndon Johnson, and lacerated Barry Goldwater as unfit for the presidency. Benjamin Spock, the Solomon of child care for millions of parents, said he found Goldwater's views on education "shocking." Admiral William F. Raborn (retired), popularly known as "father" of the Polaris submarine, said Goldwater's views on military preparedness "don't make sense." Harold Urey, Nobel laureate in chemistry, described the Republican candidate as a "blustery, threatening man, who talks often without thinking, shoots from the hip. . . ." Herbert York, director of Defense Research and Engineering under President Eisenhower, described himself as "appalled" that Goldwater, a major general in the Air Force Reserve, "could be so wrong on the basic facts of our weaponry." Jerome B. Wiesner, science adviser to the late President Kennedy, replied, "He's an amateur general." And George B. Kistiakowsky, who held the science advisory post under Eisenhower, said he considered Goldwater's policy positions "rash and primitive."

The program was presented immediately following the Sunday professional football broadcasts in most communities and, presumably, was seen by millions.

A few weeks earlier, a Republican sponsored advertisement in the Houston *Chronicle* cited the heart attack that Johnson suffered in 1955; it said that medical statistics favored Hubert Humphrey's succession to the White House before the expiration of a full term for Johnson. The same edition of the *Chronicle* carried a news story in which "a world famous heart surgeon," Michael DeBakey, chairman of Baylor University's department of surgery, deplored the "irresponsible use of medical statistics." DeBakey was quoted as saying that the Goldwater advertisement was "the grossest evidence of irresponsibility."

At about the same time, Senator Goldwater attacked the Johnson administration for what he described as poorly conceived space policies. Shortly afterward, press reports carried a rebuttal by York, the former Defense research director. He referred to the Republican candidate as "rash and irresponsible," and said that his record on space was "inconsistent, ill-considered." The rebuttal received wide press coverage.

Meanwhile, a 40-page booklet, titled "The Alternative is Frightening," circulated around the country. The cover carried serious-faced, formal portraits of Johnson and Humphrey, and a photograph of a narrow-eyed, grimacing Barry Goldwater in an aviator's helmet. It was written, financed, and distributed by Scientists and Engineers for Johnson, which was instigator of the DeBakey and York rebuttals to Goldwater, producer of the TV panel show (at a cost of $36,000, which it paid out of its own funds), and source of a ceaseless, nationwide assault on the Goldwater candidacy. At every turn, as the Republican candidate addressed himself to issues with scientific or technological components—and there are few issues without them in public affairs today—he found himself under virulent attack by prestigious men of science, engineering and medicine.

How these professional communities organized for the political campaign was described in the first installment of this series. Why they organized is a more difficult question, and the answers are less certain. Looking at the other professions and campaign groups we find, for example, that lawyers set up an organization to support the Johnson candidacy, but its activities were largely restricted to fund-raising and name-listing in behalf of the ticket. Professors for Johnson established chairmen in all 50 states and signed up 22,000 members, but it, too, was largely a fund-raising and prestige organization.

On the Republican side, apparently in response to the impact of Scientists and Engineers for Johnson, two counterpart organizations were set up late in the campaign: an advisory task force on Space, Science and the

Atom; and Scientists and Engineers for Goldwater. The first was in the traditional pattern of a campaign brain trust. It produced several position papers—which instantly drew attacks from the Johnson organization—but there is no evidence that it played a significant role in Republican policy-making or attracted much public attention. The second made no attempt to emulate the nationwide structure or activities of the Scientists and Engineers for Johnson. Republican Party professionals are tight-mouthed about both organizations, but it is known that they had difficulty attracting members, and the public announcement of both was repeatedly delayed until a respectable membership could be rounded up.

Why, then, did the scientists and engineers flock to Johnson, as did no other professional groups to either side in the campaign?

In seeking the answers, it is tempting to speculate that scientists and engineers, because of their training and work, acquire a particular type of political perception. For example, it has been suggested by some members of Scientists and Engineers for Johnson that these professions are especially attuned to the maintenance of an ordered world, and felt threatened or offended by the social and political discontinuities implicit in many of Goldwater's proposals. Unquestionably, many of them felt just that way, but lots of other people, from shopkeepers through architects, looked upon Goldwater as a threat to an ordered world; nevertheless, it was only the scientists and engineers who set up a Washington headquarters and 48 state chapters to do something about it.

Speculation on the source of motivation has also focused on the fact that the scientific and engineering communities outdistance the general public in knowledge of the effects of nuclear warfare. Again it is difficult to see how this can account for much of the intensity and scope of the energy that was turned against Goldwater. The general public may not have a professional understanding of the effects of nuclear blast and radiation, but it understands, or misunderstands, enough of the general picture to be as concerned as the most knowledgeable professional.

It has also been suggested that many scientists and engineers selfishly feared that Goldwater would disrupt the laboriously built structure of federal support for research, development, and education. To some extent, this may provide a clue to the ferocity and depth of the reaction that he inspired in the scientific and engineering communities. But the clue does not carry very far. Goldwater's frequently stated aversion to federal support for education conflicted with the interests of many segments of American society, but none of them chose the path taken by the scientists and engineers. And as for the dollar and cents matter of next year's grants and contracts, Goldwater never revealed himself to be an opponent of federal support for research. He was frequently berated during the campaign for having at times voted against increased appropriations for federal research agencies, but a look at the record reveals that in those votes he often was in the company of some of the most liberal and knowledge-loving members of the Senate. Furthermore, in his voluminous pre-campaign writings, and throughout the campaign, the Senator said virtually nothing that could reasonably be intepreted as conflicting with the immediate professional interests of scientists and engineers. Thus, there is little support to be found for the theory that the scientists and engineers were simply looking out for their own needs when they banded together to oppose Goldwater.

It has also been suggested that some of Goldwater's followers served to freshen up memories of the suspicion and hysteria that the late Senator Joe McCarthy directed toward the academic settings where many scientists and engineers work. (One senior scientist who played a leading role in founding Scientists and Engineers for Johnson not only cited McCarthy but recalled his own student days in Germany in the 1920's. "Goldwater," he said, "cannot be likened to Hitler, but some of the people around Goldwater reminded me very clearly of the types that I saw going to Hitler's support.") But McCarthy's works weren't felt only in the academic world. He produced havoc across the board. He tore apart the entertainment world, but, again, Hollywood and Broadway didn't set up a nationwide network to support Johnson.

Finally, some skeptics on the Republican side offer the theory that Scientists and Engineers for Johnson was a sheeplike movement, initiated by the Democratic Party professionals through a relative of the President's (Donald M. MacArthur, director of the organization and husband of Mrs. Johnson's niece), led by the beneficiaries of federal support for research, and held together by an unspoken and subtle fear of difficulties with grants and contracts for those who declined to cooperate. However, there isn't any evidence to support the theory that such forces were either consciously or unconsciously at work. Threats, implied or explicit, are unlikely to move Nobel laureates in physics to devote their evenings to addressing envelopes; and for every scientist, engineer, and physician whose participation was initiated by a direct invitation, there were probably half a dozen who voluntarily presented themselves to seek campaign duties.

In some places, it appears, long hours at campaign headquarters became a sort of social distinction. (Many of the volunteers would proudly complain of the cruel hours they donated to the cause.) But, though it unquestionably became the thing to do at many institutions, it was quite a simple matter at these same institutions for any individual to go abut his life as though no election were taking place. As one such nonparticipant put it, "I was asked to join and I told them I was too busy, and that was that."

BOND OF ANTI-GOLDWATERISM

A more likely analysis is that a number of factors simultaneously came together to produce the nationwide effort of Scientists and Engineers for
Johnson. The most basic was the Goldwater candidacy. Justifiably or not,
it frightened many people; it particularly frightened that small segment of
the technical community which for the past decade has been a principal
architect of this nation's military systems and arms control policies. Goldwater, in proposing a more truculent attitude toward the Soviet Union and
more aggressive development of new weapons, was calling for a break with
policies formulated over a decade under the leadership of these men. Quite
understandably, they didn't like it. But it wasn't written in the stars that
their dislike would manifest itself in a nationwide organization. In fact, it is
probably that if MacArthur with his political connections hadn't come
along with ambition to get into the thick of the campaign, the anti-Goldwaterism of the senior scientists would probably have taken the traditional
form of brain trusts, fund raising, and occasional public statements. It
seems unlikely that, without the central direction and drive that was provided by a well-financed Washington headquarters and a professional organizer, any sort of nationwide scientists and engineers campaign effort
would have come into being. It is one thing for a political novice to feel
inclined to get into the campaign; it is another to get an invitation from one
of the leading figures in the scientific community, and a follow-up from a
professional organizer who provides the a-b-c's of political action. MacArthur's access to the White House made it possible for him to accomplish
easily what many other persons probably thought about and gave up as too
difficult. And, networks of personal and professional relationships that run
through the scientific and engineering communities made it possible to put
together a nationwide organization in a matter of weeks. The networks all
run through Washington—which has become the principal paymaster of
American research—and, since Washington is in the hands of the Demo-
crats, there were telephones, secretaries, and offices already at hand to
facilitate the early organizational work.

Finally, it appears that, midway in the campaign, the President himself
took attentive notice of Scientists and Engineers for Johnson and decided
that it was a promising device for turning the public against his opponent.
As one high Democratic Party leader put it, "The President saw that it was
the nuclear issue that was killing Goldwater, and he decided that the best
way to hit Barry on the bomb was with the scientists who made the bomb:"
The President's interest in the scientists and engineers supporting him was
fed by MacArthur, who saw to it that news clippings about the organiza-

tion and other material were included in the pile of night reading that was regularly assembled for the Chief Executive. It was the President, according to party officials, who suggested the TV panel show as a sort of technical community haymaker against Goldwater on the nuclear issue; he scanned the numerous newspaper advertisements that Scientists and Engineers for Johnson ran in his behalf, and even complained to party officials that one such advertisement, in the New York *Times,* failed to mention his name often enough. And, again, according to party leaders, it was Johnson who suggested that Scientists and Engineers for Johnson employ spot radio announcements in his behalf.

"SHOCKINGLY IRRESPONSIBLE"

These may well have been in the works before the President suggested them, but in any event they were potent stuff. Featuring Wiesner, Urey, Spock, Raborn, and York, these spot announcements consisted of a series of statements of support for Johnson and denunciations of Goldwater. They were broadcast some 3000 times throughout the country. On one tape, Urey said that "many Goldwater statements regarding the use of nuclear weapons are shockingly irresponsible." And in another, Spock introduced as the "famous child care expert," said, "I don't see how any parent who is serious about the education and happiness of his children can do other than vote for President Johnson and Senator Humphrey." (Inez Robb, the newspaper columnist, later quipped that Spock's appearance in the campaign marked "the exact moment at which all hope for victory oozed away from the Republican candidate. . . . Millions of mothers and grandmothers in the United States," she wrote, "would as soon question Dr. Spock as they would Holy Writ.")

Thus, with Johnson taking a personal interest, and the scientists and engineers flocking to their well-organized local chapters to seek campaign duties, the organization prospered, and expanded to fill the campaign role carved out for it.

Clearly, a large part of the story of Scientists and Engineers for Johnson can be summed up as expert cultivation on fertile soil.

Does the experience of the past campaign mean that scientists and engineers are in the process of emerging as a well-defined political force in national elective politics? The available evidence and the judgments of many of those who were centrally involved in Scientists and Engineers for Johnson suggest a negative answer. But, at the time, as one scientist put it, "having tasted political blood, we'll never be the same."

Perhaps the most important thing to be said about the genesis of Scientists and Engineers for Johnson was that it developed in response to a particular political circumstance: the candidacy of Barry Goldwater. If the Republican candidate had been William Scranton, Richard Nixon, or Nelson Rockefeller, it is improbable that the leadership or the rank and file of the scientific and engineering communities could have been so easily mustered in behalf of Johnson. Repeatedly one was told the organization should have been called Scientists and Engineers Against Goldwater. Anti-Goldwaterism was, in fact, so clearly the only unifying basis for the organization that Washington headquarters and the state chapters recognized at the outset that it was mandatory to stay away from local and state issues. And, unless a future campaign presents a presidential candidate so far from the political center as Barry Goldwater, it is improbable that large segments of the scientific and engineering communities can be rallied as they were for the 1964 campaign.

But going farther afield into speculation, the fact is that lots of scientists who were once apolitical have indeed tasted the heady stuff of politics, and they have found that they can be effective. Though their thoughts do not yet seem to be fully clarified, a number of them—especially some younger people in California and Massachusetts—hope that some portion of Scientists and Engineers for Johnson can be preserved to function as a sort of political action organization. But most members seem to be indifferent to this interest, and a good number are actively opposed, for a variety of reasons: that many Republicans were brought into the organization with the understanding that it was a one-shot affair conceived in response to Goldwater; that the scientific and engineering communities will tarnish their public prestige by regular involvement in national politics; and that professional societies and regular party organizations are the appropriate channels for scientists and engineers interested in affecting public matters.

REGIONAL LOBBYING

Nevertheless, it is difficult to believe that the intense activity of the last campaign is not going to leave some political progeny. Future campaigns may well see a kind of escalation producing science and engineering groups on both sides. Scientists and Engineers for Johnson did not in any way function as a political lobby for science and engineering—possibly because these professions can't really gripe very much about the way the federal government has treated them. But it is possible that the tightening of federal funds for research and development may turn thoughts toward the sort of collective political action that worked so well in the last campaign. Clearly, the scientific and engineering communities are too distinct from each other, and each is too diffused throughout the country, for them to reenact their 1964 performance for bread-and-butter goals. But there are common regional interests—such as the location of federal research facilities—that could provide the basis for political action on a less-than-national scale.

In any case, more than 50,000 scientists, engineers, and physicians have just passed through an exciting and successful political baptism. It is not likely that they are going to consider that experience to be irrelevant to their future professional and political concerns.

DONALD R. FLEMING

The Big Money and High Politics of Science

Francis Bacon said that science is power. Today science is politics. Scientific institutions, plus an impalpable essence thought to emanate from them, "scientific excellence," are in the process of becoming one of the main things that American politics will be about for as far into the future as one can imagine. The domestic power struggle is rapidly coming to a new focus upon the location of federal scientific installations and the allocation of federal contracts for research and development. That is the new definition of pork barrel.

Pork barrel, though the only recognizable name for the phenomenon in question, is an unnecessarily invidious term for the inevitable process of deciding how the economy is going to be energized by federal projects. If there is little reason to despise the general process, there is still less occasion for assuming that the particular projects are unworthy. The improvement of rivers and harbors and the construction of dams were socially useful under the old dispensation. The seeding of the country with scientific installations is nothing to be ashamed of today.

Potentially, there is a great deal of scientific pork to be divided, for the federal science budget is approaching $15.5 billion a year. In 1940 the figure was $74 million. As the old forms of pork are phased out by the Great Annihilator, McNamara, there will be no dearth of new projects for resilient communities. In Boston, there are lamentations about the imminent demise of the old Watertown Arsenal; but Cambridge is going to have a new NASA Electronics Research Center, with an ultimate spillover of some $40 million a year in subcontracts. The people who are let out at the arsenal will probably not be hired by NASA, but Boston as a community has successfully negotiated the perilous transition from old-style pork to new. Every American city and region must do the same.

The historical backdrop for this new kind of politics is the long process of continentalizing American science and culture. To populate the entire continent was one thing; to curb the financial dominance of the Northeast over the rest of the country was another and more difficult; but the most difficult of all has been to level the cultural gradient from Boston and New York to the Pacific. For one thing, the stakes were always being raised. By the time the Midwest had constructed a network of vigorous liberal arts colleges on the old New England model, the idea of the graduate school was ready to explode, and the leveling upward had to begin all over again.

So far as the Midwest was concerned, the balance was amply redressed by the founding of the University of Chicago. From 1895 to 1920, the University of Chicago was the most important American center of research in physics, not only holding its own with the Eastern universities but outstripping them. Albert A. Michelson at Chicago was subverting classical physics by his measurements of the speed of light. Robert A. Millikan at Chicago was measuring the charge of the electron and quashing the residual doubts about the atomic theory. In one field, chemistry, the leading institutions in the period up to 1920 were Harvard and M.I.T. One man, Arthur A. Noyes, was the pivot of the M.I.T. school of chemists.

It was a major divide in American cultural history when Noyes was induced to abandon M.I.T. for Cal Tech in 1919. George Ellery Hale, the promoter of giant telescopes and destined to be the architect of the 200-inch instrument at Palomar, was already at Cal Tech. (He had moved to Los Angeles to get the benefit of the pellucid night air, little suspecting that it would develop into the greatest smog belt in the world.) When in 1921 Hale and Noyes induced Millikan to leave Chicago for Cal Tech, the foundation was laid for making Cal Tech what it clearly became in the 1930s, the greatest technical university in the world. When the physical sciences experienced an almost simultaneous upsurge at the University of California at Berkeley, the center of gravity of American science and in some degree of American culture had shifted to California.

In the last generation, the principal countervailing forces to Cal Tech and Berkeley, the Eastern end of a seesaw that still tilts to the Pacific, have been Columbia in physics and Harvard in chemistry and biology and medicine. The greatest single focus of strength in between has been the tradition in physiology at Washington University, St. Louis. The overwhelming majority of American Nobel Prize winners in science—a fallible index—have been divided among these five institutions: Berkeley, Cal Tech, Columbia, Harvard, and Washington.

Up to 1940, the continentalizing of American science, the shifting incidence of basic research, seemed to be merely a matter of institutional prestige and vague regional pride, and for anybody except an academic scientist, a marginal form of psychological gratification or chagrin. The situation began to change radically with the coming of the Second World War and the creation by the federal government of major research facilities in leading universities: the Radiation Laboratory at M.I.T., the nuclear pile at the University of Chicago, the Applied Physics Laboratory at Johns Hopkins, the laboratory for chemical separation of uranium isotopes at Berkeley. At the point where the cost of scientific research was soaring to astronomical heights, the universities saw an opportunity to unload an ever increasing part of their scientific budget onto the federal government. The scientific prestige that would attract federal grants became a ponderable asset on the books of a university.

Even this, however, did not turn the incidence of research into a political issue. For almost twenty years there was a surprising acquiescence by Congress in the unargued proposition that the federal research dollar should go to the best men at the best institutions, that the only appropriate test was their reputation for "excellence" in the eyes of their peers. This inevitably entailed a heavy concentration of grants upon a small number of towering institutions, with a conspicuous geographical imbalance. But congressmen did not bestir themselves about it.

This self-restraint—or, more realistically, failure to grasp the political implications of what was happening—has begun to break down in the last five years. The question is, why this sudden awareness? Part of the answer is evident. The loudly trumpeted rationalization of the Defense Department by liquidating arsenals and navy yards has hit the politicians where they live—under the steely gaze of their constituents. For the record, congressmen duly squawk about the closings, but they know that the only real solution is to get a new grip on the federal budget. Pragmatically speaking, that means a big scientific installation or major research and development contracts for local industry, preferably both.

Only one further element was required to perfect the logic of the new politics: the rising conviction that a vigorous scientific program at a major university is an irresistible magnet for the location of government research facilities that have no direct academic affiliation, and more than this, for the location of industrial plants with a scientific or engineering orientation —industrial "spin-off." University science is increasingly perceived as the great catalyst for the whole economy of a metropolitan district or geographical region.

Once it was generally accepted that great universities inevitably attract independent federal installations, that became an argument for putting new facilities near the greatest universities. This was the clinching factor in awarding the NASA Electronics Center to Cambridge, Massachusetts. Senator Edward Kennedy was first elected on the slogan "He Can Do More for Massachusetts," but even he could not have delivered NASA unless he had had Harvard and M.I.T. to throw onto the scales.

No politician could fail to read the omens. In the years to come, the raw power grab among cities and regions will have to be camouflaged by persuasive invocations of the towering strength of the local university. There is the rub. If the local university is Harvard or M.I.T.—let alone both, a daily double on the Charles—or Chicago or Berkeley, the case is made to begin with. Yet the prospect of seeing the research dollar virtually monopolized by about two dozen universities (38 percent of federal grants to ten universities in 1964, 59 percent to twenty-five universities) became politically intolerable once the distribution of university science was seen as affecting the ultimate distribution of wealth and power in American society. It will be a matter of economic survival for less favored cities and regions to get federal grants for their universities, to build them up on the scientific side by the only possible means, a gigantic infusion of federal money.

The circle appears to be vicious. How can a university that is not already supremely prestigious ever break into the big money? One answer is to federate with neighboring institutions, either formally or psychologically, to make a whole greater than the sum of the parts. The University of North Carolina, North Carolina State College, and Duke University have acquired a collective identity as the "Research Triangle," and the union has just been blessed by the award of a $25 million installation of the United States Public Health Service: the National Center of Environmental Sciences. One of the things that took John F. Kennedy to Dallas on the last day of his life was to lend his countenance to the Graduate Research Center of the Southwest, a new federation of five universities with an adjoining "Research Park" for "science-oriented industry and research facilities."

Even universities which have already been doing well with the government by objective standards have banded together to banish feelings of deprivation at not receiving more. Consider the story of MURA, an acronym for Midwestern Universities Research Association. The universities in question include Minnesota, Wisconsin, Illinois, and Indiana. At the beginning of the 1960s, they felt aggrieved at not having a giant accelerator— atom smasher to the popular press—among them. All grants for this purpose are included in the budget of the Atomic Energy Commission. MURA was a planning and lobbying organization to get $170 million from the AEC to build a high-intensity accelerator in Wisconsin.

In May, 1963, an advisory panel headed by a Harvard physicist recommended construction of the MURA accelerator but only on the condition that it not interfere with higher-intensity machines for the East and West coasts. This was exactly the kind of report that Midwestern scientists, however unfairly, had come to expect from a committee with a Harvard chairman. The view was hardened into the orthodoxy in the Midwest that the East and West coasts are conspiring to arrogate all major projects to themselves. One might say that Midwestern scientists have taken up a kind of nuclear Populism, but this time facing both ways.

The advisory report left the White House understandably confused, but by mid-November, 1963, Senator Hubert Humphrey, already the most conspicuous figure in public life from the MURA country, felt optimistic that the President was about to commit himself irrevocably to the MURA accelerator.

A week later that President was dead. A new President was reopening the budget and looking for economies. In the end, Johnson asked his principal scientific adviser, inherited from Kennedy, Jerome B. Wiesner, on leave from M.I.T., to prepare a memorandum stating the case against MURA. It does not follow that this was Wiesner's own position. When, just before Christmas, the President met with a group from MURA, he read from this hostile memorandum prepared by Wiesner's office on his own instructions and told the dumbfounded MURA people where it had come from. Then the President dismissed them without any opportunity for rebuttals. The MURA accelerator was dead. The MURA people stamped out of the White House denouncing Wiesner as an agent of the bloated East and vowing in retaliation to block any accelerators on the East or West coasts.

Senator Humphrey let the President know how strong the feelings were running. Johnson did not retreat from his basic decision, the MURA accelerator was out, but he did make what appeared at first to be the empty gesture of saying that henceforth MURA should have a bigger role at the Argonne National Laboratory, on the outskirts of Chicago, operated for the AEC by the University of Chicago but intended to cooperate with other universities in the Midwest. It was notorious that the great state universities had never hit it off very well with Argonne. By the end of 1964, however, the President's pledge had taken on real substance, for Argonne was reorganized under the joint direction of the AEC, the University of Chicago —and MURA.

What was far more important, Johnson in his correspondence with

Humphrey endorsed, a trifle patronizingly, "the development of centers of scientific strength in the midwest," called for "fairness" in the distribution of federal research funds, and implied that the best test of fairness would be direct correlation of research grants to a region with its population. The implication seemed to be that funds for research ought to be distributed more or less on the same principle as money for highways or public schools.

It is now clear that he meant what he said and did what he meant. With the hearty cooperation of Congress, he has embarked upon a drastic remedy for inequality among universities in the receipt of research grants, a deliberate policy of equalization imposed from Washington by reducing the proportion of federal funds going to major academic powers. The catch-phrase, openly avowed by the National Science Foundation, is to build up "the second 20 centers of excellence." Why "20" is mysterious, except as a round figure commensurate with the size of the country and promising shares for all. The National Defense Education Act, as amended and expanded in 1964, is frankly biased in favor of helping the needy institutions to catch up. To this end the additional graduate fellowships authorized by the amended legislation, rising to 7500 per year by 1967, are to be assigned to graduate schools rather than students. Most prospective graduate students, in order to benefit from these fellowships, will have to go to institutions they would not have chosen in a free market.

It is no derogation from President Johnson's sincerity about public health to point out that his proposal for thirty-two regional centers for medical research and treatment, correlated where possible with existing institutions, would have the identical effect of spreading the federal bounty evenly through the country, to the advantage of struggling universities. Johnson was here acting upon a recommendation from a distinguished commission dominated by medical scientists. The principle of regional equalization of medical research did not originate with the politicians. Yet no billion-dollar program of this kind would have a chance in Congress without a built-in guarantee that the centers would be evenly distributed through the country.

Disadvantaged universities, like disadvantaged individuals, races, and regions, are to be given a leg up in the Great Society. Whether by design or unerring instinct for political opportunities, Lyndon Johnson is speedily implementing the most coherent program of leveling upward that the United States has ever seen.

The historical implications of this development are tremendous. It is hardly an exaggeration to say that the main stuff of American history has been the recurring sense of regional deprivation as a deliberate infliction by favored regions upon the rest of the country. That was the point of the armed risings of the backcountry against the tidewater in the colonial South, of the infuriated assault upon Eastern bastions of privilege by the Populists of the South and West at the end of the nineteenth century; the point, above all, of the great constant in American history, the steady unappeased grievance of the South against the North. To compare great things with small, it was the point only yesterday of the new Populism of MURA. To take regional equalization as a national purpose will not miraculously iron out existing inequalities or prevent the emergence of new ones. It might, however, divest them of their single most galling aspect in past generations, of appearing to flow from the absence of a national commitment to appropriate remedies. Fierce combats will continue to be fought over the allocation of individual projects but in the mitigating context of a general recognition that all parts of the country are entitled by explicit national policy to share equally in the largesse from Washington.

In one sense, we are witnessing the absolutely definitive triumph of regionalism—the adoption of regional equalization as an undisputed national goal. At the same time, we are witnessing the death of regionalism as the political expression of distinctive ways of life generated in the matrix of distinctive natural environments. Today the regions are speedily becoming interchangeable units for participation in the federal bounty; they are no longer independent focuses of vitality expressing regional personalities but units to be plugged into the national grid for receipt of an energizing current from Washington. Regions survive and flourish, but increasingly in the character of a mere administrative convenience to the federal government, a means of breaking down the total lump to be distributed.

Many factors operating over many generations have been pushing the country in this direction. If, however, we are now prepared to acknowledge that the redefinition of regionalism has been desirable as well as inexorable, a consummation to be deliberately hastened in our own time, one of the principal factors has been the current anxiety about the distribution of science. In the end, the distribution of science is the distribution of scientists, and in a free society they will not distribute themselves evenly over the country if the country is unevenly attractive. By the same token, no region in pursuit of scientific facilities can afford to displease them. Yet the scientific and technical classes are radically antiprovincial and devastatingly implacable in demanding an end to social strife and social anachronisms as disturbing elements in their own environment. Wherever they go, they seal the doom of regional idiosyncrasies.

This is part of the logic that is painfully liquidating the peculiarities of the South, the great American exception and the one surviving pocket of the old regionalism. The state of Alabama has been publicly warned by an official of NASA that the big rocket and space-research installations at

Huntsville could be lost if Alabama does not provide a congenial society for scientific and technical personnel to raise their families in. Threats of this kind, either express or tacit, put a price tag on Wallacism. The price is too high. The South is discovering the paradox that a region must surrender its distinctive identity to reap the benefits of the new regionalism.

In the context of civil rights, most Americans would feel that the old regionalism was well lost as a refuge for social inequities. The most difficult question remains of the impact of regional equalization upon the quality of American intellectual life. One thing is certain. The catchword of this generation of Americans, in and out of Washington, is "excellence." There is little reason to think that the politicians, and still less the President, are out to induce the reign of mediocrity. The "second 20" universities are supposed to be raised to the level of the first twenty, rather than the latter reduced to the present condition of the second group. The leveling is to be upward.

Yet grave perils remain. All these revolve about the problem of "critical mass" in graduate education. The great danger in all other forms of instruction is that classes will be too large. The problem in graduate training is that the number of students in any given field may be too small to create the shared excitement and mutual criticism by which graduate students educate one another fully as much as the professors educate them. For this purpose, the relevant definition of "field" is not chemistry or physics but inorganic chemistry or solid state physics. Two doctoral candidates in solid state physics in each of four universities do not equal six candidates in a single university. Even if the sheer numbers materialized to enable all universities to achieve critical mass in all major fields, the question would still remain whether there were enough truly "excellent" people in the same field at any one place to keep each other up to snuff, or whether they would be fatally dispersed among forty universities and seldom attain critical mass among themselves.

Another aspect of the same problem is that the whole strategy of leveling upward presupposes the invulnerable excellence of the first twenty universities. It is virtually certain, however, that by any conceivable specification of the first twenty, some of these are operating on an insufficient margin of excellence and glamour to sustain the new, artificially stimulated competition of the second twenty. They might find the first twenty contracting to ten and the rest plummeting into the second category. Even if the average level of the second group did rise, that might still entail a net loss in excellence.

Whatever consequences one may envision, is there anything to stop the Johnsonian Revolution? Probably not. Any favored regions or entrenched academic powers would find themselves in an inherently false position if they tried to resist the logic of regional and institutional equalization. They would inevitably appear to be cloaking their selfish interests with a specious concern for the general good.

One practical factor may still operate as a check upon the Johnsonian Revolution: the tendency of private industry to concentrate on a few already supreme localities. If electronic firms think that Route 128 around Boston is an ideal place to locate because Harvard and M.I.T. are in the offing, the buildup of other universities in other regions by federal policy will not necessarily produce the full economic benefits intended for the surrounding communities. Yet here too the government is in a position to apply substantial pressures. Scientifically oriented industry is dependent in considerable degree upon government contracts. Firms that pile up too densely in regions that the government regards as already receiving a "fair share" might find themselves silently passed over in favor of others that spread themselves out in keeping with the new politics. Nevertheless, the preferences of private industry will probably remain the greatest single brake upon regional equalization. It does not follow that this or any other brake will keep the motor from accelerating in that direction.

Even the endeavor to move in that direction as a primary national purpose is enough to constitute a new epoch in American history. The President undoubtedly hopes to achieve a definitive continentalizing of science and high culture with no sacrifice of quality. If he can make quality and equality march together in this fashion, he will have brought off one of the greatest and most beneficent revolutions in American history. It is a big if. The prospects of excellence in American life are riding on the outcome.

WARNER R. SCHILLING

The H-Bomb Decision
How To Decide Without Actually Choosing

President Truman made his first H-bomb decision on January 31, 1950. He ordered the Atomic Energy Commission to continue its efforts to determine the technical feasibility of a thermonuclear weapon. The rate and scale of the effort were to be fixed jointly by the AEC and the Department of Defense. He also ordered the Department of State and the Department of Defense to re-examine the nation's strategic objectives and plans, both diplomatic and military, in light of the forthcoming developments to be expected in Soviet nuclear weapons capabilities. Both directives had been recommended to the President in a report submitted the same day by a special committee of the National Security Council, composed of the Secretaries of State and Defense and the Chairman of the Atomic Energy Commission.[1]

The report of the special committee and the President's subsequent decision marked the first resolution of a policy discussion that had begun in September, 1949, with the discovery that the Russians had exploded a fission bomb. This discussion had been broadly concerned with the implications of the Soviet explosion for American security and with the question of what actions the United States should undertake as a result of it. The first purpose of this article will be to contrast the content and form of the President's decision with that of the policy discussion that had preceded it. The point of this contrast will be to illustrate the "minimal" character of the decision made on January 31st. Of all the courses of action considered and debated during the preceding five months, that chosen by the President represented one which seemed to close off the least number of future alternatives, one that left the most issues still undecided. The second and third purposes of this article will be to advance an explanation for the min-

1. See Harry S Truman, *Memoirs* (New York, 1956, 2 vols.), vol. 2, p. 309.

From the *Political Science Quarterly,* March 1961, Vol. LXXVI, No. 1. Reprinted by permission.
   This article is based on part of the research conducted on the H-bomb decision by the present writer in connection with the Civilian-Military Perspectives Project of the Institute of War and Peace Studies, Columbia University. Research and article have both benefited greatly from the guidance and criticism of the Institute's Director, William T. R. Fox. Earlier versions of the article were prepared for discussion at the Arms Control and National Policy Seminar, California Institute of Technology, and the December 1960 meeting of the American Historical Association.

imal character of the decision and to indicate some of the policy consequences that followed from its having been made in this manner.

THE POLICY BACKGROUND

The explosion by the Russians of a fission bomb on August 26, 1949, was
an event which took American policy-makers by surprise and one for
which they had prepared neither specific plans nor a general strategy. The
Joint Chiefs of Staff, taking what many believed to be a pessimistic view,
had not expected the Soviet Union to detonate a fission weapon until 1952.
Although steps had been taken prior to August, 1949, to provide for the
detection of such an explosion, nowhere in the government had any formal
attention been given to the question of what actions might be appropriately
taken once the evidence of an explosion had been detected. The absence of
forward planning can be attributed in part to the absence of any formal
deadlines or pressures compelling planning groups in State, Defense, or the
Commission to undertake it. It can also be attributed to the absence of any
generally agreed-on body of strategic thought regarding the foreign policy
implications of nuclear weapons which could have served as a point of departure and frame of reference for more specific plans.

Since the end of the Civil War, the continental security of the United
States had been doubly insured. First, by virtue of its superior military potential which completely overshadowed that of the other Great Powers, the
United States had no need to fear any nation. The weapons of World Wars
I and II and the distribution of the people, skills, and resources necessary
to make and use these weapons were such that no single foreign nation
could conceivably mobilize enough military power from inside its own
frontiers to assault successfully the American continent. Secondly, by vir-
ture of the balance of power abroad, the United States could afford to leave
its potential largely unmobilized. The interests and arms of the other Great
Powers were so committed one against the other that none was free to direct its strength against the United States. In time of peace these Powers
did not dare turn their backs on more immediate enemies, and in time of
war their hands were full fighting them. The American continent was subject to only one serious military threat: the possibility that through conquest and alliance the people, skills, and resources of the Old World might
be gathered together into one hostile combination. Only in this event could
the United States be confronted with a military potential roughly equivalent
to its own. The result, if not in all instances the intent, of American intervention in World Wars I and II had been to remove this contingency from
the realm of reality.

Following World War II two revolutionary changes occurred in this security position. The first was the inability of the European Powers to re-establish a balance of power on the European continent. The nations of Western Europe were in no position to prevent the Russians from achiev-ing at their ease what had just been so painfully wrested from the hands of the Germans: an empire from the Urals to the Atlantic embracing all the peoples, skills, and resources of the Old World. The United States moved resolutely to meet this situation, both through policies designed to substi-tute American power for European (the Truman Doctrine, the North At-lantic Treaty) and through policies designed to restore to the Western Eu-ropeans themselves the capacity to balance the Russians (the Marshall Plan, the Mutual Defense Assistance Program).

These policies, which constituted the main burden of American security policy between 1945 and 1949, were addressed to a real and immediate problem. They were, however, essentially pre-nuclear in their rationale. The advent of nuclear weapons had not influenced the American deter-mination to restore the European balance of power. It was, in fact, an ob-jective which the United States would have had an even greater incentive to undertake if the fission bomb had not been developed. Nor were nuclear weapons believed to have qualitatively altered the military problem of achieving that objective. The American monopoly of the atomic bomb was seen as greatly facilitating the task of defeating the Red Army (and hence in deterring an attack by it), but in the judgment of at least two of the three services it would still be necessary to maintain sufficient ground strength on the continent to permit the mounting of the large-scale land offensive which they believed would be required in order to terminate the war.[2]

In the summer of 1949 the second revolutionary change in the American security position, that occasioned by the advent of Soviet nuclear weapons-systems, had yet to occur. This was a development destined to change com-pletely the strategic significance of the traditional components of American security. The new weapons were so cheap and so destructive, relative to the old, that the Soviet Union would have the ability to mobilize from inside its own frontiers enough military power to accomplish what had heretofore been beyond the means of any single foreign nation: the capacity to strike a mortal blow at the American continent. The consequences were two-fold: the industrial superiority that had guaranteed victory in two World

2. For the rationale of the American interest in restoring the European balance of power, see   Walter Millis and E. S. Duffield, editors, *The Forrestal Diaries* (New York, 1951), pp. 341, 349–351. For military doctrine regarding a war in Europe, see e.g. General Omar Bradley, "This Way Lies Peace," *Saturday Evening Post,* vol. 220, October 15, 1949, and Walter Millis, Harvey C. Mansfield, and Harold Stein, *Arms and the State* (New York, 1958), pp. 237–245, 247–249.

Wars was no longer the equivalent of overwhelming military potential, and the United States could no longer afford to leave its potential largely unmobilized during time of peace. Unlike the case of the Kaiser's or Hitler's Germany, the conquest of the people, skills, and resources of the Old World would not be a necessary first step in a Soviet attack on the United States. As a result, the United States would no longer be able to count on the unfolding of such conquest (1) to provide time for Americans to alert themselves to danger and to arm to meet it, and (2) to provide allies to preoccupy the enemy until they were ready. In fact, the import of the second revolution was to diminish that of the first. The more developed Russian transcontinental nuclear striking power, the less important would be the addition of Western Europe's people, skills, and resources for a Soviet attack on the United States and, perforce, the less significant the distribution of power on that continent for the security of the United States.

The implications of the advent of nuclear weapons for American security were stark. American policy between 1945 and 1949 had by no means been blind to these possibilities, and two major policies had been formulated to meet them. The first was the proposal made for international control of atomic energy, which by the fall of 1947 appeared to have little prospect of being accepted by the Soviet Union. The second was the development of a military doctrine to cope with the contingency of two-way nuclear war. The character of this doctrine can be seen in the report released in January, 1948, by the President's Air Policy Commission. Bluntly entitled "Survival in the Air Age," the Finletter Report called for a "new strategy" to provide victory in an atomic war if it came and, hopefully, by confronting the enemy with the "prospect of a counterattack of the utmost violence," to persuade him not to attack in the first place.

According to the Report, this strategy would require an Air Force capable of smashing the Russian cities and factories. The prospect of such a "devastating price" would make the Soviets hesitate to attack. The Air Force would also need the capability of launching a counteroffensive against the Russian air forces "at the earliest possible moment" in order "to silence the attack on the United States mainland and give us the time again to build up our industrial machine and our manpower to go on to win the war." The Soviet objective, on the other hand, would be to smash American industrial power "at the outset" and to destroy the American air defense and counterattack forces. Basically, however, what was outlined in the Finletter Report was not so much a "new strategy" as the problems and choices over which the discussion of strategy was to ponder for years thereafter. The Report took no note of the possible conflicts between a strategy designed to deter atomic attack and a strategy designed to win an atomic war. Neither did the Report confront the question of why, if the United

States could achieve a counter-offensive blow of the magnitude described against Russian cities and delivery forces, the Russians could not do the same or better with their attacking blow, and, in this event, against what and with what would the United States launch its counterattack? [3]

These, then, were the three major postwar security policies that the United States had evolved by the eve of the Russian explosion: the effort to restore the European balance of power; the effort to secure international control of nuclear weapons; and the effort to evolve a force for two-way atomic war and a strategy to guide it. The three objectives were by no means carefully interrelated. Just as the strategy to restore the European balance of power made no provision for the time when American security would cease to turn on the stability of that balance, so the strategic doctrine outlined in the Finletter Report, while correctly anticipating that the future pivot would be the stability of the Soviet-American balance of terror, made no provision for the possibility that the United States would continue to have a political and military stake in the independence of Western Europe. As for the proposal for international control, this, if accepted, would require a substantial revision of the forces required to implement both of the other objectives. It should also be noted that each of these three policies had the potential of pointing the American response to the Russian explosion in a different direction. With the passing of the American monopoly on the atomic bomb, the defense of Western Europe might now require a larger commitment of ground forces than had heretofore been necessary. The need to prepare for two-way atomic war, on the other hand, would seem to call for the allocation of additional resources to the weapons for air attack and defense and an expansion in the size of the nuclear stockpile. Finally, the development by the Russians of their own nuclear weapons could be seen as the proper occasion to reopen and redouble the effort to secure their control by an international agency.

It was against this background of policy that discussion began in September, 1949, on the question of what should be done now that the Soviet Union had exploded an A-bomb. The major participants in this discussion came from five government institutions: the Departments of State and Defense; the Atomic Energy Commission (including a number of scientists employed in full or in part by the Commission or its subcontractors); the Office of the President; and the Joint Committee on Atomic Energy of Congress. By far the bulk of the policy discussion among these participants took place informally, and the degree and effect of the initiative exercised

3. See *Survival in the Air Age,* A Report by the President's Air Policy Commission (Washington, 1948), pp. 6, 10, 12, 14, 20, 23–25.

through these informal contacts fully support the insight of the observer who commented that the Federal Government is the last stronghold of private enterprise in the United States. Although a number of the participants had begun by December, 1949, to leak some of the subject matter of the discussion to the press, the policy discussion was for the most part closed to the general public.

The formal development of the policy discussion was tied to the bureaucratic history of a particular issue, that of whether to undertake an intensive effort to make a thermonuclear weapon. This matter was placed on the agenda of the Atomic Energy Commission on October 5th for reference to the Commission's main scientific advisory body, the General Advisory Committee. Both the report of the GAC, submitted on October 30th, and that submitted by the five Commissioners to the President on November 9th made it clear that the issue was hardly one that could be decided without reference to political and military as well as technical considerations. For this reason, and because he was well aware of the differences that were developing both between and within the major governmental bodies involved in the issue, the President referred the issue on November 10th to the previously noted special committee of the National Security Council. Under the auspices of this committee a working group was set up, composed of representatives from each of the three Executive agencies concerned: State, Defense, and the AEC. In addition to the work done jointly by this group, each agency also conducted a variety of independent studies into aspects of the problem, and the ultimate products of this activity were the recommendations submitted by the special committee to the President on January 31, 1950. It should be noted that throughout this period the Joint Committee on Atomic Energy was active in exploring the issue and voicing its views, through letters and personal visits by the Chairman to the President.

It will be the purpose of the following section to present a summary description of the issues and alternatives that were developed during the course of these proceedings. Although there will be occasional references to individual or institutional views, the purpose of the section is not to describe in any detail the positions held by particular individuals or government bodies with regard to the issues and alternatives discussed. The views of most of the individuals concerned were quite complex, and individual views within the same government bodies were by no means uniform. Many individuals and agencies took similar policy positions but for quite different reasons, and the views of some individuals and agencies changed over the time period involved. The summary is meant to delineate not individual or institutional positions but rather the range and content of the major policy proposals and considerations that were produced as a result of these five months of debate and deliberation.[4]

ISSUES AND ALTERNATIVES

The discovery that the Soviet Union had exploded an A-Bomb several years before it had been expected to do so suggested to many that one response should be to step up the pace of America's own nuclear weapons program. Since plans had just been completed to provide for a major expansion in the facilities for producing fissionable material and to undertake the development of fission weapons of much larger power and varied size than those heretofore fabricated, the focus of attention turned to the prospects for making a fusion weapon. The possibility of such a weapon had first received detailed study in 1942, and it had been a continuing concern of the atomic energy program ever since. It had proved, however, a recalcitrant technical problem and, both during the war and after, work on it had been given a much lower priority than work on the development and improvement of fission weapons.

The idea, in the fall of 1949, that a greater effort to make a fusion weapon was now in order received some stimulus from what were believed at the time to be some promising new technical approaches to the problem, but the major motive for reconsidering the state of the program was provided by the Russian explosion. Those who advocated a greater effort were moved by two considerations. One was the idea that if the United States could develop a bomb with thousands of times the energy release of the Hiroshima bomb, it would be able to maintain its qualitative lead over the Soviet program and thereby minimize the political and military disadvantages of the loss of its fission monopoly. Even more compelling, in the minds of most advocates, was the possibility that if the United States did not move more energetically to explore this possibility, the Soviet Union might be the first to achieve such a capability.

4. The information in the preceding paragraphs and the sections that follow can largely be found in two published sources: Truman, *op. cit.*, vol. 2, ch. 20, and United States Atomic Energy Commission, *In the Matter of J. Robert Oppenheimer*, Transcript of Hearing before Personnel Security Board (Washington, 1954). The article also draws upon extended personal interviews during 1956–1958 with sixty-six of the participants in the events discussed. Given the character of interview data and the particular focus of this article, it is the present writer's conclusion that the best way to meet scholarly obligations to both readers and participants is by omitting citation for the points that follow. The same considerations are responsible for the fact that these pages omit reference to individuals except where stylistically infeasible. Detailed description and citation will, of course, be later available with the publication of the whole study of the H-bomb decision.

This reasoning seemed so persuasive to its advocates that many did not bother to think through in much detail, especially in September and October, exactly what advantages the United States could get from such a weapon that it could not secure through its superior stockpile of fission bombs or, for that matter, just what it was that the Russians might do if they secured an H-bomb first. It seemed sufficient and obvious that in the first instance American interests would be advanced, and that in the second they could only be hurt. Nor were the advocates of a greater effort very definite during September and October with regard to the rate and scale of the effort they had in mind. The analogy of the effort made during the war to develop the A-bomb came naturally to mind, and it was in these terms that the proposal was formally placed on the agenda of the Commission.

The issue of the rate and scale of the program could not be left in such ambiguous terms. The particular thermonuclear design which most of the participants had in mind, the so-called "Super," required as one of its major components a large amount of tritium. The most feasible method of making tritium was to bombard lithium with neutrons, and neutrons which were used to make tritium would not be available to make plutonium. Accordingly, the manufacture of tritium for the Super would mean foregoing the manufacture of fission bombs. Moreover, the scientific talent of the nation, as well as its supply of neutrons, was limited. Scientists put to work on the Super would be scientists not available to work on the new fission weapons. A more intensive effort to make an H-bomb would, in short, involve costs to the nation's A-bomb program.

The discussion that developed among the participants about the costs that an expanded H-bomb program would entail for the A-bomb program proved to be one of monumental confusion and misunderstanding. The least of the difficulties was that no one knew just how much tritium the Super would require. The major difficulty was that (a) the participants were reasoning from diverse premises about the kind of effort to be made and about the value of the weapons involved, and (b) the divergent character of these premises were by no means always made clear in the arguments that were then joined.

Thus, the development of any consensus with regard to the plutonium costs involved was handicapped by the fact that some participants were thinking in terms of making only enough tritium in the Hanford reactors to support a test program, others contemplated a larger diversion of those piles in order to have a stockpile of tritium immediately on hand with which to fabricate a number of usable weapons in case the Super proved feasible, and still others were thinking in terms of building a number of new reactors for the production of the tritium stockpile, and it was not always clear whether they expected those reactors to be in operation before or after a demonstration of feasibility. The discussion of the talent costs was similarly complex. Some scientists did not see how additional talent could be put to work profitably on the problem even if it was made available. In their view the Los Alamos Laboratory was already doing about all that could be done. Others were convinced that the problem had been starved for talent all along. The development of a consensus on this point was further complicated by the fact that some thought the additional talent could be secured by bringing in scientists not then working on fission weapons, and others believed that if more people were put to work on the Super they would have to come mainly from those already engaged in fission work.

Difficult as it was for the participants to reach any common conception of what kind of expanded H-bomb program they were talking about and what kind of cost it would bring to the A-bomb program, this was only half the problem in reaching a conclusion about the rate and scale of the effort to be made. A judgment about the desirability of foregoing any given number of plutonium bombs or incurring the delay or loss of any given number of improvements in the development of fission weapons would depend on the application of some criteria for comparing the relative military utility of A-bombs and H-bombs. One of the major reservations expressed by the scientists on the GAC about the idea of embarking on a large-scale H-bomb program was the result of the application of such criteria. They were by no means confident that the Super could be delivered by air, and they thought there would be few targets for which a bomb of such large yield would be suited. They concluded that the military purposes of the United States would be much better served by the A-bombs and A-bomb developments which would otherwise have to be foregone or postponed.

Illustrative of how different participants were talking about different things is the fact that the GAC judgment cannot be directly compared to that of the Joint Chiefs of Staff. At the time of the GAC report, the Chiefs were on record before the Joint Committee as desiring an accelerated effort to develop the Super, but they had not been specific about the rate and scale of the effort they had in mind and, hence, the A-costs they were willing to incur. When the Commissioners submitted their report, guidance on this point had yet to be produced by the military, and this was one of the questions to which they urged the President to secure an answer before making his decision.

The issue of the rate and scale of the effort to be made on the H-bomb thus turned, in part, on the issue of the relative military utility of H- and A-bombs. Thus discussion of this issue was conditioned, in turn, by the issue of what strategic doctrine should guide American military policy. It was here, at the level of general strategy, that some of the most significant differences existed among the participants. The three issues were so inter-related, however, that the participants were not always able to distinguish against what (and even for what) they were arguing.

The GAC report is a case in point. Many of its members were by no means persuaded that the doctrine of strategic bombing was a desirable military policy. Their views were not far removed from those of the Ad-miral (who was also a member of the Military Liaison Committee to the AEC) who had argued before the House Armed Services Committee in October, 1949, that strategic bombing was militarily unsound, morally wrong, and not suited for achieving the kind of political conditions the United States would want to obtain at the conclusion of a war. The GAC's recommendation against the development of the H-bomb was grounded, in part, on the belief that its only utility would be for the bombing of large cities and the objection to a military doctrine which would lead to the mass slaughter of Russian men, women, and children. The point was blurred, however, by their failure to carry through and make clear that they had equivalently strong objections to the use for this purpose of the products of the expanded fission program which they did support.

Another issue of doctrine interjected into the debate related to the condi-tions under which the United States would use nuclear weapons. It was ar-gued by some that a decision with regard to the H-bomb program could not be rationally made until it was first decided for what purpose the United States was accumulating nuclear weapons: for the purpose of deterrence and retaliation only, or with the intent of so incorporating them into mili-tary plans and structure that the United States would initiate their use re-gardless of whether they had been employed by the enemy. The point to the argument was the idea that if weapons were being accumulated for the first purpose only, given the great value which the Russians attached to their industrial plant, a limited number of fission bombs would be sufficient to serve it.

The preference for a strategy based on last-resort use and for a clear-cut rejection of the principle of first use was strong among those who had major reservations about the desirability of strategic bombing and those who doubted the capacity of the American public to conduct itself ration-ally in a world in which conflict with the Soviet Union would continue to be deep and basic but in which a resort to violence would become increasingly suicidal. Among the participants in the Department of Defense, however, these arguments received a different reception. There was no great interest in adopting a strategy which seemed to bind the United States to fight only on terms of the enemy's choosing, and there was determined opposition to the idea that the need for an H-bomb program turned on the making of such a choice. It was the judgment of these and other participants that for an effective performance of the task of deterrence as well as that of fighting a victorious war the armed services would need the most powerful weapons they could secure.

The idea that an over-all review of national policy and a decision with regard to these strategic issues should precede the further development of the H-bomb was energetically pressed at the NSC level by the Chairman of the AEC, David Lilienthal. One reason why he did so relates to still another issue: that of the relative utility of conventional as compared to nuclear weapons. During the NSC discussions, Lilienthal was shocked to learn just how dependent the military were on nuclear weapons, and he became convinced that what the United States needed far more than the H-bomb was a large-scale increase in conventional armaments. This conclusion was influenced in part by the prevailing military judgment that nuclear weapons alone could not win World War III, but it also reflected Lilienthal's own conviction that the foreign policy purposes of the nation would be better served by a military posture that was not so dependent on the use of large bombs against urban targets.

It was Lilienthal's contention that the decision on the Super should be delayed until an effort had first been made to review the nation's strategic doctrine and to consider the desirability of reducing the nation's dependence on large-yield nuclear weapons by increasing the size of its conventional forces. He believed that if the decision to press for the Super was made first it would prejudice the chances for a later review of that choice and greatly lessen the opportunity to secure conventional rearmament. There would be little prospect of persuading Congress and the public to support an expensive conventional rearmament program, he argued, once the Super program was announced, for most would conclude from the announcement that the security of the United States was in good shape and that the answer to the Russian A-bomb had been found.

One other major issue was raised in connection with the H-bomb debate and that was the question of its relationship to the effort to secure international control of atomic energy. The feeling was strong among many, especially the GAC and members of the Commission, that with the development of the Russian A-bomb the world had reached a crossroads in history. From this point it stood fair to continue into the mounting tensions of a nuclear arms race and perhaps, in time, into the horrors of nuclear war. The most appropriate thing to do at this time, so it seemed, was not to rush to try to make even bigger bombs but rather to make a last determined effort to reverse the direction that international politics had been taking since 1945. To those who thought in these terms the urgency of those who advocated a more intensive H-bomb program seemed both intemperate and short-sighted. To those who thought negotiation with the Russians fruitless, the insistence on delay seemed quixotic and dangerous.

The specific ideas advanced by the GAC and some of the Commissioners as to what might be done to reopen the international control negotiations or to otherwise try to move the world away from a nuclear arms race were, however, most indefinite and not very clearly stated. Some suggested that the United States increase the scale of its research on the H-bomb but not go all-out on the H-program without first reopening the international control negotiations with the Russians. Others recommended not pushing ahead at all on the H-bomb until it and the control of nuclear weapons in general had been first discussed with the Russians. (The minority annex of the GAC report suggested, in this connection, that the two Powers might agree not to make the H-bomb. Since its successful development was believed to require a test, violation of the agreement could be easily detected.) The most extreme position was that taken by the majority of the GAC, which recommended that the United States unilaterally announce that it was not going to make the weapon.

This last recommendation illustrates the interconnection among all the issues involved in the discussion. The judgment of those who made it was that the United States would not be losing much: a weapon that looked as if it would be very hard to make; one which would cost more in A-bombs than its military utility was worth; and one which if used would be employed in a manner highly repugnant to the values for which American culture was supposed to stand. It was believed that the Russians would not try very hard to make it themselves, given the cost of the weapon, the uncertainty that it could even be made, and the American example. Renunciation, so it was thought, was an opportunity for America to gain considerable moral prestige at very little cost and to make some contribution to the possible limitation of warfare in the future.

THE DECISION EXAMINED AND EXPLAINED

It is appropriate at this point to recall the content of the President's decision on January 31st: that an effort be made to determine the technical feasibility of a thermonuclear weapon; that the rate and scale of the effort be fixed jointly by the AEC and the Department of Defense; and that the State and Defense Departments undertake concurrently to review the nation's foreign and military policies in light of the prospective nuclear capabilities of the Soviet Union.

This decision stands in some contrast to the issues and alternatives just described. Had the President decided the issue of the rate and scale of the H-bomb program? Had he decided that the military utility of the Super would be worth the A-costs involved? Had he made a decision about the military and political desirability of strategic bombing? Had he decided whether military doctrine with regard to nuclear weapons was to be governed by the principle of first use or that of last resort? Had he decided that the nation needed bigger nuclear weapons more than it needed large-scale conventional rearmament? Had he decided not to renew negotiations with the Soviet Union on the subject of international control?

The President had decided none of these things. This is not, of course, to say that he had decided nothing at all. He had quite definitely decided that the United States would not unilaterally renounce the effort to make an H-bomb. Although a literal reading of his directive with regard to the determination of feasibility would indicate that he had ordered the AEC and Defense only to continue what they had already been doing, there was certainly an implication that they should approach the task with a greater sense of urgency than had heretofore been the case. The directive also made it evident that the President had not endorsed an intensive H-bomb program. The directive said nothing about production facilities for the Super, nor did it even specify that the determination of feasibility was to include a test program.

The President had also decided to order the re-examination of the nation's strategic plans that so many had urged. He further decided not to wait until the completion of that review before making his H-bomb choice. He had similarly decided against two other alternatives which involved a delay in his making that choice: the alternative of first exploring the possibility of international control, and the alternative of first endeavoring to secure a large increase in conventional arms.

The President did make choices, but a comparison of the choices that he made with those that he did not make reveals clearly the minimal character of his decision. It bears all the aspects of a conscious search for that course of action which would close off the least number of future alternatives, one which would avoid the most choice. Thus the President had affirmed his interest in exploring the feasibility of an H-bomb, but he had said nothing about testing a device if one were fabricated, nothing about producing a weapon if the device were ever tested, nothing about how many weapons would be produced if any were made, nothing about whether such weapons would ever be used if produced, and nothing about the purposes for which such weapons would be employed if ever used.

An explanation for the minimal character of this decision is to be found partly in the views and power of those who shaped the recommendations of the special committee of the NSC, partly in the character of the American governmental process, and partly in the perspectives with which the participants approached the problem of choice. With regard to the first factor, the decisive influence on the outcome of the H-bomb discussion proved to be that of the State Department. It was the Secretary of State who spoke with authority, so far as the President was concerned, with regard to the various foreign policy hopes and fears that had conditioned the views of many of the other participants. It was also the Secretary of State who held the balance of persuasion, so far as the President was concerned, on those issues on which the representatives of the Department of Defense and the Atomic Energy Commission were divided.

The State Department was responsible for rejecting the various alternatives which involved some approach to the Russians with regard to international control before undertaking to accelerate the American H-bomb program. It was, in the opinion of Secretary of State Dean Acheson and those who assisted him on the NSC committee, simply not a time period in which the Russians were interested in serious negotiations. All that could be expected from approaching them would be stalling tactics which might embarrass or perhaps even completely inhibit the American program while leaving the Russians free to push ahead on their own.

The State Department sided with the Secretary of Defense, Louis Johnson, in stressing the importance of not delaying in the effort to discover whether the Super could be made, although the reasoning in the two Departments was somewhat different. A number of planning groups within the Department of Defense had given careful study to the military utility of the Super, and the suggestions that it was in all probability not worth making struck them all as unsound, to say the least. (One member of the GAC was later to observe that the GAC report had the unprecedented effect of unifying the services.) If the judgments of some of the scientists were grounded on a concern for what the world would look like after an H-bomb war, and those of the military on a concern for what it would be like to have to fight an enemy who had a monopoly on such a powerful weapon, those of the State Department representatives reflected a concern for the diplomatic opportunities the Russians would gain from such a monopoly for political blackmail around the Soviet periphery. Most of Acheson's advisers took this possibility very seriously, as did the Secretary himself.

The State Department's strong interest in avoiding the possible consequences of the Russians getting the H-bomb first also led Acheson to side with Defense with regard to the alternatives of reviewing the nation's strategic plans and of securing an increase in conventional weapons before making a choice about the H-bomb program. Acheson was quite willing to undertake such a review concurrently (as was Defense), and, as the Department's work on this review in the spring of 1950 was to show, he was prepared to push hard for an increase in conventional weapons. But he wanted no delay on the H-bomb research.

Lilienthal's arguments for the priority of a conventional weapons program might plausibly have been expected to win him some allies in the

Pentagon, especially in the Army. They did not, largely because they were suspect. The fact that they associated Lilienthal with many of the GAC views led most of the military representatives to discount his argument as a device to delay the H-bomb for what were, really, other reasons. There was, moreover, a history of AEC-Defense disputes over the rôle of the AEC in determination of military requirements that made the defense representatives especially unresponsive to what was considered AEC meddling. President Truman, who had the greatest stake in not dissipating the persuasive lever that the Russian A-bomb gave him if he was later to press for a large-scale rearmament program, was not in the habit of examining the decision immediately before him for its implications for his future choices, and he, too, proved unresponsive to the argument.[5]

The character of the President's decision owes much to the coincidence of State and Defense views. It must also be attributed, however, to one of the major necessities of the American political process: the need to avert conflict by avoiding choice. The distribution of power and responsibility among government élites is normally so dispersed that a rather widespread agreement among them is necessary if any given policy is to be adopted and later implemented. Among the quasi-sovereign bodies that make up the Executive the opportunities to compel this agreement are limited. Agreement must be given, and it will not long be given for nothing. This condition of mutual dependence, the need, as it were, to "build a consensus" that includes one's enemies as well as one's friends, produces a strain toward agreement in the political process that is as fully characteristic of that process as the conflicts in which the participants are continually engaged.

There are many occasions when the necessary amount of coöperation can be achieved only by the device of avoiding disagreement, that is, by postponing the consideration of issues over which long and determined conflicts are certain to be waged. The H-bomb decision is a case in point. The issues which the President did *not* decide were all matters which, if he had endeavored to resolve them, would have pushed one group or another of his subordinates into passionate opposition. The President's position in the political process, however unique, is one which finds him, too, dependent upon the coöperation of others for the success of his policies, and Truman, in this instance, saw no reason to go out of his way to stir up a momentous struggle within his administration. Although he carefully read all the documents involved, from the GAC report through the NSC studies, Truman's own position on the H-bomb issue was the same in

5. For Truman's decision-making style in this respect, see Richard E. Neustadt, *Presidential Power* (New York, 1960), pp. 172–173.

January as it had been in October when he first had heard of it. If the bomb could be made, he did not see how the nation could afford to let the Russians get it first, and he was therefore prepared to back whatever program made sense to the Departments concerned.[6]

If the President had no interest in maximizing conflict, neither had the members of the special committee. Acheson was quite aware of the gulf between Lilienthal's views and those of Johnson. Indeed, he was obliged to meet each separately, since Lilienthal's and Johnson's personal relationship had deteriorated to the point where they could not profitably meet together. He was therefore consciously searching for the common ground between them. The military representatives on the NSC working group, for their part, proved not only willing but eager to follow the lead of the State Department and back a recommendation that called for only a determination of the feasibility of the Super. The responsible officials in the Department of Defense had never been among those demanding an H-bomb program on the scale of the Manhattan District. They were determined primarily in their opposition to the views and recommendations that had been advanced by the GAC and some of the Commissioners.

The final factor conditioning the character of the decision was the nature of the perspectives with which the participants approached the problem of choice. The influence of Truman's "one decision at a time" approach has already been noted. The perspective that the military members of the NSC working group brought to the decision was: "what needs to be decided *now?*" What needed to be decided now, in their view, was whether the government would make an urgent effort to determine the feasibility of the weapon. This would settle the immediate problem of defeating those who argued for delaying the program, for one reason or another, and those who argued that the weapon was of insufficient value to justify diverting any more neutrons and talent to pursue it. What need at this point, they reasoned, to stir up discussion regarding the production or use of the weapon. By avoiding these issues, Defense would avoid certain conflict with the AEC and possible conflict with State. Avoiding these issues would also permit the Department to present a unified front to its enemies. The Army and Navy were as persuaded as the Air Force that the nation had to have this weapon, if it was to be had, and that it should be secured before the Russians got it. But there was real potential for disagreement among the services once the issues of production and use be-

6. The analysis in these two paragraphs owes much to the stimulation of Gabriel Almond, *The American People and Foreign Policy* (New York, 1950), pp. 143–145; Neustadt, *op. cit.,* esp. ch. 3; Roger Hilsman, "The Foreign-Policy Consensus: An Interim Report," *Conflict Resolution,* December 1959; and Samuel P. Huntington, "Strategic Planning and the Political Process," *Foreign Affairs,* January 1960.

came operational. If very large amounts of tritium were to be manufactured, the plutonium foregone might well cut into that which the Army and Navy hoped would soon be available for their use, and at this point the doctrinal issues that divided the services with regard to the relative importance of strategic bombing as compared to other approaches to victory would be certain to arise.

The perspective with which the State Department representatives approached the decision was one that worked, in this instance, to the same end as that of the military but was significantly different in its rationale. Instead of asking "what has to be decided *now*," they asked: "what is the *least* possible that can be decided." The purpose was not so much to avoid conflict as it was to keep as many alternatives open for the future as possible, in order to be in a position to take maximum advantage of new information or changed conditions. It was with this perspective in mind that State drafted the recommendations that the special NSC committee later submitted to the President.

Of the three agencies, the perspective of the Commission representatives came closest to that of "what is the *most* that has to be decided." In fact, both State and Defense representatives had the feeling that the Commission was deliberately holding up the H-bomb program as a means of trying to force them to confront some of the major choices involved. The end result of the tactics of State and Defense, however, was to leave Lilienthal with very little to argue against or to argue for. Rate and scale? No one was urging an all-out program that would entail extremely large fission costs. Military utility? All that was being advocated was an effort to determine whether and at what expense the Super could be made; what better way to treat the question of its military value. Issues of strategic doctrine? State and Defense were to start immediately to review them, and an H-program so modest as not even to specify the conducting of a test could hardly be said to prejudice the results of such a review in advance. International control and the need for conventional weapons? Both of these matters would be given intensive study by the State-Defense review. Lilienthal could not shake the feeling that even in its minimal form the decision would prejudice the opportunity to depart from a big bomb strategy and he so argued to the end, but he had by now the feeling that there was no one at the NSC level with whom to argue.

CONSEQUENCES OF THE DECISION

One consequence of the minimal character of the President's decision was that all the issues on which he had avoided making any choice came back at him again. Thus, by the winter of 1951–1952 the disputes and dissatisfaction regarding the rate and scale of the program had reached such proportions that Air Force officials were considering setting up a weapons laboratory of their own. Similarly, in 1950 new investigations indicated that the tritium required for the Super would be much greater than that estimated at the time of the President's decision. This information, together with the concern that the Korean War might soon develop into all-out war with Russia, served in December, 1950, to reopen the discussion of the military utility of H- as compared to A-bombs and the desirability of incurring significant costs to the fission program in the effort to make it.

The State-Defense review, which became NSC-68, addressed itself boldly to the need to increase America's conventional weapon strength, but it did not really come to grips with the issues of nuclear strategy that had been raised during the H-bomb debate. Thus in December, 1951, when a group of scientists were active in urging the development and production of a large number of A-bombs for tactical use in the ground defense of Western Europe, the rationale for the proposal was in part the search for a strategy that would serve American security without requiring the bombing of cities. Their hope was that if the Red Army could be defeated through the battlefield use of A-bombs, the Strategic Air Command would be relieved of the burden of deterring a Soviet ground attack and free to exercise an option as to whether it struck the Soviet cities and initiated, thereby, an exchange that would bring bombs down on European and American cities as well. The issue of strategic bombing remains partly unsettled even today, as does the issue of last-resort use versus the principle of first use, although the terms are now "city-busting" versus "counter-force" and "second-strike" versus "first-strike" strategies. Similarly, the issue of conventional weapons versus nuclear weapons constituted a major source of debate during the whole of the Eisenhower administration.

The H-bomb decision is hardly the only occasion on which the policy process has produced a minimal decision. The continuous winnowing and worrying of the same old issues is an inevitable consequence of a political process that depends on the voluntary coöperation of independent and competing élites for the formulation and conduct of policy. Major policy changes can, for the most part, be effected only through slow and incremental change. However, as the same issues come around for the second, third, and nth time, they do so in a context slightly altered by the previous minimal choices to which they have been subjected.

The unilateral renunciation idea, for example, could hardly be advanced, after the President's decision, in the same form that the GAC had recommended it in October, 1949. It had to reappear in the form advanced by some other scientists in February, 1950: that the United States pledge itself not to be the first to initiate the use of H-bombs. Similarly, when the international control issue reappeared in November, 1952, with the proposal that the United States not set off its hydrogen device until it had first tried to negotiate an agreement with Russia not to test H-bombs, the conditions of the problem were not quite those that had prevailed when the same proposal was made in the minority annex of the GAC report. In place of an agreement on a device which no one even knew how to make, agreement would now have to be made with regard to a device which one side knew how to make and the other, presumably, did not.

The question might well be asked if there is not a possibility that through a sequence of minor "tactical" or minimal decisions the Government might some day find itself occupying a new "strategic" position without ever having made the major choice to get there. The answer, in a word, is yes, and again the H-bomb decision provides an illustration. On February 24, 1950, scarcely three weeks after the President's decision, the Joint Chiefs of Staff submitted a memorandum to the President requesting "an all-out development of hydrogen bombs and means for their production and delivery." The Chiefs, Johnson reported, wanted to undertake quantity production of the H-bomb as soon as possible.

Once again, Truman summoned the special committee of the NSC with Sumner Pike now serving in place of Lilienthal, who had submitted his resignation in November, 1949, but had stayed on to see the H-bomb decision through. On March 1st, this committee recommended that, without prejudice to the State-Defense review which was still under way, the research program should proceed to a test stage as soon as possible and that preparations be made for the quantity production of the H-bomb without waiting for the results of the test. The President so ordered on March 10th, and construction began shortly thereafter on the Savannah River reactors.

So far as those who in the fall of 1949 had advocated an intensive H-bomb effort were concerned, the program instituted in the spring of 1950 represented all that they had ever had in mind. The AEC and the Department of Defense had no basic policy disagreements in the design of this program. Although initially skeptical of the military need for an all-out H-bomb program, Pike believed that if a determined effort was going to be made to make an H-bomb a parallel production program should accompany it. Having alerted the Russians to the fact that the United States was urgently trying to make the bomb, it was to be expected that the Russians would move fast themselves and the United States had therefore better do the same.

So far as the Department of Defense was concerned, the memorandum of February 24th was designated to "button down" the decision of January 31st. What had to be decided *now* was the issue of production. Defense had no more interest than Pike in ending up in 1951 or 1952 with a handful of successful test devices and no plant with which to make the weapon. Neither did it want weapons without carriers, although in this respect the February memorandum was somewhat redundant since the January decision had also authorized the Air Force to undertake a carrier program. Unlike the Department of State, Defense had no interest in keeping the issues of production and use open. The orderly development of military plans and programs required a clear and early decision, not the flexibility and freedom sought by State. The February memorandum was, then, an invitation to State and the AEC to dispute now, if they wished, the decision to produce the H-bomb in quantity and to develop a capability to use it.

For the reasons noted, there was no dispute from the AEC. What of the Department of State and the idea that the decision to determine feasibility left open the decisions to test, to produce, and to use? There was no dispute from the Department of State either, despite the fact that the State-Defense review of strategic plans was not completed. Some of the State Department representatives have advanced the argument that a decision to produce the means for production was not yet a decision to produce the weapon, but this is to stretch words further than reality. A more accurate reading of the reasoning in the State Department would be that, while their responsibilities did not dispose them to push for quantity production, they saw no good reason for opposing it. In retrospect, it would seem that Lilienthal's sense of what was afoot on the 31st of January was not mistaken. The minimal decision permitted the Department of Defense to achieve its objectives in two bites and to take its possible opponents one at a time, and while the January decision might not have prejudiced the chances for an unfettered look at the H-bomb program, the March decision certainly did.

One cannot draw a straight line from January-March, 1950, to the present. The decisions here discussed are but two of the points from which one would have to plot the course of American policy from then to now. Whether the subsequent choices with regard to nuclear weapons policy were of the same order as those just described is, so far as the present writer is concerned, an unknown matter. Given, however, the propensity of the political process for minimal decisions, it would be plausible to expect that they were.

The H-bomb decision is essentially a tragic story. The GAC was "right" in sensing that the development of the H-bomb would drive twentieth century man deeper into the box that he has been building for himself with his military technology, doctrine, foreign policy, and cultural ethos. The GAC was also "right" in asserting that it was a time to stop, look, and think. But the GAC was not alone in seeing the dimensions of the box. It was every bit as apparent to most of the advocates of the Super program. The trouble was that no one had any good ideas of how to get out of the box. Nor are they apparent today.

Basically, the H-bomb decision is a story of international rather than domestic politics. It affords a classic example of the traditional security dilemma. Both the Soviet Union and the United States would no doubt have preferred a world in which neither had the H-bomb. Each, however, wished to avoid a world in which the other had the H-bomb and it did not. Both rushed to make it, and they ended in a worse position than that in which they had begun.

ROBERT GILPIN

The Intra-Scientific Conflict over a Nuclear Test Ban: The Problem of Conflicting Expertise

Thus far this study has demonstrated (1) that the intra-scientific dispute over nuclear weapons policy is due in large part to the scientist's sense of social responsibility, (2) that in matters of high public policy political and technical factors are often too intertwined to be isolated from one another in the advice of scientists, and (3) that therefore the non-technical assumptions of scientists legitimately and frequently become part and parcel of the scientist's advice. As a consequence of these facts the problem of conflicting expertise has arisen. Even though scientists agree on the technical facts, their interpretations of the significance of the facts for public policy can be at great variance. This situation is well illustrated by the following juxtaposition of conflicting advice from two equally eminent scientists, Hans Bethe and Edward Teller, on the *technical feasibility* of a control system to monitor a nuclear test ban:

> HANS BETHE: "I believe, therefore, that it is *technically feasible* to devise a system of detection stations and inspections which give

reasonable assurance against clandestine testing, with the possible exception of very small, decoupled tests." [1]

EDWARD TELLER: "This is the impasse at which we find ourselves today. We can say simply, surely, and clearly that if we agree on test cessation today, we have no way of knowing whether the Russians are testing or not. *There are no technical methods* to police a test ban." [2]

Each scientist has interpreted the scientific facts according to his own political predispositions. To Bethe, a strong advocate of nuclear disarmament and a disbeliever in the strategy of limited nuclear war, the facts mean that the United States could have "reasonable assurance" that Russia is not cheating. To Teller, a strong advocate of a strategy of limited nuclear war and an opponent of nuclear disarmament, the same facts indicate that there are no "technical methods to police a test ban."

It is impossible to speak of either scientist as being correct because, although they speak as if the issue were solely a technical one, the questions dividing them actually are non-technical in nature. What constitutes "reasonable assurance" for Bethe does not do so for Teller. The significance of small, decoupled tests for Teller is not the same as it is for Bethe. Teller's judgment of the capacity of the "technical methods" to *deter* Russian cheating contrasts with Bethe's. Such differences in opinion cannot be settled by the methods of science. They rest on assumptions which are outside the scientific realm such as those concerning the military value of tactical nuclear weapons, the technological intentions of the Soviet Union, and the political desirability of disarmament.

This situation illustrated by Teller's and Bethe's conflicting advice reveals how significant it is in the determination of public policy whether political leadership listens to the "scientific" advice of a Teller or of a Bethe. How perplexing, though, it must be for the politician or the administrator to decide between the advice of two such competent and convincing scientists. Yet choose between them he must, and the choices that have been made have had a profound and perhaps not always a beneficial consequence for American nuclear policy. For this reason, unless American political leadership learns to appreciate the nature of the problem of conflicting expertise, this problem will become an increasingly serious hazard to the formulation of an effective policy toward nuclear weapons and toward other products of the scientific revolution as well.

1. Hans Bethe, "The Case for Ending Nuclear Tests," *The Atlantic Monthly,* Vol. 206, No. 2, August 1960, p. 48. (Italics mine.)
2. Edward Teller, "The Issue of Peace," Unpublished paper, p. 6. (Italics mine.)

The Nature of the Problem of Conflicting Expertise

That eminently capable natural scientists trained in a rigorous method of analysis can disagree so strongly with one another over a long period of time on the technical aspects of fallout or the technical feasibility of a nuclear test ban is quite amazing to most observers; since most people do not comprehend how such differences can honestly occur among scientists, the cause of the disagreement is often believed to be the dishonest behavior of one side or the other. It is frequently reasoned that scientists, if they are intellectually honest, should be able to agree on the precise issue dividing them, to define their terms, and thereby to reach agreement on the scientific facts as well as on the scientific unknowns.

Actually, the scientists, even in the midst of their most violent controversies, really have been able to attain a high degree of agreement on the scientific facts. Nevertheless, even though the intra-scientific debate over a subject such as the technical feasibility of a nuclear test ban leads to broad areas of consensus, the debate over the central issue continues without final resolution. The reasons for this dynamic quality of the debate must be understood if one is to appreciate the problem of conflicting expertise.

The dynamic or irresolvable nature of the intra-scientific debate over the technical feasibility of a nuclear test ban and other allegedly technical issues is due to certain elements which are found in the arguments of each side. This does not mean that these elements are deliberately contrived; if this were the case the professional conscience of the scientists would soon overcome what could be legitimately regarded as a case of intellectual dishonesty. Instead—and this accounts for the tenacity with which a scientist defends his position—the elements are implicit in the arguments of the scientist and the scientist himself is unaware of the manner in which they influence his judgment and his argument.

The first element which gives an irresolvable or *ad infinitum* quality to the intra-scientific conflict over the technical feasibility of a nuclear test ban is the conviction of each side that its position represents that of the "objective" scientist. Its scientific opponents, on the other hand, are regarded as having based their position on political grounds. As a consequence each side defines the issue in a manner which is consistent with its belief that it represents "objective" truth. Because neither side appreciates the fact that it has defined the issue in terms favorable to its own political position, the opposing positions cannot possibly define the issue in a way agreeable to one another.

Thus, for the proponents of a nuclear test ban, the debate seems to be between those scientists who like themselves believe that a test ban control system would have a good probability of catching, and consequently of deterring, a violator and those scientists who demand a control system with 100 per cent probability of catching a violator. As a 100 per cent certainty is scientifically impossible, the scientists favorable to a nuclear test ban tend to regard their opponents as deliberately distorting the scientific situation. They regard the demand of the anti-ban scientists for a foolproof system as an unfair and impossible technical requirement intended to destroy the confidence of the public in the efficacy of *any* inspection system.

The opponents of a test ban also define the issue of control in terms of their own political predispositions and thereby at times cast doubt on the integrity of the position of the pro-ban scientists. The debate, according to the anti-ban scientists, is between those scientists who like themselves believe that a test ban should have a good probability of catching a violator and those scientists who want a test ban based solely on trust in the Russians. Since the question of whether or not one can trust the Russians is a matter of political judgment, these scientists believe the proponents of a test ban are distorting their advice on technical feasibility in terms of their political judgment.

The second element of the debate which confounds any attempt to reach an overall consensus within the scientific community on the technical feasibility of a nuclear test ban is the impossibility of defining certain key terms such as "good probability." Both sides, unfortunately, use the term "good probability" as if it were clearly defined and were therefore a standard by which the adequacy of the control system could be measured. Yet, as has been indicated previously, each side actually defines the term in a way which supports its own political position. Thus whereas a 1-in-10,000 chance of a test being caught may seem to one observer to be a good probability, another person will not accept as a good probability anything with less than a 1-in-10 chance.

In actuality, one's view of how *good* the probability of catching a violator is and of how high it must be to deter violations of the control system is the composite of a number of judgments on certain qualitative matters: the probable efficacy of on-site inspection; the cleverness of the Russians and their determination to cheat; and the capabilities of a control system not yet in existence. For these reasons there is wide latitude for conflicting interpretations of the technical feasibility of the control system.

The problem of conflicting expertise is further complicated by the fact that the great number of unknowns, the unpredictable nature of scientific advance, and the latitude for qualitative judgments permit the continuous interjection into the debate of *ad hoc* hypotheses to reinforce a crumbling intellectual position. For example, when the anti-ban scientists introduced the decoupling theory and thus weakened the Geneva System, the pro-ban scientists countered with the argument that the theory was impractical even though valid theoretically and that non-technical means such as defectors and semi-technical means such as the possible observation of the large scale earth moving activities necessary to create a "big hole" would ensure Soviet compliance. A similar substitution and utilization of *ad hoc* hypotheses have been apparent as the anti-ban scientists have defended their basic position when it has been challenged by new findings of the pro-ban scientists.

As a consequence of these elements—opposed definitions of the issue at stake, differing definitions of qualitative terms, and the use of *ad hoc* hypotheses—the scientists are unable to devise a "crucial" experiment by which to resolve their differences. For this reason one cannot depend upon the methods of science to validate or invalidate the conflicting cases of the scientists; instead he must turn to an examination and evaluation of the non-technical assumptions which really divide the scientists. Fortunately, the debate over a nuclear test ban has brought these conflicting ideas to the surface. Following a discussion of the opposed technical positions of the scientists, therefore, this study will turn to a consideration of these underlying sources of disagreement.

The Conflict over the Technical Feasibility
of a Nuclear Test Ban

THE POSITION OF THE PRO-BAN SCIENTISTS

Despite the extreme disappointment of the pro-ban scientists over the technical and political setbacks to a nuclear test ban, their basic attitude throughout the negotiations has been that, whatever the technical weaknesses in the Geneva System, they are minor when compared to the supreme political goals being sought. These scientists believe that establishment of control posts in the Soviet Union would be the first step toward disarmament, the opening of the Soviet Union, and the solution to the Nth country problem.

Until the breakdown in the test ban negotiations in September 1961 these scientists held that too much progress had been made toward the establishment of a nuclear test ban to permit the negotiations to fail. The concessions that they believed the Soviet Union had made indicated to them that the Russians were as interested in a test ban as was the United States. Therefore they felt that, until the United States had exhausted every possibility of overcoming the obstacles encountered since the Conference of Experts and all rays of hope had vanished, the test ban should be pursued with continued energy. As the Federation of American Scientists put it in July 1960: ". . . we do not know that our efforts have failed because of Soviet intransigence. Our efforts have not been complete enough for us to be confident that we would have found a basis for agreement if such existed. Our Government has not undertaken on a sufficient scale the hard work and intensive research that are necessary for an informal political judgment on specific arms control proposals." [3]

The pro-ban scientists have based their confidence that a nuclear test ban, whatever the apparent obstacles, would prove feasible upon the assumption that the Russians would not cheat because the incentive for the Soviets to cheat would be outweighed by their incentive to obey the ban. The interest of the Soviet Union in a successful nuclear test ban was believed to be far too great for the Russians to jeopardize the chance for the ban's success through nuclear testing in a covert fashion. Thus it was believed that even a remote possibility of discovery would deter the Soviet Union from any attempt to infringe on the test ban. As Russia was believed to be more interested in preventing the rise of new nuclear powers than it was in increasing its own armory of atomic weapons, these scientists argued that it would have a strong incentive not to wreck a nuclear test ban. [4] "I do not think," Hans Bethe has written, "the Russians intend to violate a treaty banning weapon tests; I do not think that the Russians could risk cheating, even if there is only a small likelihood of being detected. Even if we had no system of physical stations detecting nuclear tests, the Russians would not risk having some defector tell us about a clandestine nuclear explosion. If there were such a defector telling us of a Russian violation, it would not be very difficult to find physical evidence of it. I believe that the Soviet Union, which is posing as a peaceloving nation, whether rightly or wrongly, simply cannot afford to be caught in a violation, and therefore I think that it will not try to cheat." [5]

On the basis of this conviction that the Soviet Union would not dare to attempt to cheat under a test ban, the pro-ban scientists made their requirements for a control system far less stringent than the capabilities of the system believed necessary by the anti-ban scientists. Consequently, unlike the latter group, they tended to discount the decoupling theory as providing a serious obstacle to the policing of the test ban. Bethe again summarized the pro-ban view of the decoupling theory with the observation

3. Federation of American Scientists, Press Release, July 16, 1960.
4. U.S. Congress, Joint Committee on Atomic Energy, *Hearings on Technical Aspects of Detection and Inspection Controls of a Nuclear Weapons Test Ban,* 86th Congress, 2nd Session, 1960, p. 184.
5. Hans Bethe, *op. cit.,* pp. 45–46.

that "we are all behaving like a bunch of lunatics to take any such thing as the big hole seriously. . . ." [6]

These scientists argued further that even if the Russians wanted to cheat and to carry out a new test program the "restrictions imposed by any detection system, even a very imperfect one, would greatly impede their progress and slow it down to a snail's pace." [7] They believed any covert testing program would be detected long before it had made any significant progress. There are, these scientists argued, a variety of methods by which covert testing would come to the attention of the control system other than through agreed technical methods, e.g., defectors, location of suspicious events in an aseismic region, evidence of decoupling cavities such as abnormal brine concentration in rivers, and repetitive suspicious seismic events in the same location.

Among these informal policing methods the most potent, these scientists held, would be the fear of exposure through defectors. According to one pro-ban scientist, the Russians would be deterred from violation because cheating "places the whole Russian system at the mercy of any defector." [8] Another of these scientists believed that the "right of defection" ought to be incorporated into the treaty itself and thus "a citizen . . . would have a [legal] duty to report knowledge of secret testing to the International Control Commission." [9]

Furthermore, the pro-ban scientists argued that if the Soviet Union really desired to develop small yield tactical weapons they would not go to all the trouble of accepting the principle of control, of agreeing to a moratorium on small tests, and of pressing so hard for a nuclear test ban. As Hans Bethe put it: "If the Russians really want tactical nuclear weapons —that is, nuclear weapons of small yield—then the best thing for them to do would be to resume testing of such small weapons officially, exactly as was suggested in the original proposal by President Eisenhower on February 11. The fact that they asked instead for a moratorium on small tests indicates to me that they do not put much weight on development of these weapons." [10]

In the light of all these considerations the pro-ban scientists argued that

6. "The Test Ban and the Big Hole," *Scientific American,* Vol. 202, No. 6, June 1960, p. 81.
7. U.S. Congress, Joint Committee on Atomic Energy, *Hearings on Technical Aspects* . . . . , *op. cit.,* p. 184.
8. Quoted from testimony by Richard Roberts, *ibid.,* p. 217.
9. Jay Orear, Letter to *The New York Times,* January 6, 1960. It is interesting to note that Edward Teller made the same suggestion in 1946 with respect to the Baruch Plan (see Chapter Three). Orear later expanded his suggestion; "A New Approach to Inspection," *Bull. Atom. Sci.,* Vol. 17, No. 3, March 1961, pp. 107–10.
10. Hans Bethe, *op. cit.,* pp. 49–50.

the United States should take "positive" steps toward achievement of a nuclear test ban. They believed that American emphasis on obstacles to the test ban such as the decoupling theory was unhelpful and actually insulting to the Russians. Such an approach they maintained, was not creating the "mutual trust" necessary to build the peace.

Nevertheless, in order to decrease the unavoidable risk which would be inevitably inherent in a nuclear test ban, the pro-ban scientists have favored a vast research program in techniques of detection. They have argued, in the words of Hans Bethe, that "the next round [of scientific advance] ought to go to the detection rather than to the concealment." [11] In this connection the pro-ban scientists rightfully have pointed out that in the techniques of detecting and identifying underground nuclear explosions there were, and are, avenues of research as yet relatively unexplored that might reduce the possibility of evasion. Certainly the further study of the properties of the seismic waves generated by underground explosions and earthquakes could well discover positive criteria by which to distinguish underground nuclear explosions from earthquakes. Similarly, research on space testing might make it possible to detect nuclear explosions millions of miles distant from the earth.

Because their case for the technical feasibility of a system to police a nuclear test ban has been largely dependent upon the acquisition of new knowledge, these scientists have advocated an extensive program of seismic and other types of research. They have been resentful that efforts were made to discredit the Geneva System and that so little had been done to improve its capabilities. As a result of this dissatisfaction, much credit for the establishment of an extensive research program in detection methods (Project Vela) must be given to these pro-ban scientists. This is not to imply, however, that their scientist opponents have not also supported increased research on detection as well as on evasion techniques.

In addition to indicating possible future improvement of the Geneva System based on the acquisition of new knowledge, the pro-ban scientists have argued that a very substantial increase in its capabilities could be achieved within the bounds of available knowledge. Several proposals, all involving an increase in the number of control posts, have been put forward by these scientists. For example, Bethe proposed a network of about 200 robot seismograph stations to be placed in the seismic regions of the USSR. Such a network would be able to identify a high proportion of the earthquakes equivalent in yield to a 20 kiloton explosion even though it were fully decoupled. Bethe argued that the remaining unidentified events requiring on-site inspection would be of a manageable number.

11. U.S. Congress, Joint Committee on Atomic Energy, *Hearings on Technical Aspects* . . . . , *op. cit.*, p. 177.

Most scientists agree that Bethe's network would cancel the reduction which decoupling would cause in the capability of the Geneva System. They disagree, however, on the question of whether or not the network would reduce sufficiently the number of necessary on-site inspections. In fact, anti-ban scientists have argued to the contrary that the number of suspicious events requiring on-site inspections recorded by the Bethe-proposed network would be as high as 560 per year for seismic events which register two kilotons or more. Furthermore, the number of robot stations would have to be increased to 600 if the whole of Russia were to be covered, and the Russians have rather consistently rejected any such use of robot stations, as their use would undoubtedly open all of Russia to roving teams of foreign inspectors to insure that the robots were operating properly.

In summary, at least prior to the Soviet resumption of nuclear testing in September 1961, the pro-ban scientists believed not only that the Geneva System could be improved sufficiently to make it much more reliable but also that the sheer effort involved in carrying out a covert test program, the uncertainty of its results, and grave fear of "getting caught" would deter the Russians and any other nation from cheating. For the most part this conviction of the pro-ban scientists rested on their assessment of Russian motives and of the efficacy of the Geneva System. In addition, however, one senses in the case of many of these scientists a feeling that the internationalism of science itself would operate as a policing mechanism. Through personal contacts with Soviet scientists, professional gossip, and "defectors," it was believed that American scientists would be able to judge whether or not the Russians were cheating. In addition, Soviet scientists, acutely aware of the dangers of the nuclear arms race, would have presumably been able to resist the pressures of the Soviet military for continued testing; professional conscience and awareness of the dangers in the nuclear arms race would deter these Russian scientists from supporting illicit activities if they knew their American colleagues were equally restrained.

Indicative of this unspoken assumption of many pro-ban scientists that Soviet scientists could be depended upon either to prevent Russian cheating or to make such cheating known to their American colleagues was the following portion of an interview given by Harrison Brown of the California Institute of Technology:

> *Question:* "Would there not be the risk that the Russians might cheat during [a moratorium on testing] . . . ?"
> *Answer:* "They might, but I doubt that they would. First of all, I have talked with many top Russian scientists during the last 2 years and I believe that they seriously want an agreement. Further,

should they cheat there would always be the possibility that we would find out. The disadvantages to them, should this happen, would probably outweigh the advantages to be gained from clandestine testing."

Question: "Is there any direct evidence that the Russians are testing now?"

Answer: "There is no evidence. Indeed, Russian scientists of my acquaintance are as incensed at American suggestions that they might be testing, as we were incensed by Communist charges during the Korean War that we were resorting to the use of bacteriological warfare." [12]

Although not all pro-ban scientists would go as far as Brown in his dependence upon the statements of Russian scientists, the American scientists who favor a nuclear test ban tend to remain convinced that the international community of science is a force for peace. There is an implicit faith underlying many of their activities, such as the Pugwash Movement, that through appeals to Russian scientists the Soviet Union can be guided toward a more rational pattern of behavior. Many American scientists believe that a test ban would mean the most significant opening of Soviet society since the beginning of the Soviet thaw. In their view, it would give real substance to the belief that the international cooperation of scientists in both scientific and political areas constitutes a major factor working for peace.

THE POSITION OF THE ANTI-BAN SCIENTISTS

The anti-ban scientists have based their case against a nuclear test ban on the argument that the probability of detection of a test violation would be too small to overcome the powerful military incentive to advance nuclear technology through a covert test program. In the view of these scientists the technical situation was and continues to be such that the only guarantee against covert testing would be the good faith of the parties involved; and the past history of the relationship between East and West as well as the potentialities inherent in further weapons development have made "good faith" too weak a basis for a decision to enter into a test ban agreement. Furthermore, they have argued, the technical and political situation which has been unfavorable to the success of a test ban is likely to continue to exist for a long time to come. These scientists have believed that, unless the Soviet Union becomes an open society, programs of covert testing could progress almost as easily under a test ban as have the well publicized testing programs.

12. Interview of Harrison Brown by *Los Angeles Times,* December 25, 1960. See *Congressional Record,* January 30, 1961, p. A566.

In contrast to Bethe's belief that a covert test program would have to proceed at a "snail's pace," the anti-ban scientists have made the case that truly effective test programs could be carried out. In fact, these scientists believe, such test programs could be carried out even under a surveillance system far more stringent than any proposed systems and even under Bethe's proposed radical revision of the Geneva System with its 200 robot stations.

To illustrate their argument, the anti-ban scientists have pointed out that "the basic principles of most new [nuclear weapons] designs could be developed at energy releases below a few tens of kilotons" and consequently could be tested underground with little fear of detection. "Outer space testing would permit the checking of the data at full scale." In summary, these scientists have argued that "if a violator can cheat with explosions up to 1 kiloton, he can do all the work necessary to the development of small tactical weapons. If he can cheat to 20 to 30 kilotons he can do a lot, but not all he would probably want to do in developing strategic weapons. If, in addition, he can cheat in outer space in the megaton range, the full range of energy releases are available to him to conduct a full-scale weapons development program." [13]

In both space and underground testing, according to these scientists, the probability of "getting caught" is far too low to be a sufficient deterrent to cheating. They have noted that nuclear weapons of extremely small yield could be decoupled so as to create very small seismic waves. Furthermore, even if these waves were detected and the event located, it would be extremely difficult, and more likely impossible, to discover and therefore identify an underground nuclear explosion by drilling for radioactive debris. Lastly, these scientists have pointed out that when one speaks of the *location* of a seismic event he means only the definition of a 100–400 square mile area within which the event occurred. The event cannot be pinpointed more accurately because the level of scientific knowledge about seismic waves' travel time is too scanty. Some of these scientists suggest that the earth's crust is so irregular that it will never be possible to locate events very accurately because of the variation in travel time of seismic waves with varying geographical locations.

The anti-ban scientists would undoubtedly agree with the assessment of the difficulty of identification through on-site inspection made by James Fisk at Technical Working Group II: Fisk told the delegates that a scientist would seek "an almost infinitesimal target, within an area of 200 square kilometers, for example. If it were ever the purpose of a violator to attempt to hide such an event the task of an on-site inspection group

13. U.S. Congress, Joint Committee on Atomic Energy, *Hearings on Technical Aspects* . . . . , *op. cit.*, p. 404.

might be so great and so difficult that the probability of success would be close to zero." [14]

With respect to space testing, the anti-ban scientists have argued that whereas such testing is feasible as shown by Project Argus, a developed capability to detect space tests would not be possible for many years. In accordance with the conclusions of Technical Working Group I, even after the control system had been installed it would be extremely limited in capability. And even if suspicious events could be detected there would be no means by which they could be unquestionably identified as nuclear explosions or by which it could be proved which country had been the violator.

The anti-ban scientists grant that research in seismic and space detection methods would improve considerably the detection capabilities of the Geneva System. However, they have discounted the significance of such improvements for a number of reasons. Barring the discovery of a distinguishing and completely reliable characteristic for the seismic waves caused by nuclear explosions, the number of on-site inspections would have to be increased as improvement in detection capabilities increased, and then the strong opposition of the Soviet Union to on-site inspection would be encountered. Also, these scientists maintain, it is rather meaningless to speak as Bethe does of 200 or 600 seismic stations in the USSR when that nation has not yet agreed, even in principle, to having 21 stations on its soil.

These scientists have believed that the possibilities for evasion due to the imbalance between the art of detection and the art of evasion will be increased by future research. They have argued that the knowledge of evasion techniques is at a very primitive level, and that research has been seriously pursued in only one area, namely that of decoupling through the use of large chemical explosions in earth cavities.

The anti-ban scientists have pointed out that a number of other possible evasion techniques exist which, like decoupling, will prove feasible. Three of the possibilities which have been outlined by these scientists illustrate their argument.

The first suggestion is to test underneath the floor of a large body of water, such as an ocean, sea, or large lake. This procedure would have many advantages for a nation desiring to evade a nuclear test ban. As shore-line areas tend to be highly seismic, the recording of a seismic event might not in itself cause suspicions to arise. Also, even if detected and suspected, the location of the event would be very imprecise and its iden-

14. Conference on the Discontinuance of Nuclear Weapons Tests, Technical Working Group II, *Verbatim Transcript of Thirteenth Meeting,* December 10, 1959, p. 66.

tification extremely difficult because the area probably would not be surrounded by seismic control stations. Of decisive importance, the most crucial techniques of on-site inspection would not be available; the investigating team would be unable to depend upon aerial surveillance to reduce the suspicious area to manageable proportions for drilling purposes. As a result the investigating team would have few clues to guide it in selecting a spot to drill in an area hundreds of miles square. If an underwater shot were also decoupled, the difficulties of discovering the violation might be even more considerable. Ominously, they have pointed out, the most propitious place to carry out such a procedure would be the narrow Kamchatka Peninsula of Siberia and near Karafuto Island which have 60 per cent of Russia's earthquakes.[15]

A second possibility for an evasion technique which has been suggested by these scientists would be to mask the first motion of a nuclear explosion through the use of multiple explosions. As Edward Teller explained to the Joint Committee on Atomic Energy, it was conceivable, although admittedly difficult, that a series of nuclear explosions could be detonated in such a way that the explosions ". . . can wipe out the characteristic signature of a nuclear explosion." [16] As a result of such a procedure, Teller argued before the committee, the seismic events would pass unrecognized by the control posts.

These scientists also have discussed the possibility of another evasion technique, i.e., the employment in the decoupling cavity of certain materials that would absorb the energy from the explosion and consequently reduce the resulting seismic waves. Scientists in the anti-ban school believe that through the use of this technique the decoupling factor could be increased ten-fold; i.e., a 3000 kiloton explosion could be made to appear as a one kiloton explosion (300 present decoupling factor times ten).

Essentially, then, the position of the anti-ban scientists has been that evasion techniques could increase much faster than could methods for detecting nuclear explosions. Not only do they believe that detection through technical means would be infeasible but these men have felt that reliance upon non-technical means, such as defectors and espionage, could not remedy the situation. There have been, these scientists have pointed out, no Soviet defectors as yet who have told the West of the progress of Soviet nuclear research, and the West has been surprised by the first Soviet atomic bomb, by its first hydrogen bomb, by its first earth satellite and, they might add, by its resumption of testing in September 1961.

In response to the argument that one should not expect perfection in a

15. For discussion on this evasion method see U.S. Congress, Joint Committee on Atomic Energy, *Hearings on Technical Aspects* . . . . , *op. cit.*, pp. 232–38.
16. *Ibid.*, p. 160.

system to police a test ban, these scientists have replied that there should at least be *some* chance of detecting a violation. They have argued that without an open world the probability of catching a violator would be negligible while the consequences of successful covert testing could be decisive for the outcome of the struggle between East and West.

The Underlying Sources of Intra-scientific Conflict

The task of elucidating the non-technical assumptions underlying the conflicting interpretations of the scientists concerning the technical feasibility of a nuclear test ban has actually been carried out largely by the scientists themselves. The confrontation of opposed scientists before Congressional committees and in print over the past few years has made quite obvious the non-technical assumptions which influence their presentation of the technical facts. While it often remains difficult to know where scientific agreement ends and political polemics begin, the discerning non-scientists can find exposed the non-technical views upon which the scientist bases his case.

Essentially the conflict among scientists with respect to a nuclear test ban has been due to differing views over the questions of Western military strategy, the motivation of the Soviet Union, and the political desirability of a nuclear test ban. While this distinction between military and political views is necessary for analytical purposes, those views are intricately joined in the thought of each set of protagonists.

CONFLICT OVER WESTERN STRATEGY

The strategic issue at stake in the struggle over a nuclear test ban has been whether or not limited nuclear warfare constitutes a feasible alternative to massive retaliation. Universally rejecting the doctrine of massive retaliation, most scientists have realized a need to substitute for it some form of military power as long as political tension and conflict characterize the world. Here, however, agreement ends and for a variety of reasons each side of the nuclear test ban issue has favored a different Western strategy. The opponents of the test ban have advocated a strategy based primarily upon the employment of tactical nuclear weapons; the proponents generally have argued for a strategy based solely upon conventional weapons.

The strategic view of the anti-ban scientists. The infinite containment or anti-ban scientists have accepted as basic the notion that "the idea of massive retaliation is impractical and immoral." [17] It is immoral because

17. Edward Teller, "On the Feasibility of Arms Control," Unpublished paper, May 6, 1960, p. 13.

it involves the slaughter of innocent civilians; it is impractical in a world where the Soviet Union also possesses a long-range nuclear capability. The only reason for possession of megaton weapons is to deter their use by the Soviet Union. "We keep them," Teller and Latter write, "as a counterthreat against the danger that we . . . should be subjected to a devastating attack. . . . We believe that the role of nuclear weapons in a future war is by no means the killing of millions of civilians." [18]

In the view of these scientists, if the doctrine of massive retaliation is to be discarded, a new Western strategy must be developed which counters the apparent Communist military advantages of "central location, superiority in massive conventional weapons and in manpower, and finally, a political orientation which permits them to assume the initiative without any moral scruples." [19] Such an alternative strategy, these men have argued, can only be created through the development of a capability to wage limited nuclear war. "Tactical nuclear weapons could enable us to build up a counter force which would neutralize . . . Soviet advantages." [20] Even though the Russians might have these weapons as well, they would still lose their natural advantages. Indeed ". . . the main role of nuclear weapons might well be to disperse any striking force so that the resistance of people defending their homes can become decisive. Nuclear weapons may well become the answer to massed armies. . . ." [21] and thus serve to eliminate from political life the scourge of major war.

The development of tactical nuclear weapons, in the opinion of the infinite containment scientists, is bringing about a military revolution equal to the change wrought by the original atomic bomb. It will enable small mobile forces to be in possession of very great firepower and thus to accomplish the same ends which have required the employment of mass armies in earlier wars.[22] In addressing the Association of the United States Army on the need for a nuclearized army, Teller has argued: "I believe that this warfare of extreme mobility and dispersion will turn out to be the key to real military power." [23]

In the view of these anti-ban scientists, the argument that any use of nuclear weapons in limited war would lead to total nuclear war is a specious one. Wars, they have argued, are limited by their objectives and ge-

18. Edward Teller and Albert Latter, *Our Nuclear Future,* Criterion Books, 1958, pp. 141–42.
19. Edward Teller, "On the Feasibility of Arms Control,' *op. cit.,* p. 14.
20. *Ibid.*
21. Edward Teller and Albert Latter, *op. cit.,* p. 171.
22. Edward Teller, "On the Feasibility of Arms Control," *op. cit.,* p. 14.
23. Edward Teller, "The Impact of Nuclear Weapons on Future Organization," *Army Information Digest,* Vol. 12, January 1957, p. 18.

ography and not by their weaponry. For this reason they believe the use of nuclear weapons in limited war would not pose a danger of world wide nuclear conflagration. Indeed, according to these scientists ". . . the distinction between a nuclear weapon and a conventional weapon is the distinction between an effective weapon and an outmoded weapon." [24] These scientists believe that the Russian argument that limited nuclear war will lead to total nuclear war is an attempt to forestall the development of a limited nuclear war capability by the West; the Russians, through a subtle threat of nuclear blackmail, seek to prevent the development of this strategy which is disadvantageous to the achievement of Russia's goals.

If the Western allies are to develop a strategy based on a capability for limited nuclear war, it requires "very special kinds of nuclear weapons which are hard to develop and harder to perfect." [25] The development of these weapons is at a very primitive level. As the anti-ban scientists believe that these weapons could greatly contribute to the stabilization of the world by giving the West an alternative to massive retaliation, they believe there is an urgent need to continue the development of tactical nuclear arms.

The infinite containment school has argued further that continued testing will have three major effects on nuclear weapons technology. Firstly, testing will improve the economy and the performance of present weapons; deliverability could be improved; and yield could be increased. Secondly, continued testing will enable the West to develop an arsenal of the "clean," small yield nuclear weapons it needs to counterbalance Soviet conventional strengths. Principal among these military requirements are radical new designs for battlefield weapons; other nuclear weapons which these scientists include in any list of possible advances through continued research are an anti-missile missile, an anti-submarine depth charge, and improved missile warheads.

The third and most important argument for continued research, according to the infinite containment scientists, lies in the future. These scientists believe that nuclear weapons research stands at the threshold of a major breakthrough which will greatly affect all warfare. For example, Freeman Dyson, who is not himself a member of the infinite containment school, wrote in April 1960: "I believe that radically new kinds of nuclear weapons are technically possible, that the military and political effects of such weapons would be important, and that the development of

24. Edward Teller, "The Nature of Nuclear Warfare," *Bull. Atom. Sci.*, Vol. 13, No. 5, May 1957, p. 162.
25. Edward Teller and Albert Latter, *op. cit.*, p. 142.

such weapons can hardly be arrested by any means less drastic than international control of all nuclear operations." [26]

In particular Dyson had in mind what has come to be called the "neutron" bomb. It was the possibility of such a development which Teller had
in mind in 1957 when he advocated continued testing to perfect a
"clean" bomb. Apparently agreeing with Teller, Dyson has written: "A
fission-free bomb, containing a small quantity of heavy hydrogen and no
fissionable metal, is logically the third major step in weapon development
after the existing fission and hydrogen bombs." [27] Such a neutron bomb
would release a lethal ray of neutrons in all directions. There would, however, be little accompanying destruction caused by blast effect; furthermore, although this fissionless warhead would not be completely clean with
respect to radioactive fallout, it would be "enormously less" dirty than existing nuclear weapons. Such a weapon, these scientists believe, would be an
ideal anti-personnel weapon for limited war. In addition, some reason, its
neutron ray might make it the ideal warhead for an anti-missile missile.

These scientists have argued that the exploitation of these potential
breakthroughs would revolutionize ground warfare. Nuclear weapons with
a yield from one ton to one kiloton TNT equivalent would give small tactical units immense firepower; furthermore, this firepower could be employed without fear of indiscriminate destruction in densely populated
areas like Western Europe. The infinite containment scientists believe that
through the exploitation of these possibilities for the development of tactical nuclear weapons the outbreak of limited war could be deterred in the
same fashion that strategic strength deters total nuclear war.

The military significance of these potential nuclear developments is so
important, these scientists have argued, that the Soviet Union would have
great incentive to continue work in the area, regardless of any test ban;
and the West cannot risk unilateral Soviet development of such new weapons. If the Soviet Union should be the first to develop fission-free or

26. Freeman Dyson, "The Future Development of Nuclear Weapons," *Foreign
Affairs*, Vol. 38, No. 3, April 1960, p. 457. For Dyson's latest views on the neutron
bomb see *Bull. Atom. Sci.*, Vol. 17, No. 7, September 1961, pp. 271–72.
27. Freeman Dyson, "The Future Development of Nuclear Weapons," *op. cit.*, p.
458. His statement is the most authoritative and, in fact, the only one on the possibility of a "neutron" bomb by a scientist acquainted with the American nuclear
weapons program. Scientists have been exceedingly uncommunicative on this subject.
The only other statements of substance have been made by Senator Thomas Dodd.
As a consequence the exact nature of the weapon at issue when someone refers to
"neutron bomb" can mean many things in addition to a fission-free bomb. The only
available technical discussion of these various possibilities known to the writer is the
following by a British scientist: Nigel Calder, "Notes on the 'Neutron Bomb,'" *New
Scientist*, Vol. 11, No. 244, July 20, 1961, pp. 145–47.

"clean" nuclear weapons, it would secure a military advantage which would enable it to dominate future limited conflicts with the West. In this connection Dyson has noted that Russian physics journals indicate that their physicists have been working in this area since at least 1952.[28]

The theoretical possibility of a "clean" nuclear warhead well illustrates the primary argument of the infinite containment school for continued research, development, and testing of nuclear weapons. This argument is that the science and technology of atomic energy are very young. The attempt to arrest them in the immediate future would be comparable to the prohibition of the further development of chemical energy after the introduction of gunpowder in Europe. The possible implications of atomic energy for future warfare are no less revolutionary than were those of gunpowder when it was first introduced.

The strategic view of the pro-ban scientists. The pro-ban scientists, on the other hand, reject as infeasible the basing of Western strategy on the use of atomic weapons in limited war. Atomic weapons, according to their view, are by their very nature weapons of total war. Whereas in the years following the outbreak of the Korean War many of these same scientists advocated that the West develop tactical nuclear weapons, they came to the conclusion after the arrival of nuclear parity that tactical nuclear weapons were not to the advantage of the West; furthermore, their use might trigger the widening of any limited war into total nuclear war. David Inglis, a spokesman for this group, has written in opposition to the sharing of atomic weapons information with America's Europeans allies that "the policy . . . is based on an unproved and essentially unprovable proposition (probably a myth) that a 'small' nuclear war could be fought in Europe without very great danger of growing into a 'big' nuclear war that must be avoided." [29]

The only reason for maintaining *any type* of nuclear weapon in one's arsenal is, in the view of the pro-ban scientists, to deter their use by one's opponents. The present Western capabilities in nuclear technology, are, these scientists believe, more than sufficient to achieve this goal. Accordingly, there is little need to continue the development of weapons that the West dare not use except as a last resort. Also, these scientists have argued, the United States could continue laboratory research on nuclear weapons and be prepared if the Soviet Union should unilaterally resume testing.

The pro-ban school believes that the West must maintain sufficient conventional military power to deter Communist limited aggression, especially in Europe. It fears the possibility that the West might become so depen-

28. Freeman Dyson, "The Future Development of Nuclear Weapons," *op. cit.,* p. 459.
29. Letter to the editor, *The New York Times,* July 22, 1959, p. 26.

dent upon nuclear weapons that it could not defend itself against limited advances by Communist satellite nations except by means which might result in a nuclear holocaust. Inglis, in the letter referred to above, stated the concern of these scientists that an emphasis on nuclear weapons among America's European allies as desired by the infinite containment scientists would make likely ". . . the degeneration of NATO capabilities to wage a non-nuclear war against the Eastern satellites." [30] If such an eventuality were to occur, the West could not meet limited encroachment by Communist conventional forces without a major nuclear war. In time this could lead to the piecemeal capitulation of Europe and the rest of the Free World.

These scientists deny that limited nuclear warfare would be to the advantage of the West. They argue that in limited nuclear war the nation with the greatest reserve forces would be the winner, as this type of war would consume far more troops than conventional war. In addition, tactical atomic weapons could be used by the Communists to destroy port facilities, to interdict supply lines, and to bomb American overseas bases. The high attrition rate, the vulnerability of Western supply lines, and the political costs of this type of war are viewed by these scientists as but three cogent reasons against dependence upon tactical nuclear weapons. However, even if feasible, these scientists point out that one result of a limited nuclear war might be the obliteration of the country the West is seeking to defend and that such a consequence might well make other Communist threatened nations more susceptible to nuclear blackmail.

These scientists base their case against the feasibility of a limited nuclear war on the fact that whereas there is a clear qualitative distinction between nuclear and conventional weapons—such as the presence or absence of radioactivity—which provides an upper limit on the war which both sides can observe and know that the other is also observing, this would not be true in the case of "limited" nuclear war. In the latter type of war, under the pressures and excitement of battle, there could be a gradual acceleration in the size of the weapons employed. As a mutually understood upper limit would be lacking, a nation might be forced against its will to increase the magnitude of nuclear weapons used until the limited war actually became total.

In addition, these scientists argue, the proponents of limited nuclear war fail to recognize the possible political advantages which would accrue to the Communists if the primary Western response to Communist conventional aggression were with tactical nuclear weapons. While technically the only difference between nuclear and conventional weapons is one of their relative efficiencies, in political terms there is a considerable differ-

30. *Ibid.*

ence, at least in the eyes of the great majority of the world's peoples. The use of nuclear weapons to counter a limited Communist aggression undertaken with conventional weapons would carry a high political cost for the West. In such a case there is little doubt that the Communists would find many ways to utilize to their advantage the universal fear of all nuclear weapons.

For all these reasons, then, a major strategic purpose of a test ban, in the view of at least some pro-ban scientists, would be to emphasize the fact that nuclear weapons *are* different. A test ban would serve notice to all that these weapons are too dangerous to be employed. In effect, they would become outlawed by each nation for reasons of self-interest. No nation, this argument goes, would seek to gain advantage in limited war by the employment of nuclear weapons at the risk of plunging the world into nuclear conflagration.[31]

The proponents of a test ban have argued further that its cost in potential military capabilities would be negligible. Nuclear technology, they believe, has reached a point of relative stagnation. Any gain such as the proposed neutron bomb which might be made through continued testing would be minor compared to the political-strategic advantages of a test ban. The beneficial results which a test ban would bring make it a course of action far preferable to opposition to a test ban based on the speculation that nuclear science is on the verge of a major breakthrough.

In the view of these scientists, the so-called "clean" or neutron bomb is technically and militarily questionable. The high temperatures required to bring about the fusion of hydrogen nuclei, these scientists argue, are unlikely to be created by conventional means such as high explosives. Even though theoretically possible, such a development is at least many years in the future. And, even if it could be perfected, they question the possible military significance of the weapon.

Furthermore these scientists are convinced that further progress in nuclear technology would not be to the advantage of the United States—nor to the Soviet Union for that matter. Whereas the infinite containment scientists look with favor upon the possibility of a research breakthrough which would, in their estimation, give a military advantage to the United States, the pro-ban scientists disparage the effects of new advances in nuclear weaponry. The advance of nuclear weapons technology by further

31. For an excellent presentation of this argument see Donald G. Brennan and Morton Halperin, "Policy Considerations of a Nuclear Test Ban," in Donald G. Brennan, ed., *Arms Control, Disarmament and National Security,* George Braziller, 1961, pp. 234–66. Brennan is a physicist; Halperin is a political scientist. Whether or not one agrees with the conclusions of their analysis, it does indicate the benefits to be derived from this type of cooperation between natural and social scientists.

testing would only simplify the state of atomic art and thus make it easier for smaller nations to become nuclear powers. Such an unwanted development would result if the present nuclear powers proved the feasibility of making a neutron bomb which does not require costly fissionable materials.

In fact the dubious nature of any advantage accruing to either the United States or the USSR through further testing has constituted the basis for the hope of these scientists that a test ban would be observed. Whereas the loss which would be suffered by a nation caught cheating on a ban would be known, the possible gain through covert testing would be unknown. It has been argued that, given these two alternatives, the Russian incentive to test new concepts and thus to infringe on the ban would be small.

CONFLICT OVER THE POLITICAL DESIRABILITY
OF A NUCLEAR TEST BAN

The underlying difference among the scientists on the political desirability of a nuclear test ban rests on contrasting assumptions concerning the nature of the Soviet Union, of the nuclear arms race, and of international politics. An understanding of these differing assumptions is therefore essential if the conflict among scientists over nuclear weapons is to be comprehended.

The view of the pro-ban scientists. These scientists believe that the Soviet Union is characterized by an internal conflict between an irrational political heritage and the modern rational forces represented by Soviet science. They believe the refusal of the USSR to see the inherent danger in the nuclear arms race and to seek meaningful measures to end it to be due to the continued supremacy of vestigial irrational forces such as communist ideology and the Russian military services. The pressing need, in the view of these scientists, is therefore to strengthen the forces within the Soviet society which are working toward a rational solution to the problem of atomic energy. A fundamental political purpose of a nuclear test ban would be to accomplish this goal. These scientists believe that unless this occurs there is no hope for the world, as the rapid advancement of scientific technology is incompatible with an irrationally ordered world.

The view of these scientists concerning the nature of current international politics reinforces their conviction of the nature of Soviet society. They believe that the destructiveness of modern weapons has ushered in a new era of history where the old rule of power politics that disarmament must follow political settlement no longer applies. Today, in the words of the Franck Report, as all nations "shudder at the possibility of a sudden disintegration" and have a mutual interest in self-preservation, "only lack of mutual trust . . . can stand in the path of an efficient agreement for the prevention of nuclear warfare."

A number of corollaries flow from this premise; whereas in the past disarmament was presumed to be dependent upon prior guarantees of security and the settlement of political disputes, now the overwhelming interest which all nations are believed to have in nuclear disarmament has reversed this rule. For this reason disarmament can presently be viewed primarily as an autonomous problem which can be solved wholly or at least in part by technical means. Thus the pro-ban scientists believe that the criterion of technical feasibility could become the *modus operandi* in at least one area of international affairs and, in this way mankind would, in time, rid itself of the instruments of war and thus begin to substitute a more reasonable method than war for the settlement of international disputes.

The scientists who favor a nuclear test ban have approached it as an experiment by which to test their theory that mutual distrust is the major barrier to general disarmament; if the test ban could be agreed to and succeed it would prove to the nations that the criterion of technical feasibility in international negotiations opens the way for the far-reaching disarmament agreements they all desire. As one test ban proponent, Bernard Feld, has put it, "although such measures [to police a test ban] can hardly be said to constitute serious disarmament,[32] the difficulties are in many respects characteristic of the types of technical problems which will be encountered in future arms-limitation negotiations." [33] Or, in the words of Hans Bethe, "the main importance of our negotiations on the test cessation agreement comes . . . not from this agreement itself, important as it is, but from further agreements which must follow." [34]

It has been believed that through their experience in making a test ban work the nations would overcome the fears and insecurities which supposedly prevent them from realizing their mutual interest in the international control of atomic energy. Then, through technical measures such as those detailed in Seymour Melman's *Inspection for Disarmament*,[35] the nuclear powers could proceed step by step to disarm themselves.

As they believe that irrational and "traditional" thinking still predominates in the governing councils of nations, these scientists have assumed a

32. Feld's footnote, "This fact may diminish their significance, but not their importance."
33. Bernard Feld, "Inspection Techniques of Arms Control," *Daedalus* (*Arms Control* Issue), Vol. 89, No. 4, Fall 1960, p. 862.
34. Hans Bethe, *op. cit.*, p. 51.
35. Seymour Melman, ed., *Inspection for Disarmament*, Columbia University Press, 1958.

responsibility to hasten mankind's achievement of a social consciousness appropriate to the facts of the atomic age. Herein lies the meaning of the oft-repeated remark that the most important point in achieving a nuclear test ban is a political one, since a nuclear test ban would break the pattern of traditionalist thinking that prevails among men and would be the first step to a new "political atmosphere in which . . . the use of highly destructive weapons becomes increasingly an unthinkable, inhuman act." [36]

The progress which these scientists believed the Geneva negotiations had made toward the achievement of a test ban confirmed, for a time at least, their conviction that a ban represented an opportunity to bring about fundamental changes, particularly in the supposedly irrational behavior of the Soviet Union. For example, this appears to account for Bethe's reluctance to have the technical difficulties of the Geneva System stressed too much; he feared that emphasis on evasion and cheating might insult the Russians and cause them to regress to what some would call an irrational position. It was no doubt this concern which led Bethe to write in August 1960: "I had the doubtful honor of presenting the theory of the big hole [decoupling] to the Russians in Geneva in November, 1959. I felt deeply embarrassed in so doing, because it implied that we considered the Russians capable of cheating on a massive scale. I think that they would have been quite justified if they had considered this an insult and had walked out of the negotiations in disgust." [37]

Within the United States the test ban advocates believe that they have succeeded in accomplishing a major political breakthrough. For the first time since 1946 they feel that they have been victorious over the internal forces within the American government which have opposed any attempts to end the arms race. Although the way in which this was achieved was in part through Pauling's appeal to emotion and fear, they believe a new atmosphere has been created in which rational solutions can be found and will be met with favor.

In addition to being a first step toward disarmament and a moderating influence in the Cold War, the scientist-proponents of a nuclear test ban have tended to argue that it would be the solution to the Nth country problem. However, there are varying ideas of the way in which a test ban would arrest the spread of nuclear weapons to other nations.[38]

The most popular or prevalent view among these scientists—and within

36. Seymour Melman, "The Political Implications of Inspection for Disarmament," *Journal of International Affairs,* Vol. 13, No. 1, Winter 1959, p. 44.
37. Hans Bethe, *op. cit.,* p. 46.
38. For a sobering discussion of the Nth country problem see *1970 Without Arms Control: Implications of Modern Weapons Technology,* Report of the Special Project Committee on Security Through Arms Control, National Planning Association, Washington, 1958.

both the Eisenhower and Kennedy Administrations as well—of the way in which a nuclear test ban would limit the number of nuclear powers is that the force of world public opinion would act as a restraint. Thus, when asked by a United States Senator to explain how the ban would operate, John McCone, then chairman of the AEC, replied that "the thinking is . . . that a combination of logic and world opinion would develop adherence by other countries." [39] Essentially the same point was made to another Senator by John McCloy, who at the time was President Kennedy's disarmament advisor.[40]

A far more sophisticated view has been presented by a natural scientist working in conjunction with a political scientist.[41] In the view of Donald Brennan and Morton Halperin, a nuclear test ban would symbolize to the world the intention of the Great Powers not to use nuclear weapons in limited war. The ban, by serving to emphasize the danger of such weapons, would discourage the present have-not powers from investing their scarce resources in nuclear armament.

The third suggestion for the manner in which a nuclear test ban could solve the Nth country problem has been made by Herman Kahn, although he himself does not necessarily subscribe to it. This is the notion that a nuclear test ban could be enforced by the nuclear powers. In effect a ban would constitute a Pax Russo-Americana, and Kahn as well as his reader is aware of the improbability of such a political realignment of the nuclear powers.

In the eyes of the proponents of a nuclear test ban continued testing offers no solution to the problem of atomic weapons; a test ban at least holds a promise of reward in this area of threatening disaster. In the last analysis, these men would argue, one has to take a chance—an act of faith—which would enable mankind to get ahead of the nuclear arms race. In this light they have asserted that a test ban is a calculated risk which is well worth taking.

The view of the anti-ban scientists. In contrast to their scientific opponents, these scientists believe that a nuclear test ban would be neither a step toward disarmament, a means to lessen the aggressive nature of Soviet policy, nor a solution to the Nth country problem. Indeed, they argue, rather than solving these problems a nuclear test ban would bring dire consequences.

The real danger, these scientists believe, is that the West will be lulled

39. U.S. Senate, Committee on Foreign Relations, *Hearings Before a Subcommittee on the Geneva Test Ban Negotiations,* 86th Congress, 1st Session, 1959, p. 16.
40. Letter from John McCloy to Senator Stuart Symington. See *Congressional Record,* June 12, 1961, p. 9275.
41. See Donald Brennan and Morton Halperin, *op. cit.,* pp. 234–66.

into accepting an agreement which incorporates a policing system inadequate to prevent covert weapons advancement. They believe that the opportunity and the incentive to test will always be so great that the arms race can only be arrested by a radical change in the degree of openness in the world. "Once we have accomplished that," Teller told a Congressional committee, "then the way toward disarmament and toward peace lies open before us. Without it, however, we are just inventing one method after another how to fool ourselves." [42] In turn, these scientists believe, an open world must await the settlement of the political issues dividing East and West and the "withering away" of closed totalitarian societies.

Specifically, these scientists expect that a test ban would create the illusion that all was well with the world and that an atmosphere of complacency would then envelop the West. If the West let down its guard, made far-reaching concessions to the Russians, and disarmed itself, the Communists would be emboldened to seek their objectives through military aggression. At the very least, in the opinion of these scientists, a test ban would deprive the West of the major strategic advantage it now has over the Soviet Union. Not only would a ban prevent the development of the additional new varieties of nuclear weapons needed by the West, but it would cast an aura of illegitimacy about all nuclear weapons that might make them too immoral or too dangerous to use as a counter to Soviet conventional military power. In fact, these scientists argue, the main purpose of the Soviet Union in the nuclear test negotiations actually has been to outlaw the nuclear weapons upon which the United States has and must base its defense.

These scientists maintain that the hope that a test ban would open Soviet society is entirely illusory. Even though one were to agree with the pro-ban scientists that the Russian stress on secrecy and fear of espionage is in part "irrational," these scientists would still argue that the Russians are quite thoroughly convinced that it is more in their interest to maintain territorial secrecy as a strategic asset than to permit the establishment of an inspection system which would decrease significantly the extent of this security curtain. For the Russians, secrecy has become a major element in the balance of power as it protects their missile sites from discovery and consequently protects them from destruction. In fact, they believe that secrecy may be of such significance as to give the Soviet Union the strategic edge over the United States. The United States is only deceiving itself, these scientists contend, in believing that the Soviet Union will be induced by the promise of a nuclear test ban to open its territory and expose the whereabouts of its missiles.

42. U.S. Congress, Joint Committee on Atomic Energy, *Hearings on Technical Aspects* . . . . , *op. cit.*, p. 167.

The impact of a prolonged nuclear test ban on the American nuclear weapons program would be disastrous, these scientists further contend. Contrary to the argument of the pro-ban scientists that research could continue, these scientists point out that the continuation of such research is dependent upon testing just as other types of scientific research are dependent upon laboratory experimentation. Furthermore, America's successful weapons teams would break up as scientists left Los Alamos and Livermore for more interesting and socially approved work. In contrast, the Soviet Union could force its scientists to continue research and to search for potential breakthroughs which would make covert testing or a repudiation of the test ban worthwhile.

As for the Nth country problem these scientists argue that the diffusion and utilization of knowledge is far too rapid to be controlled except by a world government. Regrettable as it may be, this fact is of the essence of the scientific revolution which is making scientific knowledge available to all nations; the United States through its own generosity in the Atoms for Peace Program and in technical assistance programs has actually contributed to this process.

As a matter of fact, these scientists believe, the only nations which might be deterred by a nuclear test ban from testing nuclear weapons would be the nations of the democratic West. And even the belief that these nations would be deterred can be questioned. The constant threats of Soviet nuclear blackmail and general world insecurity are powerful incentives for have-not nations to develop their own nuclear capabilities. In addition to these factors the desires for national grandeur and an equal voice in international councils offer further motivation to possess nuclear arms.

Fortunately, these scientists argue, the next nations to become nuclear powers will be the European allies of the United States, and this is necessary for the security of the West. Furthermore, the United States through cooperation with them can control the dissemination of nuclear weapons to its NATO allies in a manner which will lessen the anarchistic spread of nuclear capabilities. Perhaps, these scientists hopefully reason, this experience will teach the world how to control nuclear weapons.

With respect to the enforcement of a nuclear test ban, these scientists ask how public opinion could deter a nation from testing. Even if one grants that a nation would not dare defy world public opinion—an assumption made highly questionable by the Russian recommencement of testing in September 1961—there must be some way to assign responsibility for a test which might be detected. However, since a test program could be carried out at high altitudes, in space, and in the oceans without any evidence by which to determine responsibility if the test were detected, then the guilty party could easily accuse other nuclear powers of having been the violators of a ban.

The events of the twentieth century have caused the infinite containment scientists to be especially concerned with the question of whether or not democracy has the determination and skill to meet the challenge of despotism. Prior to both World Wars, these scientists point out, the democracies failed to build their strength but instead they listened to talk of disarmament and were lulled to sleep. There is a fear among these scientists that political leaders cannot negotiate sound arms control agreements and at the same time call forth from the Western peoples the effort required if the West is to survive and war is to be deterred.

Instead of seeking to eliminate nuclear weapons through disarmament, these scientists believe that man must solve the problem of war itself. Modern science, including atomic weapons, seems to these scientists to have become a major force for peace. In the first place, man has reached that point in his technological evolution where he can gain more through scientific cooperation than through international conflict; through such cooperation man can build a world community where war would be unthinkable. In the second place, science has provided the threat of nuclear destruction as a deterrent to war. Just as the threat of strategic bombing deters total war, tactical nuclear weapons can be made to deter limited war. Thus, echoing the advice of the science advisory panel to the Interim Committee in 1945, these scientists believe that the military exploitation of the atom holds greater promise for the prevention of war than the benefit to man of the possible elimination of nuclear weapons.

Conclusion

The problem of conflicting expertise, as exemplified by the debate over the technical feasibility of a nuclear test ban, is one which in a sense has always existed for the public and for the policy maker. However, the increase in the complexity of the issues facing society and in their importance has accentuated the problem. Of great significance in complicating this problem is the fact that scientists believe they have a social responsibility to assist society in solving the problems created by scientific advance. This new social commitment of scientists has made it increasingly difficult for the scientist and the non-scientist to separate the expert's advice concerning *what is* from that concerned with *what ought to be*.

In no area does the problem of conflicting expertise present a more grave challenge to policy-making than in the vital area of national policy toward nuclear weapons. Even more discouraging is the fact that the complexity of the problem has increased through the years. At the time of the

Baruch Plan the political assumptions of the scientists had recently been made fairly explicit in the Franck Report, and their effect on the Acheson-Lilienthal Proposals was fairly obvious. At the time of the hydrogen bomb controversy the General Advisory Committee scientists did try, although without success, to separate their political and scientific judgments in their report. Today, however, the intensity of the intra-scientific conflict over nuclear weapons and the resultant increased politicalization of the scientist's advice have made it ever more difficult to know where scientific facts stop and political opinions begin.

Nevertheless, . . . the development of an increasing sense of social responsibility (and, therefore, political involvement) among scientists should not be regarded as cause for alarm. While it does exacerbate the problem of conflicting expertise, it can also constitute a source of great national strength. It is the task of political leadership to utilize more effectively than it has in the past the legitimate desire of scientists to contribute to the formulation of national policy toward nuclear weapons and other products of the scientific revolution.

V
SCIENCE AND FOREIGN POLICY

The emergence of the United States as a great power with interests and commitments throughout the world has coincided with the coming of the scientific revolution. These two developments have become increasingly interrelated until, in recent years, foreign policy problems seldom arise that do not involve some technological considerations. In fact, a number of the more critical international problems with which nations must be concerned are themselves the product of scientific advancements. The Damoclesian sword of nuclear war and the population explosion are obvious examples.

Warner R. Schilling opens the chapter with the observation that the entry of scientists into the decision-making process presents no problems that really differ from those common to the participation of any other type of expert in policy formulation. As he sees it, the contributions of science and technology to international politics are more dependent upon their effective utilization by statesmen than upon the positioning of scientists at high levels in the policy-making machinery.

The uneven performance of the State Department's Office of International Scientific and Technological Affairs is described by Eugene B. Skolnikoff as a highly regrettable situation in view of the need of the chief foreign policy adviser to the President to deal with issues that often include sophisticated scientific and technological components. The prompt appointment of the right scientist to direct the office, and then the placing of appropriate emphasis upon his advice, are obviously of great importance.

In an article by John Turkevich the recent growth of science and technology in the Soviet Union is examined. The nature of the programs and the degree of success of these enterprises will have direct effects on both the foreign and science policies of the United States. How a relatively static science program can be influenced by the accomplishments of a potential adversary was clearly illustrated in the American reaction to Sputnik in 1957.

An organized and continued endeavor by scientists from many nations to establish rapport and lines of unofficial communication with their opposite numbers is the subject discussed in the final reading. Although the ability of the Pugwash conferences to produce solutions to international problems is treated with some skepticism, the basic concern of the author is that Western delegates, with some exceptions, do not have the background or disposition to deal with issues that are primarily political when they are confronted with the official representatives of the Soviet Academy of Sciences who have been selected to attend the conferences at least partially on the basis that they are politically reliable.

WARNER R. SCHILLING
Scientists, Foreign Policy, and Politics

> [W]e must take, so far as we can, a picture of the world into our
> minds. Is it not a startling circumstance for one thing that the
> great discoveries of science, that the quiet study of men in labora-
> tories, that the thoughtful developments which have taken place in
> quiet lecture rooms, have now been turned to the destruction of
> civilization? . . . The enemy whom we have just overcome had at
> its seats of learning some of the principal centres of scientific study
> and discovery, and used them in order to make destruction sudden
> and complete; and only the watchful, continuous cooperation of
> men can see to it that science, as well as armed men, is kept within
> the harness of civilization.[1]

These words were spoken in Paris, in January, 1919, by Woodrow Wilson, addressing the second Plenary Session of the Peace Conference. Wilson believed he had found a watchdog for civilization in the League of
Nations. In this he was mistaken. Science and armed men have indeed
been harnessed, but in order to promote and maintain the goals of conflicting polities. Whether in the pursuit of these ends the cause of civilization will yet be served remains, it is to be hoped, an open question.

The cooperation of scientists and armed men was not a new relationship, even in Wilson's day. In the United States, for example, the president of the American Association for the Advancement of Science had
declared in 1861:

> [I]t is easy to see that there are few applications of science which
> do not bear on the interests of commerce and navigation, naval or

1. State Department, *Papers Relating to the Foreign Relations of the United States,
The Peace Conference* (13 vols., Washington, D.C., USGPO, 1942–47), III, 179.

From *Scientists and National Policy-Making,* copyright 1964 by Columbia University
Press. Reprinted by permission of Robert Gilpin and Christopher Wright (eds.). This
essay is a revised version of an article published in *The American Political Science
Review,* LVI, No. 2 (June 1962), and is reprinted by permission of the American
Political Science Association.
An earlier version of this essay was prepared for discussion at the Fifth Congress of
the International Political Science Association in Paris, September, 1961. The points
made in the essay owe much to the comment and counsel of William T. R. Fox.

military concerns, the customs, the lighthouses, the public lands, post offices or post roads, either directly or remotely. If all examination is refused . . . the Government may lose a most important advantage.[2]

As a result of the interest of a number of American scientists and government officials, the National Academy of Sciences was established in 1863 for the purpose of providing scientific advice to the United States government. The use made of this Academy by the War Department between 1863 and 1913 bespeaks a bygone era. During those years the Department requested that the Academy constitute scientific committees on exactly five matters: "On the Question of Tests for the Purity of Whiskey; On the Preservation of Paint on Army Knapsacks; On Galvanic Action from Association of Zinc and Iron; On the Exploration of the Yellowstone; On Questions of Meteorological Science and its Applications." [3]

It would be incorrect to presume from this list that the War Department was uninterested in new weapons systems. Until about the turn of the century, military technology, like industrial technology, generally developed independently of advances in basic scientific knowledge. Thus, in 1915, when Wilson's Secretary of the Navy decided to establish a "Department of Invention and Development" in the hope of securing effective weapons with which to combat that "new and terrible engine of warfare . . . the submarine," it was the inventor, Thomas Edison, who was asked to head the new organization.[4] Although the contributions of university and industrial scientists to the fighting of World War I were marked enough to have caught Wilson's imagination, it was not until a generation later, with the advent of World War II, that the mobilization of scientists brought military results which were of great and in some instances decisive importance to the course of combat.

What has transformed the relationship between science and war has been the fact that in the twentieth century the development of technology has become increasingly dependent upon advances in basic knowledge about the physical world. Moreover, in the technically advanced nations, both the rate of technological innovation and the growth of new scientific knowledge have been increasing exponentially. As crudely measured by the volume of scientific publication, scientific knowledge has been dou-

2. Quoted in U.S. Congress, Staff Study of the Senate Committee on Government Operations, *Science and Technology Act of 1958,* 85th Congress, 2d Session (Washington, D.C., USGPO, 1958), p. 110.
3. *Ibid.,* p. 115.
4. See Daniels's letter to Edison, in Josephus Daniels, *The Wilson Era: Years of Peace, 1910–1917* (Chapel Hill, N.C., The University of North Carolina Press, 1944), p. 491.

bling every ten to fifteen years.[5] In a non-Wilsonian world, the consequences of these conditions for national security policy have been as necessary as they are obvious. As the United States and the Soviet Union throw one weapons system after another into the effort to maintain at least a balance of terror, neither dares fall behind in either the discovery of new physical relationships or in the application of scientific knowledge to military hardware and political-military strategy. Thus, by the end of the first decade of the Cold War, about 50 percent of the engineers in the United States and 25 percent of the scientists were employed by the federal government, either directly or on contract, and about 65 percent of the scientific research in universities and 57 percent of that in private industry was government-financed.[6]

Indicative of the new relationship between science and war, figures and graphs comparing the Great Powers with regard to numbers of scientists and engineers have become as familiar as those in the 1930s which compared the Powers with regard to their output of steel, coal, and oil. Nor is it only in the military field that science and technology have become vital to the course of foreign policy. Science has been harnessed to the advancement of foreign policy goals in such diverse fields as the exploration of space, birth and disease control, weather modification, economic development, and global communications.[7]

Present and future developments in science and technology are certain to bring a host of problems and opportunities to those responsible for the conduct of foreign policy. In recognition of this fact, the governments of the major Powers have endeavored to find ways to make themselves more alert to such developments and more active in determining the course of science and technology. The United States and the Soviet Union are the most extensively engaged in this effort, but it should not be forgotten that the nations of western and central Europe were among the pioneers in cultivating the relationship between science and government. The three elements that have revolutionized current military technology and strategy (electronics, missiles, and nuclear weapons) had their harbingers in the

5. Ellis A. Johnson, "The Crisis in Science and Technology and its Effect on Military Development," *Operations Research,* VI, No. 1 (January–February, 1958), 14–15.
6. See Lee A. DuBridge, "The American Scientist: 1955," *Yale Review* (September, 1955), p. 13, and the *Bulletin of the Atomic Scientists,* XIII, No. 3 (March, 1957), 82, and XVII, Nos. 5–6 (May–June, 1961), 254. The figure for private industry is for the year 1959; the others are for the year 1955.
7. For a more detailed treatment of some of the points in the preceding paragraphs and a general discussion of the effect of science on international relations, see Warner R. Schilling, "Science, Technology, and Foreign Policy," *Journal of International Affairs,* XIII, No. 1 (Winter, 1959), 7–18.

World War II development of British radar, the German V-2, and the American A-bomb, and it is noteworthy that the two European developments were conceived, initiated, and directed by officials and employees of established government organizations. In contrast, the American A-bomb was the result of conceptions and initiatives that came from outside the government—and primarily from exiled Europeans at that.

As an integral part of the efforts of governments to become both more responsive to and responsible for the development of science and technology, scientists have been invited into the highest councils of government, and it is with some of the problems occasioned by the presence of these "new" participants in the making of national policy that the remainder of this essay will be concerned. Although some illustrative material will be drawn from the experience of other governments, this essay focuses on problems associated with the participation of scientists in the American policy process.

Needless to say, the problems in policy-making that may arise will vary greatly with the kind of scientist participating (oceanographer, theoretical physicist, specialist in space medicine, industrial chemist), with the nature of the policy issue at stake (weapons development, science education, public health, the exploration of space, the allocation of funds for basic research), and with the manner in which the scientist is involved in the policy process (member of the attentive public, adviser to the President, worker in a government laboratory, official in an executive department or agency). This essay will make no attempt to deal systematically with the combinations possible among these three variables (profession, issue, and involvement). The discussion will be confined to a few of the central problems that the layman and the scientist are likely to encounter in working together on national security issues, and the treatment, as will become evident, will be of a very general and suggestive order.

The central problems occasioned by the participation of scientists in the determination of high policy are not nearly so novel as is generally supposed. The scientist has been brought into the councils of government because he possesses specialized skills and information believed relevant to the identification and resolution of particular policy problems. His relationship to the policy process is therefore a familiar one, that of an expert. Just as Sputnik I precipitated the establishment of a Special Assistant to the President for Science and Technology, so the earlier problems of fighting World War II and insuring postwar employment had brought the Joint Chiefs of Staff and the Council of Economic Advisers into the Offices of the President.

The central problems in policy-making posed by the entry of scientists into the policy process are thus formally no different from those associated with any other expert involved in the determination of national security policy. In particular, four such problems can be noted. (1) Like all experts, scientists will at times disagree, and the nonscientist (be he politician, administrator, or an expert in some other field) will confront the problem of choosing a course of action in the face of conflicting scientific advice. (2) Like all experts, scientists will at times manifest certain predispositions toward the resolution of the policy problems on which their advice is sought, and the nonscientist will confront the problem of identifying the policy predilections peculiar to scientists and being on his guard against them. (3) The nonscientist and scientist will confront one problem in common, and that is how to organize themselves to maximize the contribution that science can make to the government's programs, opportunities, and choices. (4) The scientist will confront a problem common to all experts who participate in the American policy process, and that is how to engage in politics without debasing the coinage of his own expertise.

THE PROBLEM OF CONFLICTING ADVICE

The difficulties the nonscientist confronts in choosing a course of action in the face of conflicting scientific advice seem inherently no more formidable than those a nonexpert would face in deciding what to do in the event of conflicting advice from economists, soldiers, or specialists on Soviet foreign policy. There are at least seven procedures that the nonexpert can follow in such circumstances, singly or in combination, and they appear to have about the same promise, for better or for worse, regardless of the kind of experts involved.[8]

The first step the nonscientist can take is to make certain that it is really conflicting *scientific* advice he is receiving. In the fall of 1949 President Truman asked Secretary Acheson to look into the disputes then current within the Atomic Energy Commission and elsewhere about the consequences of undertaking an intensive effort to make an H-bomb. Upon investigation the Secretary of State concluded that the scientists involved were not really very far apart except on the foreign policy issues that were his and Truman's responsibility to decide.[9]

Procedures two and three are simple: the nonscientist may be guided by

8. *Cf.* the implication in the following remarks of Glenn T. Seaborg, the Chairman of the Atomic Energy Commission: "Scientists don't necessarily have to make the final political decisions, but it might be easier to let a capable scientist learn political reality than to teach a politician science." Quoted in the *Bulletin of the Atomic Scientists*, XVII, No. 2 (February, 1961), 79.

9. In this and subsequent undocumented references this writer has drawn upon personal interviews during 1956–58 with participants in the H-bomb decision.

quantitative or qualitative features of the division (he can side with the majority, or with that side whose past record is the more confidence-inspiring). Failing these, there is, four, the "principle of least harm," and, five, the "principle of minimal choice." In the former, one chooses that course of action which appears to involve the least cost if the technical premise on which it is based proves to be wrong. Thus in World War II, given the American belief that the Germans were hard at work on an A-bomb, it seemed more sensible to spend $2 billion on the assumption that the bomb could be made than to do little or nothing on the assumption that it could not. In the case of the "principle of minimal choice," one chooses that course of action which seems to close off the least number of future alternatives. This was the character of President Truman's first decision on the H-bomb. He decided to go ahead in the effort to explore the feasibility of an H-bomb, but nothing was decided about technical steps of a greater political or military consequence (for example, testing a device if one were fabricated, or preparing to produce the materials that would be required for weapons production in the event of a successful test).[10]

In the case of procedure six the nonscientist can make his choice among conflicting scientists on the basis of whichever technical estimate is most in accord with policy on which he was already intent. (In contrast to the first procedure, where the nonscientist endeavors to factor out of the conflict the policy preferences of the scientists, here he is factoring into the conflict his own policy preferences.) In the spring of 1942, the British scientists Henry Tizard and F. A. Lindemann (Lord Cherwell) diverged by a factor of five in their estimates of the destruction that could be accomplished by an all-out campaign to bomb the homes of German civilians and also in their judgments about the consequences that even the lesser amount of destruction would have for the military course of the war. (Lindemann thought that it would be "catastrophic," Tizard that it would be "most damaging" but not "decisive.") The importance of the issue lay in the fact the Naval Staff was pressing Churchill to allocate some of the bombers that the Air Staff planned to use in the campaign to the Naval Staff's own anti-submarine effort. The Air Staff, which had long been persuaded of the efficacy of strategic bombing, found Lindemann's calculations "simple, clear and convincing." The Naval Staff was similarly impressed by Tizard's. The final decisions were Churchill's, and he was greatly influenced by Lindemann's estimate—an influence presumably not unrelated to his own inter-

10. For the "principle of least harm," see Bernard Brodie, "Strategy as a Science," *World Politics,* I, No. 4 (July, 1949), 479n. On the H-bomb choice, see Warner R. Schilling, "The H-Bomb Decision: How to Decide Without Actually Choosing," *Political Science Quarterly,* LXXVI, No. 1 (March, 1961), 37–38.

est in presenting the Russians with a dramatically visible contribution to the war against Germany.[11]

In procedure seven the nonscientist is guided by his own sense for the scientific and technical problems involved. In the 1949 H-bomb debate, some of the politicians involved were little deterred by the fact that the scientists were by no means confident that they could make such a weapon and by the possibility that an all-out but failing effort might entail very high costs for the A-bomb program. These politicians were willing to press ahead in part because of their belief that the scientists were not really aware of their own potential. Similarly, when the German soldiers, scientists, and engineers engaged in the development of the V-2 divided on the question of whether it should be launched from mobile or fixed batteries, Hitler's own technical enthusiasm for large, hardened bunkers led him, unwisely as it turned out, to decide on behalf of the latter.[12]

In concluding this survey of the problem of conflicting advice, it should be noted that one of the more likely outcomes is that the actions of the contending scientists may prove much more influential than the procedures followed by the nonscientist. Divided experts will not always be equal in their physical or personal access to the decision-maker, in the persistence with which they state their case, or in the force and clarity of their arguments. Thus, in the H-bomb debate, there were instances where equally qualified scientists differed greatly in the time and energy they spent circulating their views of the technical (and political) prospects, and such differences were by no means without consequence for the judgments of others.[13]

11. See Sir Charles Webster and Noble Franklin, *The Strategic Air Offensive Against Germany, 1939–1945* (London, H.M. Stationery Office, 1961), Vol. 1, chap. 6, especially 331–36, 340–43, 371, and Winston S. Churchill, *The Second World War: The Hinge of Fate* (Boston, Houghton Mifflin, 1950), pp. 121, 328, 333–34. For more spirited accounts, see C. P. Snow, *Science and Government* (Cambridge, Mass., Harvard University Press, 1961), p. 47–51, the review of this book by P. M. S. Blackett in *Scientific American,* CCIV, No. 4 (April, 1961), 192–94; the Earl of Birkenhead, *The Professor and the Prime Minister* (Boston, Houghton Mifflin, 1962), pp. 257–67, and C. P. Snow, *Appendix to Science and Government* (Cambridge, Mass., Harvard University Press, 1962), pp. 23–30.

12. Maj. Gen. Walter Dornberger, *V–2* (New York, Ballantine Books, 1954), pp. 97, 158–60, and Lt. Gen. James M. Gavin, *War and Peace in the Space Age* (New York, Harper and Bros., 1958), pp. 76–77.

13. Note should also be taken of the problem the policy-maker faces when all his experts *agree.* This writer is unable to suggest a useful procedure here (other than variations on procedures five, six, and seven above); but that the problem is a real one can be seen in the conclusion of the German physicists that it would be infeasible for any Power to develop an atomic bomb during World War II. Some of the

THE PROBLEM OF BIAS

Discussion of the policy predispositions displayed by scientists must be entered with considerable caution. The major theoretical premise involved is that all experts will evidence certain predilections with regard to policy and policy-making which are the result of the character of their expertise: their skills, knowledge, and experience. Since experts differ in the skills, knowledge, and experience they command (or in the responsibilities with which they are charged), they will differ in the biases they characteristically exhibit. Thus scientists, soldiers, and diplomats jointly concerned with a policy problem are likely to approach the question of how and in what manner it should be resolved with rather dissimilar predispositions.

These points, however, are easier stated than demonstrated. To begin with, it should be clear that insofar as policy is concerned "the scientific mind" is as much a chimera as "the military mind." Scientists, like soldiers and the rest of us, differ greatly in the ideas they have about the political world and the things that will (or ought to) happen in it, and their views on foreign policy matters are far more likely to be reflective of these differences than conditioned by their common professional skills and interests. Moreover, even if differences in expertise or responsibility were the only factors determining the views of policy-makers (and they certainly are not), one would still have to take account of the fact that scientists are as varied in their professional skills and pursuits as soldiers. The perspectives of a theoretical physicist engaged in basic research are no more to be equated with those of an organic chemist engaged in applying extant knowledge to the improvement of an industrial product than is the outlook of a staff officer in Washington drafting a war plan to be considered identical with that of a general in charge of a theater of operations.

In addition to these difficulties, analysis must also contend with the fact that it is directed toward a moving target. The policy perspectives that a physicist may have developed as a result of two decades in a university laboratory are unlikely to endure without change after a few years on a

German scientists later stated that political considerations were partly responsible for their advice and for the fact that they made so little progress themselves on an A-bomb (*cf.* procedure one).

The German work on the A-bomb during World War II is described in Samuel A. Goudsmit, *Alsos* (New York, Henry Schuman, 1947). For various appraisals of the influence exercised by political considerations, see Robert Jungk, *Brighter Than a Thousand Suns* (New York, Harcourt, Brace and Co., 1958), pp 88–104, Hans A. Bethe, "Review of *Brighter Than a Thousand Suns," Bulletin of the Atomic Scientists*, XIV, No. 10 (December, 1958), 427, and William L. Laurence, *Men and Atoms* (New York, Simon and Schuster, 1959), pp. 90–93.

Washington advisory committee. Many American scientists are well along the same route that transformed the policy perspectives of large numbers of the American military profession during the war and immediate postwar years. As a result of new problems and new responsibilities, these soldiers acquired new skills, knowledge, and experience. In consequence, with regard to their approach to foreign policy, some are, for all practical purposes, interchangeable between the Pentagon and the State Department, and one could wish that there were more diplomats equally well equipped to work on both sides of the Potomac.

With these reservations in mind, six policy perspectives will be presented here which seem moderately characteristic of many scientists, most of them physicists, who have participated in national security policy in recent times. Most of these predispositions were first evidenced during their work with the military during World War II, and the extent and manner in which they have been later operative in reference to larger foreign policy issues is not always easy to document, since most of the sources are still classified. Needless to say, in outlining these predispositions, one is presenting a cross between a caricature and a Weberian ideal type, not describing real people. In discussing these predispositions, this writer does not mean to convey the impression that they are either "good" or "bad" from the point of view of policy or policy-making, or that one or another of these predispositions may not also be evidenced by groups other than scientists. The point to this discussion is that if certain orders of scientists are indeed prone to these or other policy predispositions, the nonscientist will be wise to be alert to them, even if on occasion he should conclude that they are all for the good.

Naïve utopianism or naïve belligerency. C. P. Snow has described the scientist as an impatient optimist in his approach to social wrongs; he is quick to search for something to do and inclined to expect favorable results.[14] Certainly, the scientist's profession inclines him to look at problems in terms of searching for a solution to them. When this perspective is turned to problems of international politics, however, the scientist's approach often appears open to the characterization of "naïve utopianism or naïve belligerency."[15] His approach to international relations appears simplistic and mechanistic. It is almost as if he conceives of policy being made primarily by forward-looking, solution-oriented, rational-thinking types like himself.

In these perspectives the scientist is likely to find little in common with the diplomat (who is inclined to believe that most of his problems have no

14. C. P. Snow, *The Two Cultures and the Scientific Revolution* (New York, Cambridge University Press, 1959), pp. 9–11.
15. The author is indebted to Hans Speier for the phrasing of this point.

solution, and who is in any event too busy with the crises of the day to plan for tomorrow), or with the politician (whose approach to problems is so spasmodic as to seem neither analytical nor rational, and whose policy positions are anyway soon blurred by his efforts to accommodate to the positions of others), or with the professional student of international politics (who, when the opportunity permits, lectures the scientist on the elegant complexity of the political process, but who never seems, to the scientist at least, to have any really good ideas about what to do). It is perhaps these differences in perspective that lead the scientist on occasion to seem "intellectually arrogant"; it is as if he concludes that those who have no promising solutions or are not seeking them cannot be very bright. In his predisposition toward action and solutions, the scientist comes closest to sharing the predilection of the soldier for decision, which may be one reason why their partnership has been so spectacularly successful.

The "whole-problem approach." The first grant made by the United States government for experimental research was in 1832 to the Franklin Institute. The scientists were asked to investigate the reasons for explosions in steamboat boilers. They reported back not only with a technical explanation but with a draft bill to provide for federal regulation of steamboats.[16] In this they evidenced the scientist's predilection for the "whole-problem approach." The reluctance of scientists to apply their expertise to mere fragments of the total problem, especially under conditions where those who prescribe the fragments do not reveal the whole of which they are a part, was evident in the work of both British and American scientists during World War II. Military officials initially approached the scientists with requests for the development of particular weapons and devices without revealing the military problems or reasoning responsible for their requests. The scientists objected to this procedure, and they were eventually able to persuade the soldiers to inform them of the general military problems involved in order that the scientists might reach their own conclusions about the kinds of weapons and devices the military would need to meet those problems.[17]

In 1952, in connection with an Air Force project on air defense, a group

16. Don K. Price, *Government and Science* (New York, New York University Press, 1954), pp. 10–11.
17. This persuasion was largely accomplished through demonstrations of the military utility of the scientists' taking such an approach, although in the early history of the M.I.T. Radiation Laboratory a certain amount of polite bargaining was apparently practiced. One scientist involved, whenever told that the reason for a request was a problem for Washington, not him, to worry about, adopted the practice of working on something else until he was given a description of the problem involved. For a brief summary of the British experience, see Alexander Haddow, "The Scientist as Citizen," *Bulletin of the Atomic Scientists,* XII, No. 7 (September, 1956), 247.

of American scientists were asked to review the prospects for improving the nation's continental air defense. The scientists concluded that some new and promising systems were possible, and they submitted an estimate of what the developments might cost. They also recommended that the money be spent. The Air Force did not approve the recommendation, and as is customary in Washington the disputants on both sides began to search for allies and to leak their cases to the press. Certain Air Force officials, who feared that additional funds for air defense would come at the expense of dollars otherwise available for the Strategic Air Command and who were convinced that this would be militarily undesirable, charged that the scientists by entering into matters of military strategy and budget policy had exceeded both their assignment and their expertise. Commenting on this charge, one of the scientists involved later explained that he would have little interest in working on a study project that did not have the potential for leading into the question of whether the conclusions should be acted upon.[18]

The predisposition to want to be told and to deal with the whole problem no doubt has its base in the professional experience of scientists (and one of the central credos of science) that good ideas on a problem may come from the most unexpected quarters and that the widest possible dissemination of information about a problem will significantly enhance its chances for an early solution.[19] Still, there are problems and problems; some are open to determinate solutions, and others can be resolved only through the exercise of political power. The point about the "whole-problem approach," as the air-defense example illustrates, is that it not

18. *Cf.* the following exchange between Gordon Gray and Jerrold Zacharias during the Oppenheimer hearing. Gray: "If you were directing a study which had to do with electronics, a pretty clearly defined field, and it started to come up with recommendations with respect to foreign policy, would you feel that an official of the Defense Department who urged that you stick to electronics was acting with impropriety?" Zacharias: "I think I would not direct a project that was as restrictive as that, sir, as to be restricted only to electronics." Atomic Energy Commission, *In the Matter of J. Robert Oppenheimer, Transcript of Hearing Before Personnel Security Board* (Washington, D.C., USGPO, 1954), p. 930.

For some of the issues involved in the 1952 air defense study, see *ibid.*, pp. 598–99, 749–50, 763–65, 923–24, 930–31, 935, and 938, and also the account in Price, *Government and Science*, pp. 136–38.

19. General Leslie Groves, who directed the Manhattan Project, was especially sensitive to the scientists' tendency to take on the whole problem. (Some even advised him on how the garbage should be collected at Los Alamos, an act which may possibly have reflected self- rather than scientific interest.) One reason for his effort to compartmentalize the work scientists were doing was his fear that "if I brought them into the whole project, they would never do their own job. There was just too much of scientific interest, and they would just be frittering from one thing to another." *Oppenheimer Transcript*, p. 164.

only helps propel the scientists from an advisory to a political role but it serves to make the scientist somewhat blind to the fact that he is so moving. In its most extreme form, the "whole-problem approach" coupled with the "intellectual arrogance" perspective can lead to instances like the following: on one high-level advisory committee concerned with several areas of national security policy, a scientist whose formal claim to participation was a knowledge of infrared-ray phenomena was reportedly quite free with his proposals for what political policies should be adopted with regard to the United Nations.

Quantum jumps versus improvements. A number of scientists have advanced the proposition that the military tend to be more interested in improving existing weapons than in developing radically new ones, and they have urged that a separate civilian agency be established to undertake such development. Both scientists and soldiers have explained this difference in their approach to military research and development, "quantum jumps versus improvements," with the hypothesis that the soldier's interest in developing entirely new weapons must always be inhibited by his concern for the possibility that war may come in the near future, since in this event his interests are best served by improving existing weapons. It has also been suggested that military leaders, who must be prepared at any time to ask others to take up the weapons at hand and fight with them, cannot afford to let themselves or others become too impressed with the deficiencies of those weapons as compared with others that might have been developed.[20]

An explanation for this difference, less flattering to the military, is the occasional assertion by scientists that theirs is a profession which stimulates original and creative thought, while that of the military tends to develop minds which accept the existing situation without too much question. As indicated in the discussion of the first predilection, this is a judgment which the scientist may extend to the diplomat and the politician as well.

The difficulty with quantum jumps in foreign policy, however, is that the structure of both the domestic and the international political process is normally such as to make them infeasible. Thus, diplomats and politicians are accustomed to seeing the same old policy problems come around year after year, and they are generally intent on policies which promise only slow and modest change. Scientists, on the other hand, have been demanding and searching for quantum jumps in foreign policy ever since the end of World War II. It is symptomatic that the first proposal developed by the Advisory Committee on Science and Technology to the Democratic National Advisory Council, established in 1959, was for the creation of a new scientific agency, independent of the State and Defense Departments,

20. See, for example, Lloyd V. Berkner, "Science and National Strength," *Bulletin of the Atomic Scientists,* IX, No. 5 (June, 1953), 155, 180.

whose function would be "to face all the problems of disarmament." [21]

Technology for its own sweet sake. In the summer of 1945, after the A-bomb had been tested but before the first drop on Japan, the Director of the Los Alamos Laboratory, J. Robert Oppenheimer, suggested to his superior, General Leslie Groves, that if some improvements were made in the design of the bomb it would be more effective. Groves decided against the improvements because he did not want to incur any delay in the use of the bomb, which he expected would end the war with Japan. In the summer of 1943, after the Director of the German V-2 project, General Dornberger, had finally secured a first-class priority for the use of the weapon, those responsible for producing it in quantity were increasingly handicapped by the scientists and engineers who kept improving but changing its design. Dornberger was finally obliged to issue a flat order against any further improvements. [22]

There was nothing irresponsible in these scientists' actions. Charged with the technical development of weapons, they would have been remiss in their responsibilities if they had failed to call attention to the prospects for improvement. The point to the examples is that scientists and engineers, in the pursuit of their own responsibilities and interests, may easily lose sight of those of the policy-maker.

The scientists on the General Advisory Committee to the Atomic Energy Commission who recommended against the development of an H-bomb in 1949 did so in part because of their concern for the foreign policy consequences of introducing a weapon of such destructive power into the world. Oppenheimer, the Chairman of the Committee, later stated that the thermonuclear design developed by Edward Teller in 1951 was "technically so sweet" that if it had been available in 1949 the Committee would probably not have made the recommendation that it did. Since with a technically more promising design at hand one might suppose that the Committee's foreign policy concerns would have been all the greater, some observers have concluded that in the pursuit of his technical interests the scientist can also easily lose sight of his own policy concerns. [23]

Such a judgment ignores the complexity of the Committee's position. For example, one of the reasons why the Committee thought the United States should take the initiative in renouncing the H-bomb was precisely because the device then in view seemed likely to be both difficult to make and of dubious military value. It was thought that for this reason the Russians might be willing to follow the American example and that if they did

21. See the *Bulletin of the Atomic Scientists,* XV, No. 10 (December, 1959), 412.
22. *Oppenheimer Transcript,* p. 33, and Dornberger, *V–2,* pp. 134–37.
23. *Oppenheimer Transcript,* p. 251. For an extreme judgment, see Jungk, *Brighter Than a Thousand Suns,* p. 296.

not the United States would not have risked much by the delay. These were considerations which obviously would have been changed if a technically more promising design had been available in 1949.[24] Still, the comments of several scientists close to these events are not without relevance. It is their feeling that there are times when the technician does take over, that when the scientist is faced with an interesting and challenging problem his inclination is to get to work on it, and that under these circumstances he should not be the first person to be expected to keep large policy considerations in balance.

This predisposition, "technology for its own sweet sake," appears to have its roots in two more of science's central credos: the belief in the value of pursuing knowledge for its own sake and the belief that the best motivation for the direction of research is the strength and character of individual curiosities. But the direction and strength of scientific interests and curiosities is not necessarily coincident with the requirements of military or foreign policy. One of the most recent examples of the scientist's capacity to get caught up in a challenging problem (assigned, to be sure, by policy-makers) is afforded by the ingenious ideas scientists have conceived for evading nuclear-test detection systems and for the design of new systems to detect those evasions. In the light of the later course of negotiations, an American statesman who believed there was considerable foreign policy gain in a test-ban treaty and who believed that the Russians were at one time seriously interested in such a treaty might well conclude that the formula developed by the British scientist Watson-Watt for meeting wartime military requirements—"Give them the third best to go with; the second comes too late, the best never comes"—was not without its implications for meeting peacetime foreign policy requirements.[25] This observation is not intended as an argument that the interests of the United States would have been better served by a test-ban treaty with a "third best" detection system than by no treaty at all. The point is rather that the policy-maker must be sensitive to the prospect that because of the constant advance of technology his only real choices may be of this order.

The sense for paradise lost. This predisposition is likely to be more characteristic of the scientists who had their graduate training and early professional experience in the years before World War II than of those who have known only war or Cold War conditions.[26] The prewar scientists

24. See Oppenheimer's statements in *Oppenheimer Transcript,* pp. 81, 251, 897, and Schilling, "The H-Bomb Decision: How to Decide Without Actually Choosing," pp. 30–36.
25. Sir Robert Watson-Watt, *Three Steps to Victory* (London, Odhams, 1957), p. 74.
26. In 1955 slightly more than half of the active research physicists in the United States were under forty years of age and had received their doctorates after December 7, 1941. DuBridge, "The American Scientist: 1955," p. 1.

took it as an article of faith that certain conditions were essential for the progress of science, in particular that scientists be free to select their research problems and that both scientists and scientific information be free to move among as well as within nations.[27] All of these conditions were violated during World War II, and as a result of the Cold War they were never fully reestablished. The nuclear physicists had had perhaps the most highly developed sense of international community. They were relatively few in number, had close personal relationships at home and abroad, and had been experiencing an exciting exchange of discoveries since Rutherford identified the nucleus in 1911. They also lost the most, for theirs was militarily the most sensitive knowledge, and the pages of the *Bulletin of the Atomic Scientists* offer eloquent testimony to their ideological disturbance.

The result is that the senior scientists tend to be especially sensitive to possibilities which hold some promise for restoring the former order. They may usually be found on the side (or in front) of those urging freer exchange of scientific and military information with allied governments, less secrecy in the circulation of scientific (and sometimes military) information, and more extensive cultural, and especially scientific, exchanges with the Soviet Union. Similarly, the major activities of the Foreign Policy Panel of the President's Science Advisory Committee (PSAC) and of the Office of the Science Adviser to the Secretary of State have been in connection with the Science Attaché program, the facilitation of international scientific programs and conferences, and the exchange of scientists with the Soviet Union.[28]

Science serves mankind. For at least 300 years the Western scientific tradition has assumed that the unrestricted generation of new knowledge about the world was a social good. Over these years science in its purest form (the discovery of the facts of nature for knowledge's sake alone) became increasingly an autonomous social institution; research scientists were largely disassociated from the practical applications of their discoveries, but they took it for granted that these discoveries would ultimately benefit mankind.[29] The advent of nuclear and bacteriological weapons systems which have the potential of destroying so much of mankind and his

27. These assumptions are excellently set forth in Margaret Smith Stahl, "Splits and Schisms: Nuclear and Social," unpublished doctoral dissertation, University of Wisconsin, 1946, chap. 4.

28. For the activities of the Panel and the Office, see James R. Killian, Jr., "Science and Public Policy," address to the American Association for the Advancement of Science, December 29, 1958, as printed in U.S. Congress, Report of the Senate Committee on Government Operations, *Science Program—86th Congress,* 86th Congress, 1st Session (Washington, D.C., USGPO, 1959), pp. 12–13, and *The Science Adviser of the Department of State* (Washington, D.C., USGPO, 1960), State Department Publ. No. 7056.

29. See Stahl, "Splits and Schisms," chap. 4.

works has called this faith sharply into question. It does not take much imagination to wonder if man, in view of his apparent inability to escape from the order of conflicts which have historically resulted in war, would not be better off in a world where the knowledge that has made the new weapons possible did not exist. For some of the senior nuclear physicists this is more than a philosophical question. They are unable to avoid a sense of personal responsibility; they reason from the premise that they were few, and if they had acted differently weapons development might not have taken the turn it did.

In the immediate postwar years, the apparent contradiction between the good of science and the evil of war was resolved by the expectation that the very destructiveness of the new weapons would lead man to renounce at last the folly of war. The course of foreign policy in later years has weakened these expectations but not destroyed them, as the recent flurry of arms-control proposals premised on the rational self-interest of both sides in avoiding mutual destruction testifies.

The need to preserve their sense of service to mankind led some American scientists to refuse to work on weapons. Similarly, there are reports that several Russian scientists were imprisoned, exiled, or placed under surveillance for refusing to participate in weapons work between 1945 and 1953, and a number of Germany's elite physicists announced in 1957 that they would have no part in nuclear weapons work.[30] Such cases are dramatic, but nowhere have they prevented the development of weapons on which governments were determined. The more consequential resolutions have been those in which scientists have simply identified the good of mankind with the strength of their nation or have endeavored to develop new weapons systems which would be as effective as the old in promoting national policy but which would result in less slaughter if used. This was part of the rationale behind the recommendation made by a group of American scientists in 1951 that the government undertake the development and production of a large number of A-bombs for tactical use in the ground defense of Western Europe. Their hope was that such an innovation would relieve the United States of the burden of having to rely solely on the threat of strategic bombing to contain the Red Army.[31]

The failure of the United States to orbit a satellite before the Soviet Union did was the result of the State Department's insensitivity to the po-

30. See Arnold Kramish, *Atomic Energy in the Soviet Union* (Stanford, Calif., Stanford University Press, 1959), p. 105. Kramish states that it is not certain whether the objections of the Russian scientists were technical or political. For the declaration of the German physicists, see the *Bulletin of the Atomic Scientists*, XIII, No. 6 (June, 1957), 228.

31. *Oppenheimer Transcript*, pp. 584, 594–95, 891–94.

litical implications of the event and the decision of the President and the Secretary of Defense not to let a satellite program interfere with military missile programs. A small part of the story, however, is to be found in the reluctance of some of the American scientists involved in the programming of the International Geophysical Year to see an American IGY satellite propelled by an operational military weapon. Their preference for the less-developed but non-military Vanguard over the Army's Redstone appears to have reflected a combination of the "sense for paradise lost" and the "science serves mankind" predispositions, in this case an interest in showing the world the peaceful side of science and in demonstrating that the scientists of the world could cooperate in the interests of knowledge as well as compete in the interests of nations.[32]

THE PROBLEMS OF ORGANIZATION AND POLITICS

With regard to the two remaining problems to be discussed—how to organize relations between science and government and how the scientist can participate in policy-making and still keep his expert standing—four points seem deserving of special emphasis: (1) the problem of organization, especially in the area of foreign policy, is still very much in the research and development stage, and so it may long remain, considering the precedent set by the problem of how to relate military experts and foreign policy; (2) in many areas of policy it will never be possible to specify what constitutes "the best" organization; the way in which policy-makers are organized is not without influence on the kind of policies they will produce, and so long as there are differences over policy there will be no agreement about organization; (3) in the American political system, at least, the science expert at the high-policy level has no real hope of keeping out of politics; his only choice is in the character of his political style; and, finally, (4) it should not be forgotten that organization and policy-making are not the same as policy; successful instances of foreign policy capitalizing on or guiding developments in science and technology will not automatically follow just because scientists have been liberally injected into the policy-making process.

Organization. Current American organization in the area of science and foreign policy still reflects the emergency responses to the Russian ICBM and Sputnik I. One effect of these events was that scientists were rushed to the most important single center of power, the Office of the President, by means of the creation of the Special Assistant to the President for Science and Technology and the President's Science Advisory Committee.

32. See Walter Sullivan, *Assault on the Unknown* (New York, McGraw-Hill, 1961), pp. 79–81.

The President certainly needs men around him who are sensitive to the areas of interaction between science and foreign policy. But a case can be made for the proposition that the center of gravity for the input of scientific advice into the policy-making process should be at a lower level than the White House. The President's political interests lie in keeping the staff about him small and generalized. Well-developed plans and programs will have a better chance of maturing in the larger and more diversified facilities that departments and agencies can provide. Secondly, as C. P. Snow concludes in his account of the differences between Tizard and Lindemann, there are risks in having a single science adviser sitting next to the center of political power. Although it should be noted that Churchill fared better with a single science adviser than Hitler did with none ("The Führer has dreamed," Dornberger was told, "that no [V-2] will ever reach England"), Snow's point has merit and it holds for institutions as well as for individuals.[33] The President will generally find his choices facilitated by the existence of multiple and independent sources of scientific advice.

This is a condition that already prevails in the case of many of the departments and agencies whose actions have significant foreign policy consequences, especially in the use of scientists by the Department of Defense, the Atomic Energy Commission, and the National Aeronautics and Space Administration. It is, however, a condition notably absent in the case of the Department of State. As it now stands, the President has more scientists to advise him on the scientific and technical aspects of various foreign policy issues, particularly in the national security field, than has the Secretary of State.[34]

Established in February, 1951, the Office of the Science Adviser in the Department of State has yet to become a point of vantage in the determination of high departmental policy. Deprived in its original charter of any jurisdiction in the atomic energy field, the Office was moribund within four years of its birth. The number of overseas science attachés administered by the Office went from a peak of eleven in 1952 to zero at the end of 1955, and the Office itself languished without a scientist from February, 1954, to January, 1958. Resurrected in the aftermath of Sputnik I, the Office—as of

33. Snow, *Science and Government*, pp. 66–68, and Dornberger, *V-2*, p. 87.
34. There are eighteen scientists on the PSAC; its working panels also contain participants from outside the Committee. In December, 1958, the Committee and the Office of the Special Assistant for Science and Technology had together some 75 scientists and engineers serving part-time. See Killian, "Science and Public Policy," p. 8. The work of the Committee and the Office are additionally described and appraised in U.S. Congress, Staff Study of the Subcommittee on National Policy Machinery, Senate Committee on Government Operations, *Science Organization and the President's Office,* 87th Congress, 1st Session (Washington, D.C., USGPO, 1961).

February, 1962—consisted of some fourteen science attachés overseas and a Washington staff of six, of whom only three, including the Director, were professional scientists. Nor were these three scientists supplemented by technical personnel elsewhere in the Department. There were no scientists, full or part-time, in the Department's offices for space and atomic energy, political-military affairs, or policy planning. Of the Department's line offices, only the Bureau of Intelligence and Research maintained a technical staff.

As might be inferred from these arrangements, most of the policymakers concerned believed that their needs for scientific advice were adequately met through formal and informal communication with scientists employed in the operating agencies and departments and with the President's own Science Advisory Committee. The Department's Science Adviser, as a participant in the activities of both the President's Committee and the Federal Council on Science and Technology, stood available to facilitate such communication. Otherwise, both the demands placed upon the Office and its own interests served to limit its activity, as previously noted, to a relatively narrow range of foreign policy problems.

In the summer of 1962, spurred by a recommendation from the President's Science Advisory Committee, the Department reorganized the Office into the Office of International Scientific Affairs with a provision for expanded personnel (perhaps a total of eighteen, including nine scientists) and a charter designed to lead it into more active participation in the policy or line offices. Moreover, as a result of the Department's decision in the spring to disband the office for space and atomic energy and to divide its responsibilities among a variety of bureaus and offices, the new Office now shares with several other bureaus a mandate over the "peaceful" uses of space and atomic energy. Although this writing is too close to these events to assay the results of the reorganization, the Office would appear to have little prospect of becoming for the Secretary of State the functional equivalent of the President's scientific advisory apparatus, at least in the areas where science and technology impinge on national security policy. Responsibility for the military applications of space and atomic energy were distributed to the European Bureau and the Office for Political-Military Affairs, and here the use of scientists and the Department's science adviser remains as before.[35]

35. The projected size of the new Office is not out of line with that of others in the State Department. The Office for Political-Military Affairs, for example, numbers some fourteen people, of whom one has the formal responsibility for monitoring the military applications of space and atomic energy.

For information on the Office of the Science Adviser, see State Department, *The*

Whether the Department of State would be better served by an "in-house" scientific competence in these fields is a question that an outside observer cannot easily answer. Much depends on the validity of the expectations that the Department can rely on the scientists of the operating agencies and the President's Committee to alert it to developments and information relevant to foreign policy. Even more depends on how determined the Department is to play an active and influential part in shaping the scientific and technical activities of the government to conform to *its* conception of national needs and priorities. (The two conditions are, of course, not unrelated. The more influence the Department exercises in determining the goals and programs of other agencies, the more confident it can be that scientists in those agencies will call the Department's attention to goals and programs which they believe to be receiving too much or too little attention.) In the final analysis, the question of the Department's organizational needs can only be answered in terms of the strength and content of its policy interests. In the field of national security policy, the Department has yet to define its responsibilities and identify its interests in such a manner as to point to the need to expand its modest political staff, much less to create a science advisory body to help this staff monitor and direct the course of science and technology as they affect such policy.

Organization and purpose. Since administrative organizations exist for the purpose of serving policy goals and implementing policy programs, it is to be expected that those who differ on the goals and programs of policy will differ about the proper design of administrative organizations. The desire of many scientists in 1945 to see atomic energy used for peaceful rather than military purposes was one of the reasons for their political campaign to place the postwar atomic energy program in the hands of a civilian commission instead of the War Department. Similarly, more recent differences about how to organize the government's space effort reflect, in part, policy differences about whether space will or should be an area for major military operations.

The same point can be seen in the proposal to create a Department of Science and Technology which would include the variety of "little" science programs now scattered throughout the Executive structure (for example, those of the Weather Bureau, National Bureau of Standards, and the Antarctic Office), but would exclude those of the Department of Defense, the

Science Adviser of the Department of State, The New York *Times,* July 2, 1962, and September 15, 1962, and Graham DuShane, "Full Circle," *Science,* 129, No. 3291 (January 24, 1958), 175. Additional information was secured from interviews with Department officials in February of 1962 and 1963. The description and interpretation made above are, of course, entirely this writer's responsibility.

Atomic Energy Commission, and the Space Administration. The hope behind this proposal is that, combined together, the "little" programs would be able to compete more effectively in the struggle for government dollars with the "big" science programs of the military, atomic energy, and space organizations.[36]

The question of the "best" science organization is thus inescapably tied to the question of what is the "best" science policy. But who can demonstrate whether science and foreign policy would be better served by allocating dollars to a program to control weather or to a program to explore Mars? There are no determinate solutions to problems of this order. Neither, for that matter, is there any one "right" amount of the nation's scientific resources that should be allocated to basic as compared to applied research. Differences on policy questions such as these are unavoidable among scientists and nonscientists alike, and they can be resolved in but one manner: through the interplay of power and interest in a political arena.

This condition, plus the increasing dependence of scientific programs and research on government funds, plus the increasing consequences of the choices the government makes in allocating those funds, all promise to put the politicians and the scientists under increasing pressure. As the opportunities for further development in each of a thousand different scientific fields mushroom with the acceleration of scientific knowledge, whatever the government decides to support, it will be deciding *not* to support more. Indeed, it is not too difficult to see the scientists becoming practiced advocates and lobbyists for the government's support of their cherished fields and projects, or to imagine the day when the politicians start to complain about "interscience rivalry" and begin to fancy that, if only there were a single Chief of Science, competition and duplication could be ended and the nation could have an integrated science policy.

Scientists in politics. The American political system is not one that insulates its experts from the politics of choice.[37] The scientist involved in high-policy matters is likely to find himself propelled into the political arena, either by a push from behind or by his own interest in seeing that the "right" choices are made. Some of the incentives the scientist may have to follow up his advice with an effort to see that it is accepted (and to take

36. See Lloyd V. Berkner, "National Science Policy and the Future," address at Johns Hopkins University, December 16, 1958, as printed in *Science Program—86th Congress,* pp. 116–18.
37. This point, especially as it relates to science experts, is discussed in Price, *Government and Science,* pp. 61–62, and in Herman Finer, "Government and the Expert," *Bulletin of the Atomic Scientists,* XII, No. 9 (November, 1956), 331–32.

a hand in a few other matters while he is at it) were outlined and illustrated in the preceding section. It is equally important to recognize that the scientist may find himself on the political firing line, placed there by a politician interested in using the scientist's prestige as an "expert" to disarm the critics of his (the politician's) choices.

Thus, prior to the moratorium on nuclear tests, the Eisenhower administration appeared to be using scientists and their scientific facts on fall-out as a means of justifying and defending a policy that was obviously compounded of a variety of considerations besides that of the radiological hazard. The comparison with Truman's use of the prestige of the Joint Chiefs of Staff to defend his choices in the Korean War comes easily to mind. So, too, do the statements of various Republican leaders that they had lost confidence in the Joint Chiefs and their determination, when they came to power, to get rid of the "Democratic" Chiefs and to appoint Chiefs in sympathy with Republican policies.

The scientist, in short, is not likely to orbit the centers of political power emitting upon request "beeps" of purely technical information. He will inevitably be pulled into the political arena. If his participation there is to be either productive or personally satisfying, both the scientist and the nonscientist need to be highly conscious of the character of their activity and the problems involved. The scientist (and many a nonscientist) must learn that the making of foreign policy is not a quest for the "right" answers to the problems of our time. There are only hard choices, the consequences of which will be uncertain and the making of which will often seem interminable in time and irrational in procedure.

The debate and disagreement over these choices will be heated and confused under the best of circumstances, but emotion and misunderstanding can be eased if scientists and nonscientists are both alert to the limits as well as the potential of the scientist's contribution. On the scientist's part, there is the obvious need to exercise the utmost care in making clear to himself and to others the areas where he speaks as a concerned citizen and those where he speaks as a professional expert. More difficult will be the task of learning how and to whom to address himself in each of these capacities when he is dissatisfied with the outcome of a policy decision in which he has participated. There is, as Don K. Price has pointed out, no clear code in Washington to govern the conduct of dissenting experts, only a "flexible" set of possible relationships with one's immediate superiors and those whose authority competes with or exceeds that of one's superiors. In contrast to the soldier, who can find some although not complete guidance in the doctrine of "civilian control," the very nature of the scientist's intellectual habits and many of his policy predispositions may make especially difficult his task in determining the limits to which he can stretch his dissent.[38]

On their part, the nonscientists need to recognize that scientists can hardly be expected to remain politically indifferent or inactive about the policy issues with which they are involved (especially when no one else in Washington practices such restraint). It was the naïveté of this expectation that was so appalling in the conclusion of the Gray Board that Oppenheimer was a security risk because (among other reasons) "he may have departed his role as scientific adviser to exercise highly persuasive influence in matters in which his convictions were not necessarily a reflection of technical judgment, and also not necessarily related to the protection of the strongest offensive military interests of the country." [39]

It is unlikely that civil-scientist relations will ever get any worse than this. With time and experience one can expect many of these problems to be eased, but it would be unrealistic to expect them to disappear. Military experts have participated in the making of foreign policy far longer than scientists, and the question of how they can best do so is still the subject of more than a little disagreement.

Policy processes and policy. In closing this discussion of scientists and the problems of their organizational and political relationships to others engaged in the determination of foreign policy, it is important to remember that the policy process can bring minds together but it cannot make them think. It is worth noting that in the political and administrative structure of

38. See the discussion in Price, *Government and Science,* pp. 131, 133, 138–42. The point about the scientists' lacking a tradition of civilian control was suggested by William T. R. Fox.

39. AEC, *In the Matter of J. Robert Oppenheimer, Texts of Principal Documents and Letters* (Washington, D.C., USGPO, 1954), pp. 19–20. Note the policy predisposition in the phrase "strongest offensive military interests."

It should not be comfortable for an American to reflect on the career of Peter Kapitsa, a Soviet physicist who was a student of Rutherford and who worked in England from 1922 to 1934 and then returned to the Soviet Union. Kapitsa was placed under house arrest in 1947 and remained there until after Stalin's death. Kapitsa has told Western scientists and newsmen that his arrest was the result of his refusal to work on nuclear energy for military purposes. Kramish believes that his arrest was due to the government's dissatisfaction with his advice on certain technical approaches to weapons development. In either event, it is noteworthy that Kapitsa is believed to have since become, on an informal basis, one of Khrushchev's main science advisers. On the matter of his arrest, see the report by Harrison Salisbury in the New York *Times,* July 11, 1956, the *Bulletin of the Atomic Scientists,* XIII, No. 1 (January, 1957), 38, and Kramish, *Atomic Energy in the Soviet Union,* pp. 109–110. The information on his recent activity was supplied by the staff of the Subcommittee on National Policy Machinery, Senate Committee on Government Operations.

the Soviet Union no scientist is as institutionally close to the Premier as is
the Special Assistant for Science and Technology to the President of the
United States and that there is no equivalent of the Science Advisory Office
in the Russian Ministry of Foreign Affairs.[40] Yet one would not say that
the foreign policy of the Soviet Union has appeared either ineffectual or
insensitive in its response to developments in science and technology.

The circumstances attendant on the development of radar by the British
from 1935 to 1940 provide a useful insight into both the potential and the
limits of effective organization. Essential, obviously, were the scientific and
technical ideas that Watson-Watt and his colleagues had in mind in 1935,
ideas which in turn were the result of the earlier years of research they had
been free to conduct in the facilities of a government laboratory. Certainly,
it was important that there were administrative scientists in the Air Ministry who were so alert to the military problems of the Air Force that they
could see on their own initiative the need to establish a special scientific
committee for the study of air defense (the Tizard Committee) and who
were so alert to the work of the scientific community that they made their
first request for information to Watson-Watt.[41] Of consequence, too, was
the fact that the personal and political relations of the members of the
Tizard Committee with the members of the military, administrative, and
political hierarchies whose interest and cooperation were vital for the subsequent progress of the research and development program were relations
characterized by mutual ease, respect, and understanding.

But these conditions would not have led from the formation of the
Tizard Committee in 1935 to a chain of operational radar stations by 1940
and a Fighter Command practiced in their use if it had not been for the
military ideas of members of the Royal Air Force. It was they who first
thought of the formation of a committee to look specifically into the problem of detection, they who recommended more funds than those first proposed by the Tizard Committee for the development of an electromagnetic

40. On Soviet government and science organization, see U.S. Congress, Report of the
Subcommittee on National Policy Machinery, Senate Committee on Government
Operations, *National Policy Machinery in the Soviet Union,* 86th Congress, 2d Session (Washington, D.C., USGPO, 1949), pp. 24–35, 59–62, and Nicholas DeWitt,
"Reorganization of Science and Research in the U.S.S.R.," *Science,* CXXXIII, No.
3469 (June 23, 1961), 1981–91. The points made above were additionally confirmed
by the staff of the Subcommittee on National Policy Machinery.

41. The circumstances provide an interesting variation of the "whole-problem approach." The Tizard Committee was initially interested in techniques for destroying
aircraft or their crews, and Watson-Watt was asked in 1935 to investigate the possibility of using electromagnetic radiation for this purpose. He reported that such a
use was apparently infeasible. In any event, he went on to note, the aircraft would
first have to be located, and, if anyone was interested, electromagnetic radiation
might be useful for this. Watson-Watt, *Three Steps to Victory,* pp. 81–83.

detection system, and they who were responsible for the decision to start constructing the stations and training the personnel while the equipment was still under development.[42] The explanation for this interest and support is to be found in their theories about the next World War. They believed the Germans were planning to engage in the strategic bombing of Great Britain, and they wished to be prepared for it.[43]

The point is obvious but important. British scientists and science organization were in the final measure only ready tools. They were good tools, but the use to which they were put was the result of the kind of ideas the military men had about war. The same will hold in the other areas in which science may affect foreign policy. The contributions that science and technology will bring to international politics will largely turn, not so much on the particular arrangements of scientists in the policy-making process, but on the purposes of statesmen and the theories they have about the political world in which they live.

42. For the development of radar, see *ibid.*, pp. 108–9, Snow, *Science and Government*, pp. 24–38, 60–61, 74–75, P. M. S. Blackett, "Tizard and the Science of War," *Nature*, CXXCV, No. 4714 (March 5, 1960), 648–49, and Basil Collier, *The Defense of the United Kingdom* (London, H.M. Stationery Office, 1957), pp. 33, 36–39.

43. Ironically, the British were mistaken in their theory. The German Air Force had no such strategy in mind, and in 1940, when it tried to improvise a strategic bombing campaign, it had neither the equipment nor the doctrine with which to conduct the campaign effectively. See Herbert Dinerstein, "The Impact of Air Power on the International Scene: 1933–1940," *Military Affairs*, XIX, No. 2 (Summer, 1955), 65–71, Telford Taylor, *The March of Conquest* (New York, Simon and Schuster, 1958), pp. 24–30, and Adolf Galland, *The First and the Last* (New York, Ballantine Books, 1954), chaps. 2–5.

EUGENE B. SKOLNIKOFF
Scientific Advice in the State Department

The apparent inability of the Department of State to fill the vacancy in the Department's chief science advisory post—that of Director of International Scientific and Technological Affairs—brings to the fore once again the question of what kinds of scientific advice the Department needs in the formulation of foreign policy.[1] The position has been unfilled since Ragnar Rollefson returned to the University of Wisconsin in September of 1964, though strenuous efforts, so far unsuccessful, have been made to recruit a replacement.

Even if a new man is found, the uneven performance of the science office since its resurrection in 1958 in response to the Sputnik crisis (Secretary Dulles had allowed an earlier version of the office, established in 1950, to atrophy) raises doubts as to the real value of the existing scientific advisory apparatus in the Department of State. The performance has been good primarily in low-priority areas, while the most important functions have all too often gone unfulfilled, or have been performed on an *ad hoc* basis by individuals and institutions from outside the Department.

The most important function of the science adviser can be summed up simply, if academically, as ensuring that the relevant scientific and technological aspects of central issues of foreign policy are integrated in policy deliberations. For an astonishing range of policy concerns these aspects are of critical importance to the choices facing the policy maker. And for those foreign policy issues of the greatest interest, these technical aspects are not simply background facts to be provided by an "expert." Instead, representing them effectively in the policy process requires good scientific judgment, involves estimates of future developments in both science and technology, and, most important, demands a thorough appreciation of the ways in which the technological alternatives may depend on and interact with the

1. Although there is a growing body of literature dealing with foreign policy issues that have significant scientific aspects, there is very little that focuses directly on the science advisory function in the foreign policy process. My forthcoming book *Science, Technology and American Foreign Policy* (M.I.T. Press, Cambridge, 1967) is an attempt to fill a gap. Other particularly relevant literature includes G. B. Kistiakowsky, *Science* 131, 1019 (1960); R. Gilpin and C. Wright, Eds., *Scientists and National Policy-Making* (Columbia Univ. Press, New York, 1964), especially articles by H. Brooks, R. Kreidler, and W. Schilling; C. Haskins, *The Scientific Revolution and World Politics* (Harper & Row, New York, 1964).

From *Science*, Vol. 154, pp. 980–85, November 25, 1966. Copyright 1966 by the American Association for the Advancement of Science. Reprinted by permission of *Science* and the author.

political alternatives. Moreover, science and technology are also available to the policy maker as new instruments of policy—instruments that can be used appropriately only when there is adequate understanding of their special characteristics and of the relationship between those characteristics and policy objectives.

As far as the position and influence of the Department of State within the government is concerned, the quality of its scientific advice determines, in a myriad of ways, the Department's ability to keep itself free of domination by the more technical agencies of government. The Secretary of State's role as chief foreign policy adviser to the President will, in fact, be increasingly in jeopardy if the Department under him continues to be deficient in effective technical-political competence while the issues with which it must deal involve ever more sophisticated scientific and technological elements.

The current relevance of the facts or expectations of science and technology to many foreign policy issues is not entirely without precedent. Quite a few foreign policy concerns in the past were heavily conditioned by technical considerations: fishery matters, treaties on the use of common water resources, international agreements on weights and measures, and others.

However, gradually since 1900, and explosively since World War II, there has been a change in degree of dependence that is tantamount to a change in kind. Now, not only are many of the central issues of foreign policy—those that affect the fundamental international position and security of the nation—intimately tied to scientific and technological variables, but whole new areas of policy concern based on science and technology have arisen that demand the time and attention of senior policy officials.

NATIONAL SECURITY ISSUES

This new dependence of foreign policy issues on science and technology is illustrated well in issues relating to national security. The fantastically increased technical sophistication of armaments and related hardware developments means that questions of relative power, of the limitations and uses of power, of future power relationships, of agreements to control or reduce military power—all have to be considered in the light of known technological facts and, more critically, of uncertain scientific and technological estimates. Whole generations of general war weapons systems have been developed and discarded because of obsolescence without ever having been used in actual warfare. The measure of a nation's total military power—the measure of its ability to support its major international commitments—must now be based on highly complex estimates of a great variety of technical factors, such as the kinds of weapons the nation has, their effectiveness against various defensive systems which are also changing rapidly, the ability to command and control the weapons during attack, and the likely developments, immediate and long-range, in both offensive and defensive armaments. Possibilities of "breakthroughs" achieved here or by potential enemies that might have enormous impact on the effectiveness of a force must be guarded against. Yet breakthroughs cannot be anticipated in detail, simply because their parameters are unknown in advance. As John Herz has said,[2] "the new weapons developments seem to affect the system of international relations in novel fashion: where formerly innovations, even radical ones, would permit the emergence of more or less stable new systems of some durability, the dynamic of the present is such as to foreclose any kind of stability."

For the arms control side of the national security coin, there are, in addition to decisions on the technical-military questions, other judgments to be made—about the design and performance of feasible inspection and verification systems; about the possibility of clandestine weapon developments and their significance if undetected; about whether the results of permissible research and development will negate the benefits of an arms control agreement; and so forth.

Policy making in the areas of military affairs and arms control must have fully integrated within it the technological and scientific competence that makes possible sound judgments on questions like these. Such integration implies, among other characteristics, the ability to ask for the *relevant* technical information (relevant, that is, to the political choices); the ability to understand the uncertainty inherent in judgments of future scientific and technological advances, or even of new applications of existing technology; and the ability to see clearly the reciprocal dependence of technical and political variables.

Naturally, for issues in the national security area, the Department of State relies heavily on other departments and agencies of government—in particular the Department of Defense—for technical inputs in its policy deliberations. For the great majority of issues it faces, that is the most efficient and practical procedure. However, complete dependence on outside technical information in effect means that on important issues the Department is at the mercy of the technical judgments of others in situations in which the technical judgments may dictate or greatly influence the political choices. And these technical judgments—since they are usually estimates of untried systems or of future developments, and thus are inherently un-

2. J. H. Herz, *International Politics in the Atomic Age* (Columbia Univ. Press, New York, 1962), p. 19.

certain—are being made by agencies with their own policy prejudices and with parochial, or at least different, perspectives on American foreign policy objectives.

For example, in the mid-1950's, the U.S. Government's desire to deploy some missiles in Europe to counter the growing Soviet medium-range-missile threat, plus the internal competition between the various elements of the U.S. military services which were seeking strategic nuclear roles, led to excessive evaluations by the services of the effectiveness in a European environment of American intermediate range ballistic missiles (IRBM's). It is somewhat of an oversimplification of a complex issue to say that the State Department took the evaluations at face value. Yet, though the Department had doubts on other grounds, they did not seriously question the inflated technical-military estimates and did agree to the deployment of IRBM weapons systems in Europe which did not enhance, and may have temporarily decreased, the security of America and Europe.

Several years later, in a somewhat similar situation, the State Department, unable to question, on a technical basis, Air Force judgments about the effectiveness and feasibility of the Sky-bolt airborne missile weapons system then under development, went along with a plan to provide the weapons for English bombers. The plan was doomed to failure almost from its inception on technical and cost grounds. When the failure came, in late 1962, and was formally communicated to the British at the Nassau meeting between President Kennedy and Prime Minister Macmillan, the political costs to both countries and to NATO were severe.[3]

The debate on nuclear test ban policy, particularly in the last years of the Eisenhower administration, offers another example. The great emphasis placed on details of the technical capabilities of a detection and inspection system to protect against clandestine nuclear testing came to obscure the fundamental political nature of the issue. At all times the heart of the issue was the question of the balance of risks—the risk of continued testing versus the risk of unilateral evasion of the treaty. This is a question heavily conditioned by the technical situation but by no means wholly determined by it. Yet the Department of State, which had to look to the President's Special Assistant for Science and Technology and to the Atomic Energy Commission and Department of Defense for technical judgments, found itself unable to put the technical disagreements into proper focus. Each new technical concept for evasion put forward by the agencies opposed to the ban appeared as a major problem, and the Department was unable to evalu-

3. W. W. Kaufmann, *The McNamara Strategy* (Harper & Row, New York, 1964), p. 125.

ate the practical feasibility of the concepts, or their importance in the basic political equation.[4]

It would be folly to say that, for these and other national security issues, a science adviser in the Department of State, with a necessarily small scientific staff, could on his own provide the necessary technical analyses and be able to place all technical inputs in the proper perspective. But a science adviser serving as a focal point for challenging agency positions, evaluating contradictory information, maintaining substantive contact with scientists and engineers at all levels in other agencies, obtaining independent studies, and—most important—presenting the technical variables as functions of the political choices and implications, could vastly improve the Department's ability to formulate its independent recommendations to the President. It is worth noting that the creation, in 1961, of the Arms Control and Disarmament Agency, with one of its major bureaus concerned entirely with the scientific and technological aspects of arms control, has sharply improved the situation in this policy area at least.

SPACE AND ATOMIC ENERGY

Outside the field of national security are many areas of major foreign policy concern in which science and technology now figure prominently. The most obvious are those in which the advances of science and technology have created entirely new subjects for the foreign-policy-maker to deal with. Space and the peaceful uses of atomic energy are the most prominent, and provide vivid examples of ways in which science and technology can be, and have been, used for political purposes.

Viewing science and technology as instruments of foreign policy is not new. In a sense, the Lewis and Clark expedition was an attempt to use a scientific expedition to assert this country's interest in the virgin lands to the west. Today, science and technology offer the policy maker many opportunities. They provide him with political instruments for reaching elements in other populations, for enhancing the nation's prestige and influence, for bypassing political obstacles, and for directly attacking specific sources of tension. Such political use, however, must be tempered with knowledge of the special characteristics and needs of science and technology and with understanding of the dangers to long-range national objectives of diversion of scientific and technological resources for short-term political purposes. The current debate in the scientific community about the

4. The recently released book by H. K. Jacobson and E. Stein, *Diplomats, Scientists, and Politicians* (Univ. of Michigan Press, Ann Arbor, 1966), presents the most detailed and competent history of the test ban debate in the U.S. Government yet produced. The views on the debate expressed in this paragraph are my own, however.

size of the space program and the emphasis it should receive is, in effect, a debate over whether the foreign policy objectives the space program is designed to serve warrant the costs (disputed) of diverting such a large portion of the nation's scientific and technological resources into this one program.

The debate has many elements, but whatever opinion one holds about the scale of resources to be devoted to the space and peaceful atomic energy programs, it is clear that these fields are applications of science and technology that are peculiarly relevant to a nation's foreign policy interests. They require massive investment of resources; they require advanced scientific and technological competence; they are dramatic and symbolic of the age; and they are related to military capability in fact, and beyond fact in the public's view. In short, the space and peaceful atomic energy programs are highly visible and have come to represent a nation's competence and capability, whatever the actual achievements of the programs. Thus, they are obvious instruments of foreign policy, especially in an age when surrogate demonstrations of power must serve instead of the real thing.

Both the Soviet Union and the United States have recognized the foreign policy importance of these fields, though unfortunately this country had to be shown the significance of space spectaculars. It could be argued that an astute science adviser in the State Department would have realized the political significance of being the first nation to orbit an earth satellite, but one could hardly have expected any one person in the Washington atmosphere of 1955–1957 to have influenced government programs appreciably in the direction of greater expenditure on space exploration. However, once the relevance of space to foreign policy interest had been accepted, a science adviser at State should have had a major role to play in the policy decisions concerning the space program. In fact, the State Department has generally had little to say, as compared with NASA and the Atomic Energy Commission, about the development, or even the international use, of the space and atomic energy programs.

Aside from the broad relationship of space and atomic energy to foreign policy objectives, the detailed development and direction of the programs themselves involve innumerable interactions with U.S. foreign relations. Obviously the desire for international cooperation and the need for international operations calls for a continuous blending of technical and foreign policy factors. Reactor agreements with other nations, policy on safeguards, establishment of overseas tracking stations, bilateral cooperative space research programs—these and other programs and policies all mean that the AEC and NASA must have extensive foreign-program staffs and must have close relations with State for guidance and help.

Most of the interactions between the technical agencies and the State

Department on such subjects are relatively simple and straightforward; the difficulty of relating technical factors to policy objectives is minimal. But for some questions—in particular those that relate to significant shifts or modifications in the program objectives of NASA or the AEC—the difficulty may be great because of the near-monopoly of technical information enjoyed by the operating agencies.

An illuminating illustration of this problem is the early history of the steps taken within this government which led to the U.S.–U.S.S.R. space cooperation agreements. In 1961, as a follow-up to President Kennedy's inaugural address, a draft of a series of projects on which it was thought cooperation with the Soviet Union might be possible was prepared under the leadership of the President's Special Assistant for Science and Technology, Jerome B. Wiesner. The State Department participated only marginally in the work, by its own choice. Though the ideas developed were shelved that year because of the coolness of the Vienna conference between Khrushchev and Kennedy, they were revived in 1962 when Khrushchev included in his congratulatory telegram on the Glenn orbital flight an offer for space cooperation. President Kennedy asked that the space projects be staffed through the relevant government agencies so that proposals could be developed for presentation to the Soviet Union.[5] NASA thereupon prepared specific suggestions, from draft proposals of the original study plus some other ideas they had developed in the interim, for interagency discussion.

It was only at this juncture that the State Department came into the picture in any major way, yet, to all intents and purposes, by then the Department's real choices had been preempted by NASA. Possibilities for cooperation could, in principle, range from minor efforts involving exchange of data to major efforts of joint space exploration; at each point of the curve of possibilities the political costs and payoffs would be different. NASA's technical judgment of the feasibility and desirability of certain classes of projects was inevitably affected by its own objectives, its concepts of what would contribute most to American foreign policy, and its preferences with regard to international cooperation. After weighing the alternatives in this way, NASA came to the high-level interagency discussion with a list of projects that excluded, for "technical" reasons, any large-scale cooperative projects.

The State Department, with no means of arriving at an independent technical judgment, thus had no significant choice to make and no rejoinder to NASA's argument that larger-scale projects were technically unfeasible or unwise. NASA, through its technical appraisals, which were certainly conditioned, even if unconsciously, by nontechnical as well as tech-

5. *New York Times* 1962, 10 (22 Feb. 1962).

nical considerations, was determining the boundary conditions within which the State Department had to exercise political choice. In this case NASA was ensuring that U.S.–Soviet cooperation in space would be minor, involving little political risk but offering correspondingly little chance for political gain. The State Department should have been in a position to challenge those boundary conditions, not in a large interagency meeting but in the privacy of its own offices, where the political implications of a wider range of technical alternatives could have been examined. To effectively challenge the position of other agencies, State would have required, and now requires, a science adviser in the Department, able to formulate the right technical and political questions, able to obtain the necessary technical judgments, and able to analyze the political alternatives in terms of their technical and other parameters.

One could give many examples of the relevance of science and technology to important areas of foreign policy concern, and of situations of the kind in which a science adviser could play an important role. Areas such as foreign economic assistance, bilateral relationships, national influence and prestige, and affairs of international organizations all have major technical elements that influence, and are influenced by, the underlying political aspects. In all such areas a strong science office in the Department could play a major role, by assuring adequate consideration of technical matters in the policy-making process, by recognizing opportunities for capitalizing on science and technology to advance a political objective, and by reducing the Department of State's reliance on the technical-political judgments of the operating agencies of government.

The great increase, in recent years, in the international scientific and technological activities of all branches of the U.S. Government, which often have major impact on other governments or societies, has emphasized a new requirement: the need for the Department of State to be able to monitor and guide overseas technical activities effectively. If the Department is not able to do this, it will be allowing other agencies of government to carry out independent policies and programs of direct relevance to this country's broad foreign policy interests.

The State Department has also come to have a small but important share of the government's responsibility for strengthening and advancing science. The international activities and organizations of science, always important, have multiplied to an astonishing degree in the postwar world. These international activities are essential to development in fields of science that cannot be investigated within the arbitrary boundaries of states, or in fields that require cooperative attack; they are also essential to the independent exchange of ideas and information that is necessary in any field of science. The Department of State has anything but a minor role to play in facili-

tating these international activities, in keeping them free of extraneous political problems, and in helping American scientists achieve the objectives
of these activities. The science office in the Department recognizes this responsibility for strengthening and protecting the international activities of
scientists, and since 1960 the performance of the office and of the Department as a whole has been excellent in this area.

However, the Department's relationship to science and technology
should go beyond the strengthening and protecting of international scientific activities. Technological developments sponsored by the government in
the fields of defense, space, and atomic energy all have impact on foreign
policy; in many cases their importance to foreign policy is a major deter-
minant of the scale of government support they receive. But developments
in these fields can take many directions; alternative technical choices must
be faced. And developments in other fields—for example, health, transport, agriculture—can have uses for, or can influence, the conduct of foreign policy. Moreover, many technical possibilities of value to foreign policy objectives may be feasible but remain unexplored because of lack of an
advocate, or lack of funds and direction. Should development of a direct-
broadcast satellite be accorded high priority? Should federal funds be used
for developing new seed strains that will thrive in the Andes? Should the
nation be spending more R & D resources to develop limited-war weapons?
Should seismology be given major new support? These are all questions
with direct bearing on the nation's foreign relations.

The Department of State should not be an idle bystander as the nation's
technological objectives are established. At times, rare times, it has participated effectively—notably in reinvigorating seismology because of its relevance to the detection of nuclear explosions—but often its views are un-
heard or, at best, general. Of course, the Department cannot seriously attempt to play an active role in these matters if it lacks internal competence
or the ability to command competence from other agencies or from sources
outside the government, so that it can understand the technical possibilities
and alternatives and present its views intelligently in policy debate.

NEW IMPERATIVES FOR FOREIGN POLICY

Beyond the need for integrating scientific and technological elements in
policy making is another aspect of these issues which has been only
touched on above but which is of at least equal importance. That is the
need to estimate the future, to examine the ways in which international relations and perhaps the international political system will be altered as science and technology continue their explosive advance, and to explore the

likely changes in what constitutes the "national interest." This is not primarily a matter of predicting future developments in detail and guessing what their effects will be. That is a difficult enterprise and one likely to be highly imprecise. Rather, what is required is some sense of the trends in science and technology and estimates of the future impact of those trends on international relations and, in turn, on current policies and objectives.

For example, what is the meaning today and for the future of concepts of control of territory and populations? Have the revolutions in communications and transport made it impossible to prevent the entry of "subversive" ideas into a formerly closed society? Were the breaking away of the European satellites from the Soviet Union and the evolution of the Soviet Union itself inevitable because of modern technology? Can the same developments be expected in the case of China, and, if so, what are the implications for China policy today?

And what are the implications of what might be called global technology? Increasingly, new technology has effects and applications which are global in scale, requiring international agreement and a willingness to accept international control. Is technology going to cause nations, willingly or unwillingly, to give up traditional notions of sovereignty and freedom of national action? What international preparations should be made now for future technological developments that will tend to have these effects?

Or take another example. It is quite clear that the revolution in weapons systems has changed the meaning of warfare between major powers and has contributed to the present stalemate or balance. Are future developments likely to be stabilizing or destabilizing to the system? Are there implications here that call for tacit or formal agreements designed to retard the development of technology likely to be destabilizing? The test ban was, in effect, an agreement to slow down developments in a certain direction. The 1963 U.N. resolution banning deployment of weapons of mass destruction in outer space similarly impedes developments considered to be destabilizing.[6] Should this fundamental and controversial idea of inhibiting certain avenues of technological development by international agreement be examined more carefully as other possible weapons developments loom ahead?

These and other ideas need airing within and outside the government, but the Department of State must have the sophisticated competence to raise and explore these ideas on its own initiative; they are not the sole responsibility of others.

6. "U.N. Resolution Against Orbiting of Nuclear Weapons," General Assembly Resolution No. 1884 (XVIII), adopted 17 Oct. 1963.

THE SCIENCE OFFICE

These, then, are the major reasons why the Department of State should have a science office and a science adviser. The task is large and extremely difficult. It is too big for one man, or for one small office, to do in its entirety. And it would be useless to attempt to create a large scientific staff in the Department, simply because it would be impossible to build a large staff having the scientific and political competence required. But that does not mean that the most important parts of the science advisory task cannot be achieved.

Selectivity must inevitably be one of the key characteristics of a State Department science office. It is, and has been, all too easy for the office to get bogged down in innumerable issues that could have been handled by others or that do not deserve the attention they receive. A science adviser must select his primary targets, and if these are to concern war and peace and the implications of future scientific developments, his background should include relevant experience. Involvement and interest in armaments, atomic energy, disarmament, and space are prerequisites.

Of course, a science adviser, whatever his background and backup, cannot represent all fields. Thus, he must have the means to tap the nongovernment scientific community when this is required, as the President's science adviser has, and must have a staff that is able to work with the technical agencies and knows how to extract the relevant information from them. Realistically, in the great majority of cases the normal procedure would be to get the needed technical information from the pertinent agency. But where the issues are central, or where innovation is required, an independent means of forming technical judgments and of working on a basis of equal competence with other agencies is essential.

The science adviser's immediate staff represents only part of his State Department resources. He also has the far-flung science attachés, now numbering more than 20, to assist him in his task of keeping informed on important issues and helping in the policy-making process. Unfortunately, though the attachés are mainly high-caliber scientists, at only a few posts have they been able to establish the relationships within their own embassy or with the State Department in Washington that provide the political-scientific advice required. As science reporters the attachés have been superb, but their major function should be the same as that of the science adviser himself: integrating scientific elements into the foreign policy process. It is encouraging to note that recent directives from the science office and recent selections of attachés indicate a trend in this direction.[7]

7. "Functions of Science Attaches," *SCI* [Office of International Scientific and Technological Affairs] *Directive, Department of State,* 2 Mar. 1965.

Every foreign service officer, moreover, must have a hand in the process of integrating science into policy. He cannot look to the science office at every turn; often the office would lack the information and understanding needed on a particular issue, and the load on the office would be intolerable. A significant number of foreign service officers must have some competence in science as it relates to foreign affairs if they are to be able to understand the relevance of technical aspects of issues, to seek out information, and to ask the right questions. This competence can be acquired through training and experience; a small beginning has been made, on the training side, at the Foreign Service Institute and at educational institutions that traditionally train foreign service officers.

The relations that exist between a science adviser and the senior officers of the Department are of course critical to his ability to have an impact on policy formulation. Little need be said about that beyond noting that it adds one more item to the long list of qualifications required of a candidate, for the science adviser must be able to function effectively against difficult odds in the State Department bureaucracy.

It is sometimes held that the Department does not need its own advisory apparatus but should look to the President's Special Assistant for Science and Technology when it needs help. This was, in fact, the course followed on the nuclear test ban issue. But that is not a feasible alternative for any significant number of issues, if only because the staff in the President's office is too small. More important, the result of such a course would be, again, to turn over major foreign policy responsibilities to another office—in effect what happened on the test ban issue in the late 1950's. The Department must have its own internal technical competence—a science office that can survey the world from the Department's own perspective.

Lastly, need the science adviser be a scientist? If one looks only at the nature of the required "technical" inputs into policy, the answer is, preferably but not necessarily, for those inputs require as much understanding of the political side of an issue as of the technical. With good technical associates, and experience in dealing with technical questions, a nonscientist could provide the bridge. However, he would have to surround himself with individuals with good technical judgment, and this would not be easy.

There are very few nonscientists who would, in fact, qualify, and for other reasons, which have little to do with the substance of issues, a scientist—one with stature in his field—is necessary. One of these other reasons is the fact that the science adviser will often be in the position of second-guessing an agency of government, and the senior officers of the Department must have full confidence in the technical validity of the advice they are receiving. Similarly, his word must carry weight within the Department, and that requires stature, seniority, and some independence of position. In addition, the science adviser will often have to call on members of the scientific community for advice, for special studies, or for short-term assignments. A well-respected name helps enormously.[8]

Of course, scientific stature will not make any difference whatever unless the science adviser has the basic ability to relate science and technology to foreign policy matters and the force and energy to make his views known and felt within the Department. It isn't all up to him by any means. If the Secretary or the senior officers or the foreign service in general are disinterested or hostile, then the post will be doomed to continued stagnation.

But the function is too important for the post to be allowed to atrophy as it did once before. The right man must be found and the right emphasis given, so that the potential of the science office may perhaps be realized.

JOHN   TURKEVICH
Soviet Science Appraised

Soviet science has been in the public eye for the last two decades. The dramatic confrontation of Marxist theory and genetics epitomized the dangers of Communism as a thought-controlling system. The rapid development of atomic weapons by the Soviets underlined the effectiveness of the Russian scientific task force. The flights of sputniks, luniks, laikas, cosmonauts showed the world that the party leadership had made an imaginative commitment to daring scientific ventures and that Soviet technology was discharging this commitment.

The reaction in the West was immediate. The Lysenko genetics controversy produced amazement that in a modern state, a political ideology should stifle development of a science. The Soviet weapon success showed

8. The present acting director, an outstanding regular foreign service officer—Mr. Herman Pollack—has considerably improved the science office's performance even though he is not a scientist and is little known outside the Department. There is a limit to the influence a regular foreign service officer can have in that position, however, for the reasons given; the gains in performance that Mr. Pollack has achieved are in part a measure of past deficiencies and in part a measure of his own unusual competence.

that in the military area, science and technology often develop more rapidly in a dictatorship than in democracies. The space spectaculars of the Russians astonished the world. The alibi that Soviet success was based solely on "secrets stolen from the West" was broken. American education was made a scapegoat for the lack of American successes in space. On the basis of comparison of curricula and statistics, and as the result of superficial visits to select Soviet schools, a cry was raised that the United States was losing the "battle of the classroom." The average American became convinced that Soviet science and education were the best in the world. Our highschool curriculum was revised, new mathematics introduced. Government leaders were shaken into introducing new administrative agencies in Washington and new advisory councils in the White House. The Soviet challenge of a human flight to the moon was accepted by launching a multi-billion-dollar space program.

In the meantime, a cultural-exchange program was initiated to bring about understanding between American and Soviet scientists and to explore areas of scientific coöperation. The three Geneva Conferences on Peaceful Uses of Atomic Energy, massive exhibits in New York and Moscow, numerous exchange visits of prominent scientists, prolonged stays by smaller numbers of younger scholars—all these brought about a better understanding between Western "capitalist culture" and the "culture of Russian Communism."

We have learned much more about each other, and now that the change in leadership in the Soviet Union has been stabilized, it seems appropriate to assess the status of Soviet science.

II

The United States still commands the lead in world science, and America has won the battle of the classroom. Soviet scientific accomplishments have been spotty: outstanding exploits in space; solid engineering in application of nuclear science; brilliant work in mathematics, theoretical physics and astronomy; elegant experiments in certain branches of experimental physics. But in many important areas, Soviet work is either weak or pedestrian. This is particularly true of genetics, crystal and molecular structure, modern biology and most branches of chemistry. The Soviet Union has a number of leaders in science whom any country would be proud to claim as its own, but the number is much less than in the United States. Russia is particularly weak in "first-class second-class" scientists who serve as supporting cast to the scientific stars. Women occupy nearly half the posts in research institutes, mostly on the lower rungs of the ladder, and so far none has risen to a position of importance in Soviet science. Furthermore, most of the scientific work is carried out in research institutes rather than in universities, where there is a continuous flow of young scholars. These two factors contribute to the stagnation of scientific personnel.

The research base of the Soviet Union is very narrow, confined as it is to Academy institutes and four or five major universities. This may be contrasted to the diversity of research institutions in the United States: universities, government laboratories, foundations, small colleges, large corporations and small enterprises. Physical facilities for carrying out scientific investigations in the Soviet Union are barely adequate except in a small number of prestige laboratories. Old buildings poorly adapted to laboratory use, new buildings constructed with little knowledge of the best in contemporary laboratory design, are overcrowded. Scientific equipment is either copied from American models or imported. The Soviet economy has not developed an instrument industry sufficiently alert to scientific discoveries, nor adequate to give logistic support to Russian scientists. This is in sharp contrast to the help the American scientist receives from a highly developed scientific-instrument and chemical-supply industry. Time lost in waiting for scientific tools, the repair of instruments or for crucial compounds is minimal. Support facilities of this type, and on this scale, seem to be lacking in the Soviet Union.

All this emphasizes the remarkable qualities of that small group of Soviet scientists and technologists who were able to overcome an ever-present bureaucracy and a retarded economy to startle the world with their scientific discoveries and technological advances.

The Soviet space program has been both dramatic and highly successful. It is used with great effectiveness to support the conduct of foreign affairs. The first earth satellite, the first dog flight, the first lunar satellite, the first cosmic rocket, the first hard landing on the moon and on Venus, the first human in orbit, the first view of the back of the moon, the first walk in space, the first soft landing on the moon—all these achievements indicate a well-knit organization producing a new technology. The United States is giving the Soviet space effort very good competition, but it has difficulty breaking into the province of dramatic "firsts." The American space program has been more successful in using space vehicles for scientific research and for practical applications. The discovery of the Van Allen radiation belt around the earth, the photography of Mars, the probing of Venus are evidences of sophisticated American instrumentation. The use of satellites for communication, for television-program transmission, for weather-pattern recognition, for surveillance of the earth's surface for nuclear blasts and missile launchings is a commentary on American ability to apply new science and technology for routine practical use.

A conversation the writer had with Premier Khrushchev in August 1958 at the American Exhibit in Moscow was revealing. After describing the American accomplishments in space, I pointed out that American scientists and engineers were disturbed by the fact that their Soviet counterparts were orbiting much heavier payloads. When I predicted that the United States would soon surpass the Soviet Union in space exploration, Premier Khrushchev's quiet answer was, "The United States is a strong and powerful nation. It can accomplish anything it sets out to do. However, it has a difficult time deciding what to do. Tell me more." I then related an incident of the preceding day. A Soviet visitor asked, "Is it correct to compare the Soviet and American space accomplishments as an alarm clock to a Swiss watch?" After some hesitation I replied, "Yes it is, but we should remember that it was the Soviet alarm clock that woke America to build the Swiss watch." Premier Khrushchev's retort to the story was, "Let us not put needles into each other. Tell me more." The conversation then turned to the cost of scientific research and to coöperation and competition in science as a means of international understanding.

The competition between the two countries in space may reveal basic characteristics of their science and technology. The Soviet Union tends to produce bulky, unsophisticated vehicles, designed to perform a particular task in an efficient way. Limited objectives are attained with maximum dramatic effect. The United States designs sophisticated machines which are difficult to produce and reflect an affluence of ideas, people and matériel, which has made American space technology unwieldly and at times inefficient. Once it works out its internal problems in a democratic, competitive manner, it will produce vehicles for space as it has for the highways and the airways of the world.

The Soviet missile and space success has had a great impact on international relations. Both the United States and the Soviet Union have a large arsenal of weapons. No place on earth is safe from missile attack. There is no place to hide. For the first time, the continental United States is vulnerable. The Soviets have used dramatic space results very effectively to give the world "evidence of the strength of the Communistic system." They have timed their exploits to exert "psychological leverage" at important international conferences. Detection schemes, anti-missile missiles, military space stations, constant-surveillance satellites have literally introduced a new dimension into modern warfare. Truly Soviet science and technology have awakened the world to the great potentialities of space.

Atomic science and technology is another important area of Soviet excellence. Here, as in space technology, significant military accomplishments have been attained before peacetime potential has been realized. From 1952 on, the world was periodically reminded of the Soviet accomplishments in weaponeering. Underground tests are still being carried out and undoubtedly research and development of more effective nuclear weapons are vigorously pursued. Atomic-powered submarines are being constructed, and moving pictures of Polaris-type missiles have been shown on European television screens.

The peaceful uses of atomic energy have not been neglected. The First Geneva Conference of the United Nations on Peaceful Uses of Atomic Energy in 1955 clearly demonstrated the direct dependence of a nation's standard of living on its per capita production of energy. Although the development of power from nuclear energy has been slower than expected, the Soviet Union, the United States and the United Kingdom are turning increasingly to this source to satisfy the demand of growing populations and higher per capita consumption. At present the Soviet Union has a 900-megawatt capacity while the United States has more than a thousand megawatts distributed among twelve power stations. Fifteen additional power stations are under construction so that by 1970 the United States will have a 7,300-megawatt capacity, while the Soviet Union plans by then to have several thousand megawatts of power. Both countries are constructing portable reactors for remote regions, and new types of more efficient reactors are being developed. The Soviet Union has a nuclear ice-breaker *Lenin,* the United States a cargo ship *Savannah* and an aircraft carrier. Both countries have a fleet of atomic submarines. Just as in missile technology, the Soviet Union has been able to master the new atomic energy technology and to compete effectively with the United States.

In the field of power production from nuclear fusion, the situation is different. Both the Soviet Union and the United States have conceded that success is difficult. The competition and secrecy that characterized their early work have given way to coöperation and open discussion. This may be a pattern for future international coöperation in science—major countries working together on difficult problems which cannot be easily solved.

I obtained an insight into international coöperation and competition, as understood by the Soviets, at the First Geneva Conference on Peaceful Uses of Atomic Energy. I had told a Soviet Minister that it was good to compete in scientific fields rather than in military and economic areas. I used the Russian word *konkurentsia* for competition. The Soviet Minister replied, "Do not use that word! It has a bad connotation in the Soviet Union. It means getting ahead by crushing and destroying the opponent. We have a new approach to competition and a new word to designate it. The word *sorevnovaniye* means getting ahead by climbing on the opponent's shoulders." This statement epitomizes the Soviet concept of coexistence.

III

Mathematics has been an area of particular excellence in Soviet science. Deeply rooted in the glorious pre-revolutionary tradition, it has produced important results and raised the level of performance of related sciences and engineering. All branches of pure mathematics are pursued. Mathematicians dominate the Soviet scientific scene; the rectors of the Universities of Moscow, Leningrad, Novosibirsk; the President of the Academy of Sciences; the founder and director of the science city near Novosibirsk—all are mathematicians.

The advance of Soviet science has been markedly accelerated by the readiness with which its outstanding mathematicians have applied their sophisticated analyses to scientific and engineering problems. In mathematical physics L. D. Landau, a Nobel laureate, has exerted a world-wide influence with his interpretation of low-temperature phenomena. I. Y. Tamm is another distinguished mathematical physicist who received a Novel prize for his work in nuclear phenomena, and N. N. Bogolyubov is known for his mathematical elegance in dealing with a variety of problems in physics. M. V. Keldysh, President of the Soviet Academy of Sciences, is an expert on vibrations in airplanes and missiles. Many of the leading mathematicians have been concerned with fundamentals of automation and cybernetics.

Automation is the great hope of the Communist Party leadership, faced with the problem of creating a modern industrial society with so few trained people and so many inefficient workers (which is one reason why the Soviet Union has no unemployment). The productivity of Soviet labor, including farm workers, is very low and their product is often shoddy. Automation would permit the Soviet Union to leap-frog over the barrier of training millions of people to become the technicians a modern state requires. Automation is based on the science of cybernetics, the theory of regulation and electronic computers. Cybernetics was founded in 1948 by the late American mathematician N. Wiener and was further developed in America by J. Shannon and J. von Neumann. It is a science of communication, direction and control in machines and living organisms. During the Stalin period it was considered a capitalistic "false science;" now it is the most popular science in the Soviet Union. The latest program of the Communist Party calls for the development of "cybernetics, electronic computers and regulating devices in production processes in industry, in construction projects, in transportation, in scientific investigations, in economic planning and engineering calculations and in the realm of accounting and management."

The field of electronic computation in the United States is far ahead of that in the U.S.S.R., in both quality and quantity. The machines in the United States work faster, have a higher memory capacity and are more varied and adaptable to different tasks. They are also better designed and show higher reliability, and their electronic components more elegant. Far more numerous, they are fully incorporated into both our economy and technology and into every type of scientific investigation. On the other hand, Soviet scientists and engineers have been able to utilize effectively their strength in mathematics, logic and non-linear mechanics. They can rely on the help of their leading mathematicians to solve problems crucial to their national security: design of nuclear weapons, calculation of satellite orbits and navigation of rockets.

IV

Chemistry has been a weak area in the Soviet scientific scene. In spite of the glorious tradition of chemistry in Imperial Russia and a brilliant outpouring of physical-chemistry research by the N. N. Semenov school before World War II, Soviet chemistry today is pedestrian. The exception is electrochemistry, so important for the development of the portable energy source of the future—the fuel cell. Here the work of A. N. Frumkin has been preëminent for several decades.

In recent years the Communist Party has been placing great emphasis on "big chemistry" as one of the three "material-technical bases" for Communism. (The other two are automation and electrification of the country.) Fertilizers, insecticides, herbicides are now more necessary than tractors and combines if the party is to solve the perennial Soviet food problem. Petro-chemicals from abundant oil resources must be turned into synthetic fibers, plastics, elastomers (elastic substances), both for industry and for general household use. The fabrication of plastics is much faster and easier than that of metals, which are often in short supply. The Soviet consumer is developing esthetic discrimination as a reaction to many decades of drab functionalism. With lagging agriculture and limited livestock, consumer demands can be satisfied only by synthetic chemistry. Planning in this area has been handicapped by the poor contacts between Soviet chemistry and that in the United States. N. N. Semenov, the leader of Soviet chemistry, has never visited America, where chemical engineering and industries are so highly developed. The Soviet Union has only a small number of chemical research laboratories, the curriculum in chemistry is antiquated, and in undergraduate and graduate studies the proportion of women is very high. Biochemistry—the most exciting science giving us an understanding of the processes of life—is sadly under-developed in the Soviet Union.

Physics, on the other hand, is a strong area. Three times during the last six years Soviet physicists received Nobel prizes in physics: P. A. Cherenkov, Tamm and I. M. Frank (1958), for the discovery and interpretation of radiation given off by particles travelling with velocity greater than light; L. D. Landau (as noted above) for his theoretical work in the behavior of matter at very low temperature; N. G. Basov and A. M. Prokhorov (together with C. Townes of the Massachusetts Institute of Technology) for their theoretical prediction of the laser. During the last 20 years 15 Americans received Nobel awards in physics (30 in other fields of science and medicine). The Nobel prize awards to Soviet physicists reflect their particular excellence in certain branches of nuclear physics, low-temperature research and radio-electronics. In the latter field, Y. K. Zavoyski discovered in 1946 that certain materials, when placed in a magnetic field, absorb radio waves. This phenomenon of electron spin resonance, together with nuclear magnetic resonance (discovered by F. Bloch and E. Purcell in the U.S.), is widely used in almost every science. It is of interest to note that the Soviet discovery was immediately and widely exploited in the West before the Soviet scientists began to use it. Even at present the magnetic resonance instruments made in the Soviet Union are inferior to those produced in the United States and in Japan.

Radioastronomy is keenly pursued in the Soviet Union. The radiation emitted by the sun, the planets, galactic and outer-galactic space is detected, analyzed and used for understanding the structure of heavenly bodies.

Geologists have been mainly concerned with the explanation of the geological structure of the vast reaches of the Soviet Union. Geophysical methods have been utilized for mapping mineral resources, investigating the origin of earthquakes and detecting atomic blasts. Preliminary work has been carried out on boring through the crust of the earth, a project similar to the American "Mohole." Geochemical research with modern instrumentation is actively pursued. Oceanographic research reflects the Soviets' heavy dependence on fish for its protein supply. Exploration of the Arctic, so important to the Soviet Union, has been supplemented in the last decade with continuous Antarctic investigations.

V

Biology has suffered most from the impact of Marxist philosophy on science. During the last decades of Imperial Russia and almost to the start of World War I, biology was a productive science in Russia. In descriptive and systematic botany and zoölogy, anatomy, cytology, histology, embryology and physiology, Russian scholars made significant contributions. Soil bacteriology was particularly outstanding. Viruses were discovered by D. Ivanovski in 1892, and I. P. Pavlov made the "conditioned reflex" a well-recognized concept throughout the world.

In the period between the two world wars genetics was developing rapidly and the Soviet geneticists attracted scholars from all over the world to come to work with them. However, just before World War II, N. I. Vavilov, their distinguished leader, incurred the displeasure of the Kremlin leaders and disappeared to an unknown death. In 1948, Lysenko baited the followers of Vavilov into public identification with "Western" genetics. They were then summarily crushed by an *ex cathedra* pronouncement by the Central Committee declaring Marxist genetics to be the "truth of the land." Genetics as we know it in the West disappeared from the research laboratories and textbooks of the Soviet Union. Lysenko dominated the biological sciences and agricultural research in Russia, and his influence extended well beyond the life sciences. Marxist philosophy battled relativity, cosmology, quantum mechanics, basic concepts of physics, cybernetics and the theory of chemical bonding. This Marxist inquisition continued through the period of Stalin terror, then abated in the Khrushchev period. The forces of reason within the Soviet scientific leadership gradually confined Lysenko's influence to a small group of research institutes and eliminated him from key committees. Genetics and molecular biology began to develop under the protection of powerful nuclear physicists who were particularly interested in the effects of radiation on inheritance. Scientists and engineers were intrigued by the relation between information theory, molecular structure and the genetic code. Work in molecular biology was encouraged. During the Khrushchev period several attempts were made to test Lysenko's strength in party circles, but they showed that he still had Khrushchev's backing.

In the meantime, genetics as recognized outside the Soviet Union was cautiously introduced to Soviet scientists and students through translations of Western treatises on biology and genetics. On January 25, 1965, Lysenko was accused in the *Literaturnaya Gazetta* of mismanaging the model farm, Gorki Leninski, near Moscow, and of making false claims that mineral-manure fertilizer is three times more effective than plain manure, and that crossing of Russian cows with Jersey bulls produces hybrids whose milk production does not depend on the milk production of the mother cow. Four days later the Presidium of the Academy named an investigating commission which reported last September that the farm was run inefficiently and was mismanaged, that the breeding and agricultural experiments were badly designed and records not kept, and that the advances claimed by Lysenko were not substantiated. Lysenko was thus attacked in the very area which had given him a following among Soviet agronomists. A 129-page report discussing in detail these shortcomings was widely publicized. In the annual report to the Academy on February 1, 1965, President Keldysh vindicated the late N. I. Vavilov and sharply criticized Lysenko's role in Soviet biology and agriculture over a period of 18 years. It seems that this tragic chapter in Soviet science is ending.

VI

The incorporation of science and technology into society is crucially important to the welfare of a modern state. The military and economic importance of technological developments, their limitless possibilities for good and evil, their inexhaustible demands for funds from the national economy, require immense organization—for gathering significant information, for making policy decisions, for planning, allocating manpower, conducting basic research and assigning priorities to development and production. Each of the major governments of the world has its own approach to the incorporation of science and technology into its society, but many of the problems that result are common to all of them.

Maximum utilization of science for building a "material-technical basis" for Communism has been the concern of the Party leadership. It has been eminently successful in organizing research and development in the secret areas of atomic weapons, missiles and space vehicles. It has had difficulties in using the discoveries of science for the general welfare of the state. There have been many reorganizations of the Soviet scientific effort. Most recently, a State Committee of the Council of Ministers of the U.S.S.R. on Science and Technology has been organized at the highest government level. Academician V. A. Kirillin, a Vice-President of the Academy of Sciences, has been named chairman of this committee and given the rank of Deputy Premier of the Soviet Union.

The Academy of Sciences is still the stronghold of pure and applied research in the Soviet Union. Its institutes are prestige establishments, its academicians are the scientific élite. However, the size of its laboratories is about equal to that provided by the Boston-Cambridge area alone, and domination by academicians, who rule over extensive scientific "empires," has caused stagnation in policies and personnel. Some of these shortcomings have been criticized this year in *Komsomolskaya Pravda* by the elder statesman of Soviet science, Peter L. Kapitza.

In order to offer opportunity to younger scientists and to expand the scientific base in the Soviet Union, a large science city was established in Siberia. A number of energetic Soviet scientists left the comforts of Moscow for the climatic rigors of Novosibirsk. The scientific world is observing with interest this new approach to scientific productivity. As for the universities, the major scientific investigations are carried out primarily in Moscow, Leningrad, Novosibirsk and Kiev; the other 36 universities have isolated areas of excellence. Overall, basic research activity is but a fraction of that in the United States.

The Committee for Coördination of Research, which was established in 1961 to exercise overall supervision of science and development, has had its role reduced to collection of information and development work. Under its supervision is the All Union Institute of Scientific and Technical Information. A permanent staff of more than 2,000 experts scans the world's scientific literature for discoveries that will help to build the "material-technical basis" for Communism and to fill in the large gaps in Soviet basic research. The State Committee on Coördination of Research, however, is primarily concerned with applied research and development, and even here the Soviet record has not been impressive. In the West, the industrial development of a new process costs about ten times as much as the original research project. It requires engineering skills that the Soviet Union does not seem to have. For this reason the Soviets have been eager to buy processes already proven profitable in the West rather than bear the burden of independent development.

The major problem facing all major countries of the world is how to allocate the available amount of money and the available number of scientifically trained people among the various sciences and competing groups in universities, government laboratories and industrial organizations. This allocation must ensure the proper balance between pure research, with its emphasis on the "unexpected," and applied research and development, with its demand for economically profitable results. This problem we in the United States share with the Soviet Union.

WILLIAM R. NELSON
Pugwash: The Scientific Conscience and
International Politics

With the scientific revolution has come an awareness on the part of many scientists of their own societal responsibilities and of political events in general. This awareness ranges all the way from a mere sensitivity to political questions to active participation in various professional and political action groups. The Pugwash movement provides an example of the more active involvement of scientists in politics on an international level. The force underlying the movement is a concern, generally shared by the participants, that since scientists contributed to the creation of the problem of nuclear war they bear a special responsibility to try to do something to prevent it.

In January of 1947, Norbert Wiener, Professor of Mathematics at the Massachusetts Institute of Technology and father of cybernetics, made public a letter in which he refused to provide a copy of a research paper for use in a guided missile project under the rationale that to do so would not be an innocent act upon his part. By this action he was dramatizing his concern about the morality of making scientific contributions to national defense. This concern has also been expressed by other members of the scientific community. To Wiener if seemed that for a scientist to place his contribution in the hands of "irresponsible militarists," as he described them, was an act which made the scientist a party sharing full responsibility for whatever use might be made of a new weapon in the future.[1]

Although few scientists have been as outspoken or as dogmatic on the subject as Wiener, or the group of scientists who later formed the Society for Social Responsibility in Science (SSRS), his concern was undoubtedly shared by a large portion of the scientific community. With the disclosure of the existence of the atomic bomb and the tremendous damage it had brought to Hiroshima and Nagasaki, many scientists came to feel a sense of involvement in what had happened. From this came an understandable desire not only to close Pandora's Box but also to capture and return to it the unsavory denizens that had escaped when the scientists of the Manhattan project lifted the lid. For a scientist, feeling that he had made certain contributions to a discipline and that now a part of that discipline was being used to produce ever more frightening and devastating weapons, it was perhaps natural to experience pangs of conscience.

Possibly it was an underlying desire for atonement that prompted some scientists to try to turn back the minute hand of the clock of doom (as portrayed on the cover of the *Bulletin of the Atomic Scientists*). From this desire to contribute to international understanding and the cause of peace came the motivation that led to the establishment of the Pugwash conferences. With some participants it was very likely a motivation similar to that which Alfred Nobel had felt when he established a perpetual peace prize after accumulating a fortune through the invention of a devastating new explosive. This was much the same feeling that stimulated such distinguished scientists as Albert Einstein and Linus Pauling to speak out strongly in favor of pacifism and a withdrawal of scientists from any contribution to the

1. Norbert Wiener, "A Scientist Rebels," *Bulletin of the Atomic Scientists*, Vol. 3, No. 1 (January, 1947), 31. Reprinted from the January, 1947, issue of the *Atlantic Monthly*.

national defense effort.[2] Pauling, when he secured over 10,000 signatures from scientists in a score of countries in 1957 calling for an international agreement to stop atomic testing, undoubtedly felt a strong personal responsibility to pursue any controls that might be feasible to limit the destructive use of scientific discoveries. In retrospect, it seems that many of the scientists who became involved in the peace movement in its various forms may have been reacting emotionally more than from any plan to solve specific international problems.

What has been identified by participants in the Pugwash conferences as the capacity of man to destroy civilization is the specter that underlies the concern of many scientists.[3] Prompted by a sense of responsibility for the use made of their work, a number of scientists have felt compelled to take more interest in public affairs and to attempt to play an active role in the examination of problems confronting the modern world, whether these problems are primarily scientific or political.

The belief of some scientists that they have special qualifications which may be of value in solving political problems has been expressed in a number of ways. One such attempt to define the unique qualities of scientists that enable them to deal with complex political questions was made by a Soviet delegate at Pugwash. He attributed the particular contribution that scientists could make, and apparently statesmen could not, to the honesty that comes from the scientific style of thinking and the independence that comes from the application of the scientific method and the special training associated with the discipline.[4] His evaluation would probably be shared by many of the Pugwash delegates.

It was in 1955 that Bertrand Russell took the initiative in planning an international convocation of scientists to discuss what could be done to enhance the chances for avoiding nuclear war. This led directly to the first Pugwash conference, named after Cyrus Eaton's estate in Nova Scotia where it was held in July of 1957.

Most of the meetings at the various Pugwash conferences have been closed sessions, to which the public has not been admitted, and for this reason it is somewhat difficult to obtain detailed information on the actual workings of the conferences. A few public plenary meetings have been held at the end of conferences, and some of the Pugwash reports have been made available both to interested governments and to the general public

2. Even though it was a letter from Einstein that prompted President Roosevelt to investigate and then pursue the manufacture of the atomic bomb, Einstein himself did not participate in the development of the weapon.
3. *New York Times,* July 11, 1957, p. 1.
4. Daniel Lang, "The Peaceable Gypsies," *The New Yorker,* December 21, 1963, p. 53.

through such publications as the *Bulletin of the Atomic Scientists* and the reports issued by the Continuing Pugwash Committee. However, it is often difficult to determine just what the various resolutions reported from Pugwash actually signify, whether they are the product of the plenary sessions or the reports of working groups, whether they are unanimous opinions or merely a consensus of the majority of the delegates at the conference, and, generally, just exactly how many of the delegates actually approve the resolutions that are adopted.

The Pugwash conferences have grown considerably since their initiation. From an assemblage of 24 men representing 11 nations at the first conference, the program has increased until at the 15th conference held in Addis Ababa in December of 1965, 16 nations were represented by nearly 100 delegates. Although a number of delegates and observers have attended the conferences who were not scientists, most of the participants have been selected because they were well known for their work in some aspect of chemistry, physics, mathematics, or a related field.

The United States delegation at the conferences consistently has been one of the largest.[5] The delegate who attended the most conferences is Eugene Rabinowitch, editor of the *Bulletin of the Atomic Scientists,* to whom we are indebted for much of the information that has been published about Pugwash. A handful of the American delegates have had some official or semiofficial relationship to the government. This would include Jerome Wiesner and George Kistiakowsky.[6] Most of the American delegates, however, have been prominent scientists attending as private individuals with a personal interest in communicating with foreign scientists about problems that threaten world peace.

From the first, the Continuing Pugwash Committee has followed a policy of remaining outside of all existing organizations and operating solely as a focal point for a series of international meetings held at irregular intervals averaging twice a year. This does not mean, of course, that delegates who represent other scientific organizations have not been invited to the conferences. For example, officers of the Federation of American Scientists, of the National Academy of Sciences, and of the Soviet Academy of Sciences have appeared at the conferences.

The Pugwash conferences or, as they are more accurately known, the Conferences on Science and World Affairs (COSWA), got off to a rather

5. The nations represented at one of the recent conferences, the 12th, and the size of the various delegations are listed at the end of this article.
6. Wiesner attended the second Pugwash conference at Lac Beauport, Quebec, in April of 1958, the fourth conference in Vienna in 1959, and the sixth in Moscow in 1960. *New York Times,* April 13, 1958, p. 5; July 3, 1959, p. 5; December 17, 1960, p. 13. Kistiakowsky was at Stowe, Vermont, for the eighth meeting. *New York Times,* September 14, 1961, p. 6.

unfortunate start when they were financed by and closely identified with Cyrus Eaton, the Cleveland industrialist whose sympathetic views toward the Soviet Union and personal friendship with Khrushchev tended to create a public impression that the conferences were a form of left wing movement. The scientists who constituted the Continuing Committee on Pugwash, the small group responsible for planning, organizing and administering the conferences, were well aware of the controversial nature of Mr. Eaton's political views, and after the first five conferences the Continuing Committee declined to rely upon his sole financial support. This, in effect, removed him from any official status in the program.[7]

Most of the time during the five or six days that a conference lasts is devoted to deliberations in small working groups. The subjects discussed in these working groups have been extremely varied. For example, considerable attention has been devoted to examining the dangers of the atomic age and what scientists can do about them, the political problems of the arms race, the nuclear test ban, biological and chemical weapons, disarmament, inspection and control, the free exchange of scientific information, international cooperation on major scientific projects, minimum and stabilized deterrence, the long-range educational responsibilities of science, and the general responsibilities of scientists today.

Among the more controversial positions taken by the conferences are those dealing with international political matters which involve science or technology only slightly, if at all. These include such resolutions as the following: that the status of Germany should be preserved as it is and that existing borders (specifically the Oder Neisse line) should be guaranteed by all parties, that economic aid should be offered by a nation without any thought of either military or political considerations, that a non-aggression pact should be negotiated between NATO and the Warsaw Pact countries, that Red China should be admitted to the United Nations, that the Pugwash scientists oppose the creation of a multilateral nuclear force, and, as reported from the April meeting in 1965, that aircraft and other vehicles capable of carrying atomic bombs should be destroyed (the proposal for the so-called bomber bonfire). Also, the 14th Conference condemned the United States use of riot gas in Vietnam, even though the scientists acknowledged in their resolution that the effects of the gas were only temporary.[8]

It should be apparent that several of these declarations resemble the foreign policy position of the Soviet Union. In spite of the fact that the dele-

7. New York Times, November 25, 1960, p. 11.
8. New York Times, April 17, 1965, p. 2; "Pugwash XII," Bulletin of the Atomic Scientists, Vol. 20, No. 6 (June, 1964), 46; Eugene Rabinowitch, "About Pugwash," Bulletin of the Atomic Scientists, Vol. 21, No. 4 (April, 1965), 11.

gates representing Communist nations have always been in the minority at Pugwash meetings, they have been successful in obtaining enough support from Western delegates participating as free agents to pass a number of controversial resolutions.

The topic of the 16th Pugwash Conference on Science and World Affairs, held in September, 1966, at Sopot, a city in Poland not far from Danzig, was "Disarmament and World Security, Especially in Europe." The participants discussed a number of controversial questions under this general heading, including the war in Vietnam.

As in previous meetings, most of the conference was devoted to the consideration of rather specific problems by working groups in which scientists from both East and West were represented. At Sopot, two groups used the work done during the preceding year by the Pugwash Study Group on European Security, while the other two groups devoted their attention to various aspects of disarmament. There was also a report received from the Study Group on Biological Warfare.[9]

In examining the possibilities for disarmament, one of the study groups discussed in detail the proposed freeze on nuclear weapons in Central Europe. While there was consensus on the value of a freeze as a first step in the reduction of tensions in the area, the group recognized the potential difficulties in controlling and verifying the movement of the components of small nuclear weapons and their delivery systems. The region to which primary attention was given consisted of the two Germanys, Poland, and Czechoslovakia.

It was agreed in the study group that, in the interest of reducing tensions, the number of troops in Central Europe should be substantially reduced. This reduction was to include a general withdrawal of all foreign troops and a dismantling of their bases. The delegates stressed that if foreign troops were withdrawn, care should be taken to prevent a corresponding increase in national troops. The positioning of observation posts at major transportation centers was suggested as a means for verifying troop withdrawals.

Considerable attention was given by two of the working groups sitting in joint session to the prospect of negotiating a non-aggression treaty between the members of NATO and the Warsaw treaty powers. Such a pact was seen by most of the participants as a valuable step toward German reunification.[10] The emphasis upon the preservation of existing borders that had been stressed at earlier conferences no longer seemed to the conferees to loom as a real barrier to consolidating East and West Germany.

9. "Statement from the Continuing Committee," 16th Pugwash Conference on Science and World Affairs, Sopot, 11–16 September, 1966.
10. *Ibid.*

The groups considering the reduction of tensions and political settlements in Europe agreed that the eventual unification of Germany was essential to any lasting peace, although it was acknowledged that reunification would be achieved only through a long and difficult process.

A more pressing problem was identified as the need to obtain agreement on a treaty to prevent the proliferation of nuclear weapons. To facilitate agreement it was suggested that the nations who already have nuclear weapons should agree not to use them on a nation which did not have them, as long as the non-nuclear power did not permit another country to base nuclear weapons on its territory. Since there was no consensus on what measures might be taken to enforce a non-proliferation treaty, it does not appear likely that the Pugwash position will be very influential in restraining those nations that are already scrambling to develop their own nuclear warfare capability. As with other Pugwash recommendations, the delegates produced a proposed political solution without fully exploring the important intermediate problems, the allayment of distrust and the elimination of the temptation to cheat in this case, that must be faced before the proposed solution could be of any real value.

The situation in Vietnam was discussed extensively in a plenary session and by one of the working groups at the 16th Pugwash Conference, but the delegates found themselves unable to agree on the causes or the nature of the war.[11] The Conference took no position on ways to terminate the conflict, although it observed that differences about Vietnam could lead to increased tension in Europe. In avoiding any resolutions on this subject that might be construed as controversial, the delegates showed more restraint than at some of the previous conferences.

As many of the supporters of Pugwash see it, the great value of the meetings is not in just collecting a representative group of scientists to discuss important issues, but rather the opportunity that is provided to go much further and to open up whole new channels of communication between the East and the West. The avowed general purpose of the Pugwash conferences has been not only to discuss important problems of international politics but also to mobilize support for Pugwash and the suggestions coming out of the conferences, particularly among the scientists of the world.

However, individual Pugwash participants have not always been in agreement as to the specific and immediate purposes of the conferences. Rabinowitch has identified at least four different philosophies that have been evident. The first view has been that the worldwide community of scientists can institute a campaign that would lead to rapid and complete dis-

11. *Ibid.*

armament, without quibbling about the details of any verification system. A second and more cautious approach, most closely associated with certain Western scientists, has been to treat Pugwash as an opportunity to utilize unofficial channels of communication where conflicting opinions can be explored with the prospect of achieving agreement upon a gradual approach to disarmament, with provisions for systematic inspections and the extensive use of electronic detection and warning systems.

The most idealistic view of Pugwash is held by those delegates who believe that the apocalyptic specter of thermonuclear war is so dreadful that it can precipitate broad changes in traditional national attitudes, where the broadly shared interests of humanity will transcend traditional nationalistic loyalties and conflicts between nation-states. At the other end of the spectrum is the fourth position, from which the entire movement is regarded with suspicion as a tool of devious international politics.[12]

It is true that at times the Soviet delegates have appeared obviously restrained on certain questions and that at other times doctrinaire attitudes have been reflected in their positions. However, American delegates have described them as expressing continued interest in the conferences and as being willing to talk about many matters upon which the Soviet government itself had been elusive. This willingness to express personal opinions, however, has never reached the stage where Soviet delegates would support resolutions that run contrary to the foreign policy of the USSR. And when the conferences have touched upon questions that were regarded as sensitive by the Russians, their delegation has been in close contact with Moscow by telephone.[13]

Consistently, the largest delegations at the Pugwash conferences have come from the United States and the Soviet Union. Other countries of both the Eastern and Western blocs have been represented, as well as many neutrals. The Chinese Communists participated in the Pugwash conferences up until the time of the Sino-Soviet split. Since the conference held in December of 1960 they have failed to appear but have responded to invitations in such a manner as to leave the door open for future acceptance.[14]

Delegates to the conferences are ostensibly invited as individuals and not as official representatives of their governments, but this selection system has generated considerable controversy. While several American delegates

12. Eugene Rabinowitch, *Bulletin of the Atomic Scientists*, Vol. 21, No. 4, 10.
13. It was reported, for example, that Academician Topchiev frequently consulted Moscow from the 7th Conference in Stowe, Vermont, after the Russians incurred a considerable amount of international criticism by resuming nuclear testing. *New York Times,* September 13, 1961, p. 3.
14. Eugene Rabinowitch, *Bulletin of the Atomic Scientists*, Vol. 21, No. 4, 11.

have had fairly close connections with the group providing scientific advice to the President, their selection has been only an occasional phenomenon and no particular pattern has been established. However, with the Soviet Union the same thing is not true. Russian delegates to the Pugwash conferences have been invited through, and sponsored by, the Soviet Academy of Sciences, and nearly all have been members of the Academy. The officers of the Academy, in particular, have been heavily represented at the Pugwash conferences. It is therefore advisable to look at the nature of the Soviet Academy of Sciences.

The role played by the Academy in Soviet society is far different from the position of the National Academy of Sciences in the United States. The Soviet Academy does not stand apart from party and government as an association of outstanding scientific authorities. It has the official state character typical of Soviet institutions. The programs of the Academy are part of a national plan, and the emphasis and direction of Academy projects are determined largely by the priority placed upon them by the Soviet government and the Communist Party. As it has been described by some of its own members, the Soviet Academy of Sciences is a Ministry of Science.[15] On important programs and decisions it is subordinate to the Council of Ministers and the Communist Party hierarchy. Its budget is a part of the official state budget, and its activities reflect the concept that dialectical materialism is synonymous with science—that this is the only acceptable realm of inquiry, and that Marx's philosophy, being built upon the foundation of scientific investigation, points the way to science as the supreme value of Soviet society.[16]

All of this raises the question of whether the Soviet scientists who have participated in the Pugwash conferences can ever really be considered to be free agents. The Soviet scientist who at the time of his death in late 1962 had attended more Pugwash conferences than any of his countrymen, even though on occasion he was the only member of the Russian delegation who did not speak English, Alexander V. Topchiev, when asked the question freely admitted that the views of the Soviet delegates represented those of the Russian Academy of Sciences.[17] Topchiev, then the Chief Scientific Secretary of the Academy, was a fairly typical example of the interrelationship that exists between Academy leadership and membership in the Communist Party. He joined the party in 1932. The General Assembly of the Academy made the then relatively unknown Topchiev an academician in

15. Alexander G. Korol, *Soviet Research and Development* (Cambridge: The M.I.T. Press, 1965), pp. 1, 11.
16. Alexander Vucinich, *The Soviet Academy of Sciences* (Stanford, Calif.: Stanford University Press, 1956), preface.
17. *New York Times,* July 12, 1957, p. 3.

1949. At the same time he was named the Chief Scientific Secretary of the newly created Scientific Secretariat of the Presidium of the Academy. It is the Scientific Secretariat, composed of the Chief Scientific Secretary and three to five other Scientific Secretaries, that wields the real power in the Academy. Appointments to positions of Scientific Secretaries have been limited largely to party members and persons of proven political acceptability.[18]

The organization of the Soviet Academy of Sciences presents the facade of democratic centralism typical of many Russian institutions. However, this is not indicative of the degree of official control exercised over the Academy. On paper, the General Assembly, with its more than 350 academicians, is the highest organ of the Academy.[19] It elects the members of the Presidium and the officers of the Academy. As a practical matter, the jurisdiction of the Presidium is greater than that of the General Assembly, and the General Assembly merely rubber-stamps decisions that have already been made by the Presidium.[20] In fact, there have been years when the Presidium did not even convene the General Assembly. Within the Presidium the Chief Scientific Secretary plays a role much like Stalin and Khrushchev did as First Secretaries of the Communist Party. Of course, the degree of ideological control that is exercised over Soviet science is not the same in all fields, and the amount of interference from the Communist Party at times has been considerably greater in the biological sciences than it has been in many of the physical sciences. For example, Lysenko's theory of Michurin genetics, which maintained that environmental influences were inheritable, dominated Soviet biological science and was official party doctrine as long as Stalin lived.

The leadership of the Soviet Academy of Sciences is strongly oriented toward the concept that all scientific investigation in the Soviet Union owes its success to the superiority of Communist ideology, and that this supposedly superior ideology will insure the success of Communist scientific endeavors in the future. Thus, there often have been attempts to synchronize scientific achievements, such as the launching of space satellites, and the announcement of those achievements with important political meetings or holidays.

The extent of the conformity of the leadership of the Soviet Academy of Sciences to Communist ideology was evident in an open letter to the President of the United States, signed by 15 academicians in August of 1965.

18. Vucinich, *op. cit.*, p. 33.
19. By the end of 1956, just before it was reorganized, the Soviet Academy of Sciences had a staff of about 40,000, including 16,000 research scientists. Korol, *op. cit.*, pp. 22–23.
20. Vucinich, *op. cit.*, p. 22.

Entitled "We Accuse," the letter was a condemnation of the United States over the Negro riots in the Watts section of Los Angeles. A portion of the letter read as follows:

> Mankind has the right to say to you, Mr. President: Look at Los Angeles. Here it is, the 'freedom' which the United States wants to impose upon other people by bayonet and bombs. Here it is, the respect for human rights about which American representatives speak so much and so eloquently from the rostrum of the United Nations. There is no end here to the work for the statesmen and lawmakers who hypercritically worry about the good of the enslaved countries. . . . The violation of the principles of humanity, justice and morals, wherever they are perpetrated—in Vietnam, the Dominican Republic, or Los Angeles—must be stopped. We, like all Soviet people, decisively demand an end to these outrages. All people unanimously are in favor of this demand. The reason, honor, and conscience of mankind cannot put up with these actions by the racists and aggressors.[21]

Among the academicians signing the letter were the President of the Academy of Sciences of the USSR, three Vice Presidents, the Secretary of the Department of Nuclear Physics, and the Secretary of the Department of History. Additionally, the President of the Armenian Soviet Socialist Republic Academy of Science, the President of the Georgian Academy, and the President of the Byelorussian Academy signed the letter, as well as the President of the Academy of Medical Sciences of the USSR.

Since this is the type of intemperate political reaction often generated by official Soviet ideologists, the degree of political commitment of the signers is worthy of further investigation. *Who's Who in Soviet Science and Technology* and *Who's Who in the USSR* reveal that 13 of the 15 academicians signing the open letter are members of the Communist Party, with the average membership dating back more than 19 years. The President of the Academy of Sciences, M. V. Keldysh, is a member of the Central Committee of the Communist Party. P. N. Fedoseyev, one of the Vice Presidents of the Academy, was formerly editor of both *Bolshevik* and *Problems of Philosophy,* two primary journals of the Communist Party. N. N. Semyonov, another of the Vice Presidents, is a candidate member of the Central Committee of the Communist Party. The third Vice President, M. D. Millionshchikov, a member of the party for 18 years, was one of the leaders of the Soviet delegation to the 13th Pugwash conference.[22]

21. *PRAVDA,* August 21, 1965, No. 233 (17185), p. 3. The letter was reprinted in *Novoye Vremya,* August 27, 1965, No. 35 (1057), p. 3.
22. Ina Telberg (ed.), *Who's Who in Soviet Science and Technology* (New York: Telberg Book Company, 1964); Heinrich E. Schulz and Stephen S. Taylor (eds.),

Since membership in the Communist Party of the Soviet Union involves far more than a legalistic act of conformity in order to gain recognition and advancement, there can be no question that the top leadership of the Soviet scientific effort is permeated with members of the party who can be regarded as completely safe to adhere to the ideology when sent abroad as delegates to an international convention. These scientists have worked actively to obtain party membership, and in the process they have been screened for political reliability. With individuals such as these, who are actually part of the political apparatus, it is not necessary to maintain any external system of rigid control over their actions. The Soviet Academy of Sciences is controlled politically from within by its own leadership. Although the Soviet scientists selected by the Academy to attend might on occasion express their personal feelings and sentiments at a Pugwash conference, it is most improbable that they would ever take a position contrary to the policies of their government or of the Communist Party.

All of this brings us to the question, what role is there for scientists in international politics, especially in the solution of those problems that are not primarily technical in nature? Scientists, of course, have the same motivations as many other groups in expressing opinions about important public matters. But do they have any special obligation because they are scientists? Many of the questions that have been considered at the Pugwash conferences are far removed from the scientific field. In this type of situation should the scientists endeavor to limit the scope of their discussion to matters on which their particular expertise may be necessary, or at least helpful, in understanding the problems and formulating possible solutions? It would seem that if scientists do not to some degree limit the scope of their discussions and suggestions, they weaken the value of their potential contributions to the solving of any problems involving political aspects.

In the political environment existing immediately after the announcement of the dropping of the atomic bombs at the close of World War II, scientists found their views solicited on an almost unlimited range of subjects. Since that time public opinion has become considerably more sophisticated, and now the scientist finds that when he expresses himself on questions that are clearly beyond the realm of his training and experience, he can anticipate a certain amount of skepticism—a skepticism that is largely attributable to the fact that he is usually too far removed in his daily work from social and political problems to have a realistic understanding of all the considerations that they involve.

The opinion has been expressed on many occasions by scientists that they share an international language of science which makes for a world-

Who's Who in the USSR 1961/62 (Montreal: Intercontinental Book and Publishing Company, 1962).

wide community of scientists, and that they therefore understand each
other and can communicate despite their respective language barriers.[23]
C. P. Snow went as far as to assert that scientists have common attitudes,
common standards and patterns of behavior, and common approaches and
assumptions that cut across other mental patterns, such as politics and
class.[24] This ease of communication is often attributed to the fact that
scientists receive similar training in all countries and have dealt with the
same types of problems in the laboratory. However, it is well to stop and
inquire whether there really is an international language of science. And
even if we assume there is, does this necessarily signify a dedication to abstract values that overrides all other influences? Does the scientist who has
been trained in a totalitarian environment and then selected by his government to participate in an international conference really hold the same values and sentiments as his opposite number in the West? Surely there is
sufficient doubt about this to justify caution in forming any assumptions
about the existence of a worldwide community of science.

Another question for consideration is whether the more outspoken scientists who advocate a particular course of action are really representative of
the opinion of the majority of their colleagues. Is there somehow more of a
consensus among scientists than among members of other disciplines and
professional groups? Do scientists as a group have significantly different
opinions about international politics than those trained in the humanities
and social sciences? If we assume that they do, even though there is little
evidence to support such an assumption, this may be the result of some
application of the scientific method, or it may be simply the voice of the
critic who is unaware of the intricacies of the problems with which he is
attempting to deal.

The Pugwash delegates have recognized that the most serious problems
confronting the world are primarily political, yet their views, and the resolutions adopted by the conferences, often have been politically unimagin-
ative or patently impractical of implementation. The neat, structured problems of the laboratory are a far cry from the real world of international
politics. How nice it would be to discover, even belatedly, that all that is
needed to resolve the grave differences that separate the East and the West
is an application of the scientific method in a political context. To expect
this result, however, is to impute wholly unrealistic qualities to the scientific method—a method that is as well known to most statesmen and social
scientists as it is to physical scientists.

23. For example, see Eugene Rabinowitch, "The First Pugwash Conference," *The
Atomic Age,* ed. Morton Grodzins and Eugene Rabinowitch (New York: Simon and
Schuster, 1963), p. 542.
24. C. P. Snow, *The Two Cultures: and a Second Look* (New York: The New
American Library, 1964), p. 16.

If the Pugwash conferences are to be continued for their value in providing an additional channel of communication between the East and the West, as many objective observers agree they should be, the conformity of the Communist delegates to party doctrine and control makes it imperative that Western participants be aware of their own limitations in the discussion of contentious political matters. They must make a special effort to inform themselves of the facts and to understand the position that has been taken by their own government. Then, if with full knowledge of the political considerations involved they chose to differ with their government's position, at least they have sufficient information upon which to base their decision, and they have not been simply swayed by other Pugwash delegates who have a higher degree of political consciousness.

Admittedly, any attempt to avoid sensitive political issues completely will be difficult and could have the effect of diminishing the value of the conferences. However, if Western delegates will attempt in the working groups to first of all restrict the discussion of political matters to those that have a reasonably close relationship to scientific questions and then to equip themselves with the background information they need to understand all aspects of the problem, they can substantially enhance the image of Pugwash and the potential contribution of the conferences to international understanding. If they fail to do so, the objectivity of the conferences—the same objectivity that is so closely identified with science and the scientific method—will become increasingly suspect.

The following nations were represented at the 12th Pugwash Conference, held in Udaipur, India, in 1964. Unless otherwise indicated, a nation had only a single delegate in attendance.

Australia	Netherlands
Brazil	Norway
Canada	Pakistan
Czechoslovakia	Poland
France–4 delegates	Rumania–2 delegates
German Democratic Republic	Sweden–1 delegate and 1 observer
German Federal Republic	Thailand
Hungary	Uganda
India–7 delegates and 1 observer	United Kingdom–6 delegates
Israel	United States–11 delegates and 3 observers
Italy	
Japan–2 delegates	USSR–10 delegates
Malaya	Yugoslavia

Also present were observers from the United Nations, UNESCO, and WHO.

Source: *Bulletin of the Atomic Scientists,* June, 1964, p. 49.

VI

GOVERNMENT AND THE FUTURE OF AMERICAN SCIENCE

In this final chapter an overview is provided of the general position of science vis à vis government. Although a determination of where science is leading governmental policy, or vice versa, can be formulated only in speculative terms, at least we are better able to ask some of the proper questions than we were a decade ago. One fact stands out very clearly. The maker of public policy in the future will be called upon repeatedly to solve problems in which scientific and political considerations are inextricably intertwined.

Biopolitics, "the science of proving that what must be done for political reasons is biologically safe for the human race," provides Lynton K. Caldwell with a point of departure from which he develops a broader definition that treats it as the study of the role of science in society. In this context biopolitics is entitled to the highest priority in the educational system. It is apparent from his article that Edward T. Chase would agree with this observation. Chase views rapid technological change as building up a fundamental political crisis of the most serious proportions.

One possible answer to the problems that have arisen is to place more scientists in positions of responsibility and authority in government. To this proposal of George C. Sponsler, however, another observer, Emmanuel G. Mesthene, replies that simply because a man is a scientist is no assurance that he is qualified to make public policy involving science. Mesthene does not rule out scientists as policy-makers, but he maintains that the best public servant will be the official who is a scientifically literate professional policy-maker, and whether this official is himself a scientist is of little importance.

In a philosophical examination of the responsibilities of scientists in the atomic age, Eugene Rabinowitch describes their obligations of expanding their own knowledge and at the same time educating peoples and governments in the things that scientists know. He does not rule out some form of effective political action by the scientists of the world—if it were possible for them to agree on a collective program.

The last article raises the possibility that an overemphasis upon science and an ever increasing orientation toward science in our educational system may result in losing sight of our fundamental values and national goals. Science and its applications, after all, are means to a better, more secure life and not an end in themselves.

LYNTON K. CALDWELL
Biopolitics: Science, Ethics, and Public Policy

Last year a front-page column of the New York *Herald Tribune* carried a whimsical description of a new science of biopolitics. J. P. Miller, already secure in his reputation for social criticism through satire in *Days of Wine and Roses,* recounted an imaginary interview between an official government biopolitician and a newspaper reporter concerning the meaning of the "new science" of biopolitics, "the science of proving that what must be done for political reasons is biologically safe for the human race."

The reported interview occurs sometimes after 1971, when the collapse of the nuclear test ban treaty has been followed by a resumption of massive testing in the atmosphere and soaring levels of fallout. In order to relieve popular fears and prevent panics and anti-government demonstrations, official biopoliticians "prove scientifically that the previous human tolerances to radio-activity and all other by-products of nuclear testing, including strontium 90, had been estimated far too low." The official pronouncement has "a wonderful calming effect on the people." Public confidence is restored.

But, asks the reporter, suppose that an increase in bone cancer is being caused by heavy concentration of strontium 90 in human and animal marrow? Some unofficial scientists say so. But the official biopolitician replies that statements which frighten people are certainly not in the public interest. Bone cancer and strontium 90 cannot be linked, he declares. "The people wouldn't like it. Therefore, by definition it is biopolitically impossible."

In the tradition of the moralizing fable, Miller is posing one of the biggest, most difficult questions of our time: are science and politics really compatible? The philosopher-dramatist with a sociological turn of mind can put the question this way. Presumably the political scientist could too—but he rarely does. As "scientist" he finds it impractical to ask questions about the extent of man's political capacities that the present state of knowledge does not permit him to answer. Moreover the discipline of political science in America has, in its subconscious, assumed the infinite perfectibility of man. To hypothesize that political man cannot or will not reshape his goals and values in the light of scientific knowledge seems disloyal to the tradition of the discipline. But while the question cannot be usefully posed in absolute and theoretical terms, it is by implication being posed daily in limited and practical situations. In the language of politics "it is a condition that confronts us, not a theory."

An explosion of biological knowledge and technology is raising questions of public policy which until recently were hypothetic, and were therefore from a practical point of view unreal. Whether there is, can, or should be in any sense a science of "biopolitics" can easily be dismissed as facetious. But the conscientious man grows uneasy when he reflects upon the mounting problems which the life sciences (in particular) are posing for political solution. There is certain to be more biology in politics and this could mean, as J. P. Miller implies, more politics in biology.

The scientist, the politician, and the philosopher, each in his own way, is confronted by the question of how political reactions to an expanding, innovating biology will affect its application to the public happiness and welfare. And unfortunately for the policy-makers, happiness and welfare do not always follow from the same course of action. Yet there are urgencies in our present "biopolitical" state of affairs that compel a reconciliation of ethical values and scientific facts in public policies involving the biological nature of man.

"Biopolitics," then, though it certainly does not designate a science, is a useful piece of shorthand to suggest political efforts to reconcile biological facts and popular values—notably ethical values—in the formulation of public policies. It affords a selective focus on a portion of the larger issue of the relationship of science to society.

For several decades, spectacular developments in the physical sciences have overshadowed major but less readily demonstrable advances in biology. Moreover the impact of applied biology upon society often occurs on a time scale that obscures its effects—at least in the early stages. Thus the present population explosion has been underway ever since public health administration and medicine began to eliminate the "natural" controls over human reproduction. The explosion of population may be as inexorable and destructive as the explosion of nuclear energy, but the consequences of the nuclear bomb are all too readily observable whereas the potential consequences of the population bomb are inferred through the dry and less convincing medium of statistics.

Although there is widespread and profound disagreement as to its implications, the population explosion is now generally acknowledged. There is less awareness of a concurrent explosion of biological knowledge, an accelerating geometrical expansion of knowledge, the culmination of long years of accumulating inquiry in the various bio-sciences. It is the contemporary convergence of these two explosions—of people and biology—that justifies, indeed necessitates, a focus on biopolitics.

If the popular press and political behavior are taken at face value, people are nowhere (certainly not in America) ready to cope either conceptually or politically with the population explosion. This circumstance in itself is a major element in a larger body of evidence suggesting the unreadiness of most peoples and their governments to deal effectively with an impending explosion of biological knowledge. That extraordinary advances in biological science and biotechnology are imminent seems certain. To this there has been informed and responsible testimony for some time. Detlev W. Bronk, President of the Rockefeller Institute, has stated that ". . . we have learned more about the nature of living matter and the mechanisms of living organisms during recent years than in all prior human history." And the rate of learning accelerates. The revision of man's perception of himself and of nature that the biological sciences may require could be as drastic as the changes made by the physical sciences in man's perception of the cosmos. William K. Wyant, Jr. recently noted the likelihood that "the rough jolts of the future, in the way man thinks of himself, will come from studies done with the microscope."

The more sensational speculations growing out of biological congresses make news headlines and sober editorials. Commenting on the unprecedented implications of the emerging biotechnology discussed at the Eleventh International Congress of Genetics, an editorial in the New York *Times* declared that "the moral, economic and political implications of these possibilities are staggering" and then asked rhetorically "is mankind ready for such power?" In the judgment of some of the most thoughtful students of man's biopolitical behavior the answer is "No." Representative of misgivings in the scientific community is the regretful observation of Theodosius Dobzhansky that man, comprehending the meaning of his biological evolution:

> . . . should be able to replace the blind force of natural selection by conscious direction, based on his knowledge of nature and on his values. It is as certain that such direction will be needed as it is questionable whether man is ready to provide it. He is unready because his knowledge of his own nature and its evolution is insufficient; because a vast majority of people are unaware of the necessity of facing the problem; and because there is so wide a gap between the way people actually live and the values and ideals to which they pay lip service.

Public unreadiness to use an expanding biotechnology wisely is not merely a speculative conclusion. Popular behavior and political action (or inaction) indicate prevailing attitudes toward biological realities. A cursory look at some of the current biopolitical issues suggests a mixed and contradictory picture. In each case a confrontation of biological facts, political exigencies, and ethical values occurs in the course of policy-making.

Biopolitical issues tend to fall into two general groups differing chiefly in the directness and generality of their effects. The first group may be termed environmental. Issues in this category arise when environments are impaired as a consequence of deliberate or inadvertent human action. The most dramatic of these concerns radio-active fallout. The attendant confusion of counsels and political recriminations hardly need comment. Whenever biological innovation is believed to threaten public health and happiness, and when scientific evidence can be marshaled in support of opposing views, a biopolitical row is inevitable. The fluoridation controversy, chronicled recently in the *Saturday Review,* is a case in point. Another is the danger of chemical poisoning through pesticides, dramatized by Rachel Carson's *The Silent Spring,* which engendered controversies described by René Dubos as ". . . disgraceful both from the scientific and social points of view."

Biopolitical controversies, frequently as heated, have arisen over efforts to conserve scientific and esthetic values in natural landscapes and in plant and animal wildlife. More recently questions concerning the effects of noise and of crowding upon human populations have been pressed forward. But in none of these matters has public policy making been pursued with the vigor urged in most of the polemic and some of the scientific literature. Perhaps this is because a clear and unequivocally right course of action seldom emerges from the research findings and the contradictions of scientific and of popular opinion.

For this failure to deal effectively with environmental problems the scientific community bears some responsibility. In a recent critique on environmental biology René Dubos takes his fellow scientists to task for gross neglect of ". . . the problems posed by the response of the total organism to the total environment." He argues that the potentialities of medicine for human welfare will be severely restricted until medical science has been provided with adequate scientific knowledge of "the effects of the total environment on the human condition." When scientists themselves offer no adequate explanation of the responses of body and mind to the impact of modern technology, has the politician any choice other than to trim biological facts to fit political circumstances? if science cannot speak authoritatively regarding the threats to physical and mental health posed by "constant and unavoidable exposure to the stimuli of urban and industrial civilization; by the varied aspects of environmental pollution; by the emotional trauma and often the solitude of life in congested cities; by the monotony, the boredom, indeed, the compulsory leisure of automated work," how can the politics of these issues be guided by science? It may indeed be argued that science, and biology in particular, are providing society with a powerful array of tools and problems, but no adequate conceptual basis for relating tools to problems in practice.

A second group of biopolitical issues are more directly and specifically physiological than environmental. More personal in immediate impact although scarcely less general in ultimate ramification are biopolitical issues relating to individual human behavior in the use of cigarettes, tranquilizers, narcotics, and alcohol—and extending to the biochemical control of personality. Even more personal and at the same time of greater social implications are questions relating to human reproduction, to social concern for the numbers and qualities of future populations. In addition, ethics and biology become mutually involved in the political issue of public responsibility for public health and medical care. And finally the relations between biology, politics, and ethics are perhaps most starkly posed in the issue of biological warfare. In few of these areas have people demonstrated a readiness to be guided by verifiable knowledge in a search for policies equal to the problems. On many matters, inadequate as our knowledge may be, our failure to make full use of what we do know is all the more regrettable.

Biopolitical problems—particularly the major ones—grow increasingly national, international, and even global in character. The continuing flow of air and water and living organisms around the world has always tended to spread biological phenomena into any receptive environment. Modern technology multiplies and accelerates these possibilities, but it also enables us to discover and to understand the processes of dispersion and interaction. Where cause-and-effect relationships in these processes have become clear they have sometimes influenced political behavior as, for example, when the sciences of epidemiology and plant pathology led to the establishment of quarantines at national frontiers and were among the factors leading to international cooperation in public health and agriculture. Continuing difficulty in controlling international traffic in narcotics and the recent tragic consequences of the sale of the dangerous drug thalidomide in international commerce underscore the lesson that there can be no biopolitical frontiers.

A convincing argument can now be made that old-fashioned political nationalism is one of the principal obstacles to biological sanity. How much positive harm or deprivation may a nation lawfully inflict upon the rest of the world in pursuance of its alleged "sovereign rights"? Atmospheric testing of thermonuclear devices has posed the question dramatically, but a list of other major biopolitical issues, current and impending, could be extended to great length and in great variety. Obvious illustrations are found in national policies pertaining to the destruction of wildlife, allo-cation of water from international rivers, disposal of harmful wastes, con-trol of plant and animal diseases, and increase in populations.

The inadequacy of conventional political mechanisms to deal with the problems of the new age of biology is nowhere more apparent than in the oceans from which life may well have come and from which man is in-creasingly drawing sustenance. As knowledge of the influence of the oceans upon terrestrial life continues to grow, so too does apprehension concern-ing impairment of their life-sustaining qualities. Massive discharge of un-treated biological and industrial wastes into rivers, lakes, and coastal wa-ters has impaired or destroyed important resources of food supply and rec-reation; residues from oil-burning seacraft have been so harmful to marine life that international control efforts have been sought; and proposals to bury radioactive wastes in the sea have aroused fears and controversy. But deliberate pollution is not the only problem. The Surgeon-General of the United States Public Health Service reports that the insect-killer DDT in some mysterious manner has invaded the water environment of the world and is being found in surprisingly large concentrations in the fats and oils of deep sea fish.

But the most portentous biopolitical issues relate to the evolution of man himself. The coincident and related explosions of human population and of biological knowledge may conceivably represent the most critical stage in human evolution since the last great ice age. The ability and necessity to control the numbers and hence (in some respects) the genetic character-istics of future populations could create a situation without precedent in human existence. And, in addition, the availability and refinement of chemopsychiatric drugs suggests both hoped-for and frightening possi-bilities for the manipulation and control of human behavior. Never before have the necessity and the possibility of control over man occurred at so decisive a conjunction.

Popular (and political) "wisdom" tends to avoid facing issues in ad-vance of a compelling necessity. Questions as sensitive and confused as those just mentioned are especially good candidates for relegation to some indefinite future. But if society's ability to deal effectively with a problem requires policy decision *before* the matter becomes a compelling issue, then some means must be found to enable political action to anticipate the fu-ture. Practical biopolitics calls for a degree of foresight that the lexicon of conventional wisdom would term "theoretical." And practical democratic politicians find it difficult to persuade themselves or their publics of the necessity of dealing with tomorrow's uncertain problems when the self-evident issues of today press for attention.

At the root of these issues one finds the familiar dichotomies: fact and value, science and tradition, knowledge and action. If society moves ever more rapidly into an age of biology, how well can public leadership—scientific, educational, and political—bridge the gulf between the realities of popular concepts and the realities of scientific fact? If a massive reorientation of popular attitudes would be necessary for society to benefit fully from the *present* state of biology, how much more orientation may be required to develop a popular receptivity to the biology and biotechnology of the emerging future? There are wide gaps to be bridged between the biological sciences and public policies, and present resources are not adequate to the task.

The building of a better bridge between science and society leads to consideration of four basic elements in the process. These are: first, prevailing perceptions of man's relation to nature; second, the meaning of science as interpreted by formalized education; third, communication between scientists and policy-makers; and fourth, leadership toward a policy synthesis of scientific knowledge and ethical values. Whatever utility the concept "biopolitics" possesses is primarily in relation to this fourth element. But all four are ultimately interrelated.

It is commonplace that man's perception of himself in relation to his environment is influenced by his culture pattern. In cosmopolitan and dynamic societies, these perceptions may range widely, as they have for example in the history of the American people. But in the realm of politics and social policy, some perceptions prevail over others. And, with acknowledgment of the inevitable exceptions, it is generally true that man's perception of his environment has in the main been possessive, exploitative, and short-sighted. From science, society has more often sought technology than understanding. The eminent ecologist Paul B. Sears has said, "The power of applied science has been overwhelmingly employed to exploit space, while those aspects of science that could illuminate its wise and lasting use are still largely ignored."

Industrial man (which until recently meant Western man) has for the most part seen himself as separate from and outside of nature. From this inference he has frequently concluded that he may exploit nature with impunity and that where nature fails to meet his wants, science through technology will synthesize a substitute. As *The Wall Street Journal* optimistically editorialized with respect to man's insatiable needs: "Technology, as always, can serve them." There has also been in Western civilization a perception of man *in* nature and a belief that he should seek understanding of his true needs and welfare through science. But this has been a minor current in a mainstream that uses science as servant rather than as teacher.

How science is used depends in large measure upon how its meaning is interpreted in the processes of formalized education. Science has been a potent influence upon education, but educational theory and practice have also shaped the course of science. Today more than ever the development of science depends not only upon the amount but also upon the nature of the incentives and support accorded it in the educational structure. For example, progress in fields as apparently diverse as medicine, human relations, and city planning is currently retarded because of past neglect of the environmental sciences. Interpretation of the implications and the needs of science to educators and to the public at large therefore becomes a crucial element in the advancement of science as well as of society.

The expansion, specialization, and diversification of biology and of all other sciences multiplies the difficulties of communication. New sciences create a need for new syntheses to relate and interpret their findings. New interdisciplinary areas take shape to deal with the new questions emerging between diverging sciences. In time, many of these interdisciplinary areas develop into coherent disciplines—into new sciences—and the process of specialization and of divergent and emergent disciplines continues.

Throughout this process direct and meaningful communication between the highly specialized research scientist and the public-policy-maker becomes ever harder to achieve. Popularizers of science have appeared in response to popular need and interest. But their status is as uncertain as their role is difficult. The best of them may find careers in journalism and may win recognition among scientists for informed and competent reporting. But there is at present little room for them in the structure of formalized education even though the need for better communication between science and the rest of society is now widely recognized.

The problem of how to organize this communication is yet to be solved. This is perhaps because communication is not merely exchange of information. And information is itself more than mere data; it is data plus meaning, intended and understood. The possession of scientific knowledge holds no promise of its use in discovering the true needs of men or in serving the public happiness or welfare. There is need for more knowledge but even greater need for more understanding.

Development of valid and coherent concepts of man-in-nature requires an interrelating and a synthesizing of knowledge. It is a task of interpretative leadership. Committees of specialists may assist the clarification and integration of knowledge, but synthesizing insights and perceptions more often originate in the minds of individuals who only then can become the expositors, the interpreters, and the advocates of a new view of man and nature. This mediating role between science, ethics, and public policy may be filled in various ways by persons from varied backgrounds—from the sciences, from professional education, from philosophy, religion, or public affairs.

Among the more effective intermediaries between science and ethics in political life have been those public servants who have in their own ways been "biopoliticians" in the best sense. These men and women have not only seen a relationship between scientific knowledge and the public welfare, but they have acted on this insight to influence the course of public policy. One may cite as examples Harvey W. Wiley's crusade for pure food and drugs, Hugh H. Bennett's lessons in soil conservation, and Ira Gabrielson's labors to substitute science for folklore in the management of wildlife. In each of these instances and in more that could be cited, scientific knowledge, a fundamentally ethical perception, and skill in communication were fused in effective policy leadership.

Granted that some aspects of biopolitics rest upon solid scientific support, the fact remains that we have not yet laid down a comprehensive biological foundation upon which a "science of mankind" can safely be erected. The scientific basis of biopolicy is fragmentary and will most likely remain so until the need for a comprehensive, verifiable, conceptual foundation for a healthful, creative, self-renewing society is more widely felt than it is today.

Better popular understanding of the biological factors in society should follow from a more accurate popular comprehension of science in the broadest sense. George Gaylord Simpson has pointed out the integrating role of biology among the sciences: life is the phenomenon to which all principles of science apply. In certain specialized areas of biology, notably in relation to agriculture and medicine, there has been a continuous flow of knowledge from the laboratory to practical application. The histories of the agricultural extension service and of the public health movement in the United States afford cases in point. But the dual explosions of population and biology create a much broader need for the desirable kind of biopolitics that has been so effective in particular cases. To achieve this objective may require new machinery in government. More certainly, it will entail changes in the structure and content of formal education and the addition of new elements to the career development of teachers and public officials who in the long run are among the principal architects of public policy.

It is neither possible nor necessary to examine here the ways in which the machinery of government might more effectively promote and utilize scientific knowledge. Relations between science and government have been analyzed at length and are under study by several Congressional committees. There is agreement in principle that government must be adapted to the new conditions wrought by science, but less agreement on what changes should be made. The United States Public Health Service's proposed Center for Environmental Health illustrates how the growth of knowledge calls forth new agencies to extend and apply that knowledge.

The changes in education that are needed to bridge the gap between biology and politics are more clearly evident. Throughout the modern world communication and understanding suffer greatly from gaps in the structure of education—gaps that appear with specialization and with divergence among the sciences and between them and the humanities. But even C. P. Snow's pessimistic analysis of "the two cultures"—the sciences and the humanities—does not postulate a gap that is unbridgeable. And it can be argued that the structuring of knowledge in Western society is a major factor in the cleavage that he has dramatized.

There is perhaps no *one* best way to obtain a more adequate communication among the disciplines and a more effective integration of related knowledge. Among the older disciplines changes in concept and emphasis may be needed as, for example, in geography where the discredited "environmentalism" of the past generation is being replaced by search for a more valid basis for understanding man-environment relationships. We may also need new disciplines to interpenetrate the older ones—to give us syntheses—to provide the form and substance of a more comprehensive understanding of man and nature. The beginnings of answers to these needs may be discerned in some aspects of the behavioral sciences and in the emerging environmental sciences—some, such as ecology hitherto relatively neglected; others such as biometeorology, regional economics and outer-space environmental research, relatively new in concept and method.

If the conditions for a better biopolitics require more realistic popular perceptions of man-in-nature, one way to assist this popular understanding is through the re-education and training of teachers, public officials, and opinion leaders. Updating and improvement of the teaching of biology has been for some time a subject for attention by the American Institute of Biological Sciences. The development of an awareness and comprehension of the significance of scientific developments by persons *outside* the fields of science is a different although related problem. Both developments are needed in strengthening the foundation for an enlightened biopolitics.

An important but relatively neglected avenue toward broader public understanding of science is adult education in its various forms. There is special need for an interpretation of science in its most fundamental sense to be built into career development programs for executive officials in government, business, labor, and the professions. Science (and particularly the biological sciences) has heretofore received comparatively little attention in these efforts, possibly because the relevance of the sciences to most fields of career development has not been fully appreciated. If mankind is rapidly confronted by unprecedented possibilities growing out of biological research and by increasing difficulties resulting from increasing populations, the need for biopolitical reorientation may soon gain a general recognition that it does not now enjoy. But this task of reorientation will not be done well unless the implications of biology can be reduced to terms and concepts meaningful for public policy.

To bring about an up-dating of the biopolitical understandings of teachers and leaders in public affairs, a valid conceptualizing, interpretative educational leadership will be needed. Some of the leadership may come, as it has, from government itself. More will need to come from the universities, the learned professions, and research institutes. For it should not be inferred that biology offers ready answers to all the problems it defines or its applied technology creates. Closing the gaps of knowledge and restructuring that knowledge for attack upon new or persistent biopolitical problems will be, even more obviously than it has already been, a multidisciplinary task.

Some eminent scientists have shown skill in relating science to social needs and ethical values. But these extraordinary individuals have been too few and too infrequent to accomplish unaided the task of bridging the gaps between bioscience and biopolitics, between science and society. The sheer mass and specialized complexity of expanding knowledge create a need for a systematic and continuing effort toward synthesis from which intelligible conceptualization and communication may be forthcoming. As yet the task is barely attempted and then in only a few places.

Does all this then imply the need for a "science" of biopolitics for purposes quite the opposite of those suggested by J. P. Miller? The answer is both yes and no. It is no if biopolitics is understood *only* as a new formal academic discipline to deal comprehensively with social applications of biological knowledge. This is not to say that such a discipline is unnecessary—or would be impractical—or that it could not be developed. We have been concerned here with the problems and the needs suggested by the term "biopolitics," with general approaches to solutions rather than with specific remedial methods. But if a science termed "biopolitics" is not specifically implied, the need should be evident for a more effective relating of the biological to the social sciences and of both to public policy and ethics.

Without the interrelation and distillation of scientific findings into issues amenable to political action, the gap between science and politics cannot be successfully bridged. Science as technology may be readily available to the lower and more routinized levels of administration. But at the higher executive and legislative levels of the governmental hierarchy where the broad public policies are formulated, the science most relevant to the issues will be more conceptual than technical. The impact of scientific thought upon public policy will in large measure depend upon its being expressed in terms meaningful to political and administrative practitioners. The legislator and public administrator must make their own policy syntheses, but they can do their jobs more effectively if the data relevant to these decisions have been organized and reduced to understandable terms. The case for aid to the administrator in his task of synthesis has been stated with exceptional clarity by Paul H. Appleby:

> Specialist after specialist pursues analysis; who pursues synthesis, or even pursues analysis with any sensible orientation to the larger function of synthesis? It is the synthesis which involves all the heavy burdens of practitioners, and these burdens are heaviest when the social action is most complex and most complexly environed. Synthesis becomes more and more important as one goes up the hierarchy, and more and more important as one moves from the relatively specialized fields of private administration to public administration.

This synthesis does not necessarily require new sciences. Ecology, for example, has long been an established if insufficiently utilized "organizing" science. Its further development and involvement with the social sciences could provide much of the needed synthesis. It also seems probable that new emphases will emerge in established disciplines, that interdisciplinary studies will increase, and that new formalized disciplines may emerge. New arrangements to facilitate interdisciplinary studies involving synthesis of the social and biological sciences and relevant professional fields—notably architecture, engineering, public health, and natural resources administration—are already under consideration in a number of universities. From these developments might come major contributions to the formulation of public policy in the years ahead.

"Biopolitics" therefore suggests a need that may be met in many different ways. It would be difficult to argue that existing educational resources are adequate. But because few educational needs can be shown to be fully served, the question will be asked: How important is this underdeveloped area of biopolitics in relation to other unfulfilled educational demands? Restating biopolitics in broader terms as study of the role of science in society, its priority is of the highest. We have been paying heavy and steadily rising prices in dollars, health, and happiness for its relative neglect, and have entered, inadequately prepared, upon a decisive test of our capacity to avoid becoming the victims of our own ingenuity.

The "condition that confronts us" calls for more than the mere tolerance of imaginative innovation in reshaping and accelerating the education of society. Tangible and timely encouragement is needed for pathbreaking efforts, for the ever risky tasks of synthesis, for the continuing development of creative individuals capable of conceptualizing and interpreting the issues that arise at the meeting point of science, ethnics and politics. The study of biopolitics—whatever it may be called—requires an extraordinary fusion of understanding, audacity, and humility.

EDWARD T. CHASE
Politics and Technology

At last there is a dawning realization that in the United States it is rapid technological change rather than ideological strife or even economics that is building up a fundamental political crisis. This realization is evidenced in several recent symposiums involving a number of the outstanding thinkers of the times and by recent executive acts and legislation with far-reaching implications. What is happening is that technology's effects are suddenly calling into question the viability of our political institutions to a degree unknown at least since the Civil War.

There is a growing awareness that tomorrow's political convulsion will be different from what doctrinaires, obsessed with dated rhetoric about socialism vs. capitalism, have led us to expect, because it derives from the cumulative impact of technology, an impact that is impersonal, nonideological, relentless, and possibly overwhelming. Above all else our political adaptability and inventiveness are being challenged by technology. This point has seldom been demonstrated more dramatically than by last summer's Senate filibuster growing out of the dispute over whether AT&T or the government should dominate the control of the communications space satellite. Such perplexity and passion were fomented by the power problem created by this particular technological triumph as to immobilize the political process for days, until cloture was invoked in the Senate for the first time in 35 years.

Examples of political consternation provoked by technology are becoming pervasive. They range from the familiar to the esoteric. How, for instance, does a free society force human and land resources out of agriculture to adjust to the realities of modern scientific farming? And does a free society make the massive, explosive problem of retraining workers displaced by automation the responsibility of state. governments or the national government or industry, or some ingenious combination of all? Again, when technological unemployment in combination with scientific medicine produces a growing population of "retired" elderly persons in an urbanized, wage-based industrial society, how will their heavy medical costs for the inevitable chronic ills of old age be financed? Or when an essential public service is threatened with extinction as a paying proposition, owing to fatal competition from more advanced technology, is the government helpless, as in the case of the New Haven Railroad, or will our political leaders devise some successful expedient without incurring a constitutional crisis? Again, is our incapacity to adjust politically such that we must forego manifest social gains from technological progress—as almost happened in the Hanford, Washington, atomic power plant case, where an invaluable supply of reactor-generated steam for creating electricity would have been wasted had there not been an eleventh hour political resolution of the conflict between private and government ownership? When completed in 1965, this will be the world's largest nuclear power plant. The plant will be the locus of further political controversy soon over the question of what particular industries the electric power will be used for. Use in one category of industry will result in 5,000 new jobs; use in another in 10,000 new jobs; and in still another category 36,000 new jobs. Not the "market" but a conscious deliberation by officials will resolve the issue.

This Hanford example, like the communications space satellite debate, introduces problems with political implications of a new order of complexity for American society. Yet already it is being widely sensed that they are only the beginning. To be sure, man has long had to make gradual social adaptation to technological change. It is the exponential rate of change today that is uniquely challenging to our political superstructure.

What is perhaps most conducive to political controversy is the fact that advancing technology is beginning to promise immediate practical solutions to hitherto insoluble frustrations, if it is given the chance. As a practical matter there must first be expensive studies of the feasibility of technological innovations and then funds appropriated for research and development. If, as is increasingly the case, these funds must be substantial and there is no promise of relatively quick profit, then the market mechanism simply does not become engaged. Only the government can undertake the enterprise. It is true that in a modern mixed economy this does not invariably create a political dilemma. But in the United States it does more frequently than not. There may be no immediate political repercussions from the unusual amount of attention President Kennedy has been giving to conquering the problem of turning brackish and sea water into usable water. Seventy-five million dollars is being spent by the Office of Saline Water to ascertain the best of a number of competing commercial processes. Nor would there be a formidable political problem in governmental support, say, for eradicating malaria from the world (3 million deaths annually, 300 million people afflicted), which is something distinctly within reach at a cost of only $50 million spread over a ten-year period.

But consider the political reverberations should the government undertake the rescue operation that could be consummated for our moribund textile industry if technology were subsidized—as is being seriously considered in Washington—to master the task of applying high speed electronic computers to our textile looms, thus rendering American textiles competitive in the world market. Comparable practical achievements are within reach in a score of areas, were it not for the political obstacles—for instance, the revival of our East Coast shipping industry by the use of fast hydrofoil ships now anchored on drawing boards for lack of developmental money, ships quite capable of out-performing trucks (hence offering some relief to the traffic problem); or, for another example, creating a major new source of high protein food by making a systematic effort to harvest the ocean.

The questions posed by these considerations are ultimately and essentially political. They go to the heart of the political problem of how a democratic government, one that is both responsive and responsible, reconciles technological promise with the will of the public. For decisions have to be made as to what public resources are to be devoted to what technological ventures—and who is to make the choice. Throughout the lifetime of the United States, our tradition has been to depend upon the market mechanism to register the people's choices. It is the doctrine of consumer sovereignty, the revered "invisible hand" (which economist Robert Heilbroner usefully characterizes as a system "to mobilize and allocate human energies and to distribute the social produce in a manner to assure society of its continued existence"). However, the evidence is now becoming overwhelming that the traditional market mechanism of supply and demand, for all its uncanny power to articulate the public will, simply is not up to reflecting the long-range values that have to be weighed if a rational use is to be made of the new technology. The point is that this is not a doctrinaire matter, a sly triumph by creeping socialists; it is a result of technological change.

The underlying dilemma arises from the fact that a democratic government must be responsive to the present electorate, yet, since it makes decisions that determine the impact of technology upon the environment of succeeding generations, it must also be responsive to future electorates.

Government is now facing situations with increasing frequency where currently popular practices sanctioned by the market system (exploitation of natural resources is an obvious example) must be modified for the sake of this future. Rachel Carson's *Silent Spring,* about the devastating ecological impact of pesticides, has wonderfully dramatized this issue.

This is to put the matter negatively, however. The political problem is not so much a matter of placing restraints on technology. It stems more from the fact that positive forces are now building up that urge us to circumvent the market mechanism and apply public funds directly to technology, as traditionally we have done only in wartime. What is slowly being realized is that the support of technology cannot any longer be confined to what the public wants. After all, the public can only choose alternatives among things it knows; it simply does not know enough to project its wants into the future, with the result that the market mechanism cannot be depended upon to nourish technological development. For the first time in our history the government has set up a unit, called the Panel on Civilian Technology, responsive to this fact. This little-known operation was established strictly for the purpose of encouraging technological innovation on the premise that new technology, as much as or more than new plant and equipment investment, is what stimulates economic growth. The 18-man panel, composed of industrialists, academics, and bureaucrats, is especially concerned with four industries suffering from technological lag—textiles, coal, housing, and transport. It reports to science adviser Jerome Wiesner, to economic adviser Walter Heller, and to Commerce Secretary Luther Hodges. It has already become a center of controversy in certain planning circles because of its first report, on urban transportation, in which it argues against support for rail transit and instead favors express buses on exclusive rights of way.

The political inhibitions to direct government subsidy on any substantial scale remain enormous, of course. Suggestions such as those made at a Brookings Institution symposium on "The Uses of Economics"—suggestions for revitalizing our lagging economy by having the government finance research and development in areas like communications, transport, food, and industrial production—are still widely judged as heresy. In business circles they are viewed as the sure road to Communist despotism.

"To what extent should government finance or subsidize industrial research in general, or for certain industries as it has already done so productively for agriculture and defense?" asked Charles J. Hitch, former Chairman of the Research Council of the RAND corporation, at the Brookings meeting. Now an Assistant Secretary of Defense, Hitch went on to say that "relatively small expenditures" for deliberately planned research and development in the military sector "have been staggeringly, alarmingly, productive. . . . I have tried to think of any reasons why the military area should be unique in this respect; I can think of none. That it is not is suggested by our somewhat similar experience in agriculture, though on a much smaller scale. I suspect that there has been a serious misallocation of resources and that it corresponds to economists' misallocation of their effort between problems of investment and problems of technological change." Coming from so highly placed a representative of the power elite, these are words calculated to give pause. Hitch was impressively seconded in his main sentiments by Francis M. Bator, of M.I.T., whose cool disparagement of laissez-faire markets as an effective allocator of resources went unchallenged.

A fruitful way to gain a perspective on the force-feeding of technology by government is to recall the attitude of the ancient Greeks toward science. They viewed science as sacred knowledge. And, since the Greek city states placed a premium upon political and social stability, the esoteric knowledge of science, the secret of manipulating nature, was confined to the few so as to preclude the social and political disruptions bound to follow in the wake of any widespread applications of technology. Everything had to be secondary to the ideal of a stable social order.

Now between this attitude and the modern American attitude the contrast is extreme. Our operating assumption has been that the essence of the free society is to encourage the unfettered intelligence and to accept all discoveries and their applications. Whether this attitude can be maintained is beginning to be insistently questioned today for the first time. Is our capacity for political inventiveness equal to the challenge of devising new political forms, alignments, and procedures that can deal effectively with technology and simultaneously preserve democratic vitality? In three recent symposiums organized independently of one another and along quite different lines, one in Santa Barbara, another in Boston, and the third at Arden House, Harriman, New York, the common subject was the social impact of new technology. These were three highly instructive sessions, illuminating many of the conundrums under scrutiny here. The imperative but largely unanswered question that eventually emerged in all these meetings was the question of *political* control, with special emphasis upon the relations between the private sector and government.

One might assume that there is already a substantial literature on technology's impact on politics. To be sure, there are numerous allusions to it in the late-blooming literature about the changes technology has brought about in social and cultural relations (though not even a professional journal on this subject existed until 1958, when *Technology and Culture* was founded). But there are no full-scale treatments of the specifically political relationship. Economist Heilbroner (at the Arden House meeting) noted that "the steady invasion of technology is the commanding reality that shapes the economic relation of man to nature in our day; how extraordinary, then, that the two most important economists of fullblown capitalism, Alfred Marshall and Lord Keynes, have virtually nothing to say about the impact of technology on the economic system!" No doubt the key to the absence of a literature on the impact of technology on politics is due to the fact that political structure is essentially reactive to economic forces, and only lately has there even been any explicit acknowledgment of technology's undermining of the market system.

In any event, the division of opinion over the fundamentally political problem of whether man does or even can control technology became sharp and even impassioned in these symposiums. Lewis Mumford produced a characteristically eloquent paper for the Santa Barbara meeting pleading for the precedence of humanist direction. Wrote Mumford: "The quantitative over-production of both material and intellectual goods poses, immediately for the Western World, ultimately for all mankind, a new problem: the problem of regulation, distribution, assimilation, integration, teleological direction." In Mumford's view, "The most dangerous notion an age of automation can entertain is the belief that machines have goals of their own, to which man must submit if he knows what's best for him." His colleague at Santa Barbara, author and scientist Sir Robert Watson-Watt, echoed this with the words, "There can, in fact, be no more disastrous undermining of the human condition than that of regarding technology as a self-propagated, self-propelled entity not fully controllable by the appropriately designed agencies of the body politic."

The University of Bordeaux's Jacques Ellul, the chief spokesman at the Santa Barbara symposium for the view that man really no longer has any control over technology, caricatured the humanists in this passage from his hotly discussed paper: "An idea frequently to be encountered in superficial inquiries concerning Technique (technology) is the following: 'At bottom everything depends on the way Technique is employed; mankind has only to use Technique for the good and avoid using it for the bad.'" Ellul's paper is a demonstration of the, to him, impossible task of discerning the ultimate effects of technology and hence of bringing it under effective rational control. He contends that control eludes us because we never can foresee all the consequences of a given technological innovation.

The project that seems to have excited the chief alarm among the Santa Barbara participants is "Operation Chariot," the Atomic Energy Commission's plan to build a harbor by an atomic explosion. Professor Ritchie Calder of Edinburgh cited this project as exemplifying the demonic tendency of technology. It carries man along with it at a furious, mindless pace, unchecked because the public is ignorant of the full results of the project. Calder recoils at the prospect of what he calls "pseudo-technologists" such as the Atomic Energy Commission making decisions, since they have vested interests in the very technology they should be helping us to control. Calder speaks of humanity being at the mercy of "the faceless men at the elbow of the uninformed." Professor Richard L. Meier of Michigan, a specialist in resource conservation, takes comfort in his belief that there are at least 500 people of Ph.D. level in government bureaucracies dedicated to preventing the misuse of technology. The "throttling process" they carry on suppresses the bad ideas like "Operation Chariot." Professor Melvin Kranzberg contended that the fact that the RAND Corporation has been asked by the Pentagon to study the social implications of technology is most encouraging. Robert M. Hutchins, never one to suffer facile optimism gladly, complained that although the difficulties for humanity if technology is not controlled had been made clear enough, no one had yet succeeded in outlining a program for control "which would not be subject to the charge that it might be worse for the human race than technology unchecked."

Between the pessimists and the optimists it is possible to identify a pragmatic bridge or middle position. It has nowhere been better exemplified than in comments by Columbia philosopher Charles Frankel made at the 1961 National Conference on Social Welfare. Frankel takes off from the premise that "the justification of a system of decentralized capitalist competition is that it energizes and makes possible the spirit of invention and innovation. That system seems to be working very well and as a result not only do we have technological unemployment *but we can count on it as a normal feature and sign that our system is doing well.* It is the price we pay for our success, the inevitable defect that goes with our virtue."

Frankel does not say we can foresee all the consequences of technological innovation. But he does say we have known for some time now that the social impact of technology is dislocating, and therefore we should not panic, treating the dislocations as an "accident," as "something that shouldn't happen." Instead, we should deliberately establish permanent preventive institutions carefully designed to cope with such dislocations as we can anticipate. In this instance his concern was with technological disemployment, and he called for retraining and relocation agencies not created in an *"ad hoc* and retrospective basis" but as standing agencies no less a permanent and fully articulated part of our institutional framework than our school systems.

An effort along these lines is getting under way with the launching of the Manpower Development and Training Act under the newly created Office of Manpower, Automation and Training. It is one of the most significant pieces of legislation in recent years, since for the first time it establishes the national government's responsibility for the reemployment of a labor force wracked by technological change. Not only does this act provide for $435 millions over three years to retrain 400,000 of the hard core unemployed; it marks the advent of a Federal program that manpower experts in Washington say will have no end because so rapid is the pace of technology that workers must anticipate new jobs in new industries perhaps a half-dozen different times in their working lives. As (then) Labor Secretary Arthur Goldberg observed of it, "For the first time in our history we are setting out to make opportunity a matter of design, and not chance." In the Congressional hearings on the law, conservative critics expressed anxiety that this was the beginning of an unprecedented control over the nation's manpower by the central government. The law does in fact mean that a government functionary and not the individual retrainee determines what skill the latter is to be taught. It is decided on the basis of known manpower needs and on a judgment of the retrainee's potential.

Frankel's paradoxical plea is for energetic centralized planning for the express purpose of avoiding political despotism. Such planning, says Frankel, must be shaped by the goal of lessening the inevitable disruptive impact of technology and the resultant pressure for political relief through oppressively authoritarian measures. "The pressures toward centralization in our society are very great," he stated. "Without deliberate planning at the center they are going to become greater. The policies of dealing with emergencies, of creating *ad hoc* measures for problem after problem, multiply restrictions, regulations, laws and inhibitions on human energy. People misunderstand the true purpose of sound social planning. The purpose is to simplify, to rationalize, to provide a stable set of alternatives in which individuals are freer to act in security and in the exercises of their freedom of choice."

It was writer Joseph Kraft, a participant at the Boston symposium on technology, who made most concrete and vivid the need for a new political superstructure if we are to manage the new technology. He made a plea reminiscent of Frankel's for new institutions to control and direct technological change, but on a grander scale than Frankel. The author of *The Grand Design: From Common Market to Atlantic Partnership,* Kraft spoke with enthusiasm of the "important political advance" represented by the European Economic Commission, on the one hand, and the Council of Ministers, on the other. The Commission consists of highly skilled technicians. The Council is a supranational body of ministers of state charged with making the political decisions of the European Economic Community. What has impressed Kraft about the Common Market is how its political framework enables it to adjust to technological change expeditiously and rationally. He cites the fact that, with the adoption of a common agricultural policy last January, the result in the next decade will be to move a million and a half inefficient West German farmers off the farm and into labor-short industry, as France's much more efficient farmers come to dominate Continental agriculture. His point is that this necessary and rational development would never have been possible if conventional German politics, with its powerful farm lobby, had prevailed. *What has happened, in effect, is that the technical experts of the European Economic Commission have become a permanent political lobby in favor of rational response to technological change.* The European Economic Commission is able to function so effectively because the Council of Ministers, being a supranational body, can then bring immense pressure to bear upon the individual governments to adopt the Commission's recommendations. For then the individual government, in this instance the West German government, says to the farmers, in Kraft's words, "Look, we understand your interests and are doing the best we can, but we don't have absolute control. There are these other people we have to consider."

Kraft sees the Commission and the Council as "an international system for diluting the responsibility of the individual governments" and thus enabling these national governments to go along with the reforms which conventional politics would otherwise have precluded. He sees the merging of the six Common Market powers as resulting, almost by accident, in a providential device for coping with technological change and feels that some such political device must be found by the United States if it is to overcome such standing blocks to progress as our inability to solve problems like subsidized farming, tax loopholes for industry, and featherbedding labor.

As a perceptive journalist, Kraft is impressed by how conventional political obstruction to needed technological adjustments has us currently immobilized in so many important areas. Herman Somers, the Haverford College political scientist, sharply questioned Kraft's evaluation of the Common Market experience. He contended that Kraft was saying nothing more than that parliamentary procedures were simply in temporary suspension when the Economic Commission's decisions were carried out and that as the Common Market countries evolved from an economic to a political unity the same "obstructionism" of parliamentary deliberation would again prevail. Neither he nor Kraft could then clarify how to escape the dilemma. Their colleague at the Boston symposium, economist and historian Robert Heilbroner (also prominent as a writer for the Arden House symposium), sees the impact of technology essentially as mortally challenging the traditional role of the market system as the organizer and arbiter of our political and social order.

In a prophetic concluding essay elaborating his viewpoint in his new book *The Making of Economic Society,* Heilbroner, like Gerard Piel at the Santa Barbara symposium and Bator at Brookings, sees the market mechanism as having "declining functional relevance" in a society of advanced technology: "The market is an assiduous servant of the wealthy consumer, but an indifferent servant of the poor one. Thus it presents us with the anomaly of a surplus of luxury housing existing side-by-side with a shortage of inexpensive housing, although the social need for the latter is incontestably greater than for the former. Or it pours energy and resources into the multiplication of luxuries for which the wealthier classes offer a market, while allowing more basic needs of the poor to go unheeded and unmet. . . . These shortcomings are all indicative of a central weakness of the market system—its inability to formulate public needs above those of the market place." Hence planning arises in the advanced market society which has mastered technology precisely to offset that society's inherent goal-setting weakness.

Technology further accentuates this goal-setting or planning deficiency of the market mechanism for two reasons. First, as Heilbroner puts it, "In a society of very great abundance, not only these cultivated desires but even the basic incentive to maximize income or minimize expenditures may well lose the ability to direct human behavior. (Who will clean the sewers and handle the garbage, for instance?) In that event the market system would cease to wield its necessary control over individual action, and society would have to look to some other means of social control to insure the necessary accomplishment of its basic tasks." It was apropos of this that RAND economist Charles Hitch at the Brookings symposium asserted, "If we don't have an adequate theory of efficiency in a non-market economy, and we certainly don't, it is high time we developed one." Hence the underlying theme of all the symposiums—the impending political crisis.

A recurrent note was that technology demands central planning because it presents a bewildering array of alternative actions and because it creates an enormously complex order in which all enterprises are interdependent, with each action exerting a chain reaction. A political superstructure capable of central planning becomes essential if only to prevent chaos. This is to express it defensively. The offensive was taken, as noted earlier, first at the Brookings symposium on economics, which served as a platform for suggestions that technological research and development be directly organized by the government so as to achieve planned socio-economic goals. At Santa Barbara the same note was sounded (and occasioned profound alarm) and the "declining functional relevance" of the market system was implicit throughout the discussions. There economist Robert Theobald quoted a Stanford Research Institute report to the United States Senate as follows: "We have invented the art of systematic invention. Organized scientific research and development, which has become a great industry in the last few decades, is itself one of the most significant social inventions of the twentieth century. It is unlocking the secrets of nature and putting the knowledge to practical use at an unprecedented rate. Also we have invented the art of systematic innovation."

The tremendous extent to which the United States is already devoting its treasure to technological advance under direct government auspices was recently shown in the testimony of Dr. Jerome Wiesner, the Director of the Office of Science and Technology, before the House Committee on Government Operations:

> This fiscal year the President proposes to put about $12.3 billion into research and development—more in one year than the Federal Government spent for research and development during the entire interval from the American Revolution through and including World War II. This $12.3 billion, although representing but 15 percent of the total Federal budget, is in effect well over one-third of that portion of the budget which is susceptible to control; for a great part of the budget, as we all know, is inevitably committed to fixed requirements such as debt retirement, etc. In addition, the Government now accounts for at least two-thirds of the Nation's entire annual expenditure in research. That is, the Federal Government spends twice as much for research and development as all of industry, universities and private foundations combined. This budget is not only large, but it has been growing at an unprecedented rate—for what in 1950 amounted to $1.2 billion has grown in the intervening 13 years by a factor of 10.

One great effect of this has been clearly explained by Professors J. S. Dupre and W. E. Gustafson of Harvard in a paper entitled "Contracting for Defense" (*Political Science Quarterly,* June 1962). "The government has had to devise new standards in its contractual relationships with business firms. Essentially, the government now assumes the financial risk involved in innovation. Free competition no longer characterizes the process of bidding for government contracts. While private firms have thus been freed from the restraints of the open market, they have acquired new public responsibilities. They are no longer merely suppliers to the government, but participants in the administration of public functions."

What is happening is that in the past companies competed on a bid basis in the open market for government contracts. Now, with immensely complicated projects whose evolution and ultimate costs can only be roughly surmised in advance, contracting firms negotiate agreements with the government to be reimbursed for costs. These firms are selected not on a price basis so much as on a basis of technical expertise, on their management calibre and their facilities. This is posing very delicate political issues with respect to conflict of interest. "Such public goals as cost control, the insurance of competition, and protection for small business all come into conflict with the profit motives," note Dupre and Gustafson. They point out that a prime contractor must take on management responsibilities in the public interest that are unnatural for a profit-seeking, competitive corporation. As prime contractor the firm has to make all kinds of judgments in acting as the overall coordinator. All the while it has to think of its own fortunes, for example in successfully competing for future contracts, and this accentuates its reluctance to make information available to participating contractors who may later be competitors.

Action has recently been taken by the executive branch responsive to precisely this situation in another instance of political decision following directly upon the admonitions of the academic community. In September the Defense Department announced that firms doing research-and-development work ("the lackeys of the death industry," as they were referred to at Santa Barabara) were to be barred from competing also for "hardware" contracts. This is a far-reaching decision because it puts at least a temporary halt upon the practice of nonprofit corporations created by the government from intruding on the lucrative engineering and technical work of the established defense companies. This decision is the first to emerge from the analysis of the government's research and development program being undertaking by a committee headed by former Budget Director David E. Bell. The committee's underlying concern is the increasingly blurred dividing line between the economy's public and private sectors.

Dupre and Gustafson conclude that "business is no longer merely a supplier but a participant in the management and administration of a public function . . . negotiation and cost reimbursement have channeled public money into the private sector *without the use of the market mechanism. Business, like government, must then become subject to non-economic checks to avoid abuses.*" *What* non-economic checks is the precise question before the house, of course.

In his testimony to Congress pleading for more money to pay for scientists, Wiesner said that the step-up in government-subsidized research and development was bound to accelerate quite apart from defense or space work because it has now become clear that our rate of eonomic growth is increasingly dependent upon technological development. All the technology meetings noted the increased dependence of the economic growth rate on technological development. John T. Dunlop, the Harvard economist who edited the book on the Arden House symposium, said: "The industry of discovery opens up a new vista of the long future in which substantial resources in increasing amounts are devoted systematically to . . . reshaping the physical environment of mankind and to providing increased living standards and cultural opportunities . . . the rise of the industry of discovery suggests that we should be able to look forward to doubling productivity and living standards . . . every fifteen years (a rise from 3 to 5 percent in the yearly growth rate). These potentials underscore the common gains to be shared by increasing productivity and the possibilities of insuring adequately those who bear the costs of the adverse initial impacts of some technological changes. The industry of discovery also raises a host of issues and questions which are slowly coming to the fore. . . . *To what extent shall the direction of invention be left to the individual spirit and curiosity, to the market, and to what extent directed by priorities established by what bodies?"*

Thus the signs are accumulating that we are on the threshold of an increasingly hot and divisive national debate on this very question and that it may very well bring us to the brink of a constitutional crisis which cannot yet be precisely envisioned but will focus on the relations between the executive and legislative branches. It will be the central domestic issue of the 1960's and the 1970's. The manner in which the question is answered will determine our governmental framework for a generation, and especially the pattern of relationships between the national government and the other great power center, business, the administrator of the market system.

How distant, really, is the time when, as Robert Theobald stressed at Santa Barbara, the issues of biological and genetic control will be forced upon the agenda of government responsibilities under such prods as the population explosion of the senile and chronically ill, the possibilities of organ transplants, new miracle drugs and artificial insemination? Professor Somers cites the work of the British physician Ffrangcon Roberts, an expert on medical economics, who uses the wry term "medicated survival" to describe technology's accomplishments in forestalling death. He sees the market system as nourishing "antiplutic medicine," that is, treatment wherein society remains burdened despite treatment because the disease is congenital or the result of old age—"antiplutic" since the very success of the treatment exacerbates the cost to society. But the examples need hardly be so esoteric. The pressures are mounting behind such familiar questions (forcefully raised at Boston) as whether a decentralized democracy traditionally infatuated with "local initiative" can cope with automotive congestion, originating across different state and city boundaries; or whether, as open land in metropolitan areas shrinks, we can devise institutions to prevent corrupting land uses; or whether the potential of television, now about to become international, is indefinitely to be determined by its effectiveness as a sales instrument for advertisers.

As the inadequacies of the market system become increasingly evident under the impact of technological change, there is a developing consensus that we are bound to witness a kind of intervention now feared by most Americans. Practically the only precedent we have for it is the Employment Act of 1946, which for the first time in Federal law stipulated that full employment and equitable income distribution were to become an explicit governmental concern rather than be left up to the market system. That law was passed in response to the national anxiety that the economy would falter with the end of wartime spending. (As it turned out, massive pent-up consumer demand more than compensated.) It was no radical dismissal of our system, but rather an acknowledgement that, in an age of technological disruption, supplementation of the market system by political action is essential for rational allocation of resources and the meeting of public needs. This year's Manpower Development and Training Act is the most important addition to the law so far.

Almost certainly we are also going to witness the development of a new kind of national economic budget going beyond annual Federal accounting (what we essentially do now) to set forth a five or six year projection of all our national resources viewed against out national goals. We will then have something close to national programming of explicit policies, in which the overriding consideration will be the role of new technology.

Just what government body will emerge as the key agency for national planning no one could say now. But it could conceivably be the President's Council of Economic Advisers, a Council further strengthened by law and with vastly increased responsibilities and powers. It is such a body that must to a substantial extent fulfill the crucial function the European Economic Commission fulfills for the Common Market. One of the best prescriptions for such an agency as this is developed in the extraordinarily penetrating statement on automation issued by the Research Section of the Industrial Union Department, AFL-CIO. It calls for "A Permanent Commission on Technological Change" to act as "a central clearing house in which there will be gathered, analyzed, and evaluated, all pertinent information on public and private plans involving technological change." It would operate within the executive branch of the national government. Recently Arthur Burns, the former economic adviser to President Eisenhower, came forward with a surprisingly similar proposal.

The development of any such planning body and such a new kind of national economic budget to cope with technological change will no doubt create and be part of a great political ferment. But by then the domestic political context may also have been modified somewhat to ease the impact. For example, in the years immediately ahead we can anticipate some modernization of the organization of Congress. As the reapportionment movement slowly eliminates the most egregious abuses and begins to alter the complexion of our government, it may in time modify the American custom of putting local interests ahead of the national interest.

We will also witness the growing power of a new constituency in the electorate, a constituency created by technology itself. I refer to the burgeoning army of scientists and other intellectual workers of the new technological order. If Professor Daniel Bell of Columbia, a participant at the Boston symposium on technology where he first unveiled his now much-discussed vision of the "post-industrial society," is correct—and his statistically-awesome arguments were compelling—this new constituency will soon come to rival the dominant voice of the past, the business community. The rise of this constituency could be the most important single political development of the new technology. Dr. James R. Killian, Jr., Wiesner's predecessor as Presidential science adviser, has urged that scientists run for Congress. Noting that they have begun to appear in state legislatures, Killian suggested that a technological society must have scientists "in the public arena if it is to deal wisely with all the great policy matters arising out of science and technology."

In any event, one thing is clearer day by day. The American instinct for freedom, the talent of political inventiveness permitting a maximum of individual freedom combined with optimum collective performance, is to be put to a rugged test. To meet the test we will have to arrive at a far better comprehension of the full impact of technology. With planning to a much larger extent superseding the market mechanism as the director of our energies, there is bound to be much more discussion as to what worthy ends our political and social institutions should serve. There will be a growing consciousness that, as Robert Oppenheimer recently elaborated in his piece on science and culture in *Encounter*, whereas technology is a cumulative process ever building on its advances and thus moves only in the direction of progress, our moral and political life lacks cumulative growth and can at any time just as easily regress as progress. As of right now Americans are still floundering in a strange transitional state of mind, for the most part blindly addicted to the notion that the old market system will make everything come out all right; the rest uneasily awakening to the realization that only our resilience as a free people will see us through the crisis.

GEORGE C. SPONSLER
Needed: Scientists on Top

The staggering growth of science and technology has so accelerated in the twentieth century that there is today no facet of our lives which is not radically influenced by its developments. Communications, transportation, food processing, buildings, electricity, light, power, medicine, weapons, the list is almost endless—all have been the gifts of science and technology. Science is the single cultural area in which modern man can without question assert his preeminence over his forebearers. It is impossible to imagine human history without science and engineering. Today the single most potent and pervasive influence upon human existence, upon national and foreign affairs, is that of science and technology. The future of the world will be decided not by law nor military prowess nor politics nor statesmanship nor economics nor dogma but by research and development.

In spite of the unquestionable supremacy of science and technology in human affairs we in the United States still adhere to the myth that science is somehow of secondary concern, occupying a supporting role, and scientists themselves are unqualified to run any but their own immediate affairs. Occasionally they are not even allowed that; it is not uncommon for military laboratories, for example, to be headed by officers having only a modicum of research and development training and experience. Usually the corporate head is a salesman; the cabinet member a businessman or lawyer; and only one President has even been a professional engineer. The scientist is kept in the role of technical advisor—on tap but not on top.

It is interesting to contrast the respective national attitudes toward science and scientists within the USSR and the United States. In the USSR science and scientists are preeminent with representatives in the highest echelons of the communist hierarchy. Glenn Seaborg, chairman of the Atomic Energy Commission, noted in a recent speech the Soviet stress on science, illustrated by the fact that eight out of fifteen members of the Communist party presidium have a technical background, as does a similar portion of the party secretariat. Outstanding Russian scientists have been elevated to membership on the central committee of the Communist party itself. In the United States the corresponding status is held by business and businessmen spiced with a good measure of lawyers. In the Soviet Union the management of the national effort in research and development has recently been organized by establishment of the new State Committee of the Council of Ministers, USSR, for the Coordination of Scientific Research Work, to yet further strengthen the position of science and scientists in government. In the United States we have a proliferation of scientific activities independently managed with no real central control.

Russia's remarkable growth since the 1917 revolution has been made possible only through a program of industrial expansion using tools provided by modern technology. Khrushchev's current plan to surpass the American economy by 1980 probably is not based only on his belief that he can better manage his economy under communist totalitarianism but also on the assumption that he will make better use of science and technology. Science rather than communism is the real surging force of the future.

The overriding importance and promise of science is slowly being recognized outside the scientific community. For example, it is reported that former Vice-president Nixon in early planning sessions was advised to base his presidential campaign upon the assertion that America's future development depended upon a national program of scientific and technological exploitation to which he would devote his energies should he be elected. Such a campaign in retrospect would have been most interesting, especially in light of the current emphasis of the Kennedy administration upon space and weapons technology. Both political parties apparently now recognize the importance of science and technology for the future development of the nation.

Scientists, engineers, and their laboratory facilities constitute a national resource of far greater importance than the natural resources which have traditionally been the concern of government. Proper use and allocation of this new and invaluable resource demands careful and responsible planning, organization, and control at the highest national level. Today we in the United States do not have this capability.

Significantly, we have no cabinet level post for science and technology. Jerome B. Wiesner, Special Assistant to the President for Science and Technology, has little real authority. He is chairman of the President's Science Advisory Committee and of the Federal Council for Science and Technology. The first committee is composed of a group of scientists of national repute primarily drawn from outside government agencies. Both committees are without authority. The words "committee, advisory, council" are truly indicative of the roles played: the committees are advisory. On the other hand, it must be noted that the Special Assistant to the President for Science and Technology himself certainly has an influential voice in the discussion and development of national policy because of his close and confidential association with the President, but he is still only an advisor.

Just within the past few months the Office of Science and Technology has been created by executive order in yet a further step towards central management of the government's activities in research and development. This is a most salutary proposal in that, if approved by Congress, it will make available to Congress an authoritative source of information on the nation's science and technology. The Special Assistant will also serve as head of the new office, but again, as the office is now envisioned, he will only be an advisor.

IS CENTRAL MANAGEMENT NECESSARY?

When considering the management of science, the question is what part of the spectrum of research and development is amenable to, or properly subject to, management. Let us recognize that basic research is best left undirected, but provided with adequate funds to which no strings are attached. Such support in itself constitutes management, in a limited sense, and in that sense basic research must be included along with the rest of the research and development spectrum in our management domain.

The federal government provides more than half of all research and development funds spent in the United States. The magnitude of the total national expenditure in research and development is frequently unappreciated: it currently amounts to some $14 billion per year. The total ten year federal space program alone is estimated to cost from $10 billion to $50 billion. Compare these figures to the total annual budget of the entire Post Office Department, about $700 million, or only one-tenth the total federal research and development budget.

Basic research is supported by the National Science Foundation, the Atomic Energy Commission, the National Aeronautics and Space Administration, the Office of Naval Research and the Advanced Research Projects Agency of the Department of Defense, and many other government agencies. Applied research is supported by almost every government agency. A few figures derived from the budget for the fiscal year ending June 30, 1962, are illuminating. It is estimated that the net budget expenditures for federal research and development programs will amount to $9.443 billion. Of that total, the Department of Defense will spend $6.275 billion, the Atomic Energy Commission $1.116 billion, NASA $965 million, Health, Education, and Welfare $483 million, the Department of Agriculture $154 million, the National Science Foundation $119 million, and other government agencies $331 million. Why there is no central management with authority to coordinate this enormous funding is difficult to understand.

IS CENTRAL MANAGEMENT DESIRABLE?

It is speciously argued that science is a tool, a handmaiden as it were, employed by most government agencies and hence no central management is desirable even if it were possible. But although all government agencies have their own lawyers and legal problems, the office of the Attorney General is still required at the cabinet level to handle legal and related national problems. Perhaps a better example, especially as regards the feasibility of government-wide control, is provided by the Bureau of the Budget. Although all government departments have their own comptrollers and prepare their own budget requests, the Director of the Bureau of the Budget has final and overriding authority, with recourse only to the President.

Contrary to prevailing opinions, central national management of science and technology is essential. Particularly in applied research and development there is ample opportunity for duplication of effort which is wasteful of both brainpower and the taxpayers' money. For example, there is still the problem of properly coordinating the space efforts of the Department of Defense and the National Aeronautics and Space Administration. One could ask if, as another example, the research programs of the National Bureau of Standards and the AEC and Department of Defense laboratories are really coordinated. Has industry been properly employed? What about interindustrial competition—can we afford competitive efforts in research and development which leave many scientists writing proposals when they should be in the laboratory? Why can't we share information and exchange technical aid while still preserving industrial proprietary rights?

In recognition that some overall control is required it has recently been proposed that a number of new assistant secretaries for science and technology be named to various government departments. Although salutary, such a proposal would leave unsolved the primary problem of interagency coordination and centralized direction of science and technology. Various other proposals have been made in the past to overcome these defects, but all such attempts have fallen short since no overall authority was given to the coordinators. Like any other human endeavor, research and development cannot be managed by indirection or good will; authority and responsibility are demanded.

In an attempt to provide central management of federal research and development, President Eisenhower in 1959 stablished the Federal Council for Science and Technology, including representatives from the Departments of Agriculture, Commerce, Defense, Interior, and Health, Education, and Welfare, as well as from the National Aeronautics and Space Administration, the Atomic Energy Commission, and the National Science Foundation. Its purpose is to provide more effective planning and administration of the various federal research and development programs. Although decidedly a move in the right direction, the Council is hampered by a lack of authority, for it has no real power over the agencies represented. Significantly, neither does the proposed office of science and technology provide any authoritative control over the agencies it will coordinate.

NEEDED: A TOP-LEVEL DEPARTMENT

It would appear imperative that a secretary for science and technology be added to the President's cabinet to head a new department of science and replace the present Special Assistant. The first responsibility of the new secretary would be to assure that all domestic and foreign policies were made with full understanding of any scientific implications. For this reason the new secretary should be a member of the National Security Council as well. Second, he would determine what emphasis should be placed on all the various federal research and development programs, and apportion the overall research and development budget to assure that emphasis. For example, he would decide how much funding should be devoted to the space effort, what fraction should be devoted to basic research, what the ratio of military to nonmilitary spending should be, etc. He would approve major projects and select the appropriate government agency to carry them out. He would act as a watchdog to coordinate the research and development efforts of all government agencies. He would determine the relative importance of the various federal research and development projects—weeding out those of lesser value and emphasizing those of greater need. He would assess the broad progress of all federal research and development and apply appropriate corrective pressure where necessary. The third major responsibility of the new secretary would be to mobilize the scientific and technical resources available throughout the nation. A major part of this latter effort would be to improve collaboration between industries engaged in the same research areas and between industries, government, and universities. It is essential that the national research and development program be supported by truly coordinated efforts on the part of all with capability to contribute.

Let us look at a few of the problems which would confront the new secretary.

NEEDED: BUDGET CONTROL

Money is management. It has been suggested by Professor Oskar Morgenstern in his book, *The Question of National Defense,* that the Bureau of the Budget in fact rules research and development because it has the ultimate power of approval of all funds. Although perhaps overstated, the moral is easily drawn. The purse strings for research and development should be transferred to the new secretary for science.

The primary organizational problem for the proposed new department of science and technology would be its relation to the existing government departments which currently manage large research and development programs as part of their responsibilities in different areas. Organizations such as the AEC, NASA, and NSF could easily be integrated under the new secretary as they are currently practically autonomous. However, the research and development programs within the Departments of Defense, Agriculture, Commerce, Interior, etc., would pose considerable organizational problems. For this reason most proposals for a cabinet level secretary of science have not recommended that all research and development efforts within the government be directed by the one secretary, but rather have recommended that only the various semi-autonomous agencies should be integrated. There is also the concern that too great a concentration of bureaucratic power would harm, not help, the national program. But if we are to maximize our efforts nothing less than complete integration of all government research and development activities is indicated.

Could the new secretary exert control of research and development across department lines without interfering with the legitimate authority of the other secretaries? A pattern for the supra-departmental control which would be required has already been set within the Department of Defense where the Office of the Director of Defense Research and Engineering has been organized to control the research and development of the three military services. The director has the power of the budget over the research and development funds of the army, navy, and air force. Although the problems would be far more complex, the new secretary for science and technology would operate in a similar fashion, but on the cabinet level. To cope with the massive problems of such an organization the new secretary would maintain control of research and development funds to assure concurrence with his broad policy directives, while leaving actual project management and individual research and development budget formulation to the appropriate departments, subject to his review.

Coordination of the entire nation's research and development potential could raise tremendous problems in the traditional freedom of scientific inquiry, which must be maintained, and in industrial competition, but the magnitude of the problem is no excuse for not attempting its solution.

There are at least two other areas which would benefit from creating this new department.

NEEDED: SCIENTIST-STATESMEN

A current deficiency in our national management of research and development is our policy of what amounts to decision by brainstorming. From time to time we convene a group of distinguished scientists for a few days or a few hours for recommendations having the greatest and most far-reaching effects on the nation's science and technology. Most scientists most of the time are not concerned with national problems. Yet they are called upon to solve, on the basis of what is all too often a cursory investigation, problems of the gravest national importance—solutions which frequently would actually require prolonged study. The board of directors concept does not work well in research and development when the directors themselves are not intimately concerned on a day-to-day basis with national problems—problems often possessing nonscientific aspects beyond the competence or experience of the scientists. Continuity and prolonged study on the part of appropriate experts is required. There is evidence that this fact is being brought home to the President's Science Advisory Committee whose members reportedly are spending more and more of their time in Washington in fulfillment of their responsibilities. Establishment of the office of the proposed secretary for science would provide a permanent staff of professional scientist-statesmen who would assure the desired continuity and competence.

The establishment of the new department would do much to attract competent scientists and engineers into government because it would symbolize to them the new status of science and technology. Part of the present recruiting problem is, of course, related to the low salary scale in government vis-à-vis industry, but a larger problem is one of morale—respect and prestige gained only by authority and responsibility. The government currently hopes to raise the professional salaries, but that step alone will not be enough to attract high caliber scientist-statesmen. The staff responsibilities and opportunities presented by the installation of the new secretary for science and technology might well reverse the present pattern and make a period of government service most attractive to the better scientists and engineers of the nation.

Criticism has often been expressed that our national policy and philosophy are negative—we are *anti*-communist for example—that we need some unifying, positive goal. Perhaps Nixon's advisors were not too far wrong: Could not the exploitation of science and technology for the betterment of our country and the world provide the necessary focus? The Kennedy administration already appears to be well down that road without having stated the goal: Science *is* the new frontier. Perhaps we need only to recognize where we are headed.

If indeed we are to exploit science and technology fully, we must first recognize that national research today is trapped in a predicament of inadequate overall management. Often the national program seems to lack direction; it is fragmented among various agencies and is frequently uncoordinated. Important decisions affecting huge segments of the research and development effort are being made without due and prolonged consideration on the advice of individuals who, though scientifically competent, are only part-time government workers. It is inexcusable that the Post Office should be represented on the cabinet and not science and technology. This state of affairs must change. Continuity and quality of control are demanded; diffused management of research and development must be replaced by centralized coordination and direction. A secretary for science and technology, a preeminent scientist or engineer with managerial competence, is urgently required now to mobilize our invaluable national resources in research and development. It is time that a scientist be on top.

EMMANUEL G. MESTHENE
Can Only Scientists Make Government Science Policy?

The belief is prevalent that the policy problems raised by the rapid advance of science and technology are best dealt with when professional scientists are appointed to policy-making positions in the government. My own involvement in the business of science and public policy, both in Washington and in an international organization, convinces me that this is not necessarily so. Policy making, even when it concerns science, has its own problems and techniques, to the understanding of which scientists, I think, can lay no special claim.

I do not speak of individual people who happen to be trained scientists.

Individual people who happen to be trained *anything* are often very good policy makers, and scientists are certainly no exception. Indeed, other things being equal, the presumption probably remains in their favor. But other things are never equal. The issue thus concerns scientists as a professional community, scientists as such. I am questioning the myth that science policy is best handled by scientists *because* they are scientists.

It is a curious myth. Few would claim that architects or bricklayers make the best housing policy, and doubts have been raised about whether doctors make the best medical policies. There have been other such myths—for example, that generals somehow have a corner on military policy making. Economists also, nowadays, are sometimes heard to argue that they are God's chosen policy makers, because all policy involves resource allocation in the light of alternative expected benefits. That is the newest of these myths. Policy making does involve that of course, just as it often involves scientific issues or technical military questions, but it also involves much else besides.

I believe that professional scientists have in fact done an indispensable policy-making job during the past two decades. In that sense, this article could not reasonably have been written much before now. The quick succession of fission and fusion and missiles and moonshots left the traditional policy-making machinery rather groggy, unable to deal with a new generation of unfamiliar policy problems. It is to the credit of the scientist—and perhaps to the salvation of the country—that he pitched in to help, willingly, quickly, and generously.

Of course, the scientist went to Washington for reasons probably very different from those that made him welcomed there. The *Bulletin of Atomic Scientists* and others at the time argued that the nuclear scientists, inventors of potentially horrendous new power, had a special moral responsibility to guide the nation in using it for good rather than for evil. The only hope of doing this, went the argument, was to introduce the precise, rational methods of science into the working processes of traditional policy making.

As far as moral responsibility is concerned, of course, we all have it. Those of us who are not professional scientists are therefore not above feeling an occasional twinge of resentment at the scientist's wanting to take it away and keep it all to himself. Does the electrician have a special moral responsibility for the electric chair?

The question of scientific method is a nicer one. That is another myth, this one perpetrated chiefly by philosophers. Does "scientific method" mean the method of the exact sciences, based on the controlled, repeatable experiment? If it does, then it is not transferable to public policy making. Does it mean orderly, systematic thinking, as against faith, tradition, or prejudice? That is what it has meant historically. But there certainly is no more want of that in Washington than anywhere else. If it sometimes seems that there is, it is because making good policy is a far more difficult job than making good science. It must, for one thing, deal rationally with the irrational, with faith, tradition, and prejudice.

I think the reason scientists were welcomed in Washington in 1945 and since is both less romantic and more compelling than moral responsibility and scientific method. They went because the policy makers who were there at the time yelled "uncle." And both deserve a lot of credit: the scientist for responding, and the government officials for knowing enough to yell.

A PERMANENT ROLE

In one capacity the professional scientist never will and never should leave Washington. The technical content of major policy issues will not lessen. It will increase and get more technical. The professional policy maker at his best will never be able to do the job of the professional scientist. More and more, the best of professional scientists will have to advise on all policy that science touches, which is just about all policy. The scientist will forevermore have to participate in the policy-making process, along with the economist, the soldier, and the public official.

But advice is a two-way street: there must be those who know how to give it and those who know how to take it, where "to take" means to understand and to evaluate. One trouble during the last two decades has been that there have not been enough good scientific-advice-takers in government, not enough policy makers sophisticated in the new technical dimensions of policy. That is why many scientists had to go beyond their adviser role, to hold the fort by filling in also in the policy-making spots, in the White House, the Defense Establishment, the State Department, and elsewhere. It is a safe bet that most of these men would willingly go back to their own profession—to science, and to giving scientific advice to government—once they were convinced that competent professional policy makers would succeed them in the government jobs.

My argument so far is that professional scientists have been the best science policy makers available between World War II and now, but that they are not by nature the best for all time. This statement requires elaboration.

SCIENCE POLICY

Making policy relating to science—making "science policy," to use a shorthand term that is gaining currency—has two aspects. A government has to have a policy *for science,* a policy (or policies) concerned with the support, health, and growth of science and scientists. But a government must also be concerned with the role of science *for policy*—for policy in general—because the rapid advance of science and technology increasingly affects policies aimed at extrascientific national objectives, like military strength, economic development, international relations, and so forth. Actually, if pushed far enough, these two aspects collapse into the second, because few but professional scientists would much care how fast and where science went if it were not for its important extrascientific implications. The country certainly could not reasonably be expected to put billions of dollars into science just because science is good. Music is good, too, and it does not get a cent.

The science-for-policy aspect, then, is ultimately the core of science policy making. But one of the effects of entrusting science policy making to professional scientists is that the narrower, policy-for-science aspect can get emphasized out of proper proportion. That is, to put it very simply, scientists by and large tend to be much more interested in science than in policy, which certainly should surprise no one.

An example of this bias is a frequently disproportionate concern with the danger to scientific freedom implicit in the very idea of government policy making for science. Government research projects that carry rather funny titles, like "An Investigation of the Mating Habits of the South American Flea," are sometimes questioned on the ground of relevance to the sponsoring agency's mission, and because there is concern that irresponsible bandying about of such titles can compromise an agency's entire research budget. The scientists involved too often answer that this is evidence of anti-intellectualism in government, and that their professional dignity and scientific competence are being questioned. They sometimes threaten to resign if the projects are not retained, but happily they do not often do so. The interesting thing, of course, is that they rarely even try to justify their choices in the light of alternative projects that the money could be spent on. No sensible person can deny that the presence of government in scientific affairs carries a real risk of unwarranted interference and control, but crying wolf too often may weaken the response if and when the wolf really appears.

Such incidents reveal another bias: a conviction that the only criterion relevant to the making of science-policy decisions is whether a project to be supported is or is not good science. Down deep, very many scientists probably wish that the government would support all the good science there is, and otherwise keep hands off. Of course, government cannot do that, because there is more good science than there is money. Choices must therefore be made, and they must be made on grounds other than scientific. To spend a billion dollars on physics and a million on archeology, or the million on physics and the billion on archeology, is not an indifferent choice in America in 1964, even when the purely scientific claims and credentials of the archeologist and the physicist are equally good. It is perfectly clear that the government should not support bad science, but that proscription is not enough to build a science policy on.

Another source of a disproportionate emphasis on the narrower, policy-for-science aspect of science policy making has its source in the at times ineffective way in which scientific advice has been used by government, especially in the earlier days. An inevitable consequence of scientific spectaculars is that science becomes spectacular. It comes into fashion, becomes a fad. With the public uncovering of the atom bomb, everybody decided he needed his own private atomic pile, and his own personal nuclear-scientist-in-waiting. Different departments of the government all suddenly flowered with their own scientific advisory boards. No one could any longer afford to be caught with his science down.

Look at these advisory boards. By and large, they were staffed from the same small group of eminent men in science who tended to rotate from one to the other. Each was told, "Look, we know that science is wonderful, we know that we need it in this department, we don't know anything about it though, so please tell us what we should do." And the answer inevitably came back, "Support oceanography, or meteorology, or molecular biology," or, if this was still in the 1940's, "Support an atomic reactor." You ask the same question of the same people ten times, and you'll get the same answer ten times. And that is what happened. Oceanography programs, meteorology projects, and atomic reactors began to spring up ten at a time, whether or not they had any relevance to the missions and objectives of the agencies that sponsored them. Policy making thus tended at times to be replaced rather than refined by science.

Science policy making will come fully of age when science begins to serve policy, rather than the other way around. As yet, it is still missing more opportunities than it is exploiting.

When the National Science Foundation was established in 1950, it was given two principal tasks: to provide financial support for scientific research and scientific education, and to concern itself with formulating and co-ordinating Government-wide policies relating to science. It never did the second job, despite a pointed Presidential reminder in 1954. Supporting research and education was relatively easily done, and was good for science. Making science policy was a new and murky area, little understood and liable to fan interagency rivalries. The Foundation played it conservatively, partly for want of sufficient authority, and to that extent missed a chance to enrich the art of policy making and to make it adequate to the present time.

International scientific cooperation is another case in point. Why do countries cooperate in scientific programs? Sometimes, as in the case of CERN, because equipment is too costly for them to support singly, or in order to make up for their individual weaknesses in certain areas by calling on the strength of others. Sometimes because of the field—like astronomy, meteorology, or space science—which does not respect national boundaries. The first of these reasons, particularly, does not in practice apply to the United States. No single European country may have enough money to buy the latest particle accelerator, but the United States could buy ten. Belgium may be weak in physics and Italy, perhaps, in biology, but the United States is pretty strong in all departments. In other words, the United States can do without European science. But it cannot do without Europe. It needs it as an ally, and it needs it increasingly as a market. Conversely, Europe needs and wants science from America, but is no longer dependent on this country for economic aid, and is increasingly going its own way in foreign and defense policy.

Now if each of two people has something that the other wants, they are likely to start talking about a trade. But no! The argument that too often greets proposals for increased U.S. participation in international scientific cooperation is "But European countries are not cooperative these days, either in NATO or in tariff negotiations. If they're anxious to cooperate in science, it's only because they want our science, and we get little in return."

This is looking at the issue solely from the point of view of probable *scientific* benefit to the United States. The real payoff to this country from international scientific cooperation may be more *political* than scientific: science may offer an important and viable channel of international communication at a time when more traditional diplomatic, military, and economic channels are faltering. Failure to recognize the full extent of this can amount to using science to obstruct policy rather than to advance it.

Science—or rather its name—has also sometimes been used to obstruct or confuse policy in other ways. One very eminent scientist will say that we should build bigger and better and more H-bombs more quickly, because he is a great scientist and he says so. Another equally eminent scientist will say that we should destroy all our weapons immediately and unilaterally, because he is a great scientist and he says so. Congress, which can be short on science but is very long on politics, plays such people like poker chips. My scientist can lick your scientist. In the meantime, of course, the really useful work is done by the man who invents the detection device that makes the test-ban treaty possible, and by the scientists who work hand-in-glove with the disarmament negotiators in Geneva. I cite this instance only to show that professional scientists are no more immune than anybody else to bias and special pleading. Scientist A's supporters, of course, argue that Scientist B is not representative of the scientific community, and B's associates argue that A is not. Probably neither is, but it is unlikely that it matters one way or the other. The problem is not to distill the true essence of the scientific community, and then listen. It is to distill the essence of particular policy problems at particular times, and to call on scientists, among others, to help deal with them.

AN INTERDISCIPLINARY EFFORT

Such examples and arguments cast doubt on the idea that professional scientists have a special competence as policy makers because they are scientists. That is not to say that being a scientist is a disqualification for a policy-making role. It just is not a special qualification, any more than being a professional economist is, or a professional philosopher. Rather must all these specialists, and more, participate together in making policy, because making policy is as truly interdisciplinary an effort as there is.

The economist as such must contribute his special expertise in cost-benefit analysis to guide the allocation of scientific resources. The physical scientist as such must determine the purely scientific priorities: how manpower and money should be divided according to the intellectual demands of each branch of science. The political official must introduce the extra-scientific considerations. The engineer must perform his unique function of translating scientific theories into useful objects, and the political scientist must help design the institutions that can convert this variety of contributions into viable policy.

Because the job is so complex, talented policy makers are rare. Talented policy makers who are also competent professional scientists are therefore necessarily rarer still. This sometimes means that important policy jobs are filled by good scientists who are relatively insensitive to policy when they could be better manned by competent policy makers sophisticated in the facts of science. That is why we should not assume without examination that scientists as such are better qualified than anybody else to deal with science-policy problems.

Am I preaching to the converted? I believe not. Most scientists will agree up to a point with what I have been saying, and still believe that, when all is said, a scientist is really better fitted by training than anyone else to do the policy making. In their souls they feel that policy making in government is a messy, disorganized, and irrational business, and that only the clear eye and trained mind of the professional scientist can clean it up.

Too often the effect of this is that the policy problems are simply not tackled. The full-time scientist-adviser in the government can sometimes be indifferent to the value and need for detailed examination of the specific ways in which science and technology enter into the often delicate policy questions with which his agency struggles. Unused to thinking in political terms, he tends to concentrate still on the subjects that occupied him in his university laboratory.

To the suggestion that his principal concern should now be with policy rather than with science as such, he has too often been known to reply, "Yes, I see that, and I suppose it's right. I hadn't quite thought of it that way before. I generally leave these political questions to others, and concentrate my own efforts on the things I know how to do; for example, our efforts in oceanography and our new program in meteorology."

I have at times, after frustratingly frequent encounters with this kind of reaction, asked knowledgeable friends in Washington when we will learn that we don't absolutely *have* to appoint scientists to these jobs irrespective of their political sophistication. "Not in the foreseeable future," is the answer I get, "because the entire scientific community would be up in arms if we considered nonscientists for them. All these jobs have to go to scientists, even when we can't attract our first or second choices to them."

CONCLUSIONS

Two comments seem in order. (i) The failure of the traditional policy-making machinery to grapple with the new technically rich problems that have arisen over the last 20 years is adequate explanation for the development of this attitude on the part of the scientific community. By and large, it has until now been better to have scientists than nonscientists in these jobs. (ii) The country's progress in dealing effectively with the important problems of science policy will be measured by the degree to which the scientific community progressively abandons this attitude. Military policy making has on the whole been better done since the professional military man gave up his special claim to omniscience and began to cooperate rather than dominate. The analogy with science policy is clear. The specialist *may* be the best man to deal with the policy implications of his field, but he is not always or by nature the best.

Of course, professional policy makers must first become more adept than they have been in dealing with issues that touch science before the government can safely lessen its encroachment on the scientist's time. It is not clear that physicists and chemists have to be in the policy-making jobs, but it is clear that these jobs must be manned by people who know what physicists and chemists do when they do physics and chemistry. The modern public servant, in other words, has to be scientifically literate. He must be able to understand a scientist when he talks. He has to be able to sift good from bad scientific advice. He has to be able to make his superiors in the Executive branch and in the Congress understand what science is really about, understand that it is more than modern sorcery. He must also be able to explain government and its special problems to the scientist, so that the scientist can provide more relevant advice to the government. He must function as the communications link, missing up to now, between the professional scientist and the professional politician.

This is no mean task. It is one to which this country is only now beginning to awaken. It is one to which public officials, professional scientists, scholars in general, and educators perhaps above all must henceforth devote themselves explicitly and systematically, in order to understand the problem and to help breed the new, technically sophisticated public servant who can deal with it. It is only when that is done that the scientist can reasonably be asked to yield to the new professional in government. But it is doubtful that he will even need to be asked. He will probably do so willingly—perhaps even eagerly—once he is convinced that the policy-making job will not be bungled by scientific illiterates.

EUGENE RABINOWITCH
Responsibilities of Scientists in the Atomic Age

Everybody has a responsibility to the society of which he is a part and, through this society, to mankind. In addition to the common responsibility of all citizens—such as to obey laws or to pay taxes—many individuals have additional responsibilities, arising from their belonging to special groups, endowed with special capacities, possessing special knowledge, or enjoying special power. The doctor, the teacher, the minister, the policeman, the soldier have such special responsibilities, often covering not only their work or service but their behavior in general. In our time, when science has become an important force, affecting both the life of the individual and the fate of society, scientists have acquired a peculiar responsibility, originating from their special knowledge and the power associated with it. What is it?

From the *Bulletin of the Atomic Scientists,* January 1959. Copyright 1959 by the Educational Foundation for Nuclear Science. Reprinted by permission. This paper was delivered at the Third Pugwash Conference.

II

More clearly than anybody else, scientists see the senselessness and the tragedy of the present situation of mankind—the *reductio ad absurdum* by modern technology of the historical tradition of humanity divided into warring factions which threaten each other with armed might.

Despite this knowledge, scientists remain the weaponeers of hostile nations. They are caught in a vicious circle. If scientists of one country refuse to provide it with all the weapons science can invent, they may be responsible for putting their nation at the mercy of another, hostile one. This was the motivation which caused the greatest physicists of our time to urge upon the American government the development of the atom bomb at the beginning of the Second World War. Without the fear that Germany might be the first to threaten the world with an atom bomb, scientists in England and America would not have mustered up sufficient enthusiasm for the job, and the feeling of urgency which made the atom bomb a reality before the end of the war. After the war, it was apprehension—as it later transpired, a justified apprehension—that the Soviet Union might be close to the production of a thermonuclear bomb, that caused a number of American scientists to press for the development of the American H-bomb.

Some people (scientists as well as nonscientists) see the root of the tragedy in wrong personal decisions of scientists. Max Born has lamented that his former pupils and co-workers—Heisenberg, Oppenheimer, Fermi, Teller, among them—have not learned, as he himself did, the wisdom of not lending their genius to the evil purposes of weaponeering. Robert Jungk, in his book *Brighter Than a Thousand Suns,* presented the whole history of the atom and hydrogen bomb development as one of the failure of scientists to make the correct moral decision—to refuse to supply their governments with the terrible new weapons. These critics do not admit that a conflict exists between two ethical imperatives with which a scientist is confronted in our divided world—the conflict between the voice of scientific conscience, which counsels him against putting his knowledge and skill in the service of destruction, and the counsel of loyalty to his state and his society, which tells him that he is not entitled to decide on his own whether this country and this society should be left to face an enemy with inferior weapons—which is likely to mean, in effect, with practically no weapons at all, except moral strength, and consciousness of rectitude.

Some—a relatively small number—of scientists escape the conflict by becoming "conscientious objectors." This is the credo of the Society for

Social Responsibility of Scientists. Among its members are some prominent scientists—Max Born, Kathleen Lonsdale. We have been told—even if we do not know it for certain—that, in the Soviet Union, Peter Kapitza has refused to put his capacities in the service of atom bomb development. It is, however, unlikely that, in any one country a majority of scientists will choose this path, and thus effectively impose unilateral disarmament on their own nation.

III

Dr. Jungk suggests that it may have been only lack of communication that prevented an agreement between scientists on both sides of World War II not to make an atom bomb, thus escaping the dilemma of unilateral disarmament. According to his story, leading German nuclear physicists consciously and consistently evaded working in this direction, and misled the German government as to the possibility of the development of the bomb. If only these German scientists had made a determined effort to let their American and English colleagues know of their decision! Then, Dr. Jungk suggests, Western scientists could have followed the example of their German colleagues, and the American A-bomb project would have bogged down, as the German one did.

I believe that the conspiracy of German scientists not to give the atomic bomb to Hitler, as described by Jungk, is a *post factum* rationalization of a vague uneasiness which caused German nuclear scientists to drag their feet, rather than to put into the atomic bomb work the same enthusiasm and urgency that animated their British and American colleagues. The German scientists, while not outright defeatists, had not the same fear of Hitler's defeat as the Western scientists had of a German victory. They grasped at evidence that the bomb could not be made in time for use in the war; and their a-scientific, if not anti-scientific, officialdom did little to urge them on.

IV

I believe that the basic cause of the predicament, into which the discovery of nuclear energy has brought the world, lies not in the inadequate ethical standards of scientists, or in the difficulties of communication between them. Rather, it lies in the low ethical standards of national governments, and difficulties of communication between them; and this, in turn, is the consequence of the stubborn survival of an obsolete organization of mankind, its division into separate sectors which require—and receive—full and exclusive loyalty from their members. Within such a world system, only a few individuals are likely to claim and assert the right to hold to their self-set standards of moral behavior, when this behavior—if emulated by a large part of their colleagues—could inflict fatal damage on the society to which they belong, and to which they owe their freedom and their living. Scientists as a profession are not likely to assume this attitude, any more than a whole class of American draftees is likely to turn one day into conscientious objectors. Scientists may be intellectually more advanced than the average population; but this intellectual level has nothing to do with attitudes in the face of this dilemma. While scientists see more clearly than can others the terrible consequences of the use of the weapons they are developing, they see with equal clarity also the possible consequences of their nation being left at the mercy of an enemy equipped with them; they are less likely to cherish the illusion that "old-fashioned" weapons could provide adequate defense against modern technological armaments, or that these armaments may not be brought to bear on the decision in a major future war.

The conflict between loyalty to his scientific ethics, and loyalty to his nation, weighs as heavily on the conscience of an atomic physicist as it does on that of a farmer, worker, or lawyer called into military service. It is not because of insufficient moral fiber, or indifference to human suffering, or high monetary rewards, that scientists do not walk out *en masse* from weapons laboratories. It is because they, like all other human beings in our time, are trapped in an obsolete structure of mankind, which our ancestors have bequeathed to us. They are part and parcel of a humanity divided into fractions, each of which enforces a certain moral code within it, but acknowledges (whatever its leaders may proclaim) no such code for its relations with other nations. Scientists cannot hope to change dramatically this situation through passive noncooperation of individuals, but they could—and, in my opinion, they should—contribute individually and collectively toward gradual reform of the world structure, ultimately to make possible a unified, harmonious humanity.

V

The political leaders of most nations understand that the arms race cannot last indefinitely, and that, sooner or later, a form of international existence must be found which would permanently exclude war, and thus make competitive armaments to win this war unnecessary. However, they postpone acting for such a new world system until after the victory of their economic or political ideology, which they confidently expect to win. Western nations believe—and point to historical experience in support of this belief—that popular control of governments by free elections is the best guarantee against military adventures into which personal or ideological dictatorships are almost inevitably drawn. The Communist leadership —also quoting historical evidence—believes even more ardently that the capitalist economy, with its recurrent conflicts between unrealistically competing economic groups, inevitably leads to war, and that only world-wide acceptance of an economic system not motivated by profit, can put an end to them. Neither side is swayed by examples—some of them quite recent —which obviously contradict their generalizations. Both play for time, in the hope that the other side bears seeds of inner instability, and will sooner or later collapse.

But mankind cannot afford to wait. Each additional year of the arms race means an additional chance of nuclear catastrophe. However small these annual increments, the risks of subsequent years add up—and eventually they will become overwhelming.

As scientists, we should realize that at the time when the ideological lines which now separate the world into apparently irreconcilable camps were first drawn, the capacity of technology, founded on consequent application of science, to create wealth (by developing new sources of energy, by utilizing new raw materials instead of the scarce and unevenly distributed traditional ones, and by increasing productivity of labor through mechanization and automation) was much less obvious than it is now. We now know that with a well-developed science and technology and given a sensible rate of population increase) enough goods can be produced to supply the basic needs of everybody, whether the economic system is the best one imaginable or not. Socialists believe, and will keep believing, that the most equitable distribution of the products of labor can be achieved under a fully planned socialist system, and that the increase in productivity will be fastest if it is not stifled by the requirements of profit earning; and they will quote chapter and verse for their belief. However, if we at all aspire to objectivity, as scientists must, none of us will deny that an economic system based on individual initiative and profit incentive has demonstrated, in America and elsewhere, a capacity to produce enough goods to achieve a fair standard of living for all. In the same way, the belief of many Americans that because of the absence of profit motive, socialist economy cannot achieve a high level of productivity, has been revealed as demonstrably wrong by the industrial development of the Soviet Union (and of the socialized segments of industry in Great Britain and other countries). In other words, while scientists may—and many will—maintain the conviction that one economic system is not only fairer, but also more efficient than the other, they will see the difference in quantitative and not in absolute terms.

VI

An important area affected by these considerations—an area in which (I believe) scientists of all countries have an abiding stake—is the economic advancement of educationally and industrially underdeveloped peoples. For these nations, the problems of political freedom and of the best economic system are overshadowed by the immediate and urgent need somehow to pull their masses out of the desperation in which want, undernourishment, and ignorance keep them. They need help from more advanced nations, through capital investment, through the spreading of education, and through the training of technical personnel, in order to be able to win the critical race between the increase in their agricultural and industrial productivity and the growth of their population.

Scientists of all countries must feel an obligation to help human progress win against blind forces of nature—not only for humanitarian reasons, but also because they are (or should be) aware that, in our age, peace and prosperity have become indivisible, world-wide problems; so that their own, at the present time more fortunate, nations cannot remain secure and prosperous as long as large parts of the world are not on the way to sound economic growth, and consequent stability. I believe that scientists of all countries should combine efforts in this field, irrespective of their political allegiances and economic beliefs. They should urge their governments to join in providing such educational and technical help, leaving to the recipient nations the choice of economic and political forms in which to mold their aspirations. That such cooperation is possible, has been demonstrated by the International Atomic Energy Agency. I think scientists should explore together the possibilities of other creative international programs in technical, economic, and scientific areas.

VII

It is more difficult—but perhaps not impossible—to mitigate also the second ideological controversy which now divides the world: that between belief in individual freedom, and in centralized political, economic, and intellectual guidance by the state. We in the West believe that the greatest over-all human progress can be achieved if maximum scope is given to the thoughts and aspirations of the individual. True, we cannot fail to see that, in certain respects, society can be weakened or its progress slowed down by the clash and pull of contradictory ideas, desires, and impulses of different groups within it. However, in the last reckoning, we expect this weakness to be more than balanced by a greater wealth of new ideas, by the spur of competition, and by the greater enthusiasm with which people work when they are permitted to pursue their own ideas and aspirations. On the other side, the view prevails that more rapid progress can be achieved by restricting severely the play of contradictory ideas and forces, and making everyone work in a coordinated program, outlined by the ideological and political leadership of the nation.

Historical examples can be quoted in support of both views. Could we, as scientists, perhaps approach this controversy also in a quantitative, relative way, rather than as a matter of dogma? As scientists, we have a common experience—that, in science, free inquiry and untrammelled exploration by individuals are the ultimate sources of the most important progress. The greatest scientific discoveries have come through efforts of nonconformist individuals, who have asked heretical questions, and boldly doubted the validity of generally accepted conceptions—be it flatness of the earth, the necessity of continued application of force to keep a body moving, the universality of time, or the continuity of matter.

On the other hand, we have witnessed, in our time, impressive examples of organized application of science under central direction, and cannot gainsay that such efforts can produce the greatest practical results in the shortest possible time—be it an atomic bomb or a sputnik. These epoch-making feats, are, however, not the great scientific breakthroughs the public thinks them to be; rather, they are spectacular practical exploitations of scientific breakthroughs which had occurred earlier, and often unnoticed, in the quiet of fundamental laboratories, or at the desks of mathematicians or theoretical physicists.

Generalizing our experience as scientists, we may perhaps agree that society needs the free striving of individuals, as well as organized collective effort. We will disagree among ourselves as to how much scope should be given to these two forces to achieve the greatest progress of science and technology—not to speak of an attempt to extend the same approach to other areas of human endeavor, such as economic or political advancement of mankind. What we may, perhaps, agree on, is that the relative scope to be given, respectively, to the free, creative individual and to the organized collective should be considered as an empirical, experimental problem, without dogmatic prejudice.

VIII

I believe that the responsibility of scientists in our time is to bring into human affairs a little more of such skeptical rationality, a little less prejudice, a greater respect for facts and figures, a more critical attitude toward theories and dogmas, a greater consciousness of the limitation of our knowledge and consequent tolerance for different ideas, and readiness to submit them to the test of the experiment. These are the attitudes on which the progress of science has been founded in the past, and on which it remains based now. For scientists, there should be no final truths, no forbidden areas of exploration, no words that are taboo, no prescribed or proscribed ideas. Their common enemies are stubborn, preconceived ideas, prejudiced and closed minds—forces whose triumph would mean the end of science.

It is this open-mindedness that makes fruitful the international gatherings of scientists, such as the atomic energy meetings at Geneva, and the numerous other, less glamorous scientific conferences. Many believe that this type of cooperation cannot extend beyond purely scientific or, at best, technical areas. Perhaps they are right, but the sequence of our meetings is dedicated to the hope that this is not the case. Our meetings suggest that with increased penetration of science into all areas of human life, an attempt to extend to new areas the approach that has permitted men of different creeds and political or economic attitudes to work successfully together in science, is at least worth making. The fact that we are meeting for the third time, and that those of us who were present at the first and second conference left them with a certain elation and a desire to return next time, is encouraging. True, we should not fool ourselves, or others. We are still only on the periphery of mutual understanding; we talk very cautiously, trying to respect the difficulties which our colleagues from different nations face in meeting with us. We try to talk mostly about our common beliefs, not to argue out our differences. Ultimately, we will be justified in speaking about a real success of our endeavors only if we are able to explore together the whole situation of mankind, analyze both the things that divide and those that unite us, and find a common program of action—not in pretended ignorance, but in full consciousness of these differences. This cannot be achieved immediately. It will require time and patience; but to aim at less would mean soon to find our movement at a dead end.

IX

The first work in which scientists can and should combine their efforts, the first area of our common responsibility, is the education of peoples of the world and of their leaders to the understanding of the fundamental facts and implications of science for world affairs. The world must become aware of the essential irreversibility of scientific progress, of its dynamic character, of the impossibility of forcing it into pre-scientific patterns of national and international life. The leadership that will in future neglect to give to the sober facts of science priority over ideological concept, in the determination of its political conduct, as well as over established traditions or national passions, will do it not only to its own peril, but—unfortunately—also at the common peril of humanity.

A second common effort of scientists could be aimed at securing greater understanding of the importance not only of scientific fact, but also of scientific methods of solving problems, for the future fate of humanity. No scientist will be brash enough not to recognize the continuing and often decisive importance, for the behavior of nations, of irrational factors—of political and national animosities, established traditions; ideological, racial, and religious fanaticisms. Many people, skeptical of the scientists' intrusion into political areas, say that they are ignorant or wilfully neglectful of all these forces and that they naively presume that mankind can be promptly reorganized on a rational, scientific basis. This is not true; but, without underestimating the power of the irrational forces in shaping the relations between men and nations, scientists must, *first*, analyze these forces with as much objectivity and open-mindedness as they can possibly bring to bear on these matters; and *second*, try to find a reasonable compromise between these forces and the arguments of reason. In this way they help mankind to avoid the grave dangers of the dawning scientific age and to utilize fully its bright promises.

X

If, as scientists, we attempt to analyze the world situation, prognosticate on its future, and search for the best way to improve it, on a broader basis, including psychological, emotional, and traditional factors in addition to the scientific and technological ones, we will undoubtedly disagree violently among ourselves. Some will believe that they are in possession of fundamental principles and of a methodology, which can give them final answers to most if not all of the crucial questions. Others will bring into their attitudes a much greater skepticism if not agnosticism; still others, a religious or ethical attitude, based on belief in revealed truth. The one thing that could bring us together, and could entitle scientists to a certain degree of leadership, would be the demonstration of greater humility in the face of the unknown, greater tolerance of each other's points of view, and greater respect for mutual difficulties of nations and societies, than are commonly displayed in the political and ideological controversies. For us, all these disagreements and conflicts must be overshadowed by common knowledge of the great challenge which the progress of science and technology places before mankind, of the dilemma of nations either subordinating their political, ideological, and national aspirations to a common interest, or perishing together.

XI

One of our colleagues at Lac Beauport remarked after a few days of this meeting "I thought at first that we were wasting time. But now I see this is a different kind of conference. We have been accustomed to come together to call for a certain thing, or to proclaim a belief we have held in advance, and then to disband. This is a conference to which people come with doubts in their minds, to search together for truth. People must be made to understand this."

This, of course, means only that we come to discuss public affairs as scientists, and try to approach them in the same spirit in which we approach other problems in pure or applied science.

To the extent to which our scientific analysis does lead to definite conclusions, on which competent experts can agree, we can authoritatively address ourselves to the public. Our conclusions concerning the destructive possibilities of atomic warfare, the radiation dangers, or the nature and possibilities of scientific progress, belong in this category. On these matters, the clear and present responsibility of scientists is to educate the people and their leaders.

I believe, however, that this does not exhaust our responsibilities. Beyond spreading information on positively established scientific facts, it behooves us, as scientists, also to assist mankind in finding adequate answers to the many new problems of national and international life in the scientific age. This requires first of all, that we should study these problems in the spirit of scientific inquiry. It would be improper for scientists to try to advise others, without having first appraised the situation on their own, and acquired as much positive knowledge of the facts as possible. Our second responsibility, then, is, to *study* the impact of science on the affairs of man, and search for objectively adequate answers to this challenge, as fearlessly and openmindedly as we possibly can, accepting no ready-made answers from the outside—in the same way scientists would approach any other unexplored area of knowledge.

The continued Pugwash program should thus, I submit, have a twofold aim. One is to educate peoples and governments in things we know; the other, to expand our knowledge. In both directions, scientists from different backgrounds, with different political and national allegiances, should be able to work together.

Beyond these two responsibilities of *education* and *investigation*, some would suggest that scientists' responsibilities include also *action*—both individual action along the lines described at the beginning of this paper (refusal to work on military research, active participation in technical assistance programs, and similar constructive projects), and collective, concerted action, to stop the arms race and prevent the misuse of science for destructive aims.

I argued at the beginning of this paper against the belief that the crisis into which the discovery of atomic energy has brought mankind, could be prevented by the decision of individual scientists not to work on the new weapons. I am equally doubtful that similar individual decisions could now put an end to the arms race. It would be, however, something different if scientists of the world could agree on organized, collective action. However, this could occur only in an open world (for which Niels Bohr has called so eloquently is his well-known appeal to the U.N.). This world does not exist now, and is not likely to come into existence in the foreseeable future. In its absence, no common action of scientists throughout the world can be reasonably contemplated. However, the world changes before our eyes, more than ever in history. What looks impossible today may become a possibility in the next generation. In the meantime, perhaps, we should not be afraid of thinking—and even talking together —about this matter.

WILLIAM R. NELSON
Science: A Means or an End?

A few years ago C. P. Snow delivered a lecture at Cambridge in which he described what he called a dangerous split between two cultures.[1] In Snow's view the intellectual life of Western society was being split into two polar groups, and these groups had almost ceased to communicate with each other. At one pole were the intellectuals. Snow at first described this group as being only the literary intellectuals, but in the discussion he gradually expanded the definition to include all educated persons who were neither scientists nor engineers. At the other pole were the scientists.

1. C. P. Snow, *The Two Cultures: and a Second Look* (New York: The New American Library, 1964).

From *The Rocky Mountain Social Science Journal,* October 1966. Reprinted by permission.

Separating the two groups, Snow felt, was a chasm of misunderstanding and mistrust.

There was ample evidence, it seemed to Snow, that scientists, using the term in the broadest possible sense, shared a common culture. This culture was, more than anything else, a shared attitude or response. With the non-scientists and their traditional culture there was also a commonality, but it was more of a negative commonality that was distinguished primarily by the absence of those more desirable features found in the scientific culture.

Snow expressed a concern that the traditional culture was not only unscientific, but it was also to a considerable degree on the verge of turning anti-scientific. He felt that there was no place where the two cultures met, and this seemed to him extremely dangerous. The solution to this unfortunate situation lay in the field of education, Snow maintained, where persons from each culture could be exposed to the important aspects of the other. If Snow had stopped at that point, his thesis would not have provoked as much controversy as it did. However, he went on to portray the hope of the developing areas, the Western world, and of humanity in general as resting with the scientific revolution, and the educational remedy that he suggested was thus strongly oriented toward placing more emphasis upon scientific training.

A number of critics have taken Snow to task over various assertions that he made in his two cultures lecture, but his supporters have been quick to rise to his defense. That there were legitimate grounds for concern about the problem that Snow described was probably best evidenced by the great amount of discussion that his Cambridge lecture stimulated. To many educators and scientists the lesson to be learned from Snow's analysis seemed clearly to be that there was a need for additional scientific training in the educational system. Specific proposals have ranged from educating a greater number of students in science and engineering to establishing a formal requirement that all college students take more science courses.

A study conducted by a panel of the President's Science Advisory Committee reported that for academic year 1962–63 from one-third to one-half of all graduate students enrolled in engineering, the physical sciences, the life sciences, and the behavioral sciences received primary monetary support from the government.[2] Of those enrolled in the humanities, only from 5 to 15 percent were receiving their primary support from the government. This report, which is commonly known as the "Gilliland Report" after Edwin Gilliland of MIT who served as chairman of the panel,

2. David Allison, "The Science Brain Trust," *International Science and Technology* (January, 1965), p. 67.

recommended that the number of graduate students in engineering, mathematics, and the physical sciences be increased markedly, so that within eight years the number of Ph.D.'s graduating in these fields would be doubled. It now appears that this recommendation was rather conservative, since the suggested increase already has been exceeded and by 1970 the number of doctorate degrees being produced in these disciplines will be triple or quadruple the number that finished in 1962.

It may be worthy of note that advanced education in the Soviet Union is heavily oriented toward the sciences, with only about 20 percent of the graduate students working in fields other than science and engineering.[3] This fact, as dramatized by Russian achievements in space, has prompted the United States government to encourage through financial assistance greater emphasis upon graduate training in science.

A military scientist who has written extensively and testified before Congress about the poor quality of the American educational system, Admiral H. G. Rickover, while advocating an overall improvement in our education at both the high school and college level, reverted to a position much like that of C. P. Snow when he wrote that science will be increasingly influential in our daily life. If this reorientation produced some unemployment among those people whose principle qualifications seemed to be their ability to get along, to adjust, and to fit into existing organizational structures, Rickover felt this would be really good riddance. He described the "man of the future" as being the technical expert.[4] Society would be increasingly dependent upon such a man, even though he was presently subservient to governmental and industrial leaders, and his work was hampered by individuals who, Rickover believed, had the authority but lacked an understanding of the realities of the new technical age. The admiral described these nonscientists as "verbal men" who were on their way out, to be replaced by the man of the future, who would be able to handle the mysteries of complex engineering and scientific projects.

In a lecture delivered not long ago, I. I. Rabi, Higgins professor of physics at Columbia University and Nobel laureate, called for a revision in the college curriculum. Professor Rabi suggested that we should take Plato's injunction seriously and let no one enter college, and certainly not graduate, who did not know mathematics at least through calculus.[5] This knowledge of mathematics, he maintained, would provide a common language and a means of communication between the two cultures. Through

3. Anatoly Zvorykin, "Organization of Scientific Work in the U.S.S.R.," *Impact of Science on Society,* XV, No. 2 (1965), 113.
4. H. G. Rickover, *Education and Freedom* (New York: E. P. Dutton and Co., 1959), p. 19.
5. Press release from Colorado College, January 11, 1965.

this bridge the traditional culture would be able to share with the scientists the realization of the social implications of scientific discoveries, and the two groups could then plan for what action might be necessary. It is interesting that Rabi saw the answer to the problem of the two cultures as being a greater knowledge of science on the part of the members of the traditional culture.

In his Cambridge lecture, C. P. Snow had called for more generalization in the educational process, and yet he repeatedly returned to criticism of the traditional culture. For instance, he asserted that Western intellectuals, other than scientists, had never been able to understand the industrial revolution nor to accept it. Snow alleged that intellectuals were natural Luddites, bent upon ignoring or degrading technological change.[6] He asserted that few non-scientists really understood the scientific concept of acceleration, as evidenced by the fact that the rate of social change had been very slow. With this narrowness of vision prevalent in the traditional culture, the natural result was the inability of the intellectual to deal with the increasing rate of social change. Describing the three menaces which stand in the way of being able to carry out the industrial revolution in the developing areas as being H-bomb war, overpopulation, and the gap between the rich and the poor countries, Snow saw the solution as the production of more scientists and engineers and the making available of large amounts of development capital. The hope for the future, in his opinion, was dependent upon scientific advancement.

The only specific recommendation that Snow offered for providing a means of communication between the two cultures was to make the study of a particular branch of science a requirement for all schools. The branch of science that he selected was molecular biology.[7] In view of what I. I. Rabi had recommended, it is rather interesting that one reason Snow gave for selecting this scientific discipline was that it required very little mathematics to understand. So, while Snow's solution to the problem of cultural isolation was different from that of Rabi's, both men saw the answer to be more training of non-scientists in scientific subjects.

The dialogue about the two cultures, the seriousness of the lack of communication between them, and what should be done to improve the situation will continue. More proposals will be made about how our educational programs should be changed in order to meet more adequately the challenge of the scientific revolution. However, in evaluating the various suggestions that are made, it is important that we do not lose sight of the fact that the pursuit of science is not an end in itself. It is true that

6. Snow, *op. cit.*, pp. 27–28.
7. *Ibid.*, p. 69. Snow wrote this proposal in 1963 as a part of his "second look" at the two cultures.

science has already shown the capability of satisfying many of the material needs of man, even if thus far the benefits have been confined largely to the scientifically advanced nations. But there is more to remedying the ills of humanity than merely expanding our scientific education programs and exporting large numbers of scientists and engineers to the developing nations. The greatest dangers to the survival of society on something above a bare subsistence level continue to be rooted in the basic nature of man and the eccentricities of group and national behavior. For example, the technological means to prevent the outbreak of nuclear war and to arrest the population explosion are at hand, but these dilemmas persist because they involve fundamental societal and political elements. Thus their solution is not primarily dependent upon further scientific advances or a more equitable distribution of scientists among the nations of the world. If science is to be a factor in the solution of these problems, and if a solution is to be found it must necessarily be heavily dependent upon science, the solution must deal with those features of human nature that are far removed from the ordered systems of the laboratory.

It is important that Snow raised the question that he did about the two cultures, but the real problem is not that the intellectual fails to understand enough about science to make meaningful evaluations. The more serious danger is that the veneration of science will lead to it being regarded as inherently good and desirable as an end in itself.

If we can utilize science as a means, or an aid, to the solution of those fundamental problems that involve basic humanistic considerations, then there is virtually no limit to the promise that the future holds. On the other hand, if we become obsessed with the mysticism of science and a fascination for gadgetry and insist upon placing an increased emphasis upon scientific and technological training virtually as an end in itself, separate and distinct from the achievement of the goals to which our society is, or should be, committed, the result can only be the inevitable frustration that will come from man becoming the captive of technology instead of its master. It is not the failures of science or a lack of scientific progression that pose the problems for the future, but rather the question of whether we can use science effectively as a means to reach a much broader and more important end, an end that involves the betterment and basic security of all humanity.

INDEX

Abelson, Philip H., 111
Academic freedom, 28, 29, 44, 45, 471
Acheson, Dean, 321, 323, 355, 363
Adams, Brooks, 9, 10
Adams, Charles Francis, 12
Adams, Henry, 9, 10, 70, 87
Adams, John Quincy, 9, 15, 19, 73
Advanced Research Projects Agency (ARPA), 65, 134, 175, 452
Advisory Committee on Science and Technology, Democratic National Committee, 370
Advisory Committee on Weather Control, 164
Advisory Task Force on Space, Science and the Atom, Republican National Committee, 293-4
Aerospace Corporation, 83, 197, 208
Agency for International Development (AID), 62
Agricultural attachés, 63
Agricultural Society of the United States, 13
Agriculture, Department of: atmospheric sciences, 161; contracts, 156; creation, 14, 27; experiment stations, 13, 14, 47; Federal Council representation, 454; Marketing Service, 63; research, 47, 65, 76, 216, 452, 455; Research Service, 63; scientists, 121; support of foreign science, 63; water resources, 161
Air Force, Department of: air defense, 368, 369; competition with Navy, 250; H-bomb controversy, 323, 325, 327; Office of Aerospace Research, 66; Office of Scientific Research, 114; policy development, 84; research contracts, 196-7; Reserve,

292; scientific advisers, 128; Skybolt missile, 387; solid fuel, 187; Strategic Air Command, 242, 325, 369; Systems Command, 66
Aircraft Nuclear Propulsion System (ANP), 250
Allison, David, 476
Almond, Gabriel A., 181, 323
Alsos, 366
American Association for the Advancement of Science, 13, 359
American Chemical Society, 115
American Federation of Labor—Congress of Industrial Organizations (AFL-CIO), 488
American Institute of Biological Sciences, 432
American Meteorological Society, 165
American Miscellaneous Society, 167-9
American Nuclear Society, 154
American Philosophical Society, 13
American Physical Society, 115, 154
American Society of Geologists and Naturalists, 13
American Telephone and Telegraph Company (AT&T), 435
Anderson, Oscar E., Jr., 81
Anfuso, Victor L., 183, 184
Antarctic Office, 378
Antarctic research, 159, 163, 164
Antarctic treaty, 163
Antiplutic medicine, 447
Antisubmarine warfare (ASW), 263
Anton Brun yacht, 171
Appleby, Paul H., 434
Arden House, 439, 443, 446
Argonne National Laboratory, 303
Armenian Academy of Science, 416
Arms control, 261, 262, 296

Arms Control and Disarmament Agency, 128, 129, 135, 136, 388
Army, Department of: aerospace program, 66; distrust of Lilienthal, 322; Engineers, 20; H-bomb controversy, 323, 324; Project Vista, 153; rocket research, 196; Signal Corps, 18
Associated Universities, Inc., 153
Association of American Colleges, 154
Association of Land Grant Colleges and Universities, 154
Association of the United States Army, 342
Atlantic Research Corporation, 182
Atlas missile, 222
Atmospheric sciences, 160, 161, 171
Atomic bomb: costs of H-bomb program, 365; cyclotrons, 24; development, 56, 81, 140, 272, 362, 466, 467, 471; monopoly, 310; passing of monopoly, 312; power stations, 400, 436; psychological impact, 407; reactor, 461; true innovation, 239
Atomic Energy Act, 81
Atomic Energy Commission (AEC): abandoned projects, 250; aerospace support, 66; atmospheric sciences, 161; basic research support, 56, 140, 141, 452; budget, 194; chairman, 132, 153, 177, 318, 323, 351, 363, 450; contracts and grants, 65, 81, 82, 85, 191, 197, 200, 211; creation, 56; dispute on radioactivity; 135; emphasis upon engineering, 58; Federal Council representation, 454; foreign scientific activities, 64; General Advisory Committee (GAC), 131; H-bomb decision, 308, 312, 313, 318, 321, 322, 324, 326, 371; high-intensity accelerator, 303; influence upon policy, 265, 376; laboratory operation, 125; Military Liaison Committee, 317; oceanography support, 161; proposal for Department of Science, 455; report of GAC, 316, 317, 319, 321, 322, 326, 327-8, 355, 371; research advances, 68-9; rivalry within, 251; water research support, 161
Atoms for Peace Program, 353
Attorney General, 208, 453

Avco Everett Research Laboratory, 291
Axt, Richard G., 80

B

Bache, Alexander Dallas, 11, 17
Bacon, Francis, 299
Bagehot, Walter, 78
Baruch Plan, 355
Basov, N. G., 403
Bator, Francis M., 439, 444
Baylor University, 293
Beech Aircraft, 196
Bell, Daniel, 449
Bell, David E., 446
Bell Telephone Laboratories, 125, 130
Bennett, Hugh H., 431
Berkner, Lloyd V., 89, 370, 379
Bernal, J. D., 71
Bethe, Hans, 129, 134, 136, 278, 279, 328, 333, 335, 336, 338, 339, 349, 350, 366
Blackett, P. M. S., 274, 276, 278, 280, 365, 383
Bloch, F., 403
Bogolyubov, N. N., 401
Bohr, Niels, 24, 475
Bolshevik, 416
Bomber bonfire proposal, 410
Bonner, Lyman G., 184
Born, Max, 466, 467
Boston: concentration of scientific activities, 300, 302, 307, 405; symposium on technology, 439, 442, 443, 447, 449
Botanic Garden, 58
Bradbury, Norris, 131
Bradley, Omar, 310
Brennan, Donald G., 347, 351
Brodie, Bernard, 364
Bronk, Detlev W., 168, 284, 286, 289, 292, 425
Brookhaven National Laboratory, 153
Brookings Institution, 438, 444
Brooks, H., 384
Brooks, Harvey, 131
Brown, Harold, 86, 133, 284, 290, 292
Brown, Harrison, 289, 336, 337
Brown and Root, Inc., 169
Brown University, 114, 196

Bucknell University, 153
Bulletin of the Atomic Scientists, 276, 373, 407, 409, 458
Bundy, McGeorge, 131
Bureau of the Budget, 120, 188, 191, 193, 211, 219, 453, 455
Bureau of the Census, 8, 12, 58
Bureau of Commercial Fisheries, 170, 171
Bureau of Labor Statistics, 215
Burnham, James, 179
Burns, Arthur, 448
Bush, Vannevar, 56, 57, 81, 139
Byelorussian Academy of Science, 416
Byrd Antarctic Station, 164

C

Calder, Nigel, 334
Calder, Ritchie, 440
California Institute of Technology (Cal Tech), 81, 82, 131, 196, 289, 300, 301, 336
California open housing law, 288
Cambridge University, 242, 475, 476, 478
Cannell, Rogers, 290
Carnegie Foundation, 80
Carnegie Institution of Washington, 16
Carson, Rachel, 121, 426, 438
Cavendish Laboratory, 242
Center for Environmental Health, 432
"Centers of Excellence," 122, 149, 155, 304-6
Central Europe troop reduction proposal, 411
Central Radio Propagation Laboratory, 174
Chamberlain, Owen, 290
Chemopsychiatric drugs, 428
Cherenkov, P. A., 403
China, 266, 280, 393, 410, 413
Chrysler Corporation, 196
Churchill, Winston, 275, 364, 365, 376
Citizens for Johnson-Humphrey, 285
Civil rights, 305-6
Civil service, 19-21, 74
Clark, Leland, 291
Cloture in Senate, 435
Coast and Geodetic Survey, 13, 27, 58, 60, 62, 170, 171, 174, 175

Collier, Basil, 383
Columbia Broadcasting System (CBS) Laboratories, 287
Columbia University, 196, 300, 301, 441, 449, 477
Commerce, Department of: atmospheric sciences support, 161; creation, 18; facilities, 216; Federal Council representation, 454; International Indian Ocean Expedition, 170, 171; oceanography support, 161; Panel on Civilian Technology, 438; scientific activities, 47, 58, 60, 65, 455; space program, 66, 194; upper mantle project, 175; water resources support, 161
Commission on Science and Technology (proposal), 150-51
Committee on Inauguration of a National Forest Policy (NAS), 17
Committee on Medical Research, 56
Committee on Meteorology (NAS), 165
Committee on Polar Research (NAS), 163
Committee on Social Trends, 81
Committee on Space Research (ICSU), 163
Common Market, 442-3, 448
Commons, John R., 12
Communication between scientist and policy-maker, 430, 465
Communications space satellite, 435
Compensation of scientists, 202-3, 214-15, 217-18
Compton, Karl T., 81
Conant, James B., 39-40, 81, 189
Condon, Edward U., 287
Conference on Science and World Affairs (COSWA), *see* Pugwash Conferences
Conflicts of interest, 206-8
Congress, U.S.: Appropriations Committees, 86; reapportionment, 449; review of scientific programs, 143, 149-50, 188, 189; science appropriations, 188, 301, 318; scientific activities, 178, 179; testimony by scientists, 135-6
Congress of Scientists on Survival, 125
Constitution, U.S., 19, 78, 140

Continental shelf, 174
Corman, James C., 183, 186-8
Cosmonauts, 396
Cosmos Club, 128, 154
Cost effectiveness, 247-8
Coulson, Thomas, 12
Council of Economic Advisers, 362, 448
Cuban disaster, 138
Cultural exchange program, 397
Cybernetics, 401, 407
Cyclotron, 24

D

Daniels, Josephus, 360
DeBakey, Michael, 293
DeBow, J. D. B., 12
Decoupling, 336, 338-40, 350
Dedijer, Stevan, 91, 95, 97
Defense, Department of: abandoned projects, 250; Antarctic program, 163; contracts and grants, 65, 191, 211, 215, 446; control and coordination of research, 455; conventional weapons, 264; disposal of facilities, 301; dispute on radioactivity, 135; Federal Council representation, 454; H-bomb decision, 308, 312-13, 320, 326; inflexibility in development, 234; International Years of the Quiet Sun, 174; laboratories, 125, 216; missile program, 375; neglect of management responsibility, 201; nuclear weapons policy, 309, 317, 319; research policy, 235, 236, 251, 267; scientists, 60, 75, 136, 218, 256, 376, 459; space program, 181; study of implications of technology, 441; support of science, 68, 141, 161, 194, 199, 200, 452; tabu problems, 265; technical advice to State Department, 386; upper mantle project, 175
Democratic Party, 284, 285, 286, 288, 289, 296, 370, 380
Detection system, 133
Deterrence 245, 260
Developing nations, 62, 93-4, 98, 101-2
Dinerstein, Herbert, 383

Director of Defense Research and Engineering (DDR&E), 216, 284, 292, 293, 455
Director of International Scientific and Technological Affairs (State Department), 384, 394-6
Distant Early Warning system, 255
Dobzhansky, Theodosius, 425
Dodd, Thomas, 344
Dominican Republic intervention, 416
Dornberger, Walter, 365, 371, 376
Doty, Paul, 131
Dryden, Hugh, 115
Dubos, René, 426
DuBridge, Lee, 130, 131, 138, 361, 372
Duffield, E. S., 310
Duke University, 302
Dulles, John Foster, 384
Dunlop, John T., 446
DuPont Corporation, 81
Dupre, J. S., 445, 446
DuShane, Graham, 378
Dyno-Soar, 250, 255
Dyson, Freeman, 343-5

E

Earl of Birkenhead, 365
Earthquakes, 340
Eaton, Cyrus, 408, 410
Ecology, 429, 434
Edinburgh University, 284
Edison, Thomas, 360
Education in America, 397
Eights Antarctic station, 164
Einstein, Albert, 407, 408
Eisenhower, Dwight D.: farewell warning, 70, 191, 271, 275; management of research and development, 453, 454; nuclear test ban, 351, 387; reaction to Sputnik, 108, 144; science advisers, 108, 131, 284, 286, 292, 380; science programs, 170; small nuclear tests, 334; weapons debate, 325
Electrochemistry, 402
Electron spin resonance, 403
Electronic computers, 402
Elite, active scientific, 129-32

Ellul, Jacques, 440
Eltanin research vessel, 163
Employment Act of 1946, 448
Encounter, 449
Enlightenment, Age of, 71, 85
Environmental science, 426-8, 432
Escalation, 263
Executive Office of the President, 145, 179
Expenditures for scientific research: abandoned projects, 250; aerospace program, 65; Antarctic research, 164; basic research, 143; difficult choices, 461-2; growth, 36, 68, 149, 194, 445, 452; International Years of Quiet Sun, 174; Japan cooperative program, 173; oceanography, 171; ocean sediment coring program, 174; programs of Federal Council, 161; proportion supported by government, 64, 67, 195-6; rocket fuel, 182-3; upper mantle project, 175-6; weather modification, 165-6
European Economic Community, 442-3, 448
European Organization for Nuclear Research (CERN), 462

F

Fallout, 131, 135, 423, 426
Federal Aviation Agency, 62, 161
Federal Council for Science and Technology: creation, 57, 144-5; international programs, 64; national programs, 159-76; program supervision, 59, 108, 109, 124-5, 451; relations with National Academy, 75; representation, 61, 377, 454; responsibilities, 147-8
Federal Security Agency, 47
Federation of American Scientists, 137, 333, 409
Fedoseyev, P. N., 416
Feld, Bernard, 349
Fermi, Enrico, 24, 466
Finer, Herman, 379
Finletter Report, 311-12

Fisher, Warren, 73
Fisk, James, 131, 338
Floating drilling vessel, 169-70, 174
Fluoridation controversy, 426
Fonda, Henry, 292
Ford, Henry, 288
Foreign Agricultural Research Grant Program, 63
Foreign aid, 62
Foreign policy, 370-93
Foreign Science Information Program, 64
Foreign Service Institute, 395
Foreign Studies Program, 63-4
Forest Service, 18, 63
Foster, John S., Jr., 131
Fox, William T. R., 381
Franck Report, 348-9, 355
Frank, I. M., 403
Frankel, Charles, 78, 441, 442
Franklin, Benjamin, 7, 11
Franklin, Noble, 365
Franklin Institute, 11, 12, 368
Fromm, Eric, 279
Frumkin, A. N., 402
Fuel cell, 402

G

Gabrielson, Ira, 431
Gagarin, Yuri, 138
Galland, Adolf, 383
Garth, David L., 289-91
Gaspar, Peter, 291
Gavin, James M., 365
General Electric, 81
General Land Office, 74
General Motors, 196
General Services Administration, 211
Genetics, Eleventh International Congress, 425
Geneva Conferences on Peaceful Uses of Atomic Energy, 397, 400, 472
Geneva system, 332, 335, 336, 338, 339
Geological Survey, 13, 18, 27, 175
Geophysics Research Board, 175
Georgian Academy of Science, 416

Germany: Common Market, 443; post-
    war status, 410; reunification, 411-
    12; scientists, 88-9, 374, 466-7;
    World War II, 365, 383, 466-7
Gillette Company, 287
Gilliland Report, 476-7
Gilpin, Robert, 384
Glass, H. Bentley, 125, 178
Glenn, John, 390
Godkin lectures, 132, 271-2
Goldberg, Arthur, 442
Goldmark, Peter C., 287
Goldsen, Joseph M., 181
Goldwater, Barry, 113, 114, 283, 286,
    288, 290, 292-8
Gorki Leninski (model farm), 404
Goudsmit, Samuel A., 366
Government Printing Office, 58
Graduate Research Center of the South-
    west, 89, 302
Government Research Institute (pro-
    posal), 219
Grants-in-aid, 76, 79
Gray, Gordon, 369, 381
Great Britain: Air Staff, 364, 382;
    Atomic Energy Commission, 100;
    Civil servants, 19, 21, 73, 74; Minis-
    try of Supply, 236; Naval Staff, 364;
    scientists, 132, 224, 383, 466, 467;
    World War II, 382-3
Greek city states, 439
Green Bank radio telescope, 149
Grodzins, Morton, 418
Groves, Leslie, 369, 371
Guadalupe Island, 168
Gustafson, W. E., 445
Gutkowski, Herbert S., 287

H

Haddow, Alexander, 368
Hailsham, Lord, 96
Hale, George Ellery, 300
Halperin, Morton, 347, 351
Hamilton, Alexander, 8
Hamilton, J. H., 135-6
Hanford, Washington, 436
Harbison, Frederick, 92
Harbor-building by atomic explosion, 440

Harris, Milton, 287
Harvard University, 82, 101, 131, 196,
    284, 287, 290, 300, 302, 303, 307,
    445
Haskins, Caryl P., 384
Haverford College, 443
Haworth, Leland J., 132, 153, 154-5,
    169
Health, Education and Welfare, Depart-
    ment of: atmospheric science sup-
    port, 161; contracts and grants, 65;
    Federal Council representation, 453-
    4; National Institutes of Health, 59;
    oceanography support, 161; pesti-
    cides, 121; research funds, 68-9, 452;
    Social Security Administration, 59;
    water research support, 161
Heilbroner, Robert, 437, 440, 443, 444
Heisenberg, W., 466
Heller, Walter, 438
Henry, Joseph, 17
Hercules Powder Company, 184
Herz, John H., 386
Hewlett, Richard G., 81
High altitude nuclear test, 126
High energy physics, 160, 303
Hilsman, Roger, 323
Hitch, Charles J., 438, 439, 444
Hitler, Adolf, 295, 365, 376, 467
Hodges, Luther, 438
Holmes, Oliver Wendell, 285
Homestead Act, 14
Hoover, Herbert, 81
Hornig, Donald F., 112-17, 119-23, 284
Hosmer, Craig, 134
House of Representatives, U.S.: Armed
    Services Committee, 317; Commit-
    tee on Science and Astronautics, 65-
    6, 146, 151, 178, 180, 181; Inde-
    pendent Offices Appropriations Sub-
    committee, 165
Houston Chronicle, 293
Humphrey, Hubert, 293, 297, 303-4
Huntington, Samuel P., 323
Huntsville, Alabama, 306
Hussey, Charles, 280
Hutchins, Robert M., 441
Huxley, Julian, 84
Hydrofoil ships, 437

Hydrogen bomb controversy, 251, 253, 272, 308, 320-38, 355, 363, 365, 371-2, 466

I

Ikeda, Hayato, 172
Income tax law, 38
Independent boards and commissions, 18-19
Industrial research, 37-8
Industrial Revolution, 478
Information, international exchange, 38
Infrared homing devices, 280, 370
Inglis, David, 345
Institute for Defense Analysis, 83, 259
Integrating role of biology, 431
Interagency Committee on Oceanography, 171
Interdepartmental Committee on Atmospheric Sciences, 171
Interdepartmental Committee for Scientific Research and Development, 56, 57, 144
Intergovernmental Oceanographic Commission (UNESCO), 171
Interim Committee on Atomic Energy, 354
Interior, Department of: atmospheric science support, 161; creation, 18; Federal Council representation, 454; International Indian Ocean Expedition, 170-71; oceanography support, 161; science adviser, 60; scientific research, 47, 65, 216, 455; upper mantle project, 175; water research support, 161
Internal Revenue Service, 62
International Atomic Energy Agency, 470
International Business Machines (IBM), 287, 288
International Council of Scientific Unions (ICSU), 126, 162
International Geophysical Year, 62, 63, 142, 159, 161-2, 170, 173, 375
International Indian Ocean Expedition, 159, 170-72
International Labor Organization, 62

Internationalism of science, 336, 337, 412, 417-18
International Science and Technology, 114
International upper mantle project, 159, 175-6
International Years of the Quiet Sun, 159, 173-4
Interservice rivalry, 250-52
Interstate Commerce Commission, 12
Ivanovski, D., 404

J

Jacksonian revolution, 19
Jacobson, H. G., 388
Japan, 159, 172-3, 403
Jefferson, Thomas, 7, 13, 14, 76
Jet engine, 231
Jet Propulsion Laboratory (JPL), 184, 196
Johns Hopkins University, 82, 301
Johnson, Ellis A., 361
Johnson, Louis, 321, 323
Johnson, Lyndon B., 112, 113, 282-9, 291-8, 303-4
Johnston Island nuclear tests, 126, 127, 130
Joint Chiefs of Staff, 83, 309, 316, 326, 362, 380
Joint Committee on Atomic Energy, 133, 134, 179, 312, 313, 316, 340
Jungk, Robert, 366, 371, 466, 467

K

Kahn, Herman, 351
Kamchatka Peninsula, 340
Kantrowitz, Arthur R., 291
Kapitsa, Peter L., 381, 405, 467
Kaplan, Joseph, 125-6, 127-8
Kaplan, N., 100
Karafuto Island, 340
Kaufmann, W. W., 387
Kaysen, Carl, 82
Keating, Kenneth, 288
Keldysh, M. V., 401, 405, 416
Kennedy, Edward, 302

Kennedy, John F., 111, 113, 118, 126, 145, 160, 170, 172, 181, 285, 302-3, 387, 390, 436-7
Kennedy, Robert, 288
Kerr, James R., 180
Keynes, John Maynard (Lord), 440
Khrushchev, Nikita, 126, 381, 390, 398-9, 404, 410, 415, 451
Killian, James R., Jr., 111, 127, 129, 131, 133, 373, 376, 449
King, David S., 184, 186
Kirillin, V. A., 405
Kistiakowsky, George B., 70, 111, 127, 131, 137, 284, 286, 290, 292, 384, 409
Kolers, Paul A., 291
Komsomolskaya Pravda, 405
Korean War, 141, 325, 345, 380
Korol, Alexander G., 414, 415
Kraft, Joseph, 442, 443
Kramish, Arnold, 374, 381
Kranzberg, Melvin, 441
Kreidler, R., 384

L

Labor, Department of, 62, 442
Lac Beauport, Quebec, 409, 474
"Lackeys of the death industry," 446
Laika, 396, 398
Land-grant colleges, 14, 27, 47, 76, 154
Landau, L. D., 401, 403
Lang, Daniel, 408
Lasers, 250, 403
Lasker, Mary, 288
Latter, Albert, 131, 342, 343
Latter, Richard, 131
Laurence, William L., 366
Lawrence Radiation Laboratory, 131, 251, 353
League of Nations, 359
Lee, Russel, 290
Legislative reapportionment, 449
Lenin nuclear ice-breaker, 400
Lewis and Clark Expedition, 13, 388
Library of Congress, 58
Lilienthal, David, 318, 321-4, 326
Lincoln Laboratory, 196
Lindemann, F. A. (Lord Cherwell), 272, 276, 280, 364

Lindsay, John, 289
Liquid versus solid rocket fuel, 181-9
Literaturnaya Gazetta, 404
Litton Industries, 290
Livermore Laboratory, see Lawrence Radiation Laboratory
Lonsdale, Kathleen, 467
Los Alamos, 114, 130, 251, 316, 353, 369, 371
Low-temperature phenomena, 401, 403
Lowell, A. Lawrence, 74
Luddites, 478
Lunik, 396, 398
Lysenko genetics, 396, 404, 415

M

MacArthur, Donald M., 284-6, 289, 292, 295, 296
McCarthy, Joseph, 295
McCone, John, 351
McCrensky, Edward, 73
McDougall, Neil A., 91
Macmillan, Harold, 387
McMurdo Antarctic station, 164
McNamara, Robert S., 133, 138, 247, 299
Magnetic resonance instruments, 403
Maine, Sir Henry, 83
Malaria eradication, 437
Manhattan Engineering District, 3, 56, 81, 114, 131, 323, 369, 407
Manned moon rocket, 118, 137, 138, 179-81
Manpower Development and Training Act, 441, 448
Mansfield, Harvey C., 310
Maritain, Jacques, 71
Maritime Administration, 61
Mars photography, 398
Marshall, Alfred, 440
Martin Company, 196
Marxism, 8, 71, 79, 396, 414, 415
Massachusetts Institute of Technology (MIT), 81, 82, 130, 196, 284, 291, 300, 302, 303, 307, 403, 407, 439, 476; Radiation Laboratory, 130, 153, 224, 301, 368
Materials research, 160
Mayers, Lewis, 74

Medical research, 30-33
Meier, Richard L., 441
Melman, Seymour, 349
Melpar, Inc., 284, 286
Meriam, Lewis, 20, 74
Metcalf Research Laboratory, 114
Meteorology support, 461
Michelson, Albert A., 20, 300
Michurin genetics, 415
Midwestern Universities Research Association (MURA), 302-5
Migration of scientists, 90-103
"Military mind," 366
Military research: abandoned projects, 250, 254; capacity, 241-2; constraints on innovation, 246-51; development policy, 220-22, 227-30, 238-40, 243-6, 267; inflexibility of programs, 234-6; military personnel, 218-19; requirement, 49-50, 254-5, 258-62; "tabu" problems, 264-6; weaknesses in management, 237
Miller, Arthur S., 82
Miller, Byron S., 81
Miller, J. P., 423, 424, 433
Miller, William E., 290
Millikan, Clark B., 290
Millikan, Robert A., 300
Millionshchikov, M. D., 416
Millis, Walter, 310
Mitchell, Billy, 247
MITRE Corporation, 197
Moe committee, 40
Mohorovicic discontinuity, 167
Molecular biology, 461, 478
Morgenstern, Oskar, 455
Morrill Act, 14
Moscow exhibit, 399
Mosher, Charles A., 188
Multilateral nuclear force (MLF), 410
Mumford, Lewis, 440
Murdock, Bernard C., 88
Murphy, George, 288
Murray, Bruce, 289

N

National Academy of Engineering, 147
National Academy of Sciences (NAS)—National Research Council: aero-

space program, 66, 114; creation, 15, 17, 360; government requests for advice, 146, 151; military research, 49; officers, 289, 409; programs, 162, 163, 165, 167-8, 171, 172, 175; relationship to government, 75, 159, 414; research recommendations, 19, 125, 154; science policy, 147
National Advisory Committee for Aeronautics (NACA), 16, 34, 45, 56, 58
National Aeronautics and Space Administration (NASA): Administrator, 77, 138, 191; atmospheric science support, 161; contracts and grants, 65, 199-200, 211-12; creation, 58, 65; Federal Council representation, 454; funds, 180; inputs to national policy, 376, 389-91; laboratories, 125, 299-300, 302, 305; liquid versus solid fuel controversy, 181-9; programs, 68, 83, 174, 379, 452, 455; scientists, 75
National Aeronautics and Space Council, 65
National Association of State Universities, 154
National Board of Agriculture (proposal), 13
National Bureau of Standards, 18, 58, 60, 66, 174, 287, 378, 453
National Center of Environmental Sciences, 302
National Conference on Social Welfare, 441
National Defense Education Act, 304
National Defense Research Committee, 55
National Grange, 13
National Institutes of Health, 58, 70, 120, 140
National Research Council, 80
National Research Foundation (proposal), 50-55, 56, 140
National Science Board, 143, 147, 152-3, 154-5, 162, 284
National Science Foundation (NSF): aerospace programs, 66; contracts and grants, 122, 156-8, 452; creation and development, 56, 139-49, 461; Director, 132, 152-4, 191; Federal

National Science Foundation (*cont.*)
  Council representation, 454; foreign science activities, 63; future role, 149-52, 455; national research programs, 158-76; National Science Board, 154-6; recommendations, 122, 125, 304; transfer of functions, 57-8, 110
National Science Fund, 81
National Security Council, 57, 308, 313, 318, 320-24, 326, 454
Nationalism, 427-8
Navaho missile, 226, 250
Naval Observatory, 20, 27
Navy, Department of: aerospace programs, 66; Antarctic program, 163-4; H-bomb controversy, 323-4; International Indian Ocean Expedition, 170-71; Polaris missile, 250; Project Atlantis, 154; research activities, 62
Negroes, 288, 416
Neustadt, Richard E., 322
Neutron bomb, 344, 347
New federalism, 76
New Haven Railroad, 436
New York Academy of Sciences, 154
New York *Herald Tribune,* 423
New York *Post,* 128
New York State Agricultural Society, 13
New York Times, The, 297, 425
New York University, 196
Newman, James R., 81
Nichols, Caroline, 286
Nichols, Rodney W., 286, 287, 288, 289
Niels Bohr's Institute, 242
Nixon, Richard, 298, 451, 456-7
Nobel, Alfred, 407
Nobel Prize winners, 300-301, 403
North American Aviation, 185
North Atlantic Treaty Organization (NATO), 62, 346, 353, 387, 410, 411, 462
North Carolina State College, 302
Northwest Territory, 14
Novosibirsk, 401, 406
Novoye Vremya, 416
Noyes, Arthur A., 300
Nth country problem, 266-7, 332, 351, 353, 412
Nuclear magnetic resonance, 403

O

Oak Ridge Institute for Nuclear Studies, 153
Ocean harvest, 437
Ocean sediment coring program, 159, 174
Oceanography, 160, 161, 171, 287, 461
Oder Neisse Line, 410
Office of Aerospace Research (USAF), 66
Office of Antarctic Programs (NSF), 63
Office of Business Economics (Department of Commerce), 58
Office of Defense Mobilization, 57, 108, 131, 145
Office of Economic and Statistical Studies (NSF), 63-4
Office of Experiment Stations, 74
Office of International Science Activities (NSF), 63
Office of International Scientific Affairs (Department of State), 377
Office of Manpower, Automation and Training (Department of Labor), 441
Office for Political-Military Affairs (Department of State), 377
Office of the President, 362, 375
Office of Naval Research (USN), 56, 140, 252, 452
Office of Saline Water, 437
Office of the Science Adviser (Department of State), 376-7
Office of Science Information Service (NSF), 64
Office of Science and Technology (OST): creation, 57, 109-10, 452; Director, 108, 132, 209-10, 445; responsibilities, 59, 115, 124, 142, 147, 149
Office of Scientific Research and Development: accounting requirements, 54; compartmentalization of information, 45; military research, 28, 34, 44, 55, 81, 197; preparation of publications, 46; relations between scientists and military men, 49, 140
Operation Chariot, 440
Oppenheimer, J. Robert, 131, 369, 371, 372, 381, 449, 466

Orear, Jay, 334
Organization of American States (OAS), 62
Ortega y Gasset, José, 71
Oxford University, 100

P

Pacific Science Board (NAS), 172
Palo Alto Medical Research Foundation, 290
Palomar telescope, 300
Panel on Civilian Technology, 438
Panofsky, Wolfgang, 131
Pastore, John, 135-6
Patent Office, 13, 19, 53, 58, 60, 62
Pauling, Linus, 178, 350, 407-8
Pavlov, I. P., 404
Pax Russo-Americana, 351
Peace Corps, 285-6
Peck, Merton J., 82
Permanent Commission on Technological Change (proposal), 448
Pershing missile, 263
Personnel in research and development, 41, 42, 67-9, 129, 197, 217-18, 476-7
Pesticides, 428, 438
Physical Review, 225
Piel, Gerard, 444
Pike, Sumner, 326
Pinchot, Gifford, 17
Piore, Emmanuel R., 131, 287
Planning Research Corporation, 197
Plato, 477
Polar years, 162
Polaris missile, 243, 248, 250, 253, 292
Pole Antarctic station, 164
Pollack, Herman, 396
Pollution, 427, 428
Population increase, 27, 424, 478, 479
Pork barrel, 299
Post Office Department, 61, 84, 452, 457
Pratt and Whitney Corporation, 229
Pravda, 416
President's Air Policy Commission, 311
President's Club, 285, 287
President's Reorganization Plan No. 2, 57, 109, 142, 145, 155
President's Science Advisory Committee (PSAC): chairman, 108, 119; cre-

ation and development, 57, 59, 145, 375; international scientific activities, 64, 373; membership, 109, 115, 116, 125, 126, 131, 266, 286; programs, 121, 136, 138, 476; responsibilities, 85, 132, 134, 147, 377, 456
President's Scientific Research Board, 56
Price, Derek, 88
Price, Don K., 177, 280, 368, 369, 380, 381
Price, Melvin, 127
Princeton University, 82, 114, 131, 196
Problems of Philosophy, 416
Professors for Johnson, 293
Project Apollo, 137-8, 182
Project Atlantis, 154
Project Matterhorn, 253
Project Mohole, 149, 159, 166-70, 174, 403
Project Vela, 335
Project Vista, 153
Project West Ford, 130
Prokhorov, A. M., 403
Pseudo-technologists, 441
Public Health Service, 74, 135, 156, 302, 428, 432
Pugwash Conferences (COSWA): Continuing Committee, 409; creation, 273, 275-6, 408; meetings, 409-19; motivation, 337, 407; participants, 125, 126, 409, 413-14; Soviet delegates, 414-17
Purcell, Edward M., 131, 287, 403
Purdue University, 183
Pure food and drug crusade, 431

Q

Quantum jumps in science, 370

R

Rabi, I. I., 129, 131, 134, 477, 478
Rabinowitch, Eugene, 409, 410, 412, 413, 418
Raborn, William F., 292, 297
Radar, 26, 224-5, 226, 229, 362, 382-3
Ramey, James T., 254
RAND Corporation, 83, 131, 134, 197, 208, 222, 225, 227, 229, 259, 438, 444

Rate of growth of science, 88, 89, 360-61

Redstone missile, 375

Republican Party, 283, 284, 288, 290, 292, 293, 294, 295, 298, 380

Research Board for National Security (NAS), 49, 50

Research contracts, 193-5, 199-201, 211-16, 445-6

Research grants, 156-8, 212

Research Triangle, 302

Revelle, Roger, 287

Ribicoff, Abraham, 289

Rickover, H. G., 477

Robb, Inez, 297

Roberts, Ffrangcon, 447

Rockefeller, Nelson, 298

Rockefeller Foundation, 24, 80

Rockefeller Institute, 284, 425

Rocketdyne Division of North American Aviation, 185

Rollefson, Ragnar, 384

Romney, Carl F., 133

Roosevelt, Franklin D., 56, 81, 139, 408

Rosenblith, Walter, 291

Rostow, Walter, 93

Rowe, James H., Jr., 285

Royal Air Force, 382

Royal Society, Fellows, 273-4

Rubel, John H., 290

Ruina, Jack, 134, 135

Russell, Bertrand, 124, 273, 280, 408

Rutherford, Sir Ernest, 373, 381

S

St. Andrews University, 284

Salinger, Pierre, 288

Salisbury, Harrison, 381

Saturday Review, 426

Savannah nuclear cargo ship, 400

Savannah River reactors, 326

Scates, Douglas E., 88

Scherer, Frederic M., 82

Schilling, Warner R., 178, 361, 364, 372, 384

Schulz, Heinrich E., 416

Science administrators at the secretary level, 60, 61, 217, 459

Science Advisory Board, 37, 81

Science Advisory Committee, 57

Science Advisory Office (Department of State), 382

Science attachés, 63, 373, 376, 394

Science magazine, 130

Science and Technology, Department of (proposal), 378-9, 455-7

"Scientific mind," 366

Scientific-technological elite, 70

Scientists in Congress, 449

Scientists and Engineers for Goldwater, 294

Scientists and Engineers for Johnson-Humphrey, 283, 285-9, 291, 293-8

Scranton, William, 293

Scurlock, Arch C., 182

Seaborg, Glenn T., 132, 177, 363, 450

Sears, Paul B., 429

Seismograph stations, 335-6, 338-40

Semyonov, N. N., 402, 416

Senate, U.S.: Committee on Aeronautical and Space Sciences, 66, 178-9; Committee on Government Operations, 381; filibuster, 435; Foreign Relations Committee, 83

Shannon, J., 401

Shepard, Alan, 138

Shklar, Judith N., 71

Sidewinder missiles, 280

Simpson, George Gaylord, 431

Sino-Soviet split, 413

Sisson, C. H., 73

Sky-bolt missile, 387

Small Business Administration, 124

Smith, Michael E., 74

Smithsonian Institution, 15-16, 139, 161

Snark missile, 250

Snow, C. P., 72, 132, 271-6, 280-81, 365, 367, 383, 418, 432, 475-9

Social Security Administration, 59

Society for Social Responsibility in Science, 407, 466-7

Soil conservation, 431

Somers, Herman, 443, 447

Sorbonne, 100

Soviet Union: Academy of Medical Sciences, 416; Academy of Sciences, 401, 404-5, 409, 414-17; agronomy,

404-5; All Union Institute of Scientific and Technical Information, 406; Antarctic investigations, 403; army, 325, 374; atomic bomb, 308-12, 314; atomic power stations, 400; automation, 401; biology, 403-4, 415; chemistry, 402-3; Committee for Coordination of Research, 406; communism, 396, 399, 405, 469; Communist Party, 402, 404, 414, 415, 416-17, 450; Council of Ministers, 405, 414, 451; cybernetics, 401; education, 397; genetics, 404; geology, 403; H-bomb, 315, 317-23, 325-6, 328, 466; industrial development, 406, 469; mathematics, 401; military programs, 230, 240, 259, 361, 375, 387, 400; Ministry of Foreign Affairs, 382; model farm, 404; oceanography, 403; physics, 403; Pugwash Conferences, 126, 410-11, 413-17, 419; radioastronomy, 403; science city, 401, 405; scientific programs, 397-406; scientists in government, 382, 450-51; scientists' refusal to work on nuclear weapons, 374, 381, 467; space program, 161-2, 179, 181, 250, 389-91, 477; test ban negotiations, 133, 135-6, 278, 329, 331, 333-53, 372; World Data Center, 161; World War II, 365

Space Science Board (NAS), 66

Special Assistant to the President for Science and Technology: appointees, 131, 284, 449; creation and development, 57, 59, 108-9, 144-5, 362, 375; responsibilities, 108, 147, 179, 191, 382, 387, 395, 438, 451, 454; science programs, 175, 390

Special Committee on Atmospheric Research (ICSU), 162-3

Special Committee on Oceanic Research (ICSU), 162, 171

Speier, Hans, 367

Spelman Fund, 24

Spock, Benjamin, 292, 297

Sputnik, 108, 132, 133, 161-2, 179, 362, 375, 384, 396, 398, 471

Stahl, Margaret Smith, 373

Stalin, Joseph, 381, 404, 415

Stanford Research Institute, 196, 290, 444

Stanford University, 196

State, Department of: Bureau of Intelligence and Research, 377; foreign policy formulation, 265, 367, 386-7, 389-91, 395; H-bomb controversy, 308, 313, 319-27, 363; insensitivity to political implications of science, 374-5; international scientific activities, 62-3, 171, 172, 373, 392; science adviser, 60-61, 376-8, 384-5, 388, 394-6, 459; scientific programs, 83, 163, 172

Steamboat Inspection Service, 12, 74

Steelman, John R., 56

Stein, E., 388

Stein, Harold, 310

Stevens Institute of Technology, 153

Stevenson, Adlai, 289

Stigler, George J., 234

Stover, Carl F., 177

Strategic bombing, 273-4, 383

Strontium 90, 423

Sullivan, Walter, 375

Sutton, G. P., 185

Systems Development Corporation, 197

T

"Tabu" problems, 264-6

Tactical nuclear weapons, 374

Tamm, I. Y., 401, 403

Target selection, 245-6

Taylor, Diane, 284, 295

Taylor, Stephen S., 416

Taylor, Telford, 383

Technological change, 435-6

Technological plateau, 241

Technology and Culture, 439

Telberg, Ina, 416

Teller, Edward, 131, 134, 136-7, 178, 277-9, 328-9, 334, 340, 341, 342-3, 344, 352, 371, 466

Tennessee Valley Authority, 161, 219

Test ban negotiations, 131, 133-7, 178, 277, 328-55, 387, 423

Textile industry, 437

Thalidomide, 427
Theobald, Robert, 444, 447
Thomas, Albert, 165-6
Tizard, Henry, 272, 276, 364, 376, 382
Tocqueville, Alexis de, 24
Topchiev, Alexander V., 413-15
Townes, C., 403
Treasury Department, 161
Tritium, 315, 324
Trollope, Anthony, 73
True, A. C., 14
True, Frederick W., 13, 17, 75
Truman, Harry S, 56, 140, 308, 313-14, 322-3, 325-6, 363-4, 380
Turboprop, 227
Tuve, Merle A., 86
Two cultures, 271-2, 432, 475-6, 478-9

University of Novosibirsk, 401
University of Pennsylvania, 11
University of Wisconsin, 153, 302, 384
Urey, Harold, 292, 297

V

V-2 rockets, 33, 362, 365, 371, 376
Valenti, Jack, 285
Van Allen, James A., 127, 130, 398
Van Dyke, Vernon, 181
Vanguard satellite, 162, 375
Vavilov, N. I., 404
Venus probe, 398
Vienna conference, 390
Vietnam, 410, 412, 416
Von Kann, Clifton, 221-2
Von Neumann, John, 253, 401
Vucinich, Alexander, 414, 415

U

Unamuno, Miguel D., 71
Unemployment, technological, 441-2, 448
Union Carbide, 81
United Nations (UN), 370, 410, 416, 475; resolution against orbiting nuclear weapons, 393
United States Agricultural Society, 13
United States—Japan Cooperative Science Program, 159, 172-3
Universities, American, 21, 23
University of Alabama, 291
University of Bordeaux, 440
University of California, 81, 130, 290, 300, 301
University of Chicago, 81, 82, 153, 300, 301, 303
University of Colorado, 287
University of Edinburgh, 440
University of Illinois, 82, 153, 196, 287, 302
University of Indiana, 153, 302
University of Kentucky, 82
University of Leningrad, 401
University of Maryland, 82
University of Michigan, 441
University of Minnesota, 302
University of Moscow, 401
University of North Carolina, 302

W

Wall Street Journal, The, 429
War Department research, 360, 378
Warsaw Pact, 410
Washington, George, 7, 8, 13, 76
Washington University, 291, 300, 301
Water resources research, 160, 161
Waterman, Alan T., 148, 153, 165-6, 168
Watson, Thomas J., Jr., 288
Watson-Watt, Sir Robert, 372, 382, 440
Watts riots, 416
Weather Bureau, 18, 60, 66, 174, 278
Weather modification, 142, 159, 164-6
Webb, James, 138
Weber, Max, 84
Webster, Charles, 365
West Point, 20
Westheimer, Mrs. Frank, 291
Wheeler, John A., 131, 253
White, Leonard D., 19
White House, 131, 133, 145, 285, 296, 303, 376, 397, 459
Wiener, Norbert, 401, 407
Wiesner, Jerome, 111-13, 117, 118, 124, 125, 127, 131-3, 137, 138, 284, 286, 290, 291, 292, 297, 303, 390, 409, 438, 445, 446, 451

Wildavsky, Aaron, 187
Wildlife management, 431
Wiley, Harvey W., 431
Williamsburg yacht, 171
Wilson, John T., 153
Wilson, Woodrow, 78, 80, 359
Wizard war, 275
Wohlstetter, Albert, 134, 137
Wolfle, Dael, 86
Woods Hole Laboratory, 16, 114
World Data Centers, 161
World Health Organization, 62
Wright, Christopher, 384
Wyant, William K., Jr., 425

Y

Yale University, 82
Yeomans, Alice V., 88
York, Herbert, 292, 293, 297
Young, Arthur, 7

Z

Zacharias, Jerrold R., 131, 133, 369
Zavoyski, Y. K., 403
Zucrow, Maurice, 183
Zvorykin, Anatoly, 477

28830

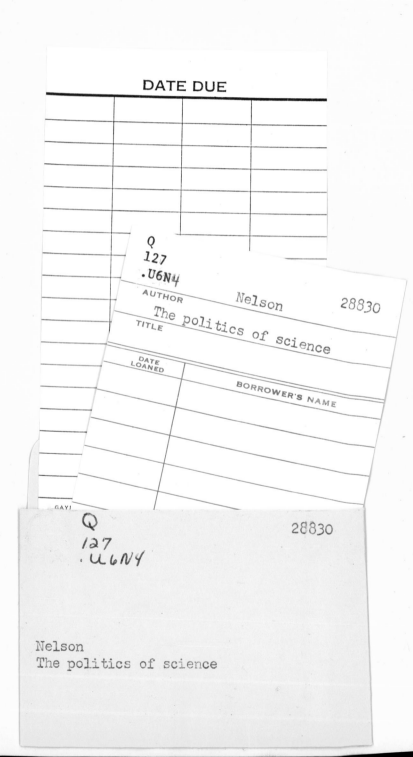

DATE DUE

Q
127
.U6N4

AUTHOR   Nelson   28830

TITLE   The politics of science

DATE
LOANED

BORROWER'S NAME

GAYL

Q   28830
127
.U6N4

Nelson
The politics of science